An Introduction

to the Chemistry of

Heterocyclic Compounds

R. M. ACHESON

Fellow and Tutor in Chemistry
The Queen's College, Oxford

Second Edition

INTERSCIENCE PUBLISHERS
a division of
John Wiley and Sons . New York . London . Sydney

First Edition 1960

Second Edition 1967

Filmset in 10/12 pt Baskerville using ⬡hemistyle diagrams.

Printed photo litho in Great Britain by Page Bros (Norwich) Ltd.

To
my B.T. and 3 L.T.'s.

PREFACE TO THE SECOND EDITION

Since the original publication of this book the flow of papers concerning heterocyclic chemistry, as in other branches of chemistry, has increased substantially. Every attempt has been made to bring this new edition fully up to date and relevant papers noted in *Current Chemical Papers* up to and including the September 1965 issue, and more recent issues of a few journals have been scanned for this purpose. A short new chapter on 7-membered ring heterocycles has been added, as well as a little information concerning heterocycles with less common heteroatoms. I will be very pleased, as in the past, if those who note errors or important omissions will kindly bring them to my attention, and I thank all those who have kindly corresponded about, or discussed, such matters with me in the last few years. In response to requests I have included a greater proportion of references to recent work.

I wish to record my grateful thanks to the University of Oregon for a Visiting Professorship, during the tenure of which most of the library work was done, to the Library staff of The University of Oregon for their willing assistance, to Mr. J. A. L. B. Caterer and Mr. C. W. C. Harvey for checking the index, and to Miss Marjorie Haycock for her typing and secretarial help.

R. M. ACHESON

The Queen's College
Oxford

PREFACE TO THE FIRST EDITION

In recent years many specialised works on specific topics in hetero-cyclic chemistry have appeared, while at the same time the more general text-books on organic chemistry have not given this important part of the subject the attention it deserves. The specialised works, while valuable to research workers and occasionally to advanced students, contain so much detail that it is virtually impossible for the average undergraduate to separate the wheat from the chaff and to recognise even the major features of heterocyclic chemistry in the time available to him. This time is proportionately too little in most teaching schools when it is considered that heterocyclic chemistry at the moment accounts for about 26% of the organic chemistry papers published. An attempt has been made, in this work, to present to the student a concise account of the more important properties, and chemical re-actions, of the basic heterocyclic systems with which he should have some acquaintance. This account, if it is to serve its purpose, cannot be complete. It is more difficult to decide on what to leave out than what to put in, and every writer has his own ideas on this matter. The present author is no exception, in consequence a great deal has been left out, including the sugars and alkaloids, which have been described at the appropriate level elsewhere. However, attempts have been made to include recent pertinent physical data, to use modern electronic and mechanistic concepts where possible, and to deal briefly with bio-chemical discoveries concerning the metabolism and biosynthesis of some important compounds. A general bibliography has been placed at the end of each chapter, references have been kept to a minimum, and review articles are quoted whenever possible.

I should be most grateful to know of errors, for which I accept sole responsibility and which have inevitably crept into this book in spite of the vigilance of many of my friends and pupils. I thank Professor R. L. Huang, of the University of Malaya, for reading most of the manuscript, and Dr. M. J. T. Robinson and Dr. R. Brettle for reading the complete manuscript and offering most constructive criticism. I am also indebted to Dr. E. Schlittler and Dr. N. F. Taylor for reading the proofs and for making valuable suggestions. I thank Professor W. C. Gibson, of the University of British Columbia, for encouragement which was much appreciated during the early stages of writing, the staff of the Radcliffe Science Library for their help and co-operation, Mrs. M. Little for the typing, and the officers of Interscience Inc., who have made my task as easy as possible. I also thank my wife for her help at all stages of the book.

R. M. ACHESON

Department of Biochemistry
University of Oxford

CONTENTS

INTRODUCTION AND NOMENCLATURE

A heterocyclic compound is one which possesses a cyclic structure with at least two different kinds of atoms in the ring. The most common types, discussed here, contain largely carbon atoms. Nitrogen, oxygen, and sulphur are the most common heteroatoms, but many other elements, including even bromine, can also serve. The heterocyclics containing the less common atoms have been subject to much investigation in recent years, but will not be considered in this book.

Heterocyclic compounds are very widely distributed in nature, and are essential to life in various ways. Most of the sugars and their derivatives, including vitamin C, for instance, exist largely in the form of five-membered (furan) or six-membered (pyran) rings containing one oxygen atom. Most members of the vitamin B group possess heterocyclic rings containing nitrogen. One example is vitamin B_6 (pyridoxine), which is a derivative of pyridine essential in amino acid metabolism. Many other examples of the importance of heterocyclic compounds in biological systems can be given. Most of the alkaloids, which are nitrogenous bases occurring in plants, and many antibiotics, including penicillin, also contain heterocyclic ring systems. A large number of heterocyclic compounds, obtainable only by laboratory syntheses, have valuable properties as chemotherapeutic agents, drugs, dyestuffs, copolymers, etc.

Heterocyclic compounds can be aliphatic or aromatic in character, depending upon their electronic constitution. In general, the aliphatic heterocyclics, where specific effects due to the constitution of the compound are excluded, are very similar chemically to their open-chain aliphatic analogues. For instance, tetrahydrofuran (**1**) has many properties characteristic of diethyl ether (**2**). In a similar way the

aromatic heterocyclic compounds have many properties resembling their aromatic carbocyclic analogues, a specific example being a comparison of pyridine (**3**) and benzene (**4**). In general, many well-developed syntheses of aromatic heterocyclic rings are available in

1

contrast to the benzene series, where very few practical syntheses of the aromatic ring itself are known. This is because while the parent compound, benzene, is readily available and easy to substitute, and in consequence direct syntheses of the ring have attracted little attention, most unsubstituted heterocyclic systems are either difficult to obtain or are not susceptible to substitution.

There are several conventions for numbering the atoms and substituents in simple heterocyclic rings which are generally accepted and are used by *Chemical Abstracts*, the world's most important and useful chemical abstract journal and index. The atoms of a simple heterocyclic ring are numbered from the heteroatom, which is counted as one. Substituents are given the lowest possible numbers and then are arranged in alphabetical order. For example, the chloromethylpyridine shown below could be numbered and described as 5-methyl-6-chloropyridine (**5**), but it is better numbered the other way round and called 2-chloro-3-methyl-pyridine (**6**). It should be found under the last name in most chemical indexes. In *Chemical Abstracts* it would be found

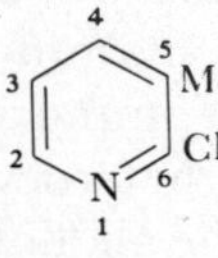

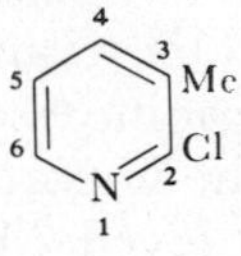

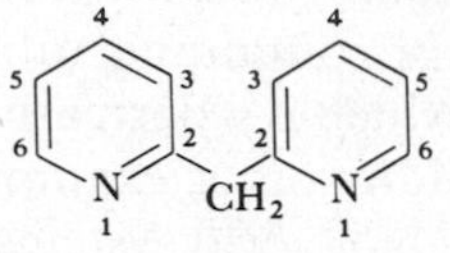

under 'pyridine, 2-chloro-3-methyl-', as derivatives are indexed under what is arbitrarily considered the 'parent' part of the molecule. Compound **6** is therefore not usually known as a derivative of methane; it could be called 3-(2-chloropyridyl)methane. However, in the case of **7**, when the pyridine ring might be considered as 'parent' and the compound named 2-(2-pyridylmethyl)pyridine, it is customary to treat the compound as a derivative of methane and to name it bis-2-pyridylmethane. Because of difficulties of this sort it is always advisable to look up the several alternative names, when ambiguity exists in the first instance, when conducting a literature search.

Where the heterocyclic ring contains more than one heteroatom the order of preference for position 1 is oxygen, sulphur, and then nitrogen. If there are two ways of numbering the ring the way which gives the second heteroatom the lowest possible number is chosen. Isoxazole (**8**) and thiazole (**9**) are therefore numbered as shown below.

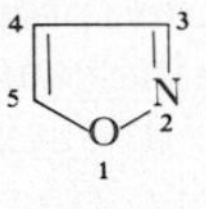

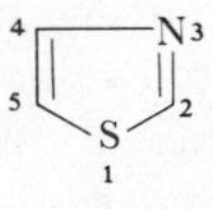

Nomenclature and numbering become more complicated for condensed or fused-ring systems, where a part of one ring is also a part of another. Generic terminology showing the genesis of the structures may be used. On this basis, the structure **11**, usually known by the trivial name of quinoline, may be called 2,3-benzopyridine, showing that a benzene ring has been fused on to the 2,3 side of the pyridine ring (**10**). Another system which is commonly used is to label the side of the heterocyclic system—*a*, *b*, *c*, . . . as shown for pyridine (**12**), starting from the atom number one. Structure **11** can then be called benzo[*b*]-

10   11   12

pyridine. These types of systematic nomenclatures are often used for complex molecules, the last system being employed by *Chemical Abstracts*.

Although general agreement has been reached for the naming and numbering of many heterocyclic compounds, agreement has not been reached with regard to others for which alternative names and numberings are used. This can lead to much difficulty in the use of original literature. It is therefore advisable to ascertain at an early stage which name is in vogue for the compound in the particular journal, when making a search, for the name can change from journal to journal, and occasionally different names are used for the same compound in the same journal. The *Ring Index* (Patterson, Capell and Walker, American Chemical Society, New York, 1960) is a most useful compilation of mainly heterocyclic ring systems with their alternative names and numbers. It is often very useful to consult this reference work before making a search for less common heterocyclic compounds in the literature.

CHAPTER I

HETEROCYCLIC ANALOGUES OF CYCLOPROPANE

All three-membered rings have one major property in common—a strained ring which confers great reactivity on the compounds in comparison with their open-chain analogues. This strain is reflected in the compression of the normal bond angles and by a shortening of the bond lengths from normal, as is shown by modern physical methods. The presence of a double bond in the ring increases the strain, and the molecular dimensions of cyclopropane (**1**) and cyclopropene (**2**) are given here for comparison with those of the heterocyclic compounds

1.53 ± 0.03 Å

49.9°

1.52 ± 0.02 Å

1.28 ± 0.04 Å

1   **2**

described later in this chapter. The bonds between the atoms are drawn straight, although it is suspected that a bent line in the form of an arc would better represent the electronic distribution in these molecules.[1]

Three-membered rings containing a nitrogen, oxygen, or sulphur atom as the heteroatom are called aziridine, oxirane, and thiirane, respectively. While the bonds between these three heteroatoms and the carbon atoms are a trifle longer than corresponding bonds in an unstrained molecule (e.g. dimethyl ether) the carbon–carbon bonds are all very similar in length but are substantially shorter than those of **1**. The rings of these compounds are much more easily opened than that of cyclopropane, since the heteroatoms facilitate the attack of ionic and free-radical reagents. The synthesis of three-membered heterocyclic rings from appropriate three-atom intermediates is on the whole quite easy, for although the 'strain energy' of the molecule must be provided, the atoms which must combine are largely oriented so that cyclization is prefered to intermolecular reaction and polymerization.

1. AZIRINE

One of the simplest heterocyclic compounds is the hypothetical azirine, or azacyclopropene. It could have structures **3** or **4**, and is yet unknown, although some derivatives of 1-azirine have been described and their structures adequately confirmed. Azirine is a nitrogen analogue of cyclopropene, one derivative of which, sterculic acid, has been found

3, 1-Azirine   **4**, 2-Azirine   Sterculic acid

in nature. No physical measurements have yet been reported on the azirine ring, which from classical considerations must be even more strained than that of the saturated aziridine (ethylenimine, p. 6).

2-Alkyl- and aryl-1-azirines are easily obtained[2] by the pyrolysis of the appropriate azide, as indicated below.

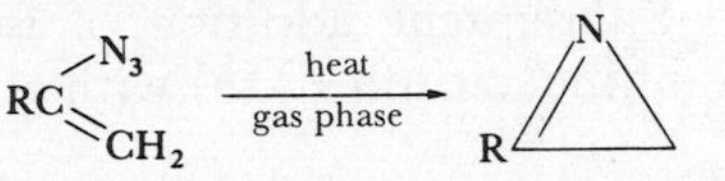

Neber in 1932 isolated an unstable intermediate in one of his syntheses of α-amino ketones from oxime 4-toluenesulphonyl derivatives. He gave an azirine structure (**6**) to the intermediate. Cram and Hatch[3] recently confirmed this structure and extended the work. Treatment of the oxime 4-toluenesulphonate with cold pyridine followed by sodium carbonate gave the azirine (**6**). This with acetic acid and acetic anhydride was converted into the acylamino ketone (**10**) of Neber, which can also be obtained from the oxime derivative (**5**) by successive treatment with pyridine and acetic acid–acetic anhydride.

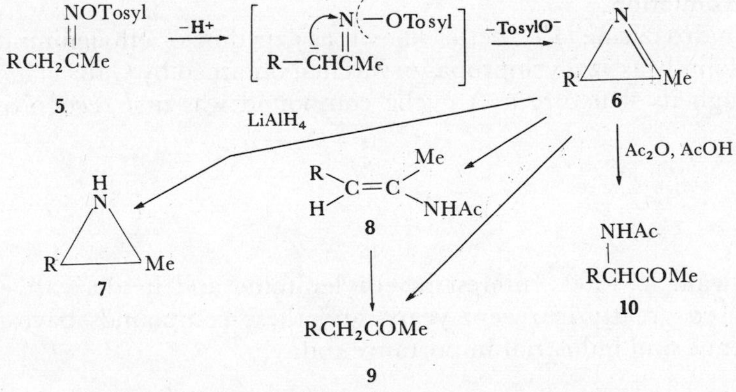

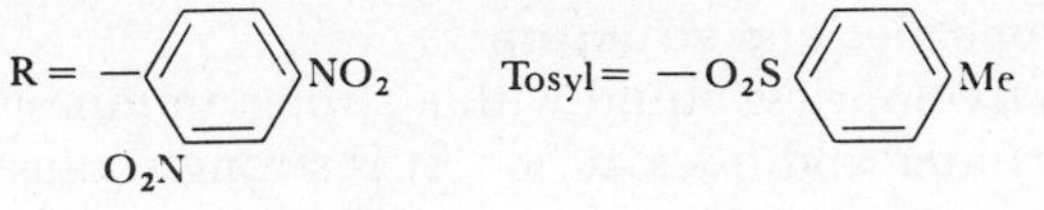

Hydrogenation of the azirine over Raney nickel, followed by purification, gave 2,4-dinitrophenylacetone (**9**) presumably via the imine. With palladium on charcoal as catalyst in acetic anhydride both *cis* and *trans* isomers of **8** were obtained, and both isomers on hydrolysis again gave 2,4-dinitrophenylacetone. Reduction of the azirine with lithium aluminium hydride also gave a small yield of the aziridine (**7**) which was characterized. It is of interest that the nitro groups were not affected by the reagents which reduced the three-membered ring. These reactions, coupled with the confirmatory infrared and ultraviolet absorption spectra of the compounds, leave no doubt as to the correctness of the azirine structure. Some attempts to prepare azirines lacking the nitro groups from oxime 4-toluenesulphonates and potassium ethoxide gave 2-ethoxyaziridines (cf. **13**), but the methiodide of the dimethylhydrazone (**11**) with sodium isopropoxide rapidly cyclized[4] to the azirine (**12**). Subsequent addition of isopropanol was base catalysed, and the resulting aziridine (**13**) with acid yielded the amino ketone (**14**).

(a) = i-PrOH and base,   (b) = azeotropic distillation with PhMe

2. AZIRIDINE

A. Introduction

Dihydroazirine (**15**), better known as aziridine or ethylenimine and occasionally as azacyclopropane, was first obtained by Gabriel in 1888, although its structure as a cyclic compound was first recognized by

Markwald in 1900. Interest in ethylenimine and its derivatives has increased greatly in recent years, and these compounds have much academic and industrial importance today.

B. Physical properties and structure

Aziridine is a colourless liquid with a strong ammoniacal smell. It is miscible with water and boils at 56°. It is strongly caustic to the skin, and it should always be used under a hood (cf. p. 16). Inhalation of the vapour causes acute inflammation of the eyes, nose, and throat, and an individual may become sensitized to it. It is strongly basic[5] (pK_a 7·98) but is much less so than dimethylamine (pK_a 10·87). The microwave spectrum[6] of the vapour has given the following structural data:

Aliphatic	C—C,	1·54 Å
Aliphatic	C—N,	1·47 Å

Me $\diagdown$ N, 111 ± 3°
Me $\diagup$

The results also indicate that the N–H bond is at 112° to the plane of the ring. The strain energy of the ring, due to the distortion of most of the bond angles and distances from normal, has been estimated[7] approximately as 14 kcal/mole from combustion data. The strain in the ring is also reflected in the change of the C–H bending frequency in the infrared[8] from normal (1465 cm^{-1}) to 1475 cm^{-1}, and the N–H vibration frequency (1441 cm^{-1}) is lower than normally encountered in secondary amines (1460 cm^{-1}). These physical data completely confirm the much earlier deduction, made from the many facile ring-opening reactions, that the aziridine ring, like other three-membered rings, must be highly strained, but nevertheless it is more easily formed than the corresponding four-membered ring (p. 39).

C. Chemical properties

Aziridine is not a very stable compound as normally obtained, but in the absence of catalysts is stable at 150°. It is best stored over sodium hydroxide in sealed bottles in a refrigerator. As may be anticipated from its formula, it has a number of reactions of secondary amines, although often the ring strain makes other reactions of more consequence. It behaves as a secondary amine to phenyl isocyanate and isothiocyanate, giving the ureas; it forms complexes, like ammonia, with metals;[9] and it gives acyl derivatives with acid anhydrides or chlorides in the presence of alkali. The product (16) from benzenesulphonyl chloride is insoluble in alkali, and this, coupled with the stability of aziridine to potassium permanganate, eliminates the possibility that aziridine could be the isomeric vinylamine (17).

16   17

As a secondary amine aziridine gives 1-chloro and 1-bromo derivatives with aqueous hypohalite[10] and will add to activated double bonds:

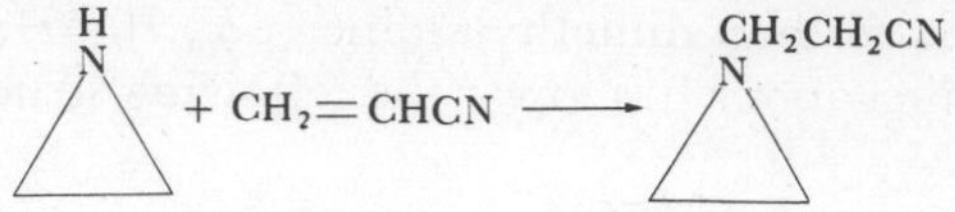

and with methyllithium the N-lithium derivative is obtained. This last compound with alkyl or activated aryl halides gives the corresponding N-substituted aziridines which are otherwise preferably obtained by direct synthesis and not from attempted N-substitution. Even 1,1'-biaziridine can be obtained from the lithium derivative and 1-chloroaziridine.[10] Aziridine with nitrosyl chloride at $-60°$ in ether yields an unstable N-nitroso derivative which could not be isolated but decomposed at $0°$ to nitrous oxide and ethylene. Although 2-chloroethyldimethylamine with silver perchlorate cyclizes to 1,1-dimethylaziridinium perchlorate (18) in 94% yield,[11] aziridine with methyl iodide gives only the ring-opened quaternary salt (19). Presumably the perchlorate anion, in contrast to the iodide anion, is too weakly nucleophilic to attack the ring.

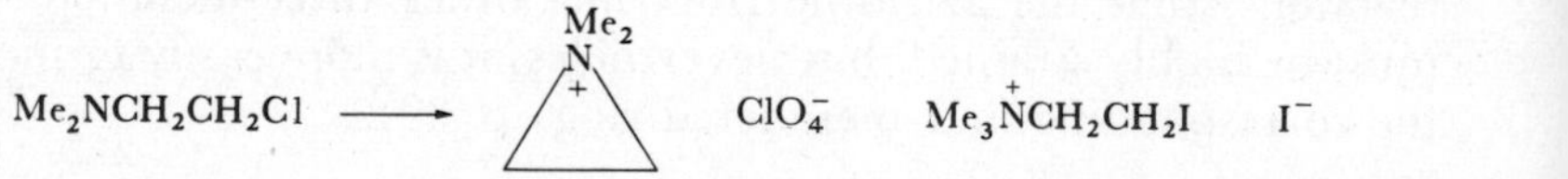

Although pure dry aziridine is comparatively stable, it polymerizes in the presence of traces of water, and rapidly and occasionally explosively in the presence of acids. Carbon dioxide is sufficiently acidic to promote polymerization. Polymerization is almost certainly not free radical in nature, as free-radical polymerization inhibitors do not affect the reaction. Aziridine is stable to bases, and it is thought that the polymerization proceeds through iminium intermediates as indicated. The polymer is linear.

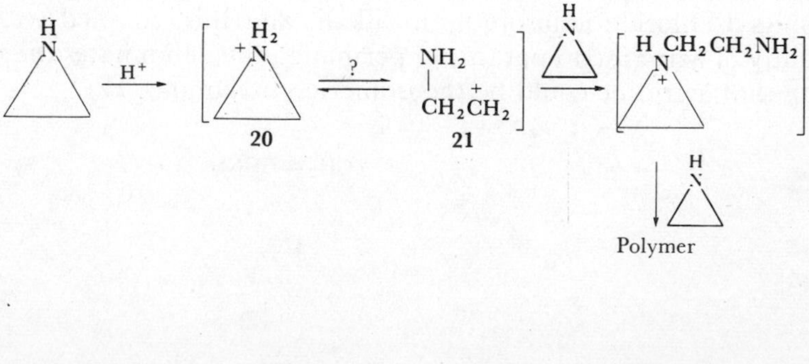

Kinetic and other evidence[12] shows that nucleophilic attack (here by an uncharged aziridine molecule) usually takes place on the cation (20) with simultaneous ring opening rather than on the corresponding carbonium ion (21).

Under proper conditions aqueous hydrochloric acid opens the aziridine ring to give 2-chloroethylamine in a similar way to its reaction

$$\overset{\overset{\text{H}}{\underset{\displaystyle\triangle}{\text{N}}}}{} \quad \underset{\text{NaOH}}{\overset{\text{HCl}}{\rightleftharpoons}} \quad ClCH_2CH_2\overset{+}{N}H_3 \quad Cl^-$$

with oxirane and thiirane. The chloroethylamine with sodium hydroxide gives back aziridine, and the kinetics of these reactions have been examined. The ring opening, in hydrochloric acid, was approximately second order, while cyclization with sodium hydroxide was first order and quantitative. The rate constants for both reactions are greatly influenced by substitution. Later kinetic studies[13] on cyclization of dialkylaminoethyl chlorides showed that reversible cyclization to the aziridine cation (22) took place in dilute aqueous solution and that this could then react with a variety of anions to yield the corresponding products. The reaction with thiosulphate is very fast and is

$$R_2NCH_2CH_2Cl \quad \underset{+Cl^-}{\overset{-Cl^-}{\rightleftharpoons}} \quad \overset{\overset{R_2}{N^+}}{\underset{\displaystyle\triangle}{}} \quad \overset{X^-}{\longrightarrow} \quad R_2NCH_2CH_2X$$

22

$X^- = HO^-, Cl^-, EtCO_2^-, PhCO_2^-, HCO_3^-, \text{ and } S_2O_3^{2-}$

used for estimating aziridines. Dialkylaminoethyl chlorides are well known for dimerizing to the cyclic bisquaternary salts (23), probably via reaction of the halide with a cation molecule (22). This side reaction is of little consequence at the low pH used in the recent kinetic work.

$$\begin{array}{c} \overset{R_2}{\underset{\displaystyle\bigcirc}{N^+}} \\ \overset{N^+}{\underset{R_2}{}} \end{array} \quad 2Cl^-$$

23

Structural evidence supports the partial formation of aziridines as intermediates in some alkylation reactions involving 2-chloroethyl-amines. Diphenylacetonitrile (24) reacts[14] with both 2-chloro-1-dimethylaminopropane (25) and 1-chloro-2-dimethylaminopropane (27) in the presence of potassium t-butoxide to give both 28 and 29.

The only rational explanation of this is that some cyclization to an aziridinium cation (**26**) must occur and that its ring can open in both ways.

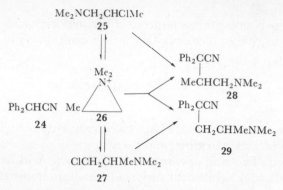

Aziridine reacts with hydrogen sulphide to give 2,2′-diaminodiethyl sulphide (**30**). The reaction has not been halted at the 2-mercapto-ethylamine stage, perhaps because aziridine reacts especially rapidly with thiols; with the essential amino acid cysteine the product is **31**. Water in the presence of dilute nitric or sulphuric acid opens the ring to give ethanolamine (**32**), aqueous sulphur dioxide gives taurine (**33**), while phenol and thiophenol behave similarly, yielding **34** and **35** respectively.

$(H_2NCH_2CH_2)_2S$ $H_2NCH_2CH_2SCH_2CHNH_2CO_2H$ $NH_2CH_2CH_2OH$

  30   **31**   **32**

$NH_2CH_2CH_2SO_3H$ $PhOCH_2CH_2NH_2$ $PhSCH_2CH_2NH_2$

  33   **34**   **35**

Aziridine reacts vigorously with carbon disulphide to give 2-thiathiazol-idone (**36**)[15]

and heating *N*-benzoylaziridine yields a polymer and some 2-phenyl-oxazoline.

Aziridine reacts with acetaldehyde, benzaldehyde, acetone, and some other aldehydes and ketones to give oxazolidines (**37**) at 5–10°, while *N*,*N*-dimethylaziridinium perchlorates behave similarly, leading to salts such as **38**.[16]

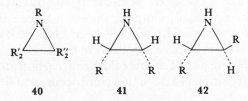

37   38

In the presence of hydrogen sulphide[17] thiazolidines (39) may sometimes be obtained.

39

D. Derivatives of aziridine

As the bonds from a trivalent nitrogen atom are tetrahedrally arranged, it would appear that aziridines of type 40 might be capable of resolution. Racemization would, of course, follow salt formation, which must be excluded. Many attempts to resolve a number of aziridines of this type have, however, been unsuccessful. It appears that the nitrogen atom inverts too easily to permit isolation of the optical enantiomorphs at ordinary temperatures. From nuclear magnetic resonance spectroscopic measurements it has been calculated

40   41   42

that the rate of inversion for N-cyclohexylaziridine is about one hundred times a second at 95°. As N-phenylaziridine inverts very much more rapidly even at $-77°$, conjugation between the substituent and the nitrogen atom is of major importance.[18]

Certain substituted aziridines can, of course, be obtained in *cis* (41) and *trans* (42) forms. A number of examples are known, and in the case where the substituent (R) is phenyl the internally compensated *cis* and the optically active *trans* isomers have been prepared.[19]

The first genuine aziridinone (43) was obtained in 1962, and its structure follows from its nuclear magnetic resonance spectra and the reactions outlined below.[20]

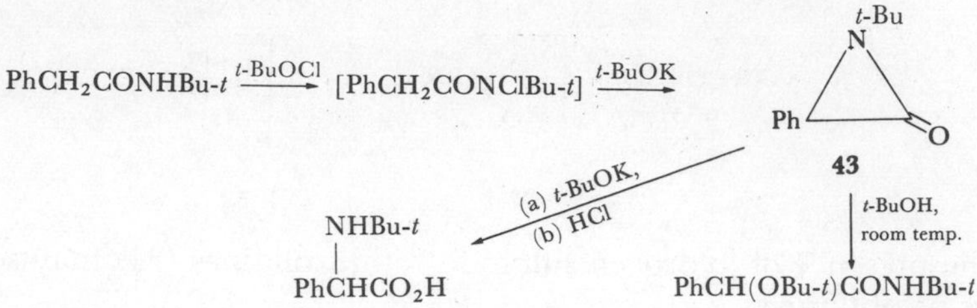

PhCH2CONHBu-t
t-BuOCl
[PhCH2CONClBu-t]
t-BuOK
t-Bu
N
Ph
O
43
(a) t-BuOK,
(b) HCl
NHBu-t
PhCHCO2H
t-BuOH,
room temp.
PhCH(OBu-t)CONHBu-t

A complementary cyclization of the bromo amide **44** has also been carried out[21] and the product (**45**) was indefinitely stable at −78° but decomposed rapidly above 30°. It behaved like **43** towards ionic and non-ionic nucleophiles, and in boiling ether the ring was opened.

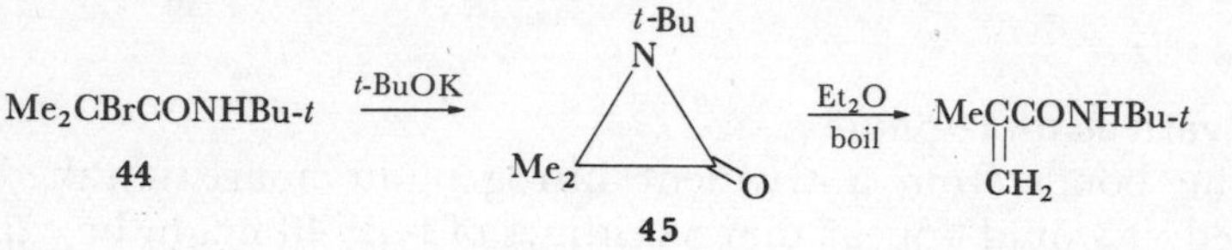

Me2CBrCONHBu-t
44
t-BuOK
t-Bu
N
Me2
O
45
Et2O
boil
MeCCONHBu-t
CH2

Many substituted derivatives of aziridine have been prepared in recent years, and in general their properties can be anticipated from those of the constituent groups.

Ring-opening reactions of asymmetrically substituted aziridines can theoretically take place in three ways, but often one product is largely obtained. Most of the reactions examined involve breaking a carbon–nitrogen bond and have been acid-catalysed, but as base-catalysed ring openings are essentially simpler, they will be considered first.

Several substituted aziridines have been cleaved by aqueous ammonia and ethylamine. The reactions were bimolecular and proceeded through attack by the amine at one of the ring carbon atoms.[22] Walden inversions at the position of attack therefore occur, and the ring openings

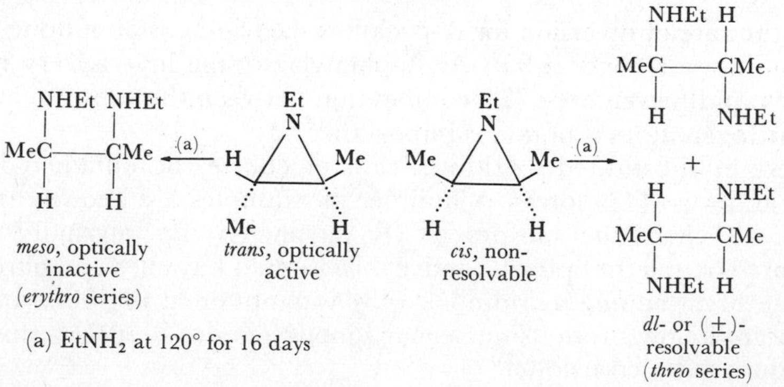

NHEt NHEt
MeC—CMe
H H
meso, optically inactive (erythro series)
(a)
Et
N
H
Me
Me
H
trans, optically active
Et
N
Me
Me
H
H
cis, non-resolvable
(a)
NHEt H
MeC—CMe
H NHEt
+
H NHEt
MeC—CMe
NHEt H
dl- or (±)-resolvable (threo series)
(a) EtNH2 at 120° for 16 days

consequently take place in a *trans* manner. Where the aziridine is un-symmetrical the attacking amine usually reacts with the carbon atom possessing most hydrogen atoms, but sometimes the ring opens in both possible directions. These reactions are similar to those of oxiranes (pp. 20–23) and thiiranes (p. 30). Phenol also reacts with 2,2-dimethyl-aziridine and gives 2-amino-2-methylpropyl phenyl ether.[23]

Acid-catalysed ring openings of aziridines give mixtures much more often than reactions carried out under basic conditions. The *cis* and *trans* isomers of 2,3-diphenylaziridine will be taken as an example. On treatment with hydrogen chloride these compounds are first con-verted into the aziridinium chlorides (**46**). Now if the chloride ion were to attack the 2 position of the aziridinium ring, then by *trans* reaction the *cis* isomer should give only a *threo* product, while the *trans* should give an *erythro* compound. In fact, a mixture of both racemates is obtained from both the *cis*- and the *trans*-aziridines. This leads to the conclusion that in these cases the cyclic cations **46** with the one open-chain form (**47**) or a similar species permitting changes in stereo-chemistry are in equilibrium. The presence of the phenyl groups, in contrast to the otherwise similar case described on page 9, will facilitate the formation of carbonium ions. In some instances, however, only *trans* reaction takes place,[24] and this implies combination of the nucleophile with the cyclic cation, or the aziridine.

The asymmetric 2,2-dimethylaziridine reacts with benzene and alu-minium chloride to give **48**, and similar openings with methanol and with hydrochloric acid have been described. This aziridine opens in the reverse way, however, with hydrogen and Raney nickel as *t*-butylamine is the sole product. 2-Phenylaziridine and its 1-*p*-toluenesulphonyl derivative open between positions 1 and 2 to give the expected products with hydrogen halides, and with hydroxylic compounds in the presence of acids. 2-Phenylaziridine, like aziridine, combines with carbon disulphide, yielding 5-phenylthiothiazolidone.

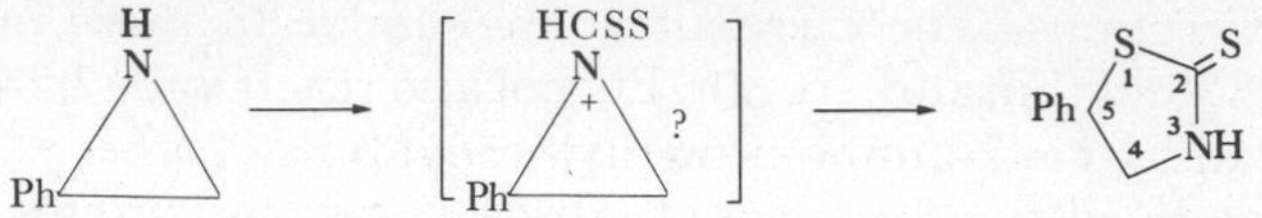

2-Methylaziridine reacts with carbon disulphide and hydrogen chloride, giving 4-methylthiothiazolidone[24] and 2-amino-n-propyl chloride[25] respectively. These results are in agreement mechanistically, but are not in complete accord with the recent report[26] that this aziridine with benzene and aluminium chloride yields **49** (80%) and **50** (20%) unless the aluminium chloride unexpectedly affects the reaction.

$$PhCH_2MeCH_2NH_2 \qquad PhCH_2CHMeNH_2 \qquad BrCH_2CH_2NBuCN$$

49   **50**   **51**

1-n-Butylaziridine gave a normal von Braun product (**51**) with cyanogen bromide while asymmetrically substituted aziridines give mixtures.[27]

Cis- and *trans*-2,3-dimethylaziridine with nitrosyl chloride yield *cis*- and *trans*-but-2-ene respectively in over 99% purity, while in the second case working at low temperatures the *N*-nitroso derivative (**52**)

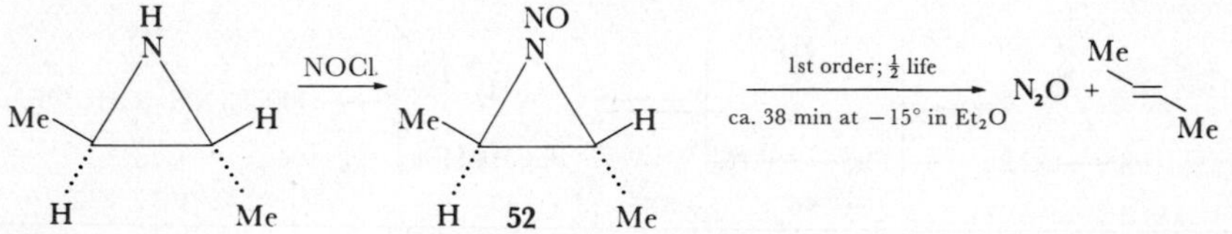

was obtained as a yellow oil decomposing explosively at room temperature.[28] Certain aziridines with electron-attracting substituents can also be opened to olefins by light[29] or acid[30]:

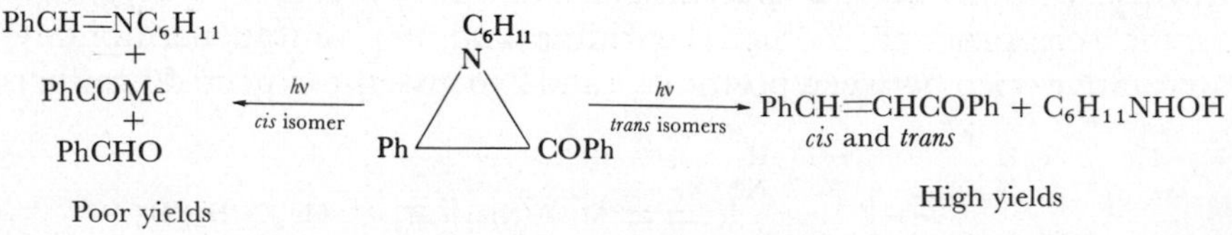

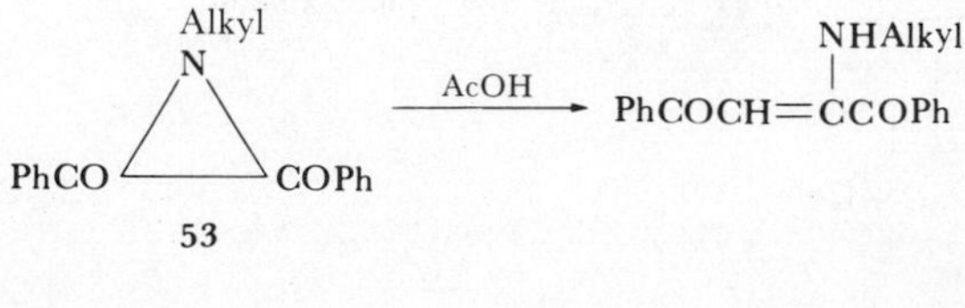

The opening of **53** can be regarded as a reverse Michael reaction.

1,2,3-Triphenylaziridine with diethyl acetylenedicarboxylate, with maleic anhydride, and with potassium *t*-butoxide gave **54**, **55**, and **56** respectively.[31] These are the first examples of the opening of a carbon–carbon bond of an aziridine.

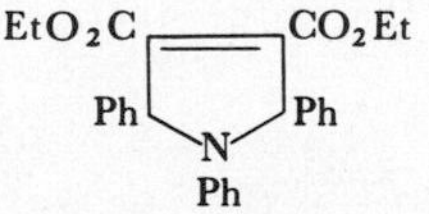

54 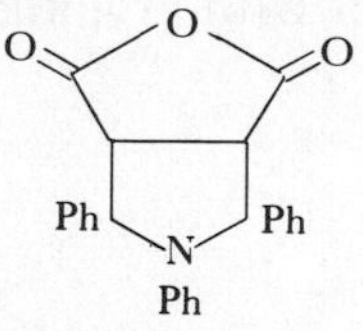   **55** 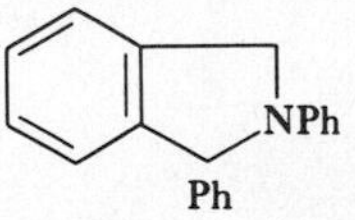   **56**

E. Synthetic methods

Attempts to prepare aziridine from acetylene and ammonia, and by heating ethylenediamine, which gives some piperazine, have failed.

It should be noted that methods (1) and (2) shown below are often complementary, and when one gives bad results the other is satisfactory.

(1) The best preparative method[32] for aziridine, also useful for the

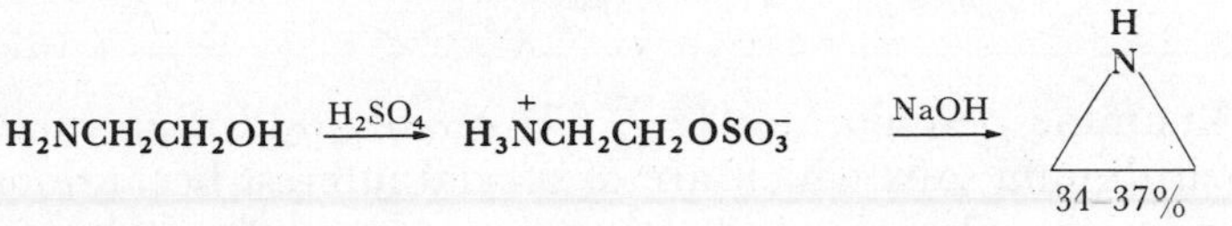

$$H_2NCH_2CH_2OH \xrightarrow{H_2SO_4} \overset{+}{H_3}NCH_2CH_2OSO_3^- \xrightarrow{NaOH} \underset{31-37\%}{\triangle} \overset{H}{\underset{N}{}}$$

synthesis of both *N*- and *C*-alkyl and -aryl[33] derivatives, is to heat 2-aminoethylsulphuric acid with concentrated aqueous sodium hydroxide when aziridine, b.p. 56°, distils over. A small amount of the dimer, 1-(2-aminoethyl)aziridine, b.p. 127°, is also formed.

(2) Another widely used method is the original one of Gabriel for aziridine, the cyclization of a 2-chloro- or 2-bromoethylamine by silver oxide or better by concentrated aqueous potassium hydroxide. The rate of reaction depends largely on the substituents, and the synthesis has also been used for the corresponding four-, five-, and six-membered

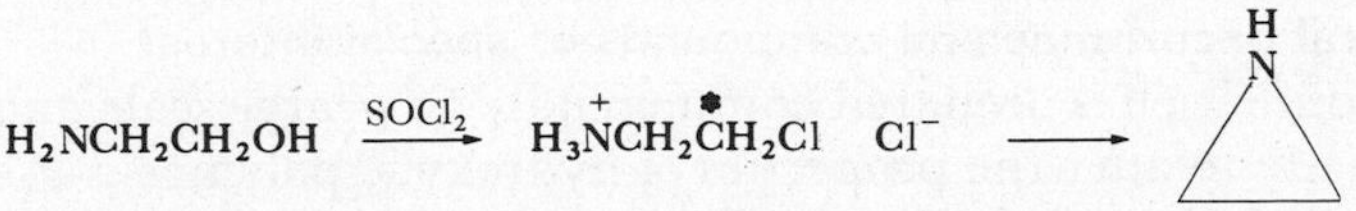

$$H_2NCH_2CH_2OH \xrightarrow{SOCl_2} \overset{+}{H_3}NCH_2\overset{*}{C}H_2Cl \quad Cl^- \longrightarrow \triangle \overset{H}{\underset{N}{}}$$

rings; the five- and six-membered rings are by far the most easily formed. When substituents are present which make observation of the centre of inversion possible it is found that a Walden inversion takes place at the carbon atom marked with an asterisk during the cyclization and a second inversion occurs if the ring is opened during a subsequent reaction,[34] as is also the case with the oxiranes (p. 23) and thiiranes (p. 33). N-Alkyl or -aryl, or benzenesulphonyl derivatives of 2-chloro-ethylamines also cyclize with alkali to the N-substituted aziridines.

(3) A remarkable synthesis of the aziridine ring occurs when alkyl- or arylmagnesium halides react with aryl alkyl ketoximes, e.g.

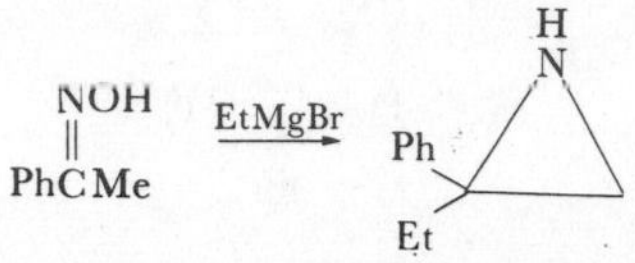

In a similar reaction dibenzyl ketoxime with lithium aluminium hydride in tetrahydrofuran, but not in ether, gives 2-benzyl-3-phenyl-aziridine.[35]

(4) The decomposition[36] of ethyl azidoformate in cyclohexene yields an aziridine:

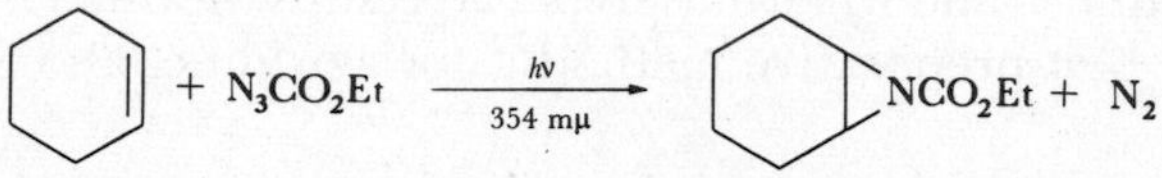

(5) Enamine perchlorates (e.g. 57) readily add diazomethane to form aziridinium salts which are of special interest because on treatment with water or alcohols azepines (e.g. 58) are formed.[37]

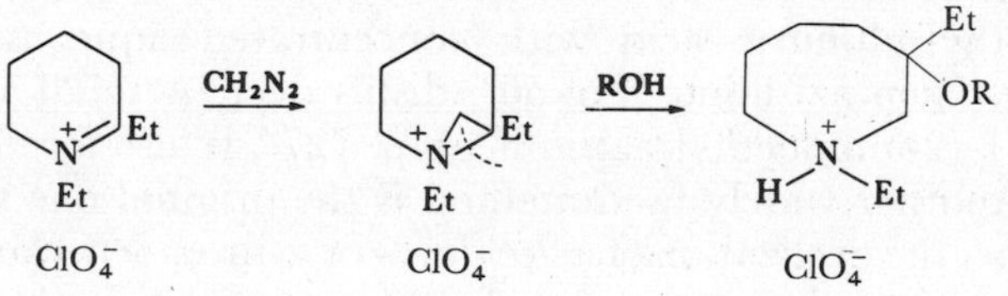

57   58

F. Natural occurrence and compounds of special interest

Aziridine itself is prepared commercially on a large scale and is used industrially to alter the properties of hydroxylic polymers.

The unpleasant handling properties of aziridine are due to its great reactivity, and it is worth noting that it has some carcinogenic activity in rats, while its N-acetyl, and many other N-acyl, derivatives are more powerful in this respect. However, some of its derivatives, notably 59, 60, and 'Tetramin', are under clinical trial as anticancer agents.

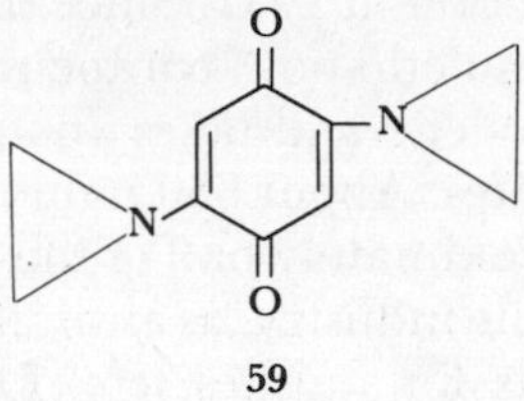

59

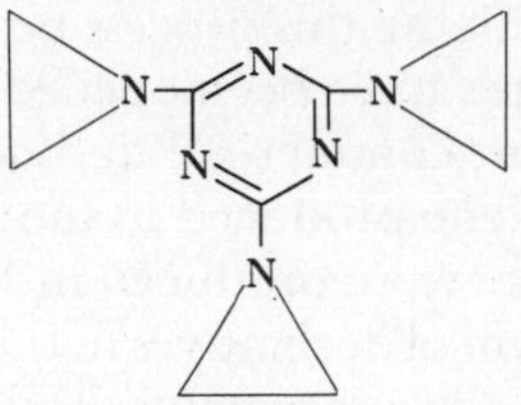

60

Tetramin[38] is the 2:1 mixture of **61** and **62** obtained from 2-vinyloxi-rane with aziridine. A recently discovered[39] class of antibiotics posses-ses both the aziridine rings and anticancer activity. One of these com-pounds, mitomycin A has structure **63**. Some of the toxic properties of

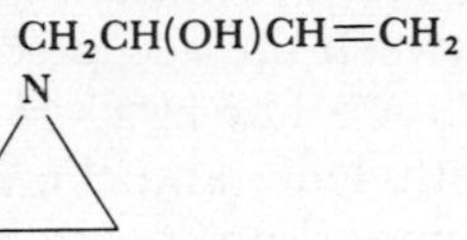

$CH_2CH(OH)CH{=}CH_2$

61

CH_2OH
$CHCH{=}CH_2$

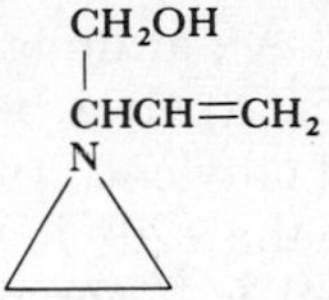

62

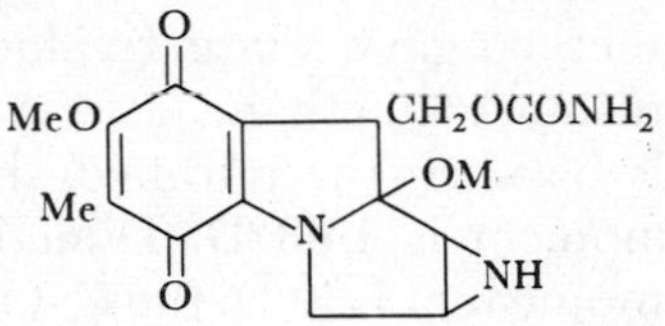

63

the 'nitrogen mustards', e.g. $MeN(CH_2CH_2Cl)_2$, which are analogues of mustard gas, $S(CH_2CH_2Cl)_2$, may be related to the fact that they cyclize to reactive aziridines under physiological conditions.

3. OXIRANE OR ETHYLENE OXIDE

A. Introduction

The simplest oxygen-containing heterocycle, oxirene (**1**), has not yet been described although there is evidence[40] that 2,3-diphenyl-oxirene is an intermediate in the oxidation of diphenylacetylene by peroxy acids. Oxirane or ethylene oxide (**2**) is also known as 1,2- or β-oxidoethane, or α,β-epoxyethane, and rarely as oxacyclopropane. It was first obtained by Wurtz in 1859, but attracted little attention until about 1925, when ethylene chlorohydrin became commercially

available from ethylene. Treatment of the crude chlorohydrin with caustic soda gives up to 95% of oxirane. In 1931 a patent was taken out on the direct oxidation of ethylene to oxirane by oxygen, and the first plant utilizing this process began production in 1937. Since then many new plants have been opened, and next to ethanol, oxirane is the most important commercial derivative of ethylene and takes about 30% of the ethylene produced in the United States. About 650 million pounds of oxirane were produced in 1954. Approximately half of this was used in the form of derivatives in the automobile industry, as antifreeze bases, brake-fluid components, resins, solvents for finishes, etc. Oxirane is clearly a very important industrial chemical.[41]

B. Physical properties and structure

Oxirane is a colourless liquid, b.p. 10·7°. The most accurate structural data for the molecule are derived from microwave spectrum measurements.[42] The C–C distance is in agreement with a recent electron diffraction value[43] (1·46 ± 0·03 Å), although earlier studies with this method gave a larger value (1·54 Å). It is between the accepted C–C distances in ethane (1·54 Å) and ethylene (1·35 Å). The H–C–H angle is between the tetrahedral and the 120° in ethylene, and the dipole moment is 1·88 D. Dimethyl ether,[44] for comparison, has a dipole moment of 1·30 D, the C–O distance is 1·416 ± 0·003 Å and its C–O–C angle is 111·5°. In water the H–O–H angle is 104·5°, while for pure p orbitals it would be 90°. Oxirane has been assumed to have p^2 bonding, with 'bent' bonds lying along the arc, tangents to the C and O orbitals.[42] The strain in the ring is also reflected by the C–H vibration frequency in the infrared,[8] which is at 1500 cm^{-1} instead of at the normal value of 1465 cm^{-1} for aliphatic compounds. The strain energy,

from combustion data, has been estimated[7] at about 13 kcal/mole, a similar figure to those obtained for thiirane and aziridine. The ring is, of course, very easily opened. Oxirane, qualitatively, has a similar effect to that of a carbonyl (C=O) or alkenyl (C=C) group on the ultraviolet absorption spectrum of a conjugated molecule.

C. Chemical properties

Oxirane, or ethylene oxide, is a well-known stable laboratory reagent which, because of its low b.p. (10·7°), is available in sealed glass tubes or metal cylinders. Care should be exercised in its manipulation, for application of even a 1% solution to human skin for 15 minutes gives bad blisters; it should always be used under a hood. Although its ring is highly strained and liable to open, oxirane does, like other ethers, form a 1:1 addition compound with boron trifluoride at $-78\cdot8°$. This compound decomposes reversibly on heating, unlike comparable

addition compounds of the four-, five-, and six-membered ring cyclic ethers, which decompose irreversibly and give some hydrogen fluoride. Oxirane is a much poorer electron donor than these other cyclic ethers, as is shown by the heats of mixing with chloroform (Table 1).

TABLE 1. Heats[45] of mixing with chloroform at $13°$

Compound	Heat of mixing (cal/mole)
Oxirane	365
Oxetane (trimethylene oxide)	760
Tetrahydrofuran (tetramethylene oxide)	750
Tetrahydropyran (pentamethylene oxide)	640
Diethyl ether	650

The oxidation of oxirane itself with platinum black and oxygen gives glycollic acid, while thermal decomposition over magnesium oxide at $400°$ yields mainly acetaldehyde and condensation products. It has been suggested[46] that the biradical $\cdot CH_2CH_2O\cdot$ is an intermediate. Homogeneous thermal decomposition at $400°$ gives ketene, acetaldehyde, and formaldehyde.[47] The reduction of oxirane with lithium aluminium hydride, or with hydrogen over nickel or palladium catalysts, gives ethanol.

Oxirane polymerizes slowly on standing with sodium hydroxide or zinc chloride, while the reaction is faster with stannic chloride. Peroxides and ultraviolet light do not cause polymerization, which therefore proceeds by ionic mechanisms. The acid-catalysed polymerization is probably similar to that of aziridine (p. 8), but under the correct condition dioxane (**3**) can be prepared and is obtained industrially in this

3

way. The alkaline polymerization, which has industrial application mentioned later, probably proceeds by the primary addition of an hydroxyl ion:

$$\overset{O}{\triangle} \xrightarrow{OH^-} \underset{CH_2CH_2O^-}{\overset{OH}{|}} \xrightarrow{\overset{O}{\triangle}} \underset{(CH_2)_2OCH_2CH_2O^-}{\overset{OH}{|}} \xrightarrow{\overset{O}{\triangle}} Polymer$$

Water, preferably in the presence of catalytic amounts of acids or in the vapour phase, converts oxirane into ethylene glycol; the first formed glycol also combines with unused oxirane to give some diethylene

$$\overset{O}{\triangle} \longrightarrow \left[\overset{\overset{H}{\overset{|}{O^+}}}{\triangle}\right] \xrightarrow{OH^-} HOCH_2CH_2OH$$
$$\xrightarrow[-H^+]{glycol} HOCH_2CH_2OCH_2CH_2OH$$

4

glycol (**4**) as a by-product. The reaction with water has great commercial importance. The use of alcohols instead of water gives the corresponding glycol monoethers, which are useful industrial solvents. Hydrogen fluoride in ether, and the other hydrogen halides, give the corresponding halogen hydrins with oxirane, while treatment with even aqueous sodium bromide or nitrate gives appreciable quantities of ethylene bromohydrin and ethylene glycol mononitrate respectively.

$$\overset{O}{\triangle} \xrightarrow{H^+} \left[\overset{\overset{H}{\overset{|}{O^+}}}{\triangle}\right] \xrightarrow{X^-} HOCH_2CH_2X$$

Acetyl chloride (reacting as $CH_3CO^+Cl^-$) and a number of other acids, including carboxylic acids, sodium hydrogen sulphite, hydrogen sulphide, and hydrogen cyanide, behave similarly. The last reaction is very important commercially, as an easy dehydration of the resulting 3-hydroxypropionitrile (**5**) yields acrylonitrile (**6**), which is a very valuable polymer intermediate used in the manufacture of Acrilan and Orlon.

$$HOCH_2CH_2CN \longrightarrow CH_2{=}CHCN$$

5   **6**

In the presence of aluminium chloride oxirane alkylates benzene and its derivatives to the corresponding 2-phenylethanols, while more vigorous conditions naturally lead to diarylethanes.

$$PhH \ + \ \overset{O}{\triangle} \xrightarrow{AlCl_3} PhCH_2CH_2OH$$

The reaction between oxirane and Grignard reagents has been used widely to obtain primary alcohols.[48] In the case of ethylmagnesium bromide an addition compound (7) is first formed, which upon distillation of the ether from the reaction mixture is thought to rearrange.

$$\overset{O}{\triangle} \longrightarrow \overset{EtMgBr}{\underset{7}{\overset{\uparrow}{\overset{O}{\triangle}}}} \longrightarrow EtCH_2CH_2OMgBr \xrightarrow{H^+} \text{n-BuOH}$$

Subsequent hydrolysis yields n-butyl alcohol, which is anticipated as the sole product but occasionally secondary alcohols are formed to some extent (10%). This side reaction can be avoided by the use of dialkylmagnesiums, instead of the Grignard reagents. Magnesium bromide, formed from the Grignard reagent, isomerizes the oxirane to acetaldehyde (see also p. 23), which then reacts in the normal way with more Grignard reagent.

$$2\ RMgBr \rightleftharpoons MgR_2 + MgBr_2$$

Oxirane combines very easily with many aromatic and aliphatic amines, yielding 'ethanolamines'. With ammonia, for instance, 'monoethanolamine' (8), 'diethanolamine' (9), and 'triethanolamine' (10) are obtained according to the conditions. This type of reaction is

$$\overset{O}{\triangle} + NH_3 \longrightarrow \begin{array}{ll} H_2NCH_2CH_2OH & 8 \\ HN(CH_2CH_2OH)_2 & 9 \\ N(CH_2CH_2OH)_3 & 10 \end{array}$$

very general, but in the laboratory secondary amines are used where possible, as only one product can then ensue.

In a similar way sodium alkoxides, phenates, and thiophenates react with oxirane, yielding the corresponding ethers.

$$\overset{O}{\triangle} \xrightarrow[\text{(b) } H^+ \text{ aq.}]{\text{(a) PhONa}} PhOCH_2CH_2OH$$

Sodium derivatives of compounds with activated methylene groups, such as acetoacetic ester, malonic ester, etc., also combine with oxiranes, lactones usually being the end products.

$$(Na^+)\ \bar{C}H(CO_2Et)_2\ +\ \underset{\triangle}{\overset{O}{\triangle}}\ \longrightarrow\ \left[\begin{array}{c} CH(CO_2Et)_2 \\ | \\ CH_2CH_2O^- \end{array} \right] \xrightarrow{-EtO^-} \underset{CO_2Et}{\overset{O}{\bigcirc}}=O$$

Aldehydes and ketones combine with oxirane in the presence of acidic catalysts such as stannic chloride to give dioxolanes, but the yields are often poor because of simultaneous polymerizations.

$$PhCHO\ +\ \underset{\triangle}{\overset{O}{\triangle}}\ \longrightarrow\ \text{(2-phenyl-1,3-dioxolane ring)}$$

2-Phenyl-1,3-dioxolane

D. Derivatives of oxirane

As in the case of the other three-membered heterocylics, very few functional derivatives involving the carbon atoms of the ring are known. Oxiranone (**11**), a hypothetical dehydration product of

11

glycollic acid, is unknown and there is only one unconfirmed claim concerning a derivative in the literature. Some 2-methoxyoxiranes (**12**) have been obtained from the α-chloro ketones and sodium methoxide. They behave as reactive acetals and decompose very easily as shown.[49] A small number of 2-acetoxyoxiranes have been obtained

$$PhCOCHClR \xrightarrow{NaOMe} \underset{\text{MeO}}{\overset{O}{\underset{Ph \rule{0pt}{1em}}{\triangle}} R}$$

R = Ph or Me

$\xrightarrow{H_2O}$ PhCOCHOHR

$\xrightarrow{AcOH}$ PhCOCHOAcR

$\xrightarrow{MeOH}$ PhC(OMe)_2CHOHR

12

from the corresponding ethylenes with perbenzoic acid and have similar properties. Many substituted oxiranes are known, and on the whole they behave as expected, considering their substituent groups. The

oxiranecarboxylic esters, often known as glycidic esters, are easily prepared by the Darzens reaction (p. 27) and are an exception. On treatment with cold alkali followed by acid, hydrolysis and rearrangement
take place, giving aldehydes or ketones, often in excellent yield.[50]
The isomerization of oxiranes not possessing an ester group usually
proceeds via a hydride shift giving mostly the aldehyde, and is catalysed
by magnesium bromide, by phosphoric acid, and by bases; ketones and
allyl alcohols are occasionally obtained, however.

$$R \overset{O}{\underset{R'}{\diagup\!\!\diagdown}} CO_2Et \longrightarrow RR'CHCOR'' + RR'R''CCHO$$

Asymmetrically substituted oxirane rings are opened by anionic
attack under alkaline conditions. The opening therefore proceeds by a
Walden inversion and is *trans*, as is the case with analogous aziridines
(p. 12). This can be illustrated by the case of *cis*-2,3-dimethyloxirane,
which with a large excess of ethylamine yields the *threo* amino alcohol,[22] which can be resolved.

$$Me \overset{O}{\diagup\!\!\diagdown} Me \quad \xrightarrow{EtNH_2} \quad \begin{matrix} Me & & Me \\ H-C-OH & & HO-C-H \\ | & + & | \\ EtHN-C-H & & H-C-NHEt \\ Me & & Me \end{matrix}$$

(*threo* series)

Where two carbon atoms are otherwise equivalent, anionic attack
usually takes place at the atom possessing most hydrogen atoms. Thus
the reactions of 2-methyloxirane (propylene oxide, **13**, R = H) and of
2,2-dimethyloxirane (isobutylene oxide, **13**, R = Me) with amines,
sodium derivatives of alcohols, phenols, acetoacetic ester, etc., yield
alcohols exemplified by **14** and **15**. 2-Ethyloxirane and lithium
borohydride give exclusively 1-methylpropanol (**16**), while 2-methyl-

$$R \overset{O}{\underset{Me}{\diagup\!\!\diagdown}} \quad MeRC(OH)CH_2NR_2' \quad MeRC(OH)CH_2OR' \quad MeCH_2CHMeOH$$

13   **14**   **15**   **16**

oxirane and ethylmagnesium bromide yield[48] pentan-2-ol. 2-Methyl-
oxirane on reduction with lithium aluminium hydride gives isopropanol largely, while Raney nickel and hydrogen give n-propanol.
The production of secondary[51] and primary alcohols respectively by
these two reagents is fairly general. However, 2-phenyloxirane with

lithium borohydride gives[52] 74% of 1-phenylethanol and 26% of 2-phenylethanol. Substituents on the benzene ring greatly influence the proportions of the two possible products.

$$\text{Ph}\overset{O}{\triangle} \longrightarrow \text{PhCH(OH)Me} + \text{PhCH}_2\text{CH}_2\text{OH}$$
$$74\% \qquad\qquad 26\%$$

In acid-catalysed openings of asymmetric oxirane rings the direction of opening is not always the same as in the alkaline reaction. Usually mixtures of products are obtained and it is difficult to predict the outcome with confidence in an unknown example.

The rates of opening of the epichlorhydrin ring (**17**), when the ring is protonated, by Cl⁻ and OH⁻ have been examined and are about 400 times as fast as the comparable basic reactions. If the protonated

$$\text{ClCH}_2\overset{O}{\triangle} \qquad \underset{R'\quad R'''}{\overset{H}{\underset{18}{R\overset{O^+}{\underset{3\quad 2}{\triangle}}R''}}} \rightleftharpoons \underset{19}{RR'\overset{OH}{\underset{+}{C}}-CR''R'''} \quad\text{or}\quad \underset{20}{RR'\overset{+}{C}-\overset{OH}{C}R''R'''}$$

17

ring can open to give carbonium ion, which can then by a fast reaction combine with the anion to give the product, then it would appear that the ring would open to give the more stabilized carbonium ion, which in general has the positive charge on the most highly substituted carbon atom. This leads to the racemization of the carbon atom bearing the charge and the opposite mode of ring opening to that obtained in the alkaline reaction. In the case of 2-methyloxirane (**21**), which would not be expected to give carbonium ions readily, acid-catalysed ring opening in the presence of chloride ions obeys second-order rate equations[53] between pH 7 and 2 when the proportion of the 'abnormal' product (**23**) increases from 14% to 39%. In this case it is clear that attack of the anion occurs on the protonated oxirane (**18**), as for aziridine (p. 9), rather than on a carbonium ion (**19** or **20**). 2-Methyloxirane (propylene oxide) with hydrogen chloride gives 80–90% of **22** with 20–10% of

$$\text{Me}\overset{O}{\triangle} \longrightarrow \text{MeCHOHCH}_2\text{Cl} + \text{MeCHClCH}_2\text{OH}$$
$$\qquad\qquad\qquad\qquad 22 \qquad\qquad\qquad 23$$

21

23. In the acid-catalysed opening with alcohols both isomers are obtained in roughly equivalent proportions. Hydrogen chloride with

2,2-dimethyloxirane gives about 60% of 2-chloro-2-methylpropanol, while in the case of 2-phenyloxirane (styrene oxide) one product (**24**) is obtained virtually exclusively. As in the case of the aziridines, substituents in the aryl or alkyl group can alter the proportions of the possible products very substantially.[52]

$$Ph \triangle \longrightarrow PhCHClCH_2OH$$
$$24$$

Epichlorhydrin (**25**) is a useful synthetic intermediate obtained from glycerol. Its reactions with secondary amines are of interest. First the oxide ring is opened normally. If more amine is present it acts as a base and reforms an oxirane, while if excess is available the diamino alcohol is formed.

$$\underset{25}{\triangle}CH_2Cl \xrightarrow{R_2NH} R_2NCH_2CHOHCH_2Cl \xrightarrow{R_2NH} \underset{R_2NCH_2}{\triangle} \longrightarrow R_2NCH_2CHOHCH_2NR_2$$

$(NC)_2 \triangle (CN)_2$	$(NC)_2C\!=\!C\overset{OH}{\underset{CN}{}}$	pyridinium $\overset{+}{N}$ $^-C(CN)_2$	$CO(CN)_2$
26	**27**	**28**	**29**

Tetracyanooxirane (**26**) reacts very easily with nucleophilic reagents, for example boiling with water displaces a cyano group yielding **27**. With pyridine at 0° the zwitterion (**28**) and mesoxalic nitrile (**29**) are obtained, while reaction with acetylene and ethylene gives the furans **30** and **31**, respectively. These are the first examples which have been found of the scission of the carbon–carbon bond of an oxirane.[54]

$(NC)_2 \underset{O}{\boxed{}} (CN)_2$	$(CN)_2 \underset{O}{\boxed{}} (CN)_2$
30	**31**

E. Synthetic methods

Attempts to cyclize ethylene glycol to oxirane have not been successful. Vigorous dehydration initially gives the enol form of acetaldehyde, which then rearranges and polymerizes, and other conditions yield dioxane (p. 20).

(1) The direct oxidation of ethylene by air over a silver catalyst under the correct conditions gives about 50% oxirane. The reaction has much industrial value.

$$CH_2{=}CH_2 \xrightarrow{\quad [O] \quad} \triangle{O} + H_2O + CO_2$$

(2) The oxidation of olefins with isolated double bonds by perbenzoic, the crystallizable 3-chloro derivative, or monoperphthalic acids[55] gives the corresponding oxirane. The reaction is carried out in organic solvents and gives excellent results. The rate of reaction depends greatly on substituents, and the reaction proceeds by *cis* addition to the double bond. If the double bond is conjugated with a carbonyl group the

$$\underset{R'}{\overset{R}{\diagdown}}C{=}C\underset{R'''}{\overset{R''}{\diagup}} \xrightarrow{\quad PhCO_2OH \quad} RR'\triangle R''R'''$$

reaction rate is extremely slow. However, in such cases hydrogen peroxide and sodium hydroxide, a combination which does not attack isolated double bonds, usually yields the oxirane. Reaction may proceed via a type of Michael addition as indicated:

$$RR'C{=}CHCOMe \xrightarrow{\quad HOO^- \quad} \left[\begin{array}{c} HO \\ RR'C{-\!-\!-}CHCOMe \end{array} \right] \xrightarrow{\quad -HO^- \quad} RR'\triangle COMe$$

(3) The dehydrohalogenation of ethylene halohydrins by alkali at room temperature is a widely used general method. There is an inversion of configuration (Walden inversion) at the carbon atom losing the halogen and a *trans* cyclization which has been amply demonstrated in the formation of substituted oxiranes. Many examples of the completely analogous cyclization of glycol monotoluenesulphonyl derivatives to epoxides with the elimination of the toluenesulphonyl group are well known in the sugar series, and an oxirane can be formed only if the OH and O-tosyl groups are initially *trans*.

$$\underset{\quad\quad X}{\overset{OH}{CH_2{-}CH_2}} \xrightarrow{\quad base \quad} \underset{\quad\quad X}{\overset{O^-}{CH_2{-}CH_2}} \xrightarrow{\quad\quad} \triangle{O} + X^-$$

Similar types of synthesis are the Hofmann decomposition of amino

$$\underset{\underset{^+NMe_3}{|}}{\overset{\overset{^-OH}{|}}{CH_2-CH_2}} \xrightarrow{-Me_3N} \left[\underset{CH_2-\overset{+}{C}H_2}{\overset{\overset{OH}{|}}{}}\right] \xrightarrow{-H^+} \triangle O$$

alcohols and the action of nitrous acid on certain amino alcohols.

(4) Condensation of an aldehyde or ketone with an α-chloro ester in the presence of sodium ethoxide or amide, the Darzens reaction,[50] gives an 'epoxy' ester. The reaction can be used with both aromatic and aliphatic compounds, and is mainly of interest as a route to aldehydes and ketones by decomposition of the acid formed on hydrolysis (see p. 23).

$$RR'CO + ClCH_2CO_2Et \xrightarrow[-H^+]{base} \left[\underset{RR'CCHClCO_2Et}{\overset{\bar{O}}{|}}\right] \xrightarrow{-Cl^-} \underset{RR'\diagdown\quad\diagup CO_2Et}{\triangle O}$$

(5) Diazomethane reacts with aldehydes and ketones to yield mixtures of higher aldehydes, ketones, and oxiranes.[56] Substitution has a very great effect on the course of the reaction, and in an unknown case it is difficult to predict the major product.

$$RR'CO \xrightarrow{CH_2N_2} \left[\underset{RR'C-CH_2\overset{+}{N_2}}{\overset{\overset{O^-}{|}}{}}\right] \xrightarrow{-N_2} \begin{array}{c} RR'\triangle O \\ + \\ RCOCH_2R' \\ + \\ R'COCH_2R \end{array}$$

(6) Dimethylsulphonium methide (32), and other methides,[57] with many aldehydes and ketones give the corresponding oxiranes.

$$\underset{32}{\underset{+}{\overset{\bar{O}}{|}}{Me_2S{=}CH_2}} + RCOR' \longrightarrow \underset{RR'}{\triangle O} + Me_2SO$$

F. Natural occurrence and compounds of special interest

The first oxirane found in nature is probably 'auraptin', a coumarin derivative (33). Naturally occurring oxiranes have been reviewed.[58]

Oxirane reacts with proteins at physiological pH and it also gives useful commercial products with nylon, a 'synthetic protein'. 2,2-Bis-oxirane (**34**) is active against certain cancer tumours in rats, and the antibiotic fumagillin (**35**) also contains two oxirane rings.[59]

33   **34**   **35**

Detergents must contain both fat-soluble and water-soluble groups in the same molecule; the fat-soluble part is largely hydrocarbon and the water-soluble group usually ionic. However, by treating crude highly alkylated phenols ('largely hydrocarbon'), obtained from phenol, olefins, and boron trifluoride, with oxirane and a trace of sodium hydroxide both addition and polymerization occur. When $n =$ 6–12, in the formula below, the oxygenated side chain has sufficient

$$ROH \xrightarrow[\text{NaOH, }150°]{} RO(CH_2CH_2O)_nH$$

hydrophilic properties which are not dependent on a charged ion to make the compound an excellent detergent.[60]

4. THIIRANE

A. Introduction

Thiirene (**1**), the analogue of cyclopropene, has not yet been prepared and derivatives are unknown. Its dihydro derivative, thiirane (**2**), was first prepared in 1920 by Delépine.[61] It is commonly known as ethylene sulphide and occasionally as thiacyclopropane; many thiiranes

1   **2**

are most commonly referred to as the olefin sulphides. Thiirane attracted little attention until 1948, when its potentialities as a reactive analogue of oxirane were appreciated. No naturally occurring thiiranes are yet known.

B. Physical properties and structure

Thiirane is a colourless liquid very sparingly soluble in water but easily soluble in organic solvents. Its b.p. is 55–56°, somewhat higher than that of methyl sulphide, b.p. 38°. The structural constants for the molecule, shown below, have been derived from microwave spectrum measurements.[42] Although the C–S bonds have almost the same length as in dimethyl sulphide (1·81 Å) the C–C bond is intermediate in length between that of ethane (1·54 Å) and ethylene (1·35 Å), and

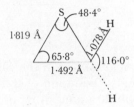

the H–C–H angle is between the tetrahedral and the 120° in ethylene. It may be noted[43] that the H–S–H angle in hydrogen sulphide is 92·1°. The dipole moment[44] (1·66 ± 0·03 D) is higher than that of methyl sulphide (1·40 D), the bond angle of which is 104°.[43] These indications that the thiirane ring is highly strained are reinforced by the small change of the C–H vibration frequency (1475 cm^{-1}) in the infrared[8] from that of a normal C–H in a CH_2 group (1465 cm^{-1}). The strain energy of the ring calculated from the heat of combustion gives[7] a value of about 9 kcal/mole, similar to that obtained for oxirane and aziridine. The ring is likewise easily opened.

C. Chemical properties

Thiirane is much less stable than oxirane, and polymerizes quite easily, even on standing in the dark. It is stabilized by small amounts of mercaptans or hydrogen sulphide, while acetic acid, mineral acids, or strong alkali greatly catalyse the polymerization. The mechanism of the polymerization has not yet been examined. Both ionic (cf. aziridine) and free-radical propagation mechanisms are possible. Substituted thiiranes are usually more stable than the parent compound.

Attempts to oxidize the sulphur atom to the tri- or tetracovalent state have so far been unsuccessful. Methyl iodide gives a crystalline product with several thiiranes, but recent work[62] has shown that *cis*-2,3-dimethylthiirane (**3**) gives the crystalline iodide (**5**) and *cis*-butene. Initial attack of the methyl iodide to give the sulphonium iodide (**4**) as a transient intermediate is not excluded by the experimental data, and is in fact supported by other work (p. 33). **3** and the *trans* isomer are also converted almost exclusively into the *cis*- and *trans*-butenes respectively by iodine in benzene[62] and by triphenyl-phosphine. Oxidation of thiirane with nitric acid gives carboxy-methanesulphonic acid, while treatment with hydrogen peroxide gives[63] 2-hydroxyethylsulphonic acid and not the expected sulphone.

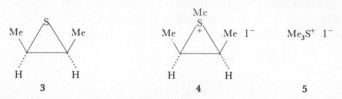

    3   **4**   **5**

The sulphone is, however, obtained in the case of the four-membered ring compound thietane.[63] Oxidation of thiirane with chlorine gives bis-(2-chloroethyl) disulphide among other products. The only thiirane sulphones known are the tetraphenyl- and 2,3-di-*p*-methoxyphenyl-2,3-diethyl derivatives, obtained from sulphur dioxide and the appropriate diazo compounds. On heating, sulphur dioxide is lost, with the formation of olefins;[64] a similar decomposition to olefins takes place with arylthiiranes and copper at 200°.

$$\underset{R'}{\overset{R}{>}}C{=}N_2 \xrightarrow{SO_2} \overset{O_2}{\underset{RR'\triangle RR'}{S}} \xrightarrow{heat} SO_2 + RR'C{=}CRR'$$

Thiirane has many similar ring-opening reactions to its oxygen and nitrogen analogues. The conditions for most of these reactions are very much more critical for good results than those of these analogues owing to the much greater tendency to polymerization. Some polymer is almost invariably obtained even under the most favoured conditions. Cold concentrated hydrochloric acid and thiirane give **6**, **7**, and **8**.

    ClCH$_2$CH$_2$SH   ClCH$_2$CH$_2$SCH$_2$CH$_2$SH

     6   **7**   **8**

Thiirane behaves in an analogous manner to oxirane with primary and secondary amines (preferably in an inert solvent at about 100°), with acetyl chloride, sodium phenoxide,[65] primary alcohols, and mercaptans (in the presence of boron trifluoride), and with phenylmagnesium bromide.[65] Similar ring openings also occur with hydrogen sulphide in methanol, and with potassium hydrogen sulphide or ethyl mercaptide.

In all these reactions the expected addition of the cationic part of the reagent to the sulphur, and the anionic part to the carbon, takes place.

$$\text{(thiirane)} \xrightarrow{\text{PhONa}} PhOCH_2CH_2SNa$$

Thiirane behaves as an epoxide with the lithium derivatives of secondary amines, but phenyllithium gives 51% of thiophenol and some butane-1-thiol.[66] In contrast to oxirane, it does not react with ethyl malonate or ethyl acetoacetate, but does so with the more reactive ethyl cyanoacetate to give[67] a cyclic product (9) along with much polymer.

$$\text{(thiirane)} + NCCH_2CO_2Et \xrightarrow{\text{base}} \left[\begin{array}{c} S^- \quad CN \\ CH_2 \quad | \\ \diagdown \diagup CHCO_2Et \\ CH_2 \end{array} \right] \xrightarrow{H^+} \text{(9)}$$

9

D. Derivatives of thiirane

No functional derivatives of the thiirane ring, such as oxothiirane (10), which would be a hypothetical dehydration product of mercapto-acetic acid, have yet been authenticated.

10

Most substituted thiiranes reported behave quite similarly to thiirane itself. The most interesting problem encountered concerns the direction of opening of the asymmetrically substituted thiirane ring. 2-Methyl-thiirane, or propylene sulphide, with hydrogen chloride gives 2-chloro-propyl mercaptan. A similar orientation is obtained with acetyl chloride and bromide, in contrast to that expected by analogy with 2-methyloxirane (p. 24). This reversed mode of ring opening is probably due to the formation of a carbonium ion more easily than with the corresponding oxirane (cf. p. 24). However, with acetic anhydride in pyridine a much slower reaction leading to the 'normal' product (11) takes place. The basic cyclization of 2,2-dimethylthiirane with

$$\text{Me}\diagdown(\text{thiirane}) \xrightarrow{\text{AcCl}} \left[\text{Me}\diagdown(\overset{Ac}{\overset{S^+}{\diagdown}}) \right] Cl^- \longrightarrow MeCHClCH_2SAc \qquad MeCH(SAc)CH_2OAc$$

11

ethyl cyanoacetate and sodium ethoxide also yields the 'normal' product (**12**) exclusively, as does the reaction with amines[67] which gives (**13**). Reduction of 2-butylthiirane with lithium aluminium hydride gives only[66] the secondary mercaptan (**14**), and 2,2-dimethylthiirane, aluminium chloride, and benzene combine to give a mixture of the two possible mercaptans (cf. 2-methylaziridine, p. 14).

12

$Me_2C(SH)CH_2NR_2$ **13**

n-BuCHMeSH **14**

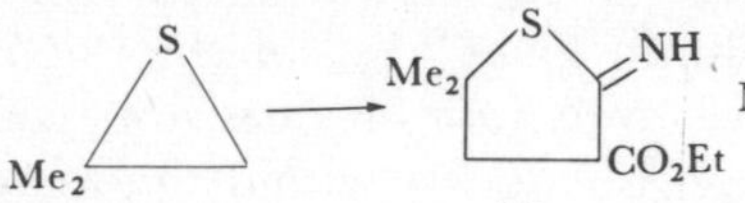

E. Synthetic methods

(1) The best synthesis[68] of thiirane is from 2-mercaptoethanol, which with phosgene in ethyl acetate and pyridine yields monothiolethylene carbonate (**15**). This can be decarboxylated to thiirane in 80–88% yield.

15

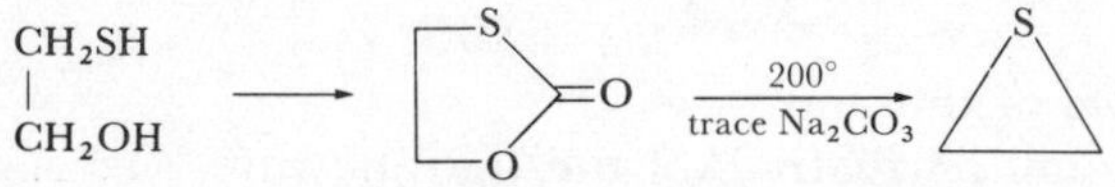

(2) Treatment of the appropriate oxirane, including oxirane itself, with aqueous or aqueous–ethanolic potassium thiocyanate,[69, 70] or less frequently thiourea,[71] at about −7° has been the most common synthesis of thiiranes. The mechanism[70] is thought to involve two Walden inversions and a rearrangement. In the case of cyclohexene oxide, where the oxide ring always opens in a *trans* fashion (p. 23), the first product must be **16**.

16 **17**

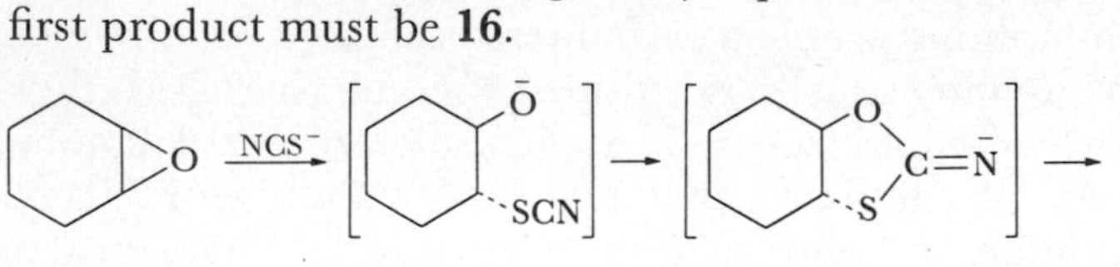

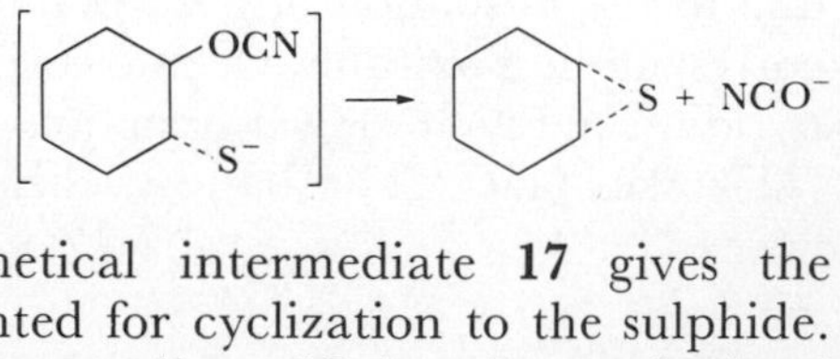

Rearrangement via the hypothetical intermediate **17** gives the *trans* ion, which is correctly oriented for cyclization to the sulphide. The protonated form of the intermediate **17** has been obtained crystalline, and the free base spontaneously loses cyanic acid in ether

solution giving the sulphide. The synthesis fails, in support of the mechanism, with cyclopentene oxide, as the requisite hypothetical intermediate would involve two fused five-membered rings and be in a state of considerable strain. Confirmation of the above mechanism has been obtained from a quantitative study of the cyclization of both the O- and S-monoacetyl derivatives of 2-mercaptoethanol during their conversion by sodium hydroxide into thiirane. From estimations of free thiol and acetyl groups it is clear that the O-acetate is converted into the S-acetate before cyclization occurs. The mechanism also explains the formation of L-(−)-2,3-dimethylthiirane from D-(+)-2,3-dimethyl-oxirane.

(3) A small number of 2-chlorothiols obtained from the hydroxy-thiols by hydrogen chloride have been cyclized to the thiiranes by sodium bicarbonate. This synthesis is complementary to the first in that it can be used for cyclopentene sulphide. The chlorothiol must be *trans*

in order to cyclize, and in this case was obtained from the *trans*-2-hydroxy compound with hydrochloric acid. A Walden inversion to a *cis* product would be expected unless a three-membered sulphonium ring can be formed as an intermediate.

(4) Other synthetic methods[70] used in a few rare instances include the thermal dehydration of 2-mercaptoethanols, the treatment of 1,2-halothiocyanates or 1,2-dithiocyanates with sodium sulphide, and the direct sulphurization of olefins with ethyl tetrasulphide.

5. DIAZIRENE AND DIAZIRIDINE

Diazirene (**1**), first obtained in 1961,[72] is a colourless stable gas, b.p. −14°, with a dipole moment of 1·59 ± 0·06 D. Its molecular dimensions, calculated from the microwave spectrum,[73] show that the molecule is highly strained and eliminate other possible structures. In contrast to 'ordinary' diazomethane, for which the diazirene structure was once considered, diazirene is decomposed comparatively slowly by sulphuric acid with evolution of nitrogen. It is non-basic, stable to potassium dissolved in *t*-butyl alcohol, but is reduced by sodium amalgam to ammonia and methylamine. Cyclohexylmagnesium bromide adds to yield the diaziridine **2**, an example of a general reaction.

Both the thermal decomposition and the photolysis of dimethyl-diazirine yield nitrogen and propene.[74]

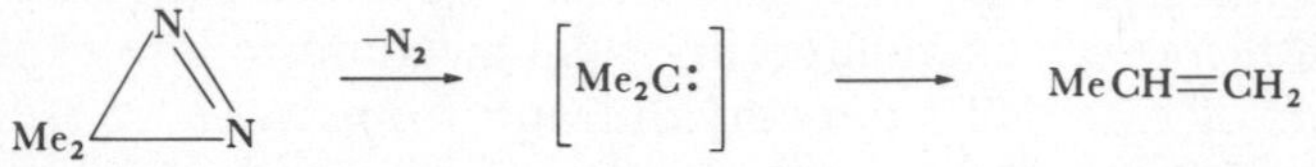

Diazirenes, including **1**, are usually obtained from the appropriate aldehyde or ketone, ammonia, and chloramine, followed by *in situ* oxidation of the resulting diaziridine, or by simple variants of this

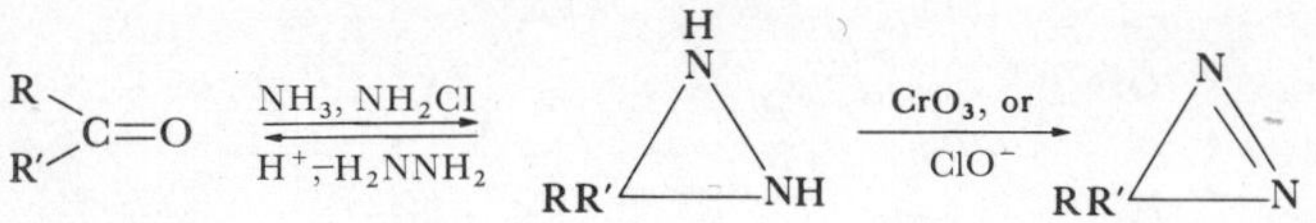

synthesis.[75] The intermediate diaziridines, which can be isolated, are hydrolysed by acid to the original carbonyl compounds and the hydrazine.

Di-*t*-butyldiaziridinone (**3**), prepared as indicated,[76] has high thermal stability and is only slowly attacked by potassium in *t*-butyl alcohol.

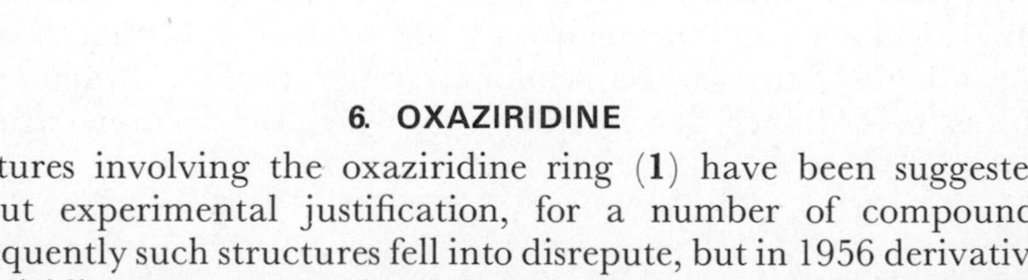

6. OXAZIRIDINE

Structures involving the oxaziridine ring (**1**) have been suggested, without experimental justification, for a number of compounds. Subsequently such structures fell into disrepute, but in 1956 derivatives of oxaziridine were prepared and their ring structures confirmed chemically beyond all doubt.[77] Oxazirene (**2**) and derivatives are not yet known.

Most authentic oxaziridines contain a substituent on the nitrogen atom and have been prepared from the corresponding imine by oxidation with anhydrous peracetic acid. The reaction is quite general and is successful when the parent imine and the resulting oxaziridine

$$\underset{R'}{\overset{R}{>}}C=NR'' \quad \xrightarrow{\text{MeCO}_2\text{OH}} \quad \underset{RR'\text{——}NR''}{\overset{O}{\triangle}}$$

are stable to the acidic conditions. Oxaziridines have also been obtained[78] by the irradiation of nitrones, for example of **4** yielding **3**, and by treating aldehydes or ketones with hydroxylamine O-sulphonic acid.[79] The simple oxaziridines are colourless liquids, and 2-t-butyl-oxaziridine has b.p. 52–54° at 75 mm.

$$\underset{R'}{\overset{R}{>}}C=O \; + \; NH_2OSO_3H \; \longrightarrow \; \underset{RR'\text{——}NH}{\overset{O}{\triangle}}$$

The ring structure was rigorously proved in the case of 2-t-butyl-3-phenyloxaziridine by the degradation sequences shown. This oxaziridine (**3**) can be considered an 'electronic tautomer' of the nitrone (**4**), but their separate identities are beyond all question. The ultraviolet absorption spectrum of the oxaziridine (**3**) is that expected of a compound possessing an isolated phenyl ring, while that of the nitrone shows a strong additional band. Oxaziridines, in contrast to the nitrones, oxidize both iodide and chloride ions to the corresponding halogens, and the iodide oxidation has been used quantitatively. A further

PhCH=NBu-t $\xrightarrow[\text{(a)}]{\text{MeCO}_2\text{OH}}$ $\underset{Ph\text{——}NBu\text{-}t}{\overset{O}{\triangle}}$ $\xrightarrow{\text{H}_2\text{SO}_4}$ t-BuNHOH + PhCHO

3

(a) LiAlH$_4$, same conditions $\underset{\text{light}}{\overset{\text{u.v.}}{}}$ $\Bigg\|$ $\underset{\text{boil}}{\overset{\text{MeCN,}}{}}$

PhCONHBu-t

5

PhCH$_2$NBu-t $\xleftarrow{\text{(a)}}$ PhCH=$\overset{+}{N}$Bu-t
| |
OH   O

4

differentiation has proved possible in the case of the oxaziridine (**6**), which has been obtained partially resolved. It contains an asymmetric carbon atom, while the corresponding nitrone (**7**) does not. Ferrous ions initiate a free-radical reaction with **3** leading to **5**.

$$\text{Me(i-Pr)C} = \overset{+}{\text{N}}\text{Pr-n}$$

Me — (triangle O / NPr-n) — i-Pr   **6** $\overset{-}{\text{O}}$ **7**

Oxaziridine rings are normally opened by acids in the presence of 2,4-dinitrophenylhydrazine, which traps the carbonyl compounds liberated. If the *N*-substituent is tertiary a migration of one group on to the nitrogen atom can take place to allow an otherwise similar decomposition; an alternative scission of the oxaziridine ring by acid is, however, mentioned in the previous paragraph. Oxaziridines are stable

$$\triangle\text{NCMe}_3 \xrightarrow{\text{H}^+} \left[\text{HOCH}_2\overset{+}{\text{N}}\text{CMe}_3 \right] \longrightarrow \left[\text{HOCH}_2\overset{+}{\underset{\text{Me}}{\text{N}}}\text{CMe}_2 \right] \longrightarrow \begin{array}{c} \text{CH}_2\text{O} \\ + \\ \text{Me}_2\text{CO} \\ + \\ \text{MeNH}_2 \ (67\%) \end{array}$$

to sodium methoxide if the substituent on the nitrogen atom is tertiary. If it is secondary the molecule decomposes to the same products as those obtained with acids. If there is no substituent *N*-acylation is effected by acyl halides.[80]

GENERAL BIBLIOGRAPHY

Heterocyclic Compounds with 3- and 4-Membered Rings, ed. Weissberger, Interscience, New York, 1964.

AZIRIDINE
Fruton in *Heterocyclic Chemistry*, ed. Elderfield, Vol. I, Wiley, New York, 1950.

OXIRANE
Winstein and Henderson in *Heterocyclic Chemistry*, ed. Elderfield, Vol. I, Wiley, New York, 1950; Parker and Isaacs, *Chem. Rev.*, **59**, 737 (1959).

THIIRANE
Tarbell and Harnish, *Chem. Rev.*, **49**, 1 (1951).
Sander, *Chem. Rev.*, **66**, 297 (1966).

REFERENCES

1. Coulson and Moffitt, *Phil. Mag.*, **40**, 1 (1949).
2. Smolinsky, *J. Org. Chem.*, **27**, 3557 (1962).
3. Cram and Hatch, *J. Am. Chem. Soc.*, **75**, 33, 38 (1953).
4. Parcell, *Chem. Ind. (London)*, 1396 (1963).
5. Buist and Lucas, *J. Am. Chem. Soc.*, **79**, 6157 (1957).
6. Turner, Fiora, Kendrick and Hicks, *J. Chem. Phys.*, **21**, 564 (1953).

7. Nelson and Jessup, *J. Res. Natl. Bur. Std.*, **48**, 206 (1952).
8. Bellamy, *The Infra-Red Spectra of Complex Molecules*, Methuen, London, and Wiley, New York, 1954.
9. Jackson and Edwards, *J. Am. Chem. Soc.*, **83**, 355 (1961).
10. Graefe and Meyer, *J. Am. Chem. Soc.*, **80**, 3939 (1958).
11. Leonard and Paukstelis, *J. Org. Chem.*, **30**, 821 (1965).
12. Earley, O'Rourke, Clapp, Edwards, and Lawes, *J. Am. Chem. Soc.*, **80**, 3458 (1958).
13. Cohen, Artsdalen, and Harris, *J. Am. Chem. Soc.*, **74**, 1878 (1952), and earlier papers.
14. Schultz and Sprague, *J. Am. Chem. Soc.*, **70**, 48 (1948), and earlier papers.
15. Clapp and Watjen, *J. Am. Chem. Soc.*, **75**, 1490 (1953).
16. Leonard, Paukstelis, and Brady, *J. Org. Chem.*, **29**, 3383 (1964).
17. Bestian *et al.*, *Ann. Chem.*, **566**, 210 (1950).
18. Traylor, *Chem. Ind. (London)*, 649 (1963).
19. Weissberger and Bach, *Ber.*, **64**, 1095 (1931).
20. Baumgarten, Fuerholzer, Clark, and Thompson, *J. Am. Chem. Soc.*, **85**, 3303 (1963).
21. Sheehan and Lengyel, *J. Am. Chem. Soc.*, **86**, 1356 (1964).
22. Ghirardelli and Lucas, *J. Am. Chem. Soc.*, **79**, 734 (1957).
23. Clapp, *J. Am. Chem. Soc.*, **73**, 2584 (1951).
24. Fanta, *J. Chem. Soc.*, 1957, 1441.
25. Gabriel and Ohle, *Ber.*, **50**, 804 (1917).
26. Braz, through *Chem. Abstr.*, **48**, 570c (1954).
27. Hageman, *Org. Reactions*, **7**, 198 (1953).
28. Clark and Helmkamp, *J. Org. Chem.*, **29**, 1316 (1964).
29. Padwa and Hamilton, *J. Am. Chem. Soc.*, **87**, 1821 (1965).
30. Turner, Heine, Irving, and Bush, *J. Am. Chem. Soc.*, **87**, 1050 (1965).
31. Heine and Peavy, *Tetrahedron Letters*, 3123 (1965); Heine and Scholer, *Tetrahedron Letters*, 3667 (1964).
32. Allen, Spangler, and Webster, *Org. Syn.*, **30**, 38 (1950).
33. Brois, *J. Org. Chem.*, **27**, 3532 (1962).
34. Walker, *Ann. Rept. Chem. Soc.*, **49**, 202 (1952).
35. Kitahonaki, Kotera, Matsukawa, Miyazaki, Okada, Takahashi, and Takano, *Tetrahedron Letters*, 1059 (1965).
36. Lwowski and Mattingly, *Tetrahedon Letters*, 277 (1962).
37. Leonard, Jann, Paukstelis, and Steinhardt, *J. Org. Chem.*, **28**, 1499 (1963), and earlier papers.
38. Bottini and Dev, *J. Org. Chem.*, **27**, 968 (1962).
39. Patrick, Williams, Meyer, Fulmor, Cosulich, Broschard, and Webb, *J. Am. Chem. Soc.*, **86**, 1889 (1964).
40. McDonald and Schwab, *J. Am. Chem. Soc.*, **89**, 4866 (1964); Stille and Whitehurst, *J. Am. Chem. Soc.*, **86**, 4871 (1964).
41. Joslin and Steele, *Chem. Eng. News*, 5311 (1955).
42. Cunningham, Boyd, Meyers, Gwinn, and Le Van, *J. Chem. Phys.*, **19**, 676 (1951).
43. Igarashi, *Bull. Chem. Soc. Japan*, **26**, 330 (1953); Abrahams, *Quart. Rev. (London)*, **10**, 407 (1956).
44. Günthard and G umann, *Helv. Chim. Acta*, **33**, 1985 (1950).
45. Searles, Tamres, and Lippincott, *J. Am. Chem. Soc.*, **75**, 2775 (1953).
46. Malinovskii and Baranov, through *Chem. Abstr.*, **49**, 8241f (1955).
47. Mueller and Walters, *J. Am. Chem. Soc.*, **76**, 330 (1954).
48. Gaylord and Becker, *Chem. Rev.*, **49**, 413 (1951).
49. Stevens *et al.*, *J. Am. Chem. Soc.*, **74**, 618 (1952); **75**, 3977 (1953).
50. Newman and Magerlein, *Org. Reactions*, **5**, 413 (1949); Ballester, *Chem. Rev.*, **55**, 283 (1955).
51. Brown, *Org. Reactions*, **6**, 469 (1951).
52. Fuchs and VanderWerf, *J. Am. Chem. Soc.*, **76**, 1631 (1954).
53. Addy and Parker, *J. Chem. Soc.*, 915 (1963).
54. Linn, Webster, and Benson, *J. Am. Chem. Soc.*, **87**, 3651 (1965).
55. Swern, *Chem. Rev.*, **45**, 1 (1949); *Org. Reactions*, **7**, 378 (1953).
56. Gutsche, *Org. Reactions*, **8**, 364 (1954).

57. Johnson, Hruby, and Williams, *J. Am. Chem. Soc.*, **86**, 918 (1964).
58. Cross, *Quart. Rev. (London)*, **14**, 317 (1960).
59. Young, Turner, and Tarbell, *J. Org. Chem.*, **28**, 928 (1963).
60. Birch, *J. Inst. Petrol.*, **38**, 69 (1952).
61. Delépine, *Bull. Soc. Chim. France*, **27**, 740 (1920); **29**, 136 (1921); **33**, 703 (1923).
62. Helmkamp and Pettit, *J. Org. Chem.*, **27**, 2942 (1962), and earlier papers.
63. Walker, *Ann. Rept. Chem. Soc.*, **50**, 233 (1953).
64. Vargha and Kovacs, *Ber.*, **75**, 794 (1942).
65. Oda, through *Chem. Abstr.*, **48**, 1935e (1954); **49**, 1626a (1955).
66. Bordwell, Anderson, and Pitt, *J. Am. Chem. Soc.*, **76**, 1082 (1954).
67. Snyder and Alexander, *J. Am. Chem. Soc.*, **70**, 217 (1948).
68. Reynolds, *J. Am. Chem. Soc.*, **79**, 4951 (1957).
69. Snyder, Stewart, and Ziegler, *J. Am. Chem. Soc.*, **69**, 2672 (1947).
70. Van Tamlen, *J. Am. Chem. Soc.*, **73**, 3444 (1951); Price and Kirk, *J. Am. Chem. Soc.*, **75**, 2396 (1953).
71. Culvenor, Davies, and Heath, *J. Chem. Soc.*, 282 (1949).
72. Schmitz in *Advan. Heterocyclic Chem.*, Vol. II, ed. Katritzky, Academic Press, New York, 1963.
73. Pierce and Dobyns, *J. Am. Chem. Soc.*, **84**, 2651 (1962).
74. Frey and Stevens, *J. Chem. Soc.*, 3514 (1963).
75. Graham, *J. Org. Chem.*, **30**, 2108 (1965).
76. Greene and Stowell, *J. Am. Chem. Soc.*, **86**, 3569 (1964).
77. Emmons, *J. Am. Chem. Soc.*, **78**, 6208 (1956); **79**, 5739 (1957).
78. Splitter and Calvin, *J. Org. Chem.*, **23**, 651 (1958).
79. Schmitz, Ohme, and Murawski, *Angew. Chem.*, **73**, 708 (1961).
80. Schmitz, Ohme, and Schramm, *Tetrahedron Letters*, 1857 (1965).

CHAPTER II

HETEROCYCLIC ANALOGUES OF CYCLOBUTANE

Four-membered rings are not as highly strained as the corresponding three-membered rings, but are more difficult to prepare by the direct cyclization of straight-chain intermediates. This is partly because the atoms which must combine, unlike those which join to give a three-membered ring, can alter their relative positions considerably under the influence of thermal motion. It is only when the cyclizing atoms happen to be suitably oriented and the appropriate stimulus applied that the ring can form. The rate of such cyclizations should therefore be much less than those of the corresponding three-membered rings. Studies of the rate[1] of cyclization of 2-bromoethylamine (**1**) and 3-bromopropylamine (**2**), and the alkaline cyclization[2] of **3** which

$$BrCH_2CH_2NH_2 \qquad BrCH_2CH_2CH_2NH_2$$
$$\mathbf{1} \qquad\qquad\qquad \mathbf{2}$$

gives the aziridine **4**, and not the less strained azetidine **5**, support this contention. Four-membered heterocyclic rings are, in general, fairly easily opened. They are, however, more stable than their three-membered analogues to ring-opening reagents, and although similar reactions ensue, more vigorous conditions are usually required. This is perhaps largely because the normal bond angles and distances are less distorted in four-membered than three-membered rings, and there is therefore less 'strain energy' associated with the larger ring.

Owing to their comparative inaccessibility, the four-membered heterocyclics attracted little attention until about 1943, when the discovery of an azetidin-2-one ring in penicillin gave new interest to the compounds described in this chapter. The first derivative of a four-membered heterocyclic ring containing one double bond was clearly demonstrated in 1961. It contains a sulphur atom (p. 58), and the ring is doubtless strained like that of cyclobutene. The preparation of compounds analogous to cyclobutadiene, such as azete, has not yet been attained and will doubtless be more difficult.

1. AZETIDINE

A. Introduction

The unsaturated compounds, azete (**1**) and azetine (**2**), have not yet been prepared. Several claims concerning derivatives remain un-

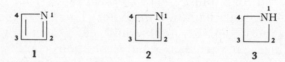

1   **2**   **3**

substantiated but one azetinone has definitely been obtained (p. 44). Azetidine (**3**), commonly known as trimethylenimine and occasionally as azacyclobutane, was first obtained pure in 1899.

B. Physical properties and structure

Azetidine is a colourless liquid, b.p. 61°, which smells like ammonia and fumes in air. It is miscible with water or ethanol, and its basic strength has not been determined. The ring is clearly strained, but its shape and dimensions are not yet available. Azetidine appears to form a much more stable complex with trimethylboron than aziridine. It has been suggested that the ring strain of aziridine increases when the nitrogen becomes tetracovalent, but the heats of formation of the other trimethylboron complexes (**4**) listed in Table 1 are not in simple agreement with this postulate.

4

TABLE 1. Trimethylboron complexes (**4**)[3]

Amine ä	Number of atoms in ring $(n + 1)$	Heat of formation (kcal/mole)	Extrapolated b.p. at 760 mm
Aziridine	3	17·59	159·5
Azetidine	4	22·48	201·4
Pyrrolidine	5	20·43	191·3
Piperidine	6	19·26	176·5

C. Chemical properties

Azetidine itself is comparatively stable, and is largely unchanged when passed over alumina at 360°. Azetidines have many properties of secondary aliphatic amines, and react similarly with potassium cyanate and thiocyanate to form the asymmetric ureas. Carbon disulphide yields the salt (5), while nitrous acid gives an oily nitroso compound (6) as a yellow oil, b.p. 197°. The methylolamine (7), obtained with formaldehyde, cannot be isolated pure, as further reaction to 8 takes place very readily. Benzoyl derivatives of some complex azetidines have been prepared by normal methods. Treatment of azetidine

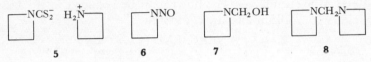

with methyl iodide causes complete methylation to the quaternary iodide; it appears difficult to halt the reaction at the intermediate stage.

The azetidine ring, like that of aziridine, can be opened quite easily, but much polymerization often takes place. With hydrogen chloride 3-chloropropylamine hydrochloride is formed, while hydrogen peroxide

$$\boxed{}\text{NH} \quad \xrightarrow{\text{2 HCl}} \quad \text{ClCH}_2\text{CH}_2\text{CH}_2\overset{+}{\text{N}}\text{H}_3 \ \text{Cl}^-$$

causes decomposition to some acrolein and ammonia. The acid conditions required to hydrolyse the 4-toluenesulphonyl derivative of azetidine are such that the first formed azetidine is instantly decomposed (see also p. 42).

D. Substituted azetidines

A few N-alkylated azetidines have been synthesized and behave very much like tertiary amines. Treatment with alkyl halides gives the cyclic quaternary halides, in contrast to the aziridines. These salts are crystalline solids, soluble in water but not in non-polar solvents. The lower members are hygroscopic or deliquescent, and some tend to polymerize. For example, 1,1-dimethylazetidinium bromide is converted into a linear polymer slowly on standing, or rapidly at 200°, but

$$\boxed{}\overset{+}{\text{N}}\text{Me}_2 \ \text{Br}^- \quad \longrightarrow \quad \text{Me}_2\text{N}(\text{CH}_2)_3\overset{+}{\text{N}}\text{Me}_2(\text{CH}_2)_3\text{Br} \longrightarrow \text{Trimer} \longrightarrow \text{Polymer}$$

the 1,1-diethyl compound does not polymerize under these conditions. The pyrolysis of some azetidinium chlorides merely yields the corresponding dialkylaminopropyl chlorides; this reaction is reversible. The azetidinium hydroxides, prepared with silver oxide and water, are similarly decomposed to 3-hydroxypropylamines. The von Braun decomposition of 1-n-butylazetidine with cyanogen bromide[4] is normal and yields the bromocyanamide.

$$\overset{\text{NBu}}{\square} \xrightarrow{\text{BrCN}} Br(CH_2)_3NBuCN$$

E. Synthetic methods

(1) Azetidine itself is best prepared by treating 1,3-dibromopropane with 4-toluenesulphonamide and alkali. The product cannot be hydrolysed to azetidine (p. 41), but it can be reduced to the base, in 42% yield, with sodium and amyl alcohol.[5]

$$Br(CH_2)_3Br \longrightarrow \overset{NSO_2C_6H_4Me}{\square} \longrightarrow \overset{NH}{\square} + PhMe, \text{etc.}$$

(2) The cyclization of 3-aminoalkyl halides by alkali gives very poor results except when substituents are present. Azetidine was first

$$X(CH_2)_3NHR \xrightarrow{-HX} \overset{NR}{\square}$$

obtained by this method, which is also applicable to the synthesis of 1-phenylazetidine[6] and azetidinium halides from the appropriate dialkylaminopropyl halides.

(3) The pyrolysis of 1,3-diaminopropane is stated to give some azetidine. Only a trace is obtained on distillation of 3-aminopropyl-sulphonic acid with sodium hydroxide (contrast aziridine, p. 15).

F. Natural occurrence and compounds of special interest

Azetidine-2-carboxylic acid (10) has been isolated from the leaves of *Convallaria majalis* Lin. (Lily of the Valley), and its structure has been

$$\begin{array}{ccc}
CH_2NH_2 & & CH_2NH_2 \\
| & \longrightarrow \quad \overset{NH}{\underset{CO_2H}{\square}} & | \\
CH_2CHBrCO_2H & & CH_2CHNH_2CO_2H \\
9 & 10 & 11
\end{array}$$

proved by degradation and also by synthesis from an amino acid (9) and barium hydroxide.[7] It is formed in the plant from methionine.[8] Both azetidine-2-carboxylic acid and the related amino acid (11) occur in *Polygonatum*.[9]

2. AZETIDINONES

A. Introduction

Staudinger,[10] before 1912, initiated work on the chemistry of the azetidin-2-ones or β-lactams. Interest in these compounds was largely lost until 1943, when it was suggested that the penicillins might contain azetidinone rings. Since then a great deal of work has been done on these compounds, including Sheehan's[11] practical synthesis of penicillin V. This synthesis is certainly one of the most outstanding of those in recent years, especially considering the very intensive unsuccessful efforts made in this direction by many groups of workers during World War II, and led the way to other methods of building penicillins.

B. Physical properties and structure

Azetidin-2-one (**1**) was first obtained[12] in 1949. It is a colourless solid, m.p. 73–74°, b.p. 106° at 15 mm, very soluble in ethanol and chloroform and moderately so in ether and benzene. Structural studies have

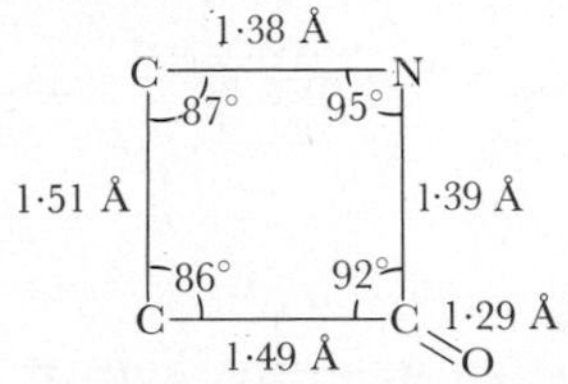

not been carried out. The data given for the azetidin-2-one ring are those obtained from x-ray studies of sodium benzylpenicillin.[13]

C. Chemical properties

Azetidin-2-one (**1**) is not nearly as reactive as oxetan-2-one (p. 53), although it is much more reactive than normal amides. Both alkaline

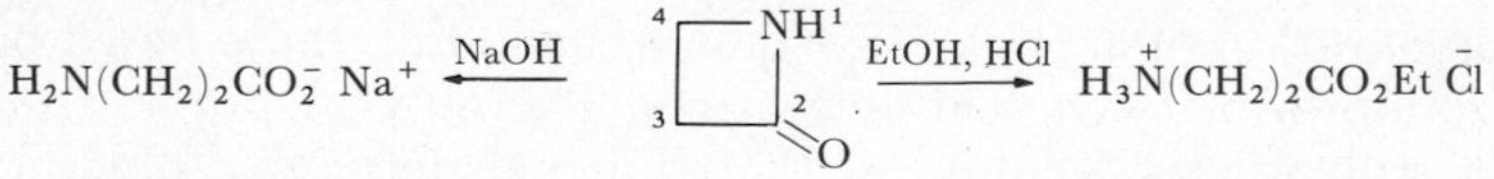

and acid hydrolyses open the ring, but no reaction occurs with saturated aqueous sodium chloride (contrast oxetan-2-one, p. 53). Alkaline hydrolysis opens the ring very much more slowly than in the case of benzylpenicillin.

D. Substituted derivatives, excluding penicillin

The most noteworthy property of alkyl-, and more particularly of aryl-substituted azetidin-2-ones is the difficulty with which they are hydrolysed by alkali. This contrasts very markedly with the easy opening of the fused azetidinone ring in the penicillins. In some cases

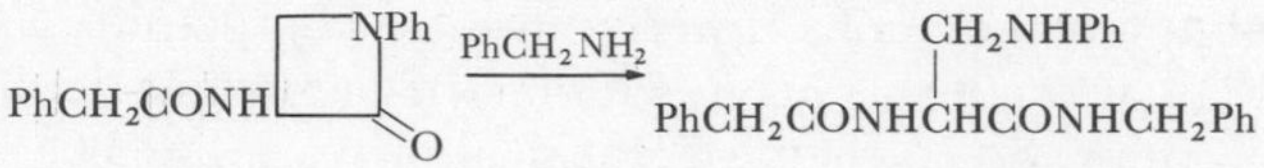

$$PhCH_2CONH-\underset{O}{\square}-NPh \xrightarrow{PhCH_2NH_2} PhCH_2CONH\underset{\underset{CH_2NHPh}{|}}{C}HCONHCH_2Ph$$

the ring has been opened with amines, as is shown above. Hydrogenation also sometimes opens an azetidinone ring, when aromatic groups

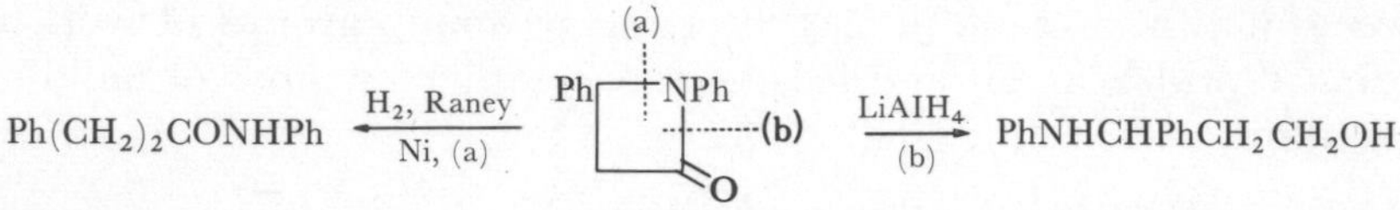

$$Ph(CH_2)_2CONHPh \xleftarrow[Ni,\ (a)]{H_2,\ Raney} Ph-\underset{O}{\underset{(a)}{\square}}-NPh\ \text{(b)} \xrightarrow[(b)]{LiAlH_4} PhNHCHPhCH_2CH_2OH$$

are present; lithium aluminium hydride can also cause both reduction to the azetidine[14] and reductive scission. Thermal decomposition of some azetidin-2-ones can split the molecule in two ways.

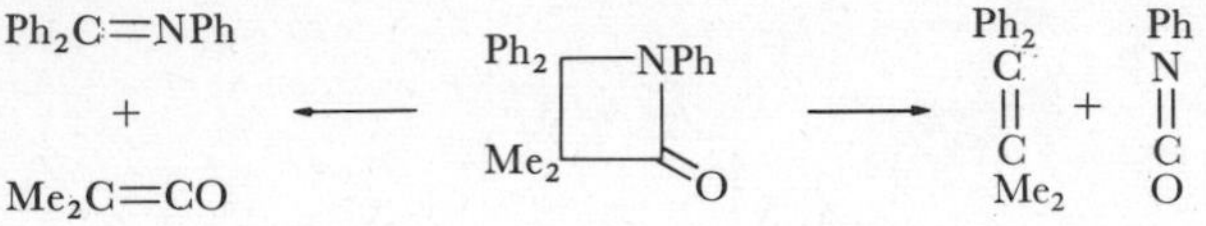

$$
\begin{array}{ccc}
Ph_2C{=}NPh & & Ph_2\\
+ & \longleftarrow & Me_2-\underset{O}{\square}-NPh \longrightarrow \\
Me_2C{=}CO & &
\end{array}
$$

$$
\begin{array}{c}
\underset{Me_2}{\overset{Ph_2}{C}}\!\!\!=\!\!\!C + \underset{O}{\overset{Ph}{N}}\!\!\!=\!\!\!C
\end{array}
$$

The first azetinone (2) has been obtained[15] by an elimination reaction, and on hydrogenation gave the known 1,4-diphenylazetidin-2-one.

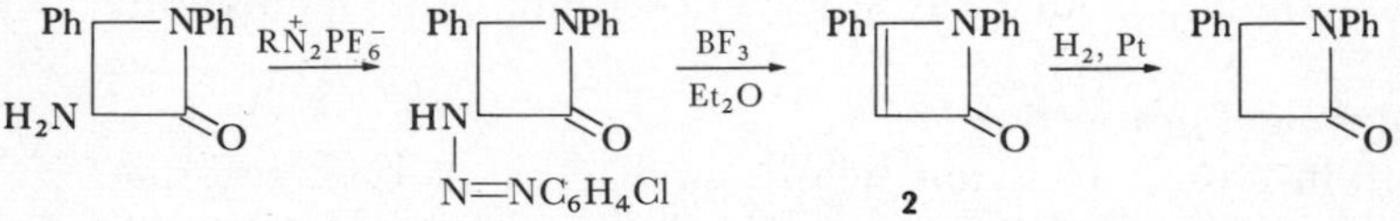

$$H_2N-\underset{O}{\square}-NPh \xrightarrow{R\overset{+}{N}_2PF_6^-} HN-\underset{O}{\square}-NPh \xrightarrow[Et_2O]{BF_3} Ph-\underset{O}{\square}-NPh \xrightarrow{H_2,\ Pt} Ph-\underset{O}{\square}-NPh$$

$$\underset{N=NC_6H_4Cl}{}\qquad \mathbf{2}$$

Recent work[16] has failed to confirm many earlier claims[17] alleging the preparation of azetidine-2,4-diones, including those based on the cyclization of malonic acid derivatives. The only azetidine-2,4-dione which still appears genuine is the triphenyl derivative obtained by Staudinger.

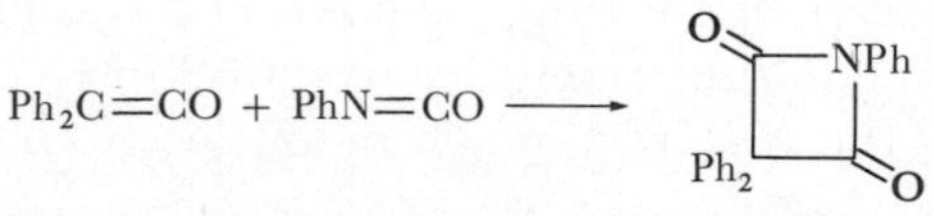

$$Ph_2C{=}CO + PhN{=}CO \longrightarrow \underset{Ph_2}{\overset{O}{\square}}-NPh$$

E. Synthetic methods, excluding penicillin

(1) Thermal decomposition of β-amino acids can proceed in two ways, but no azetidin-2-one is formed. However, cyclization in some instances has been carried out with acetyl chloride or phosphorus trichloride.

$$PhNH(CH_2)_2CO_2H \xrightarrow{heat} PhNH_2 + CH_2{=}CHCO_2H$$

$$PhNHCHPhCPh_2CO_2H \xrightarrow{heat} PhN{=}CHPh + Ph_2CHCO_2H$$

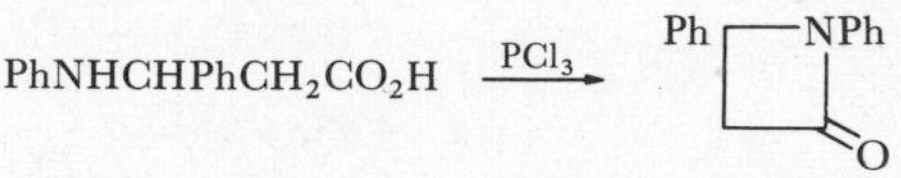

$$PhNHCHPhCH_2CO_2H \xrightarrow{PCl_3}$$

(2) Treatment of β-amino acid esters with Grignard reagents causes cyclization, although sometimes in poor yield.

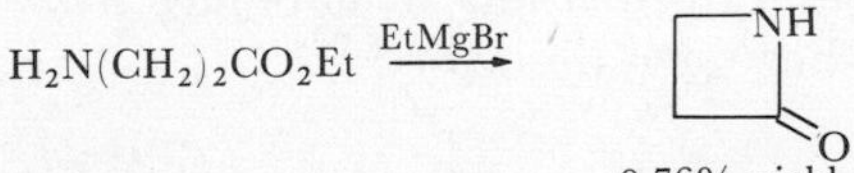

$$H_2N(CH_2)_2CO_2Et \xrightarrow{EtMgBr}$$

0·76% yield

Azetidin-2-one itself[12] and a number of *N*- and *C*-substituted derivatives have been obtained in this way. Some β-amino acid chloride hydrochlorides with dimethylaniline give azetidin-2-ones in good yield.[18]

(3) Certain amides have been cyclized[19] to the azetidin-2-ones, the carbon–carbon linkage being established at cyclization.

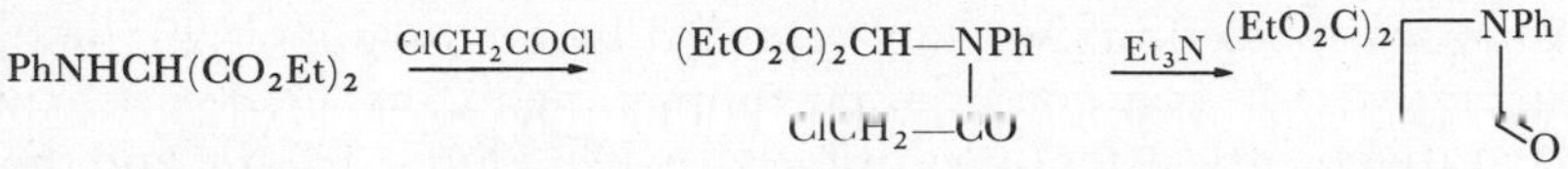

$$PhNHCH(CO_2Et)_2 \xrightarrow{ClCH_2COCl} \underset{ClCH_2{-}CO}{(EtO_2C)_2CH{-}NPh} \xrightarrow{Et_3N}$$

(4) Heating certain acylamino acids gives the azetidin-2-ones.

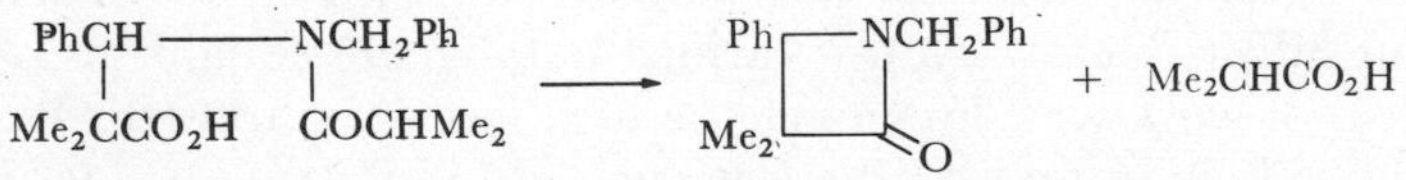

$$\underset{Me_2CCO_2H \quad COCHMe_2}{PhCH{-}-{-}NCH_2Ph} \longrightarrow \quad + \quad Me_2CHCO_2H$$

(5) The direct combination of ketones with imines was used by Staudinger to obtain azetidin-2-ones, but the reaction is not general.

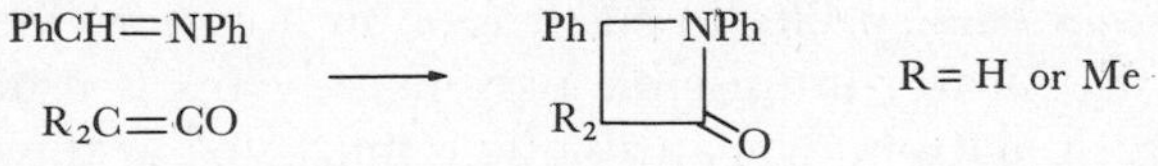

$$\underset{R_2C{=}CO}{PhCH{=}NPh} \longrightarrow \qquad R = H \text{ or } Me$$

The ketene can be replaced by acid chlorides and either zinc or triethylamine in certain cases,[19] but the ketene may in fact still be the reactive intermediate.

(6) Phenyl isocyanate and diazomethane yield 1-phenylazetidin-2-one, in a synthesis similar to that of cyclobutanone from ketene.

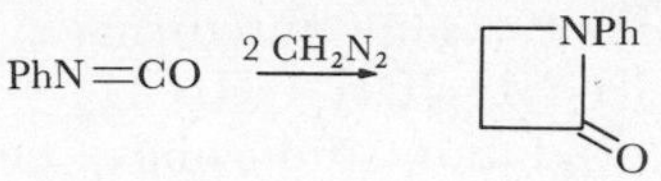

$$PhN{=}CO \xrightarrow{2 CH_2N_2}$$

(7) Cyclization of the amide **3**, under the conditions of the Michael reaction, rather interestingly give the azetidinone[20] **4** instead of less strained alternative 5-membered ring.

$$(EtO_2C)_2HC\text{—NPh}$$
$$|$$
$$EtO_2CHC\text{=}HC\text{—CO}$$

$\xrightarrow{\text{piperidine}}$

$$(EtO_2C)_2 \text{—NPh}$$
$$EtO_2CCH_2 \text{—}\text{=O}$$

3   **4**

(8) A new photocyclization which may have applications in the penicillin series has been described.[21]

$$PhSO_2NHN\text{=}CPhCON\text{—}\overset{S}{\diagup}\overset{Me_2}{\diagdown}CO_2Me$$ $\xrightarrow{\text{NaH}}$ $$PhCCON\text{—}\overset{S}{\diagup}\overset{Me_2}{\diagdown}CO_2Me$$ $\xrightarrow[3660\,\text{Å}]{h\nu}$
$$\underset{\underset{N_2}{||}}{}$$

$$Ph\text{—}\overset{S}{\diagup}\overset{Me_2}{\diagdown}$$
$$O\text{=}\text{—N}\text{—}CO_2Me$$

F. The penicillins

Although 'penicillin' was first reported by Fleming in 1929, he did not investigate it as a potential chemotherapeutic agent. It attracted comparatively little attention until 1940, when Florey, Chain, and their collaborators isolated the material in an inhomogeneous form from a culture of the mould *Penicillium notatum* and showed its enormously powerful effect *in vivo* against various pathogenic organisms. A very great deal of work was done over the next few years towards the commercial production and synthesis of the antibiotic, and in spite of very intensive efforts, a chemical synthesis confirming the structure and giving a reasonable yield was first carried out only in 1957. 'Penicillin' is prepared commercially from the fluid obtained by growing selected strains of *Penicillium* species in suspension in a culture medium. Cold extraction with water-immiscible organic solvents is usually the first stage towards isolation. The antibiotic is marketed as the calcium and sodium salts and as the salts of several organic bases.

There is a whole family of penicillins, consisting of the basic structure (**5**) with various substituent groups, which is produced by different strains of *Penicillium notatum*. The most common substituent groups (R) are benzyl, 4-hydroxybenzyl, 2-pentenyl, n-amyl, n-heptyl, and phenoxymethyl. Penicillin N, an antibiotic obtained from *Cephalosporium sp.*, also contains the same fused-ring system (**5**) but the side chain (R = $HO_2CCH(NH_2)CH_2CH_2CH_2-$) is derived from D-$\alpha$-aminoadipic acid. Degradation studies have been carried out on all these penicillins, and in almost every instance the products could have come from more than one parent structure. The rings in the molecule are very easily opened, like thiazolidines (p. 322) but unlike typical

Degradation of sodium benzylpenicillin (R = $PhCH_2$)

$$\text{5} \xrightarrow[\text{H}_2\text{O}]{\text{pH 10–11}} \text{Benzylpenicilloic acid}$$

RCONH, S, Me_2, N, O, CO_2H — **5**

$PhCH_2CONHCH$, S, Me_2, HO_2C, HN, CO_2H — Benzylpenicilloic acid

5 → Raney Ni, on Na^+ salt

Benzylpenicilloic acid → pH 2·5, 27°

$PhCH_2CONH$, $CHMe_2$, N, $CHCO_2H$, O — **6** + other products

$PhCH_2CONHCH_2$, S, Me_2, HN, CO_2H — Benzylpenilloic acid, **7**

6 → $PhCH_2NH_2$

7 → (a) $HgCl_2$ (b) H_2S

$PhCH_2CONHCH—CH_2$ $CHMe_2$
$PhCH_2NHCO$ $NH—CHCO_2H$ — **8**

$PhCH_2CONHCH_2CHO$ + — **9**

HSCMe$_2$
H_2NCHCO_2H
D-Penicillamine, **10**

azetidine-2-ones. The accepted structure was first proposed on the basis of degradative work, but it remained for Mrs. D. Crowfoot Hodgkin to provide real proof from x-ray crystallographic data. Two of the many important degradation sequences for sodium benzylpenicillin are outlined above.

The very easy opening of the fused thiazolidine–azetidinone ring by alkali is in contrast to the behaviour of known azetidin-2-ones which are quite stable under such conditions, while the benzylamine opening of **6** to **8** is normal. The opening of the thiazolidine ring of benzyl-penilloic acid (**7**) is also expected. The mercuric ion forms a complex with the penicillamine (**10**), while the aldehyde (**9**) is left in solution. It should be noted that the penicillamine is of the D-configuration as is the case with a few other amino acids obtained from the degradation of other antibiotics. This is remarkable as amino acids obtained from other natural sources usually have the L-configuration.

Sheehan and Henery-Logan's[11] remarkable synthesis of penicillin V is shown overleaf. The most notable points are (a) the use of anhydrous hydrochloric acid to split a tertiary butyl ester to the acid and butylene and/or tertiary butyl chloride, and (b) the use of dicyclohexylcarbo-diimide (11), which is hydrated to the urea (12) during the reaction, as the cyclodehydration reagent.

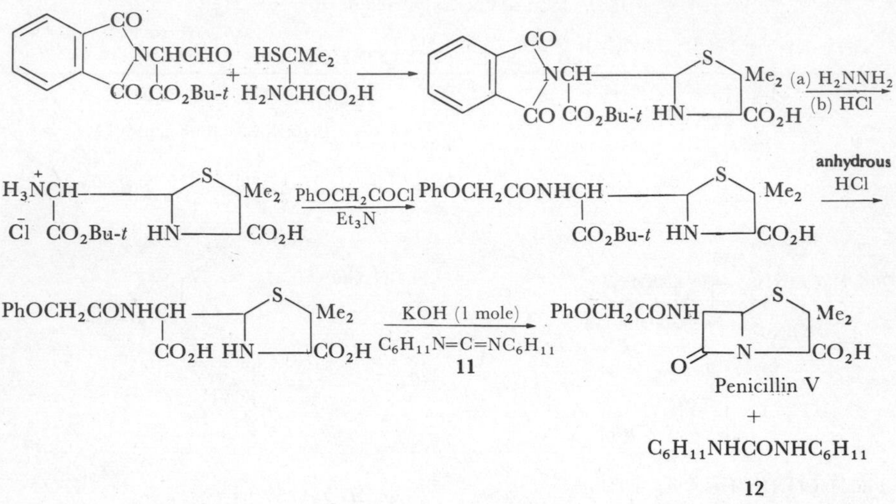

The biosynthesis of benzylpenicillin by the mould has been studied by the addition of labelled possible intermediates[22] to the nutrient media followed by isolation of the penicillin. The penicillin was then degraded by known routes and the positions of the labelled atoms (C, H, N, and/or S) in the products determined. Labelled phenylacetic acid is incorporated in the side chain, and this probably occurs after the bicyclic system is formed (see p. 49). The location of two of the hydro-gen atoms of added labelled cysteine is shown by asterisks. Using L-valine, both uniformly labelled and with individual atoms labelled, it has been shown that the whole of the carbon skeleton is incorporated into the penicillamine part of the molecule. The source of the ring nitrogen atom may be valine, but the $^{15}N/^{14}C$ ratio incorporated into the penicillin from doubly labelled valine is much lower than the ratio in the initial valine. This may, or may not, be due to exchange of ^{15}N for ^{14}N by transamination (p. 234). When the side-chain precursor is omitted from the culture medium in the case of one *Penicillium* species 6-aminopenicillanic acid (13) is obtained instead of penicillin.[23] This discovery is of great interest, as this acid can be acylated on the amino group by acids which are not incorporated by the mould to give new penicillins which have advantages over the natural ones. It also

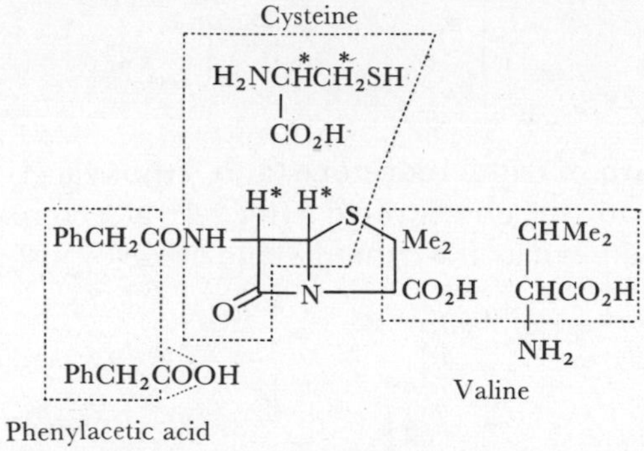

Cysteine

$$H_2NC\overset{*}{H}C\overset{*}{H}_2SH$$
$$|$$
$$CO_2H$$

PhCH$_2$CONH — $\overset{H^*\ H^*}{\underset{O}{\boxed{}}}$ S

Me$_2$ CHMe$_2$

CO$_2$H   CHCO$_2$H

NH$_2$

PhCH$_2$COOH   Valine

Phenylacetic acid

suggests that the penicillins are synthesized by the mould through the formation of **13**, which is then acylated.

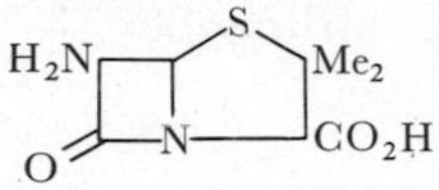

$$H_2N \quad \overset{S}{\diagup} \quad Me_2$$
$$\underset{O}{\diagdown} \quad N \quad CO_2H$$

13

The *Cephalosporium sp.* which produces penicillin N also synthesizes, by an analogous route, the closely related antibiotic cephalosporin C (**14**).[24] Treatment with nitrosyl chloride removes the side chain without opening the 4-membered ring and gives the amine (**15**), from which many new cephalosporins, for example the clinically useful **16**, have been obtained by acylation. The acetoxy group of **14** is remarkably easily displaced by nucleophilic reagents, even by pyridine, when a pyridinium salt is obtained.

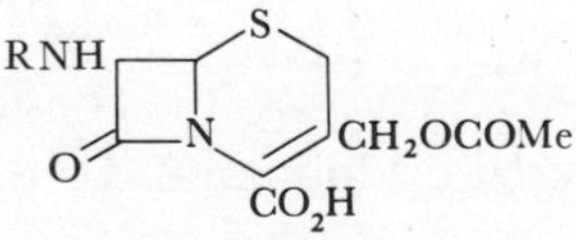

RNH $\overset{S}{\underset{O}{\boxed{}}}$

N   CH$_2$OCOMe

CO$_2$H

14, R = H$_3\overset{+}{N}$CH(CH$_2$)$_3$CO—
            |
            CO$_2^-$

15, R = H—

16, R = $\boxed{}$ CH$_2$CO—
         S

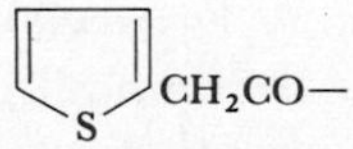

3. OXETENE AND OXETANE

A. Introduction

Oxetene and oxetane are **1** and **2** respectively. Although a few reports of oxetenes are scattered through the literature the first derivatives (**3**) clearly possessing this ring system was described in 1965. It

1   2

was obtained from trifluoroacetone and ethoxyacetylene at $-78°$, and isomerizes to the unsaturated ester (4) at room temperature.[25] Oxetane, often known as 1,3-trimethylene oxide or just as trimethylene

$(CF_3)_2CO$

$+$ $\xrightarrow{-78°}$ $(CF_3)_2$ $\begin{array}{c} O \\ OEt \end{array}$ $\longrightarrow$ $(CF_3)_2C=CHCO_2Et$

$HC≡COEt$

3   4

oxide (2), was first obtained in 1878, but until recently was little investigated. It is somewhat less strained than oxirane, which it resembles in many respects although it is much more sluggish in its reactions.

B. Physical properties and structure

Oxetane is a colourless liquid, b.p. 47–48°, which is miscible with water and most organic solvents. It can donate electrons more easily than oxirane, as it gives out the more heat on mixing with chloroform (p. 19). Electron-diffraction studies[26] have given some molecular dimensions, and microwave studies suggest that the molecule is planar

$$C \xrightarrow{1·46 \pm 0·03 \text{ Å}} O$$
$$94·5 \pm 3°$$
$$1·54 \pm 0·03 \text{ Å}$$
$$88·5 \pm 3°$$
$$C \xrightarrow{\hspace{2cm}} C$$

in contrast to the puckered cyclobutane. Its dipole moment is 2·01 D.

C. Chemical properties

Most of the reactions which have been examined are ring-opening reactions analogous to those of oxirane, but they require much more vigorous conditions. In many cases yields are good, but some polymerization occurs. Thermal decomposition over alumina at 250° yields some propionaldehyde among other products.[27]

Oxetane with hydrogen bromide gives 1,3-dibromopropane, presumably via the bromohydrin, and 1,3-dichloropropane is obtained with phosphorus pentachloride. Reaction also takes place with sodium sulphite, presumably yielding 3-hydroxypropylsulphonic acid, although with potassium bisulphite in the presence of excess sulphur dioxide the bisulphite addition compound of propionaldehyde is formed.[28] With alkyl- or aryllithiums and Grignard reagents, the ring opens as anticipated.

$$RNH(CH_2)_3OH \xleftarrow{RNH_2} \boxed{}O \xrightarrow[\text{or PhLi}]{PhMgBr} Ph(CH_2)_3OH$$

Grignard reagents, particularly those from secondary and tertiary bromides, also give 3-bromopropanol, which is formed from the oxetane and the magnesium bromide present in the Grignard reagent (p. 21). The ring opens similarly with alkali-metal mercaptides and phenoxides, with alcohols in the presence of acid catalysts, with amines, and with benzene in the presence of aluminium chloride 3-phenylpropanol is formed. Lithium aluminium hydride cleaves the ring, forming n-propyl alcohol.

D. Derivatives of oxetane

The few known alkyl- and aryl-oxetanes behave like the parent compound. Asymmetrically substituted oxetanes are reported to give a

$$EtCHOHMe \xleftarrow{LiAlH_4} \boxed{}O_{Me} \xrightarrow{HCl} \begin{array}{l} MeCHOH(CH_2)_2Cl + \langle some\rangle \\ MeCHCl(CH_2)_2OH \end{array}$$

single alcohol with lithium aluminium hydride, while hydrogen chloride and bromide yield mixtures of the isomeric halogen hydrins. The ring usually opens in the same way as that of the analogous oxirane, but variations do occur.[29]

$$Ph(CH_2)_3OH \xleftarrow{LiAlH_4} \boxed{}O_{Ph} \xrightarrow{HCl} \begin{array}{l} PhCHCl(CH_2)_2OH + \langle some\rangle \\ PhCHOH(CH_2)_2Cl \end{array}$$

E. Synthetic methods

(1) Oxetane can be prepared from 3-chloropropanol, or better its acetate (5), and potassium hydroxide. Heating propane-1,3-diol with sulphuric acid, when the disulphonic ester (6) is probably obtained, followed by treatment with sodium hydroxide, is a convenient laboratory synthesis.[30]

$$Cl(CH_2)_3OAc \longrightarrow \boxed{}O \longleftarrow HSO_3O(CH_2)_3OSO_3H$$
$$ \quad 5 6$$
$$Ac = MeCO—$$

(2) The light-induced reaction between olefins and aldehydes or ketones yields oxetanes[31] in what appears to be quite a general reaction.[32]

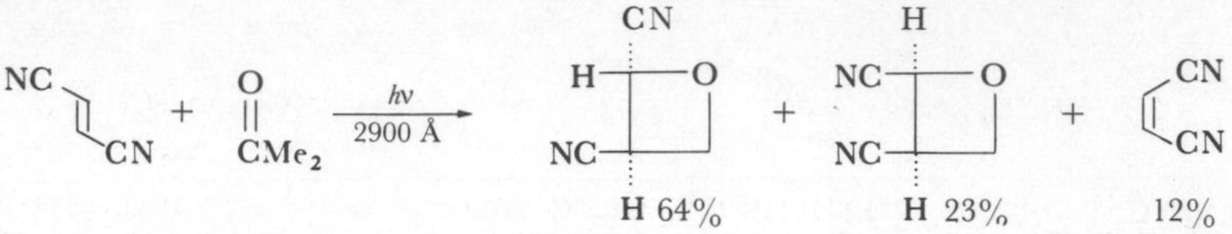

The photolysis of certain ketones also leads to oxetanes.[33]

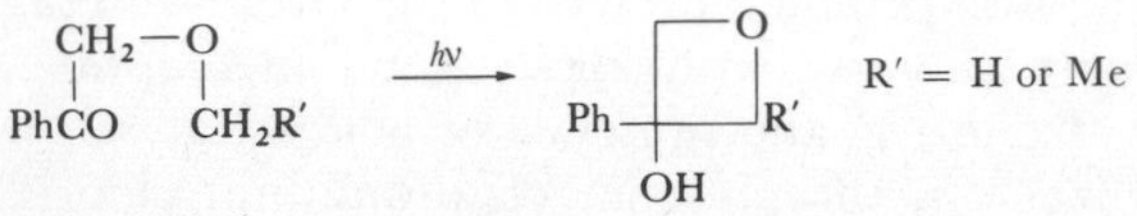

4. OXETANONES

A. Introduction

The most important functional derivatives of oxetane are the oxetan-2-ones[34] or β-lactones (**1**), while a few oxetan-3-ones (**2**) have also been

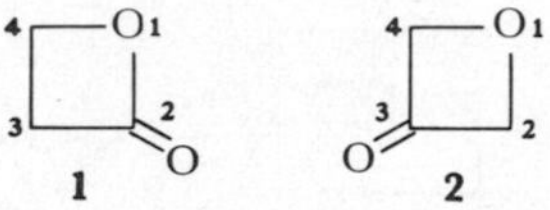

prepared. The strained ring of the oxetan-2-ones makes these compounds much more reactive and difficult to prepare than the γ- and δ-lactones. β-Propiolactone or oxetan-2-one (**1**) is commercially available, and may become an important synthetic intermediate. It is, however, a carcinogen,[35] and the technical material is both a lachrymator and a vesicant.

B. Physical properties and structure

Oxetan-2-one is a colourless liquid, b.p. 51° at 10 mm, which is miscible with water. It has a dipole moment of 3·10 D, and its structure as found by electron-diffraction measurements is shown.[36]

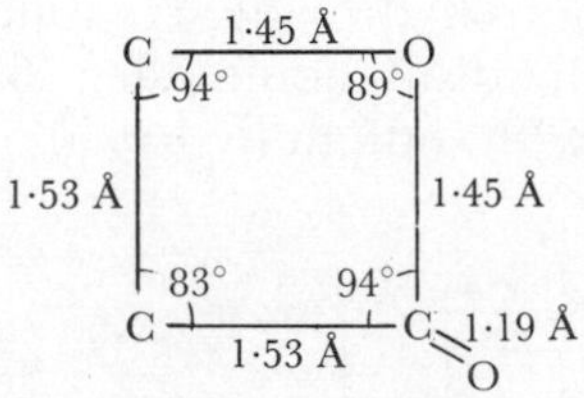

The molecule is planar.[37]

C. Chemical properties

Oxetanone polymerizes slowly on standing. The polymerization is catalysed by acids, bases, and salts and can be explosive. The polymer is linear. On alkaline hydrolysis it gives salts of 3-hydroxypropionic acid, while pyrolysis yields acrylic acid.

Oxetan-2-one can react with a reagent RX in two ways:

$$X(CH_2)_2CO_2^- R^+ \quad \xleftarrow{(a)} \quad \text{[oxetanone]} \quad \xrightarrow{(b)} \quad RO(CH_2)_2COX$$
$$\mathbf{3} \qquad\qquad\qquad\qquad\qquad\qquad \mathbf{4}$$

Ionic reagents, such as aqueous sodium salts (halides, acetate, phenate, etc.), break the bond labelled (a), yielding products of type **3** and polymer; sodium hydrogen sulphide gives a good yield of 3-mercapto-propionic acid. Alcohols, in the absence of a catalyst, slowly give 3-alkoxypropionic acids. In strongly basic or strongly acidic solution the ring opens in the alternative position (b), leading to 3-hydroxypropionic esters (**4**) and their dehydration products (acrylic esters) respectively.

Oxetan-2-one reacts easily with amines by both possible routes, giving 3-aminopropionic acids and 3-hydroxypropionamides. Aromatic

$$H_2N(CH_2)_2CO_2H \qquad\qquad HO(CH_2)_2CONH_2$$
$$\text{NH}_3, \text{MeCN} \qquad\qquad \text{NH}_3\text{H}_2\text{O}$$
$$Me_2S \qquad\qquad R_3N$$
$$Me_2\overset{+}{S}(CH_2)_2CO_2^- \qquad\qquad R_3N(CH_2)_2CO_2^-$$

amines usually give amino acids, but the course of reaction with aliphatic amines depends, in order of importance, on the amine used, the solvent, and the order of mixing the reactants. Water and aceto-nitrile are the best solvents for hydroxyamide and amino acid production, respectively. With tertiary amines and dimethyl sulphide, betaines are formed.

Grignard reagents give complex mixtures with oxetan-2-one. Some methyl vinyl ketone, polymer, and iodopropionic acid are obtained with methylmagnesium iodide; benzylmagnesium chloride gives only 32% of 4-phenylbutyric acid while alkyllithiums yield 1,1-dialkyl-propane-1,3-diols.[38]

D. Derivatives of oxetanones

Ketene dimer (**5**), the structure of which has been confirmed by x-ray and nuclear magnetic resonance measurements, is of special importance, as with ethanol it yields ethyl acetoacetate. This is an industrial synthesis of the ester.

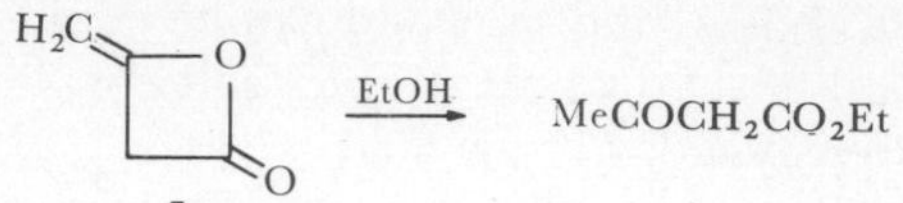

The autoxidation of tetraphenylacetone (**6**) in the presence of light gives tetraphenyloxetan-3-one, and the tetramethyl analogue has been obtained from tetramethylacetone and lead tetraacetate.[39] Hydrolysis of **7** with potassium hydroxide yielded the acid (**8**), the structure

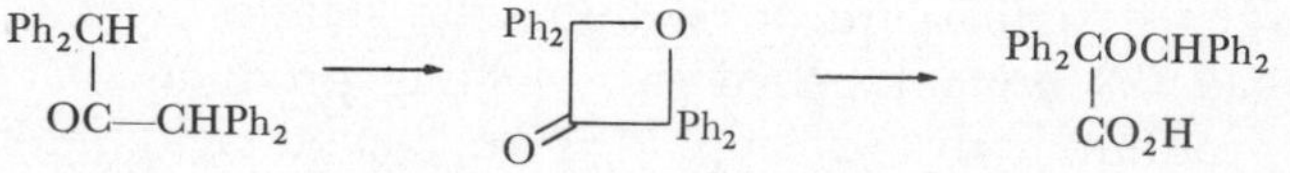

of which was proved both by hydrogen iodide reduction to diphenyl-methane and diphenylacetic acid, and by hydrochloric acid hydrolysis to benzilic acid. The oxetan-3-ones are of special interest because, in spite of their strained ring, their carbonyl group behaves normally to Grignard reagents, to hydroxylamine, and to 2,4-dinitrophenylhydra-zine. Oxetan-3-one itself has been isolated[40] as the 2,4-dinitrophenyl-hydrazone.

The few known naturally occurring oxetanes include trichothecin (**9**), an antifungal compound,[41] and anhydroscymnol which is a steroid.[42]

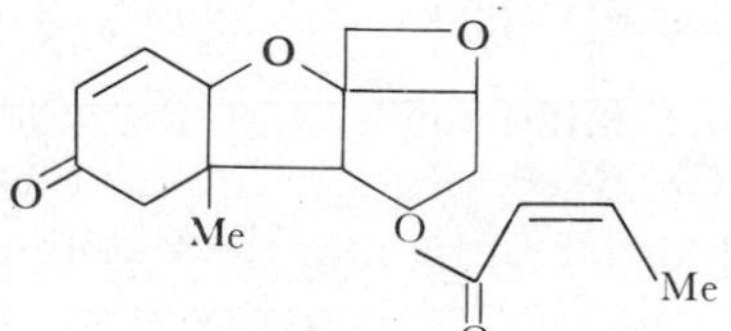

E. Synthetic methods

(1) Oxetan-2-ones cannot be obtained by the thermal dehydration of 3-hydroxy acids; acrylic acids and polymerization products are formed. However, treatment of a 3-bromo, or occasionally of a 3-iodo, acid with one equivalent of sodium carbonate, bicarbonate, or silver oxide effects cyclization. Excess base causes hydrolysis of the lactone, and ethylenes are also formed as by-products. Oxetan-2-one (β-propiolactone) was first obtained in this way in 1915. A Walden inversion at the carbon atom bearing the halogen takes place, and if steric factors render this

impossible a hydroxy acid, rather than the cyclic lactone, is the main product.

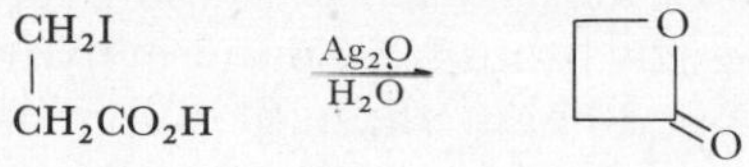

$$CH_2I$$
$$|$$
$$CH_2CO_2H$$ $$\xrightarrow[\text{H}_2\text{O}]{\text{Ag}_2\text{O}}$$

(2) Ketenes react with carbonyl compounds in the presence of acid catalysts. Oxetan-2-one is prepared commercially in this way, and

$$CH_2{=}O$$
$$+$$ $$\xrightarrow{0°-20°}$$
$$CH_2{=}CO$$

the synthesis has wide application. The self-condensation of ketene is the industrial synthesis of ketene dimer (5), mentioned earlier (p. 55).

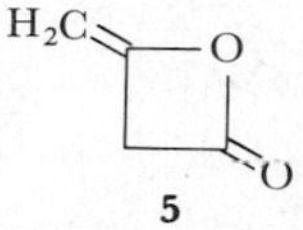

5

5. THIETANE AND THIETENE

A. Introduction

An alkyl derivative of thietene (**1**) was obtained very recently (p. 57). Thietane (**2**), otherwise known as trimethylene sulphide or 1,3-propylene sulphide was first prepared in 1916. This group of compounds has received much attention in the last few years.

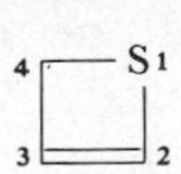

1 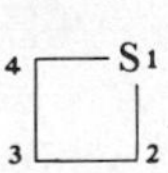   **2**

B. Physical properties and structure

Thietane[43] is a colourless liquid, m.p. −73°, b.p. 95° at 760 mm. Its dipole moment in benezene is 1·78 D, and its molecular dimensions calculated[44] from electron-diffraction data, and given below, indicate that the ring is strained.

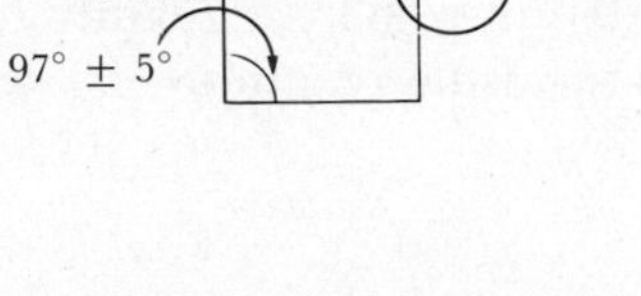

C. Chemical properties

Unlike thiirane, thietane can be oxidized by hydrogen peroxide successively to a stable 1-oxide,[45] and to the sulphone. The sulphone is reduced back to thietane by lithium aluminium hydride,[46] a procedure which does not affect open-chain aliphatic sulphones.

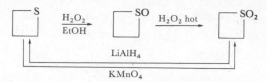

Like thiirane, the ring is cleaved by methyl iodide, perhaps via[47] a cyclic intermediate (**3**) giving **4**. Thietane is also reported to polymerize with mineral acids under conditions which leave tetrahydrothiophene unchanged. Thermal decomposition over alumina gives

$$\square^{S} \xrightarrow{\text{MeI}} \left[\square^{\overset{+}{S}\text{Me I}^-}\right] \xrightarrow{\text{MeI}} I(CH_2)_3\overset{+}{S}Me_2\ I^-$$

3   **4**

olefins, hydrogen sulphide, and hydrogen, while in the presence of hydrogen sulphide some 1,2-dithiolane (**5**) is formed.[48]

5

The ring of thietane, like that of thiirane and its heterocyclic analogues, is strained and ruptures quite easily. With chlorine in chloroform[49] it gives **6** and its oxidation products, while with butyllithium

$$Cl(CH_2)_3SS(CH_2)_3Cl \qquad \text{n-BuSPr-n}$$
$$\textbf{6} \qquad\qquad\qquad\qquad \textbf{7}$$

some **7** is formed.[50] Tetrahydrothiophene is not attacked by this last reagent. With aqueous ammonia at 200° thietane is stated to give 3-aminopropyl mercaptan.[47]

Thietanes are desulphurized[51] in the expected way by Raney nickel (p.128); for example, **10** gives isopropyl alcohol.

Thietan-3-one[52] (**9**), m.p. 63°, is readily obtained by hydrolysis of the acetal (**8**). It has the usual reactions of a ketone in forming common derivatives, and with sodium borohydride gives the alcohol (**10**). Secondary amines open the ring giving a mixture of mercaptoacetone ($MeCOCH_2SH$) and the amide ($MeCOCSNR_2$). The enamine[53] (**11**)

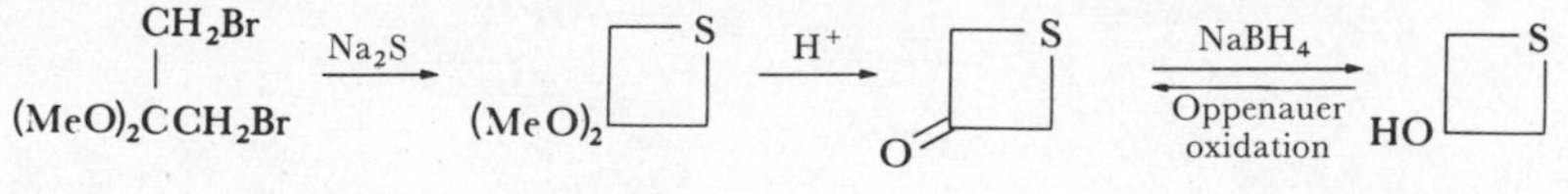

and the related sulphone[54] (**14**), below, are easily hydrolysed to thietan-3-one 1,1-dioxide (**12**) which is acidic enough (pK_a 4·1) to liberate carbon dioxide from aqueous sodium bicarbonate. No evidence for the presence of an enol form of this ketone was found in its infrared or nuclear magnetic resonance spectra. The acetal (**14**), perhaps surprisingly, is decomposed by sodium hydroxide to the acid (**15**).

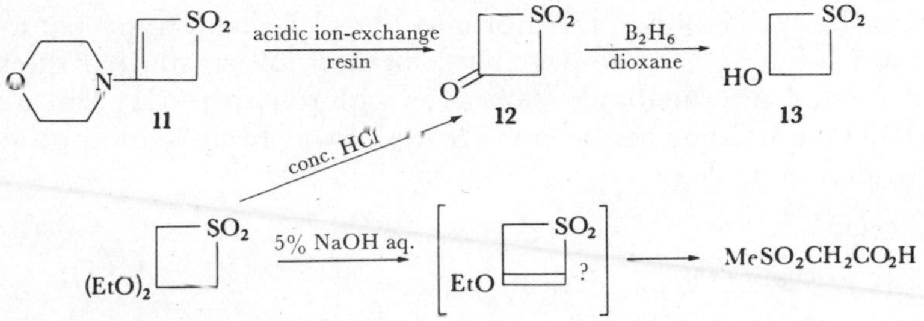

Although all attempts to convert the alcohol (**10**) and a number of derivatives into thietene (**1**) have so far failed, the quaternary iodide (**16**) with a strong base appears to undergo a Hofmann degradation yielding the thietene (**17**) which was obtained in pentane solution. This solution with perphthalic acid followed by oxidation of the resulting sulphoxide gave the known sulphone (**18**), while 2,4-dinitrophenyl-hydrazine gave the corresponding derivative of cyclohexene-1-carbaldehyde (**19**); concentration of the solution gave only a polymer.[55]

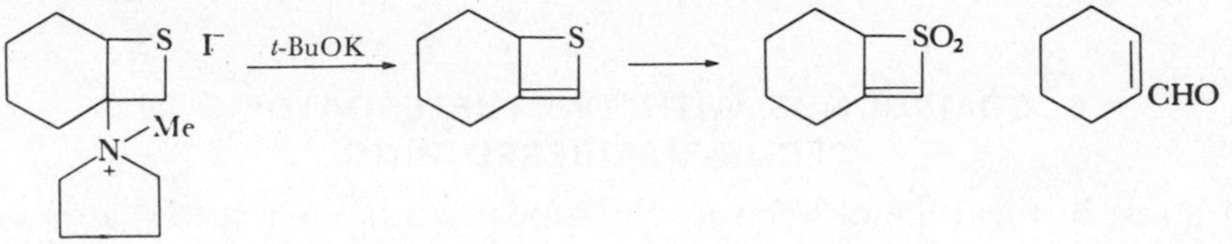

Thietene 1,1-dioxide (**20**) has been obtained from **13** by replacement of the hydroxyl group by chlorine and dehydrohalogenation with triethylamine. Its double bond is reactive, and readily adds nucleophiles.[56]

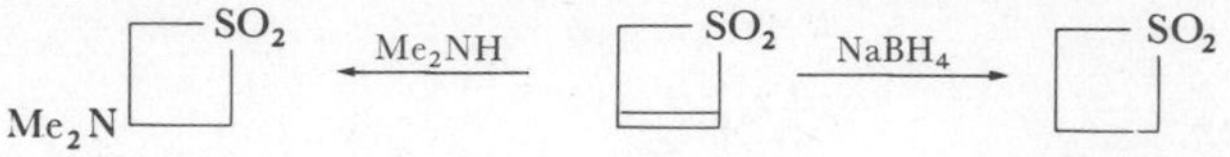

20

D. Synthetic methods

(1) The best synthesis[46] for thietane itself starts with 3-bromopropyl chloride. Treatment with thiourea gives the thiouronium salt which with potassium hydroxide is converted into thietane in 53·5% yield.

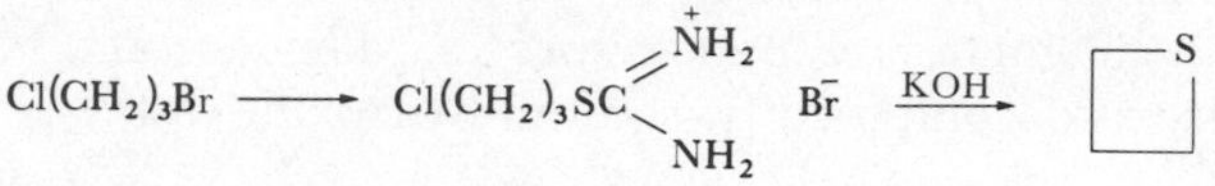

(2) The cyclization of 1,3-dibromo-[49] or 1,3-dichloro-propanes with sodium sulphide is quite a general method for substituted thietanes, and related intermediates such as epichlorohydrin (**21**) can also be used. Thietan-2-one has been made in this way from 3-chloropropionyl chloride.

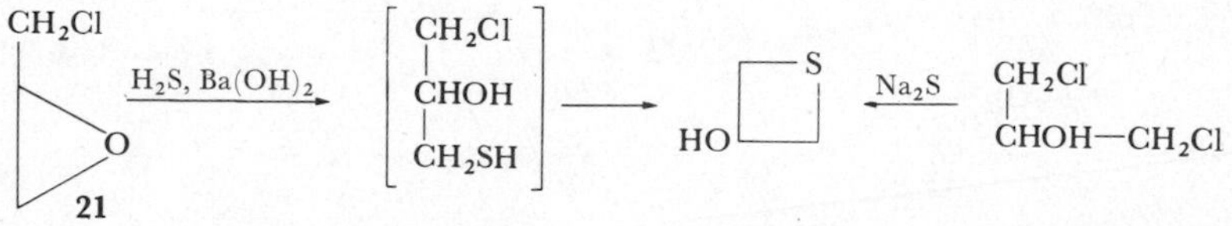

(3) Methylsulphonyl chloride and triethylamine, perhaps acting as a source of sulphene ($CH_2{=}SO_2$), reacts with ketene diethyl acetal[54] and similar compounds[53] to give thietane or thietene 1,1-dioxides; the type of product is determined by the ketene derivative used.

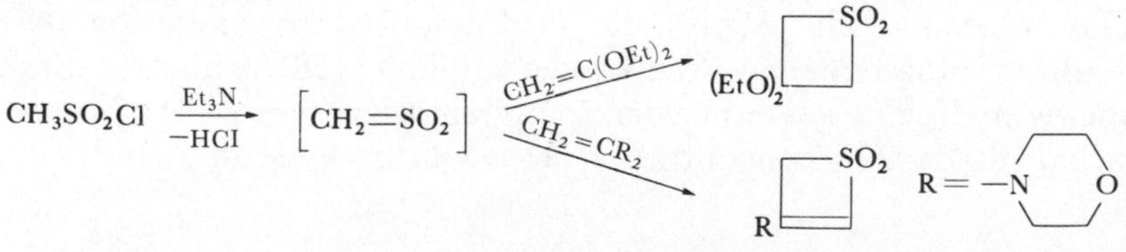

6. COMPOUNDS WITH TWO HETEROATOMS IN A FOUR-MEMBERED RING

Interest in this type of heterocycle appears to be increasing, although few data are available at present.

The structure of tetrafluorodiazetine (1) has been established spectroscopically.[57]

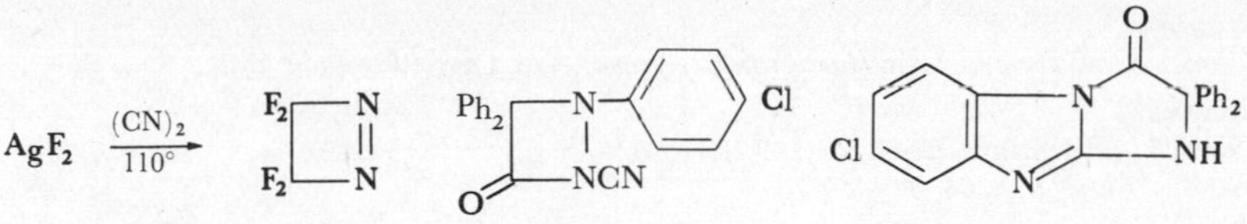

$$AgF_2 \xrightarrow[110°]{(CN)_2}$$

1   2   3

The diazetidinone (2) is obtained from diphenylketene and *cis*- or *trans*-4-chlorophenyldiazocyanide, and on heating isomerizes to 3.[58]

Four-membered rings with two sulphur atoms seem to be easily formed. Hexafluorobut-2-yne (4) with boiling sulphur gives the 1,2-dithietene (5) in 80% yield. It is a yellow liquid, b.p. 95°, which with iodine and a trace of triethylamine gives the tetrathiaoctadiene (6), and with tetramethylethylene the 1,4-dithiin[59] (7). The stability of this dithietene is in accord with the results of molecular-orbital calculations, which suggest that the parent ring system should have considerable delocalization energy.[60]

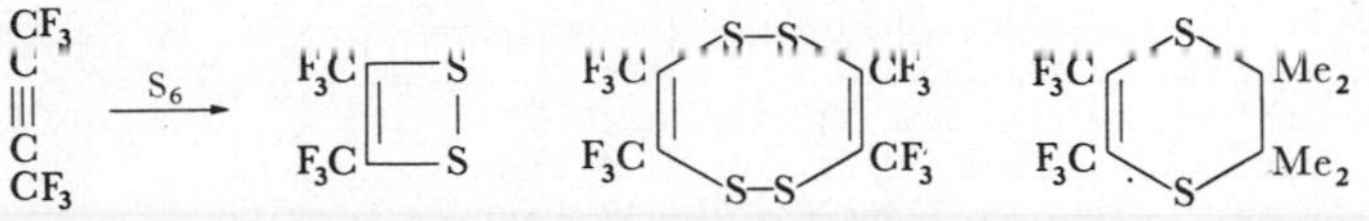

4   5   6   7

The desaurins (e.g. 8), first made and given correct structures in 1888, have been reinvestigated.[61] 8 is stable to concentrated sulphuric acid, and to zinc and acetic acid, at room temperature and is little affected by boiling concentrated hydrochloric acid.

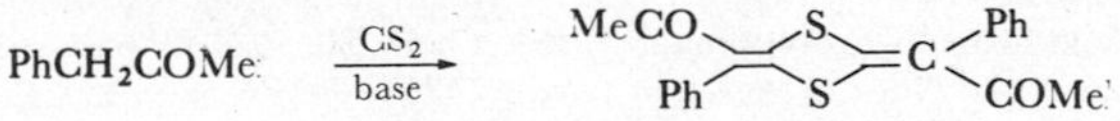

$$PhCH_2COMe \xrightarrow[base]{CS_2}$$

8

GENERAL BIBLIOGRAPHY

Heterocyclic Compounds with 3- and 4-Membered Rings, ed. Weissberger, Interscience, New York, 1964.

AZETIDINES

Ballard and Melstrom in *Heterocyclic Compounds,* Vol. I, ed. Elderfield, Wiley, New York, 1950.

AZETIDINONES, including PENICILLINS

Clarke, Johnson, and Robinson, *The Chemistry of Penicillin,* Princeton University Press, N.J., 1949.

D

Cook, *Quart. Rev. (London)*, **2**, 203 (1948).
Sheehan and Corey, *Org. Reactions*, **9**, 388 (1957).
Newton and Abraham, *Chem. Soc. (London) Spec. Publ.*, No. **5**, 97 (1956).

OXETANE

Winstein and Henderson in *Heterocyclic Compounds*, Vol. I, ed. Elderfield, Wiley, New York, 1950.

THIETANE

Tarbell and Harnish, *Chem. Rev.*, **49**, 1 (1951).
Sander, *Chem. Rev.*, **66**, 341 (1966).

REFERENCES

1. Freundlich and Kroepelin, *Z. Physik. Chem. (Leipzig)*, **122**, 39 (1926).
2. Gensler, *J. Am. Chem. Soc.*, **70**, 1843 (1948).
3. Brown and Gerstein, *J. Am. Chem. Soc.*, **72**, 2926 (1950).
4. Hageman, *Org. Reactions*, **7**, 198 (1953).
5. Vaughan, Klonowski, McElkinney and Millward, *J. Org. Chem.*, **26**, 138 (1961).
6. Bottini and Nash, *J. Am. Chem. Soc.*, **84**, 734 (1962).
7. Fowden, *Biochem. J.*, **64**, 323 (1956).
8. Leete, *J. Am. Chem. Soc.*, **86**, 3162 (1964).
9. Fowden and Bryant, *Biochem. J.*, **70**, 626 (1958).
10. Staudinger, *Die Ketene*, Enke, Stuttgart, 1912.
11. Sheehan and Henery-Logan, *J. Am. Chem. Soc.*, **81**, 3089 (1959).
12. Holley and Holley, *J. Am. Chem. Soc.*, **71**, 2129 (1949).
13. Crowfoot *et al.* in *The Chemistry of Penicillin*, above.
14. Testa, Fontanella, and Aresi, *Ann. Chem.*, **656**, 114 (1962).
15. Henery-Logan and Rodricks, *J. Am. Chem. Soc.*, **85**, 3524 (1963).
16. King and Clark-Lewis, *J. Chem. Soc.*, 3080 (1951) and earlier papers.
17. Summarized by Ballard and Melstrom in *Heterocyclic Chemistry*, Vol. I, ed. Elderfield, Wiley, New York, 1950, pp. 111–115.
18. Blicke and Gould, *J. Org. Chem.*, **23**, 1102 (1958).
19. Sheehan *et al.*, *J. Am. Chem. Soc.*, **73**, 1761 (1951) and earlier papers.
20. Bose, Manhas, and Ramer, *Tetrahedron*, **21**, 449 (1965).
21. Corey and Felix, *J. Am. Chem. Soc.*, **87**, 2518 (1965).
22. Arnstein and Clubb, *Biochem. J.*, **68**, 528 (1958); Arnstein, *Ann. Rept. Chem. Soc.*, **54**, 339 (1957).
23. Batchelor, Doyle, Nayler and Robinson, *Nature*, **183**, 257 (1959).
24. Abraham and Newton, *Endeavour*, **20**, 92 (1961); Abraham, *Pharm. Rev.*, **14**, 473 (1962).
25. Middleton, *J. Org. Chem.*, **30**, 1307 (1965).
26. Shand, in Allen and Sutton, *Acta Cryst.*, **3**, 46 (1950).
27. Yur'ev and Levi, through *Chem. Abstr.*, **49**, 3119i (1955).
28. Schenck and Kaizerman, *J. Am. Chem. Soc.*, **75**, 1636 (1953).
29. Searles *et al.*, *J. Am. Chem. Soc.*, **79**, 948, 952 (1957).
30. Schmoyer and Case, *Nature*, **183**, 389 (1959); Noller, *Org. Synth.*, **29**, 92 (1949).
31. Beereboom and Schach von Wittenau, *J. Org. Chem.*, **30**, 1231 (1965).
32. Arnold, Hinnan and Glick, *Tetrahedron Letters*, 1425 (1964).
33. Yates and Szabo, *Tetrahedron Letters*, 485 (1965).
34. Zaugg, *Org. Reactions*, **8**, 305 (1954); Machell, *Ind. Chemist*, **36**, 13 (1960).
35. Haddow, *Ann. Rev. Biochem.*, **24**, 689 (1953).
36. Bregman and Bauer, *J. Am. Chem. Soc.*, **77**, 1955 (1955).
37. Kwak, Goldstein and Simmons, *J. Chem. Phys.*, **25**, 1203 (1956).
38. Stuckwisch and Bailey, *J. Org. Chem.*, **28**, 2362 (1963).
39. Hoey, Lester, *et al.*, *J. Am. Chem. Soc.*, **77**, 391, 4430 (1955).
40. Marshall and Walker, *J. Chem. Soc.*, 467 (1952).
41. Jones and Lowe, *J. Chem. Soc.*, 3859 (1960).
42. Cross, *J. Chem. Soc.*, 2817 (1961).
43. Haines, Helm, Bailey, and Ball, *J. Phys. Chem.*, **58**, 270 (1954).
44. Goldish, *J. Chem. Educ.*, **36**, 408 (1959).

45. Tamres and Searles, *J. Am. Chem. Soc.*, **81**, 2100 (1959).
46. Bordwell and McKellin, *J. Am. Chem. Soc.*, **73**, 2251 (1951).
47. Tarbell and Harnish, *Chem. Rev. (London)*, **49**, 1 (1951).
48. Yur'ev and Levi, through *Chem. Abstr.*, **45**, 2934b (1951).
49. Stewart and Burnside, *J. Am. Chem. Soc.*, **75**, 243 (1953).
50. Bordwell, Andersen, and Pitt, *J. Am. Chem. Soc.*, **76**, 1082 (1954).
51. Searles, Hays, and Lutz, *J. Org. Chem.*, **27**, 2828 (1962).
52. Funk and Mayer, *J. Prakt. Chem.*, **21**, 65 (1963).
53. Hasek, Gott, Meen, and Martin, *J. Org. Chem.*, **28**, 2496 (1963).
54. Truce and Norell, *J. Am. Chem. Soc.*, **85**, 3231, 3236 (1963).
55. Dittmer and Davis, *J. Am. Chem. Soc.*, **87**, 2064 (1965).
56. Dittmer and Christy, *J. Am. Chem. Soc.*, **84**, 399 (1962).
57. Ebsworth and Hurst, *J. Chem. Soc.*, 4840 (1962).
58. Bird, *J. Chem. Soc.*, 5284 (1964).
59. Krespan, McKusick and Cairns, *J. Am. Chem. Soc.*, **82**, 1515 (1960).
60. Bergson, *Arkiv Kemi*, **19**, 181, 265 (1962).
61. Yates and Moore, *J. Am. Chem. Soc.*, **80**, 5577 (1958).

CHAPTER III

HETEROCYCLIC ANALOGUES OF CYCLOPENTADIENE WITH ONE HETEROATOM

Pyrrole, furan, and thiophene are all related to cyclopentadiene, from which they can be theoretically formed through replacement of the methylene group (CH_2) by the appropriate heteroatoms. They are, however, all aromatic to some degree, and must therefore possess 6 π electrons as is the case with the fully aromatic and symmetrical cyclopentadienyl anion.

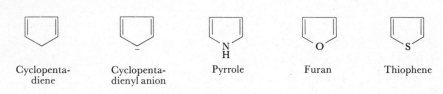

| Cyclopenta-diene | Cyclopenta-dienyl anion | Pyrrole | Furan | Thiophene |

Although superficially furan, pyrrole, and thiophene resemble each other in formula and in some properties, there are major fundamental differences. These differences affect the properties of the molecules to such an extent that a prediction of the behaviour of, for example, a thiophene based on the known behaviour of the analogous pyrrole or furan could often be wrong or misleading. The three ring systems are therefore considered separately, and a summary comparison of their aromatic properties is given in section 4 of this chapter.

1. PYRROLE

A. Introduction

Runge in 1834 found that the distillation of coal tar, bone oil, and other products derived from proteins gave an unknown substance in the ammonia fraction. It turned a pine splint, previously dipped in hydrochloric acid, a fiery red. He called the substance pyrrole, and in 1857 Anderson obtained the compound in a pure condition from a bone-oil distillate. Three years later it was synthesized by the pyrolysis of ammonium mucate. This is still a useful laboratory method, in spite of the availability of commercial pyrrole.

The pyrrole ring system soon became of great interest, as it was found in many compounds widely distributed in nature. It had been recognized in the dyestuff indigo, in haemin obtained from blood, and in chlorophyll before 1880. Two amino acids derived from pyrrole, proline (pyrrolidine-2-carboxylic acid) and 4-hydroxyproline, are constituents of many proteins. Many alkaloids also possess a pyrrole ring.

The positions of the substituents round the pyrrole ring may be shown by the use of numbers (**1**) or Greek letters (**2**). The first system is currently preferred and is obligatory when several substituents are

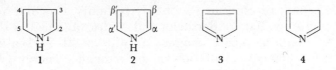

present. Two tautomeric formulations (**3** and **4**) can be written for pyrrole, and derivatives of both are known. They are named 2*H*-pyrrolenine or α-pyrrolenine (**3**) and 3*H*-pyrrolenine or β-pyrrolenine (**4**). Three dihydropyrroles or pyrrolines are theoretically possible and tetrahydropyrrole is known as pyrrolidine. The pyrrole ring,

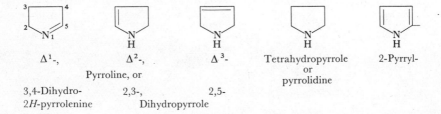

when considered as a substituent in another structure, is called pyrryl.

B. Physical properties and structure

Pyrrole is a colourless liquid, b.p. 129° at 760 mm, f.p. $-24°$, d_4^{20} 0·968, with an odour resembling that of chloroform. It turns brown on standing in air and is miscible with most organic solvents. It is somewhat soluble (6%) in water and dissolves 3% of its weight of water at 25°. Substantial intramolecular hydrogen bonding takes place and is shown both by the lower boiling point of 1-methylpyrrole $(114-115°)$ and by the infrared absorption spectrum of pyrrole itself.[1]

The structure of pyrrole, as usually written (1), was first suggested

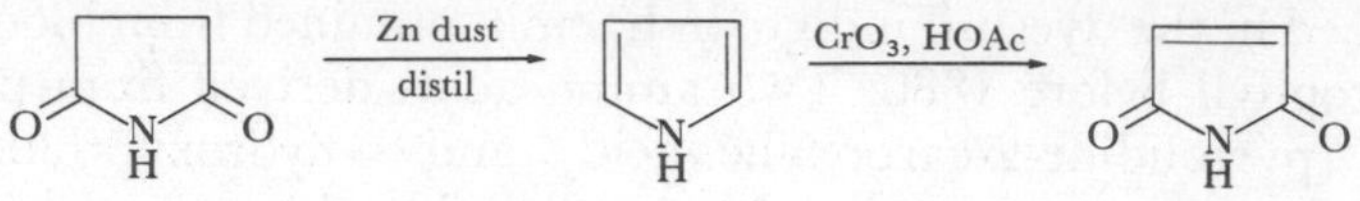

by Baeyer in 1870. This follows from the transformations outlined above.

There has been no recent determination of the heat of combustion or heat of hydrogenation of pyrrole, and so the resonance energy of the molecule cannot be estimated with any certainty. Calculations based on the combustion data of Berthelot and André, obtained in 1899 with pyrrole of doubtful purity, suggest a value of 21–24 kcal/mole. A quantum-mechanical calculation of the resonance energy gives 24·7 kcal/mole.[2]

Recent microwave studies have shown that the pyrrole molecule is completely planar[3] and have given molecular dimensions.[4] These

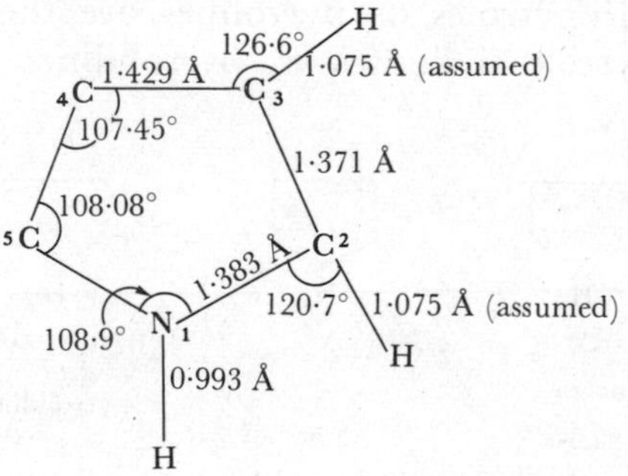

results confirm the experimental results of the earlier electron-diffraction studies of Schomaker and Pauling, but not their interpretation.

As the distances (1·37 Å) between carbon atoms 2 and 3, and 4 and 5 are greater than that between the carbon atoms of ethylene (1·34 Å), as the distance between carbon atoms 3 and 4 (1·43 Å) is less than that between the carbon atoms of ethane (1·54 Å) and approaches the carbon–carbon distance in benzene (1·40 Å), and as the carbon–nitrogen distances (1·38 Å) are less than those in trimethylamine (1·47 Å), the molecule cannot be adequately represented by the classical structure (1). It must be treated as a resonance hybrid of which the more important contributing structures are shown below; structure **1** is the major contributor. This conclusion is supported by the comparatively large resonance energy of the molecule and by dipole-moment studies.[5] These studies have shown decisively that the dipole moments of pyrrole (1·84 D) and 1-methylpyrrole (2·11 D) in the gas

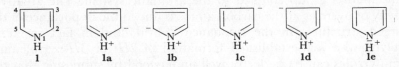

phase are directed so that the nitrogen atom is at the positive end of the dipole. Structure **1e** is therefore probably an insignificant contributor in pyrrole itself, although the anion of **1e** is the major contributor in metallic derivatives such as potassium pyrrole. As the dipole of pyrrolidine (tetrahydropyrrole, 1·57 D) is in the opposite direction, having its negative end at the nitrogen atom, experimental proof of the importance of ionic structures in the resonance of pyrrole has been provided.

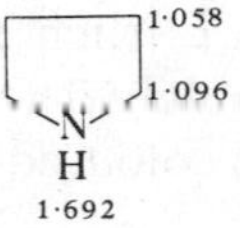

π-Electron densities calculated
by the molecular-orbital method[6]

Electron-density calculations by the valence-bond and molecular-orbital[6] methods confirm each other and that the π-electron density is high at all positions of the ring, while being greater at positions 5 and 2 than at 3 and 4. The localization energies for electrophilic, nucleophilic, and free-radical attack are all lower for position 2 than position 3.[6a] This is in agreement with the very facile electrophilic substitution of pyrrole by cationoid reagents which takes place preferentially at the positions 2 and 5.

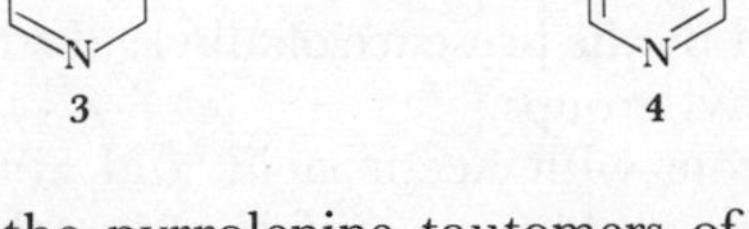

The presence of the pyrrolenine tautomers of pyrrole (**3** and **4**), neither of which can possess much resonance energy, has in the past been postulated to account for the great reactivity of the molecule at the carbon atoms. These tautomers have been shown absent in pyrrole itself through an examination of its infrared and Raman spectra.[7] The rate of iodination of 1-methylpyrrole, where the formation of pyrrolenine tautomers is not possible, is greater than that of pyrrole itself, and must therefore be due to the ordinary electron-donating properties of the methyl group coupled to the aromatic system. The great reactivity of pyrroles at the carbon atoms is due to the importance of the charged structures in the resonance hybrid, and in fact reactions involving the well-established formation of 2*H*- or 3*H*-pyrrolenines from pyrroles can be perfectly well understood by supposing that the reacting entity is one of the charged structures (e.g. **1b** or **1c**) which is a contributor to the pyrrole resonance hybrid.

C. Chemical properties

Pyrrole behaves mainly as a very reactive aromatic compound towards electrophilic reagents and has been compared to phenol in this respect. It also shows weakly acidic and basic properties, and it can behave as a 1,3-diene towards some reactive reagents. Many pyrroles, including 2,3,4,5-tetramethylpyrrole, which has only fully substituted carbon atoms, give positive Ehrlich reactions (red to violet colours with 4-dimethylaminobenzaldehyde and concentrated hydrochloric acid, see p.156) and most form coloured azo compounds with diazonium salts.

1. *Opening of the pyrrole ring*

The pyrrole ring is not readily opened by acids or alkalis, but boiling with alcoholic hydroxylamine hydrochloride causes rupture, with the formation of succindialdehyde dioxime (**5**). This is almost the reverse

$$
\underset{\substack{|\\ H}}{\overset{}{N}} \xrightarrow{\text{NH}_2\text{OH}} \quad
\begin{array}{ll}
CH_2 & \text{———} CH_2 \\
| & | \\
CH{=}NOH & CH{=}NOH
\end{array}
$$
5

of the synthesis of pyrrole from succindialdehyde (p. 85), and the hydroxylamine may function by reducing the free dialdehyde concentration so that very little pyrrole is present at equilibrium. This opening is facilitated by the presence of alkyl substituents and hindered by carbonyl or phenyl groups.

3,4-Dimethylpyrrole with acetic acid and zinc acetate gives the indolizine (**7**).[8] Presumably some of the pyrrole initially gives the dialdehyde (**6**), through the ring opening, which then combines with unreacted pyrrole.

6   7

The ozonolysis of pyrrole and derivatives[9] at $-60°$ in chloroform breaks the ring. The production of both glyoxal and methylglyoxal (**8**) from 2,5-dimethylpyrrole shows that the bond between carbon

$$CHOCHO + MeCOCHO + MeCO_2H + NH_3$$
8

atoms 2 and 3 is partly single, in confirmation of the presence of ionic structures in the resonance hybrid.

Pyrrole in aqueous silver nitrate is broken down by ultrasonic vibration into acetylene and cyanide ions.[10]

2. Addition reactions

In order to have aromatic properties the pyrrole ring must possess 6 π electrons, and as only 4 can be provided by the two double bonds of the uncharged formulation, the lone pair on the nitrogen atom must be involved. This is another way of illustrating the importance of ionic structures with a positive charge on the nitrogen in the resonance hybrid. The effect of this charge is to discourage an approaching proton, and in fact pyrrole is a very weak base ($pK_a = -3.8$).[11] Nuclear magnetic resonance spectrum measurements have shown that, in aqueous sulphuric acid, pyrrole and both its *N*- and *C*-alkyl derivatives accept protons at the α-positions to give stable cations (e.g. **10**). The position of protonation of **9** is of interest. In some cases, particularly in more concentrated sulphuric acid, up to 30% of competitive protonation yields[11] cations of type **11**. These cations (**10** and **11**, cf. furan, p. 97) have no aromatic stability due to π-electron sextets. They are very reactive and can readily polymerize by radical and/or ionic mechanisms.[12]

9   10   11

Treatment of pyrrole with 5·5 N hydrochloric acid at 0° for 30 seconds yields[12] a crystalline trimer (**13**). This is presumably formed

D*

through electrophilic attack of the cation **11** on a neutral pyrrole mole-cule leading to **12**, followed by protonation of **12** at position 4 and subsequent attack on another pyrrole. The trimer is basic, has the

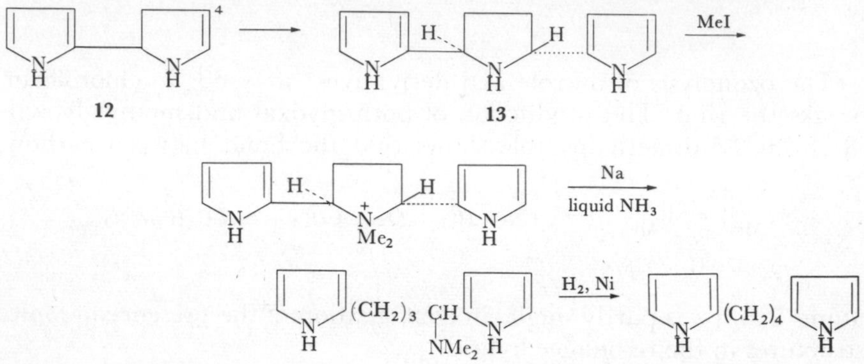

absorption spectrum required by two unreduced pyrrole rings, and forms a neutral monoacetyl derivative with an ultraviolet absorption spectrum identical to that of the parent base. The trimer was degraded as shown to 1,4-bis-2-pyrrylbutane (**14**), the structure of which was confirmed by synthesis. Pyrolysis of the trimer yields indole, pyrrole, and ammonia.

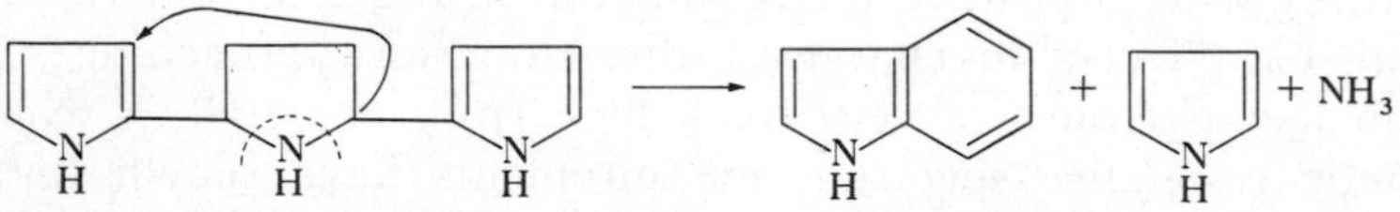

There are a few examples of pyrroles behaving as 1,3-dienes. Both pyrrole and its 1-phenyl derivative are reduced by zinc and acetic acid (1,4-addition of hydrogen occurring to the 1,3-diene system), yielding the Δ^3-pyrrolines. The reaction of pyrrole with triphenyl-methyl radicals, and with oxygen in the presence of light and eosin,[13] also gives the Δ^3-pyrrolines **15** and **16** respectively. Oxidation of the

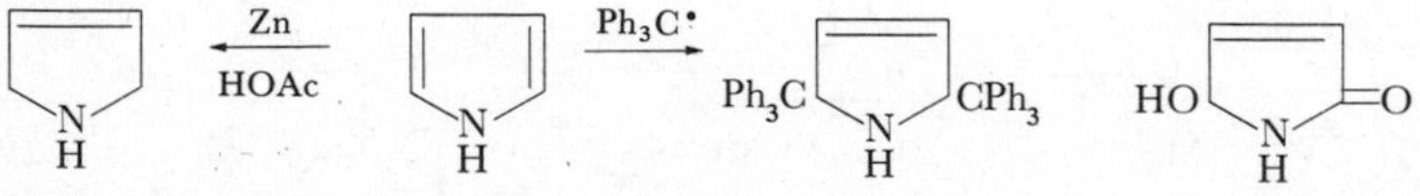

last compound with manganese dioxide gives a convenient synthesis of the maleic imide. Although adducts of the Diels–Alder type have not yet been detected in the case of pyrrole itself, a minor product (major products, see p. 78) from[13a] 1-benzylpyrrole and acetylene-dicarboxylic acid is **17**. 2-Fluorophenyllithium, probably reacting as benzyne (**18**), yields **19** with 1-methylpyrrole.[14] The structure of **19** was confirmed by successive treatment with methyl iodide and silver oxide when 1-dimethylaminonaphthalene (**20**) was formed. Pyrrole itself with benzyne, from 2-bromofluorobenzene and magnesium, gave 26% of 2-phenylpyrrole, no product corresponding to **19** being detected.[14]

The high-pressure catalytic hydrogenation of pyrrole to pyrrolidine can be achieved over Raney nickel at 180°; some Δ^1-pyrroline is formed under special conditions (p. 74). If the pyrrole is first converted into its 1-ethoxycarbonyl derivative (**21**) hydrogenation then proceeds at 70°. The effect of this group in facilitating the hydrogenation appears to be quite general, and it is easily removed afterwards by hydrolysis. Pyrrole itself is also much more easily hydrogenated over platinum in acid solution than under neutral conditions, where reaction proceeds very slowly if at all.[15] Both the proton and the ethoxycarbonyl group will reduce the availability of the lone pair of the nitrogen atom. The effect of the ethoxycarbonyl group in this connexion is well illustrated

by the fact that while pyrrole will couple with benzenediazonium chloride at position 2, even in weakly acid solution, ethyl pyrrole-1-carboxylate (**21**) will not react even with 2,4,6-trinitrobenzene-diazonium salts.[16] Pyrrole with sodium hydrogen sulphite at 100° is stated[17] to give the pyrrolidine (**22**).

3. Substitution reactions of pyrrole

a. At the nitrogen atom, and related substitutions at other positions. Pyrrole is an extremely weak acid. The anion (**23a**) may be compared with the much more highly symmetrical cyclopentadienyl anion (p. 62) and

$$\underset{\substack{\text{N}\\\text{H}}}{\boxed{}} \underset{+H^+}{\overset{-H^+}{\rightleftarrows}} \underset{\substack{\text{N}\\23a}}{\boxed{}}^- \longleftrightarrow \underset{23b}{\boxed{}}^- \longleftrightarrow \underset{23c}{\boxed{}}^- \quad K = 10^{-16\cdot5}$$

can be expected to be somewhat more aromatic than pyrrole itself. Metallic potassium, but apparently not sodium, reacts with pyrrole, with the liberation of hydrogen. Other pyrroles bearing electron-attracting substituents which facilitate the loss of the proton do form crystalline N-sodium derivatives with sodium ethoxide,[15] and pyrroles in general form sodium derivatives with sodamide in liquid ammonia. Potassium pyrrole is hydrolysed instantly by water and, unlike pyrrole itself, which does not react, combines with methyl iodide, acyl chlorides, and ethyl chloroformate, giving the corresponding 1-substituted pyrroles. This appears to be the general pattern, but the solvent and metal are important. Allyl bromide with potassium and dimethyl sulphoxide give 92% of 1-alkylation, while with sodium and tetra-hydrofuran 80% of 2-allylpyrrole is formed. A Claisen type of re-arrangement of 1-allyl- to 2-allyl-pyrrole has been excluded, and it is concluded that dissociation of the pyrrole–metal ion pair favours N-alkylation.[18] 1-Acetylpyrrole is easily obtained by refluxing pyrrole with 1-acetylimidazole.[19]

Pyrrole, in the presence of alkaline catalysts, reacts with acetylene and other unsaturated compounds, such as acrylonitrile, to give 24 and 25 respectively. With formaldehyde and potassium carbonate at

$$\underset{\substack{\text{N}\\\text{CH}=\text{CH}_2\\ \textbf{24}}}{\boxed{}} \qquad \underset{\substack{\text{N}\\\text{CH}_2\text{CH}_2\text{CN}\\ \textbf{25}}}{\boxed{}} \qquad \underset{\substack{\text{N}\\\text{CH}_2\text{OH}\\ \textbf{26}}}{\boxed{}} \qquad \text{HOCH}_2\underset{\substack{\text{N}\\\text{H}\\ \textbf{27}}}{\boxed{}}\text{CH}_2\text{OH}$$

40–55° it gives 26, while 2,5-dihydroxymethylpyrrole (27) is formed at 75–90°.

Pyrrole reacts with methylmagnesium bromide, and other Grignard reagents, giving one mole only of hydrocarbon and pyrrylmagnesium bromide. This last compound can be represented as 28 or considered as an ionic compound when the resonance forms of the pyrrole anion

$$\underset{\substack{\text{N}\\\text{MgBr}\\ \textbf{28}}}{\overset{4\quad3}{\underset{5\quad2}{\boxed{}}}}$$

are represented by **23a**, **23b**, and **23c**. It usually reacts at position 2 and to a smaller extent at position 3. Treatment of **28** with alkyl halides, and acyl halides, methyl chloroformate,[20] or ethyl formate at 150–200° yields mainly the 2-alkyl- or 2-acylpyrrole, or pyrrole-2-carboxylic ester or -2-carbaldehyde respectively; with carbon dioxide the 2-carboxylic acid is obtained. At low temperatures pyrrylmagnesium bromide and alkyl or acyl halides may form 1-substituted pyrroles, but these isomerize on heating alone to 2-substituted pyrroles. The temperature required for this isomerization is much higher than that employed for one-stage substitution at the position 2, but as the effect of the magnesium bromide, and the other substances present in the reaction mixture which leads to substitution at position 2, on the isomerization are not known, it is not possible to conclude that 'one-stage' substitution at position 2 is either direct or proceeds by a rearrangement. However, it is likely that it is direct because **28** reacts with the optically active 2-bromobutanes giving both the 2- and 3-*s*-butyl-pyrroles with complete inversion of configuration.[21] 1-Acylpyrroles on reduction with lithium hydride yield the parent pyrrole and an alcohol or an aldehyde.

b. At carbon atoms. Pyrrole is attacked by electrophilic reagents very rapidly, and primarily at positions 2 and 5. It is probable, in contrast to furan (p. 96), that these substitutions are direct and do not proceed through the formation of a Δ^3-pyrroline by addition to the 2- and 5-positions followed by an elimination.

Pyrrole cannot be sulphonated under ordinary conditions, as polymerization occurs, but with 1-proto-1-pyridinium sulphonate (p. 194) the 2-sulphonic acid is formed in 90% yield. The free acid is a very hygroscopic crystalline solid which with phosphorus pentachloride in carbon tetrachloride gives the sulphonyl chloride.

Pyrrole reacts extremely rapidly with halogens. With iodine in aqueous potassium iodide, or bromine in methanol, the products are the tetrahalogenated pyrroles, while the end product of chlorination is pentachloropyrrole. This last compound may be **29**, **30**, or **31**. No differentiation between these structures has yet been made. Boiling with water yields dichloromaleic imide, while sodium amalgam removes the halogen, giving back pyrrole.

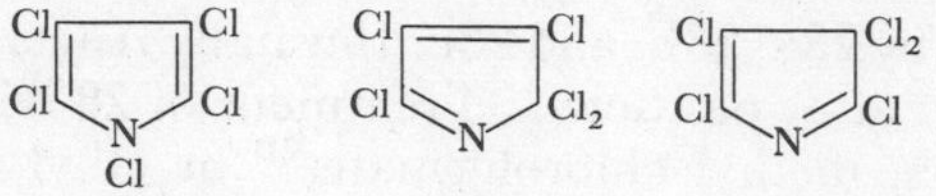

29   **30**   **31**

It is difficult to isolate pure compounds from the direct nitration of pyrrole owing to the formation of tar, but using nitric acid and acetic anhydride, best at $-50°$, 55% of 2-nitropyrrole and a few percent of 3-nitropyrrole are formed.[22] Pyrrole, ethyl nitrate, and sodium ethoxide do not give 3-nitropyrrole as commonly stated, but a 1% yield of 2-nitropyrrole (**32a**);[22] the product from the similar reaction involving ethyl nitrite is almost certainly sodium 2-nitrosopyrrole (**32b**).

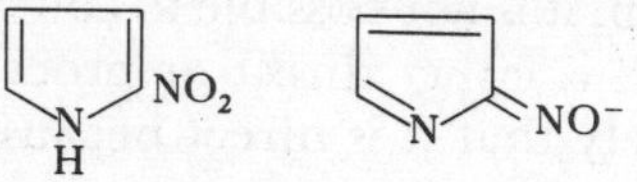

32a   **32b**

Pyrrole is extremely reactive in the Friedel–Crafts reaction and will combine with acetic anhydride on heating, in the absence of any catalyst, to give 2-acetylpyrrole. The related Gattermann reaction, involving anhydrous hydrogen cyanide (or zinc cyanide) and hydrogen chloride, fails with pyrrole itself although the reaction and the Houben–Hoesch modification, in which the hydrogen cyanide is replaced by an aliphatic or aromatic nitrile, proceed well with deactivated pyrroles. Pyrrole-2-carbaldehyde is prepared (90% yield)

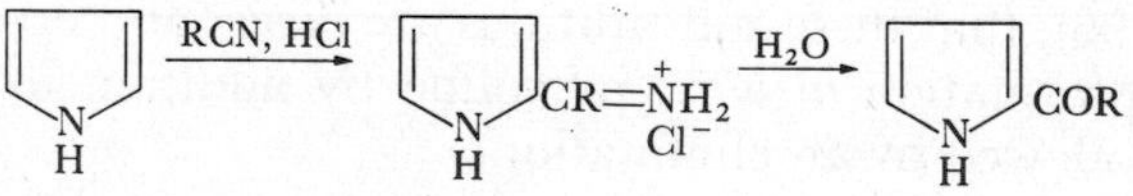

by treating pyrrole with phosphorus oxychloride and dimethylformamide and then boiling the product (**33**), which can be isolated, with aqueous sodium acetate.[23] Pyrrole, and alkylpyrroles, give[24] the corresponding phenyl 2- (or 5-) pyrryl ketones with benzoyl chloride and aqueous sodium hydroxide at 0°.

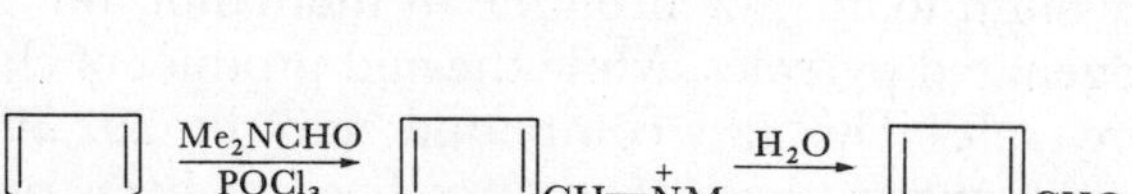

33

The Reimer–Tiemann reaction (boiling with chloroform and aqueous or alcoholic potash) with pyrrole gives both pyrrole-2-carbaldehyde (36) and 3-chloropyridine (35). It is not unlikely that the chloroform is first dehydrohalogenated by the alkali to dichlorocarbene, :CCl$_2$,[25] which then gives the bicyclic compound (34) as an intermediate; 34 can subsequently split in two ways. This explana-

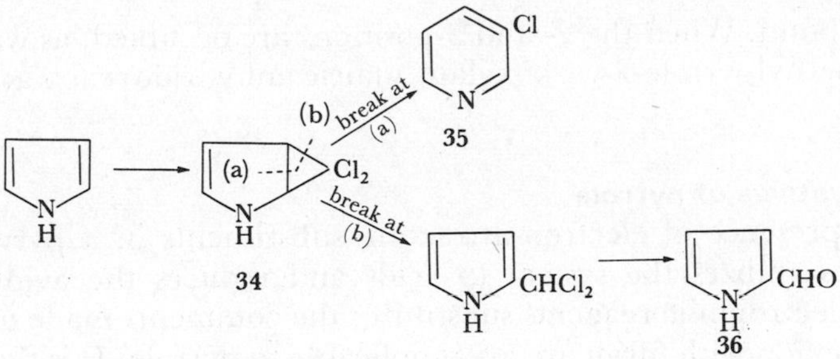

tion is attractive, as it accounts easily for both products, and also it can explain the formation of pyridine (32%) from pyrrole, methylene dichloride and methyllithium,[26] and of 3-chloroquinoline and indole-3-carbaldehyde from indole; however, the indole-3-carbaldehyde is now known to be formed in part, at least, by an alternative route (p. 160). If the chloroform is replaced by carbon tetrachloride in the reaction with pyrrole some pyrrole-2-carboxylic acid is formed; the carbene hypothesis is hardly applicable here, and another mechanism must be involved. Pyrrole, and many derivatives, couple preferentially at position 2 with aromatic diazonium compounds under weakly acid conditions to give highly coloured azo compounds; most phenols couple with benzene diazonium salts only in the presence of alkali.

Pyrrole undergoes the Mannich reaction with formaldehyde and dimethylamine, yielding 37. Conversion into the methiodide by methyl iodide, followed by treatment with alkali, gives pyrrole-2-methanol,

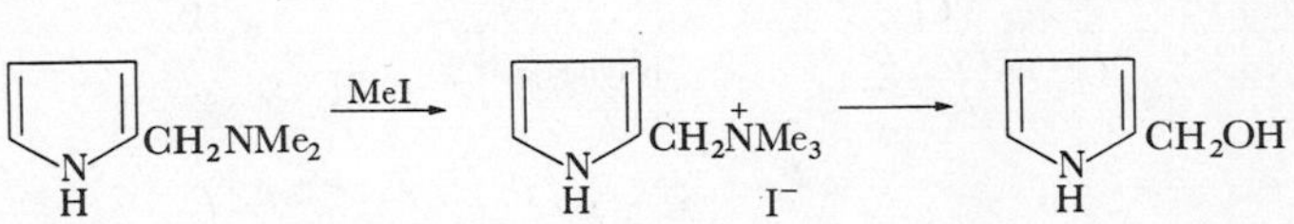

while the methiodide with potassium cyanide yields pyrryl-2-acetonitrile.

Maleic anhydride does not undergo a Diels–Alder reaction with pyrrole, but addition takes place with the formation of **38**, or **39** if the anhydride is in excess. The reaction may be, in essence, a Michael addition of the more reactive positions of pyrrole to the activated

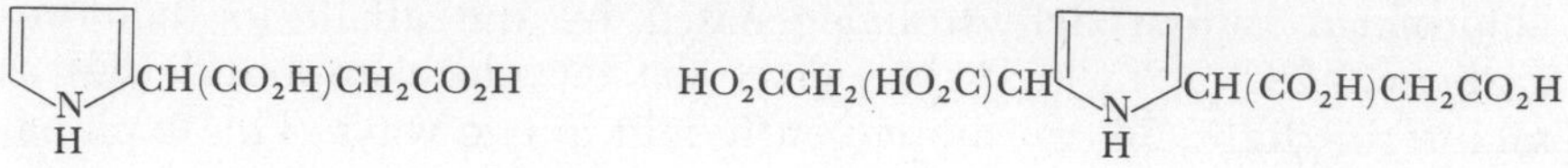

38   **39**

double bond. When the 2- and 5-positions are occupied, as with ethyl 3,5-dimethylpyrrole-2-carboxylate, maleic anhydride reacts at position 3 or 4.

D. Derivatives of pyrrole

The presence of electron-attracting substituents in a pyrrole ring greatly stabilizes the system to acids and reduces the avidity with which electrophilic reagents substitute; the comments made on p. 108 in connexion with furan are also applicable to pyrrole. It is therefore a practical proposition to monohalogenate, or nitrate, pyrrolecarboxylic acids or esters. At the same time the displacement of existing substituents by entering groups is particularly noticeable in the pyrrole series. For example, nitration of ethyl 2,4-dimethylpyrrole-3,5-dicarboxylate gives ethyl 2,4-dinitropyrrole-3,5-dicarboxylate, nitration of ethyl 5-acetyl-2,4-dimethylpyrrole-3-carboxylate gives ethyl 2,4-dimethyl-5-nitropyrrole-3-carboxylate, and bromination of 2,4-dicarboethoxy-3-methylpyrrole-5-carboxylic acid gives ethyl 5-bromo-3-methylpyrrole-2,4-dicarboxylate.

1. *Some reduced pyrroles*

Both the hydrogenation of pyrrole over a rhodium–alumina catalyst and the dehydrogenation of pyrrolidine give some Δ^1-pyrroline, which can be more readily prepared from pyrrolidine acetate as indicated.[27] It

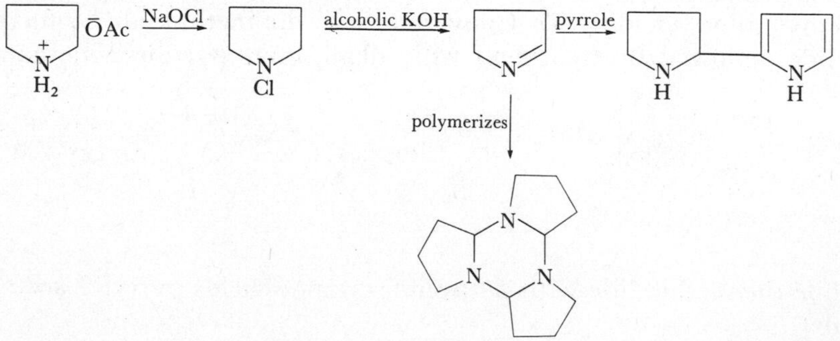

Trimer?

shows no N–H absorption band in the infrared, it reacts with pyrrole as shown, with hydrogen cyanide[28] giving the nitrile of proline (p. 86), and it also self-condenses to a trimer.

Although the partial reduction of pyrrole is claimed to yield a homogenous product, Δ^3-pyrroline (p. 68), reduction of 2,5-dimethyl-pyrrole[29] yields 80% of **40** and 20% of **41**. The Δ^3-pyrroline (**40**) has typical properties of an aliphatic secondary amine in forming a mono-benzoyl derivative and reacting with two moles of methyl iodide. It

also has the properties of an olefin in instantly decolourizing bromine water and acidified potassium permanganate. Ozone splits the double bond, giving **42**, and hydrogenation over platinum gives *trans*-2,5-dimethylpyrrolidine. The isomeric pyrroline (**41**), in contrast to **40**, shows no N–H vibration band in the infrared. It reacts with only one mole of methyl iodide, very slowly with bromine water or permanganate, and it resists ozone. Benzoylation opens the ring, yielding **43**, and hydrogenation gives *cis*-2,5-dimethylpyrrolidine. These reactions

exclude the possible alternative formulation (**44**) for the compound. The Δ^3-pyrroline (**40**) is isomerized to the Δ^1-compound (**41**) by boiling with Raney nickel in xylene. So far the authenticity of no Δ^2-pyrroline unsubstituted on the nitrogen atom has been confirmed; it appears that the tautomeric Δ^1-compounds are the more stable.[30]

Tetrahydropyrrole, or pyrrolidine, b.p. 88°, is almost a flat molecule[31] and has the properties of a typical aliphatic secondary amine. It can be synthesized by many methods, examples being the reduction of pyrrole and the cyclization of butane-1,4-diol by ammonia over alumina at 325° (68% yield). Pyrrolidines have been dehydrogenated to pyrroles by heating with platinized asbestos. Pyrrolidine rings can be opened by the Hofmann (p. 202) and von Braun (p. 203) methods.

2. Alkyl- and aryl-pyrroles

Many alkylpyrroles have been synthesized in connexion with work on the porphyrin pigments, and the Wolff–Kishner reduction of acylpyrroles obtained by Knorr's synthesis is a very common method (p. 84). The direct alkylation of some pyrroles can be effected in a remarkable manner by heating to about 200° with a sodium alkoxide. The mechanism of the reaction has not been investigated, but it is known that position 2 is attacked more easily than the position 3. It is interesting that this is the same as for electrophilic attack, but it would be very remarkable if such were the case under such strongly alkaline conditions; an uncharged molecule, such as an aldehyde, is perhaps involved.[32] In this case the resulting hydroxyalkylpyrrole with sodium

alkoxide could regenerate more aldehyde and give the corresponding alkylpyrrole, and an analogy is the conversion of 2-naphthol into 1-methyl-2-naphthol (**45**) by successive reaction with formaldehyde and sodium methoxide.

1-Alkyl- and 1-aryl-pyrroles rearrange to the 2-substituted pyrroles at about 600°. This reaction was used in the first synthesis of the alkaloid nicotine. Alkylpyrroles are in general more reactive, more basic, and more sensitive to acids than pyrrole itself, as can be anticipated from the electron-donating properties of alkyl groups. Methyl groups at position 2 are much more easily attacked than those at position 3.

The halogenation of alkylpyrroles has been widely studied, and even if the most favourable conditions for side-chain substitution are chosen, for example, by using sulphuryl chloride, all unsubstituted carbon positions on the ring are chlorinated before attack occurs on a 2-methyl group. All three hydrogen atoms of the methyl group are then successively replaced. Bromination can be more easily controlled so that substitution ceases at the monobromomethyl stage. Careful hydrolysis of the halogenated methylpyrroles (cf. $PhCH_2Cl$, $PhCHCl_2$, and $PhCCl_3$) can yield the corresponding alcohols, aldehydes, and acids, but the self-condensation of the halogenated pyrroles may prevent their isolation. For example, the bromination of **46** goes through the sequence indicated yielding the dipyrrylmethene **47**. Asymmetric dipyrrylmethenes can be obtained by using appropriate intermediates in the last stage of the synthesis.

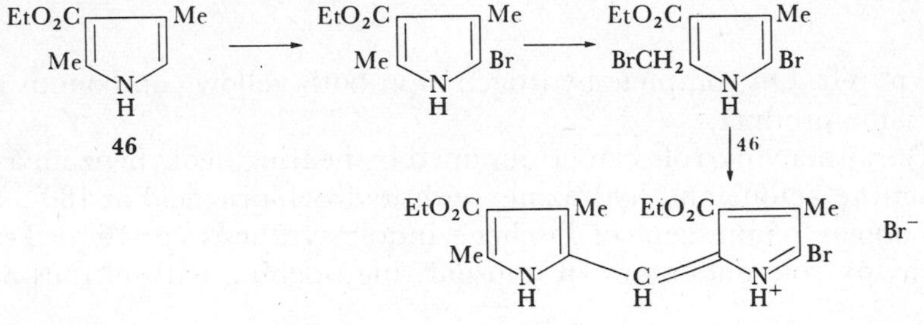

1-Methylpyrrole forms a hydrochloride. It also forms an *addition* compound with ethylmagnesium bromide, no ethane being liberated,[33] and the addition compound gives no pyrrolecarboxylic acid with carbon dioxide. With acetyl chloride the addition compound surprisingly does give 2-acetyl-1-methylpyrrole. An explanation is that magnesium bromide is present in equilibrium in the mixture, and

$$2\ EtMgBr \rightleftharpoons MgBr_2 + MgEt_2$$

alone can catalyse the condensation of the pyrrole with the acetyl chloride.[33] 1-Methylpyrrole will react with one mole or an excess of butyllithium yielding the 2-lithium or 2,5-dilithium derivative, respectively, as is shown by carbonation (dry ice) when the 2-carboxylic acid and the 2,5-dicarboxylic acid are formed.

The nitration of 1-methylpyrrole in acetic anhydride gives[22] a mixture of the 2- and 3-nitro derivatives in 2:1 ratio. These nitro compounds are of special interest, as they are among the very few nitro compounds known to undergo the Friedel–Crafts reaction. This gives an indication of the very great reactivity of the pyrrole ring which is sufficient to overcome the deactivating properties of the nitro group.

1-Benzylpyrrole combines with acetylenedicarboxylic acid[13a] giving the yellow **48** and **49**, with a small amount of a colourless compound

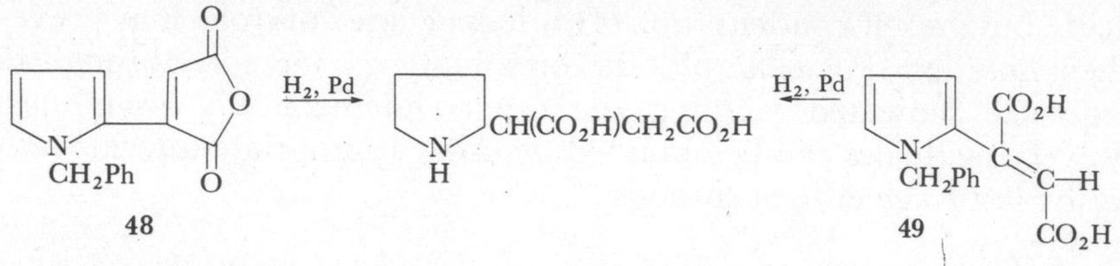

(see p. 69). On complete hydrogenation both yellow compounds give the same product.

Tetraphenylpyrrole can be obtained by heating deoxybenzoin azine (from the ketone and hydrazine) with hydrochloric acid at 180°. The reaction is reminiscent of Fischer's indole synthesis (p. 167). Tetraphenylpyrrole undergoes an unusual ring opening with nitrous acid.

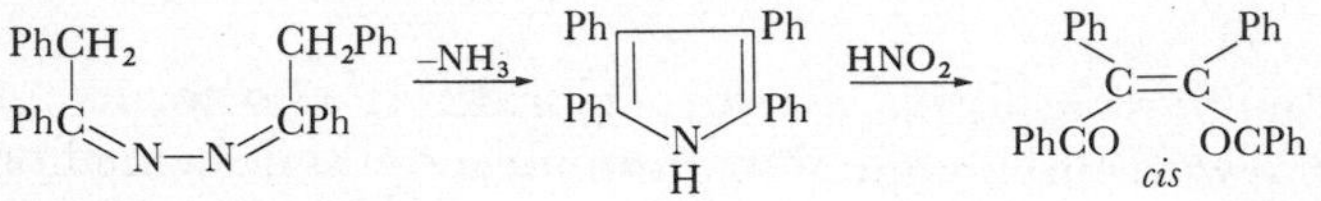

3. *Amino- and diazo-pyrroles*

Comparatively few simple aminopyrroles are known. They can be prepared by direct synthesis as shown or by reduction of nitroso- or nitro-pyrroles, or of benzeneazopyrroles obtained by diazonium coupling. Infrared examination[34] of **50** has shown the absence of bands characteristic of the imine group. The compound is therefore

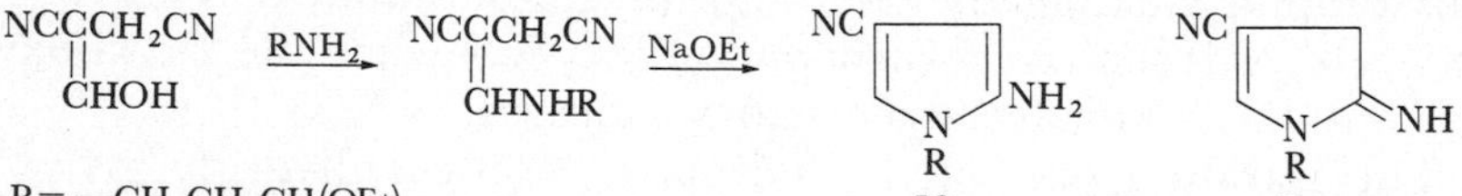

not the pyrrolenine **51**. It gives positive Ehrlich's and pine splint tests, and no ammonia is evolved on boiling with 2 N sodium hydroxide. Little is known about the diazotization and coupling of simple aminopyrroles. The diazonium compound **52** is obtained from ethyl 3,5-dimethylpyrrole-2-carboxylate by successive nitrosation, reduction, and diazotization. It is comparatively stable, perhaps because of the

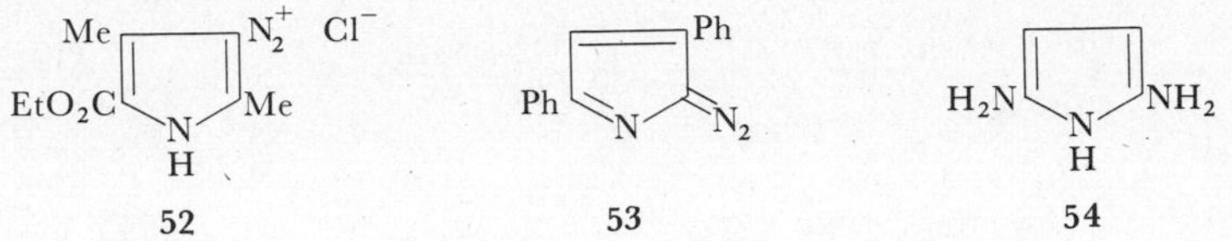

52 53 54

two electron-attracting substituents, and couples in aqueous sodium bicarbonate[35] with phenols. Buffered nitrous acid with 2,4-diphenyl-pyrrole gives first 2-nitroso-3,5-diphenylpyrrole but on prolonged treatment the 2-diazopyrrole (53) is formed.[36] 2-Diazopyrroles are more reactive and less stable than their 3 isomers, but both couple with 2-naphthol. 2,5-Diaminopyrrole (54) has been obtained from succinonitrile and ammonia. Its exact structure is uncertain, although the amino–imino tautomer is excluded by the ultraviolet spectrum of the compound.

4. Hydroxypyrroles

As the ultraviolet absorption spectra of 55 and 57 differ widely, and as 57 can only have the structure given, 55 must exist largely as the 2-pyrrolone tautomer, as is shown. By analogy 2-hydroxypyrrole probably exists in the pyrrolone form (56). It is a colourless oil, b.p. 75° at 0·05 mm, which resinifies on standing for 24 hours.[37]

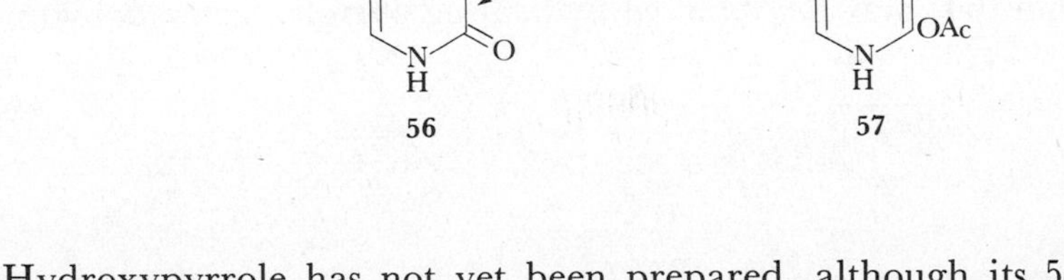

55
56
57

3-Hydroxypyrrole has not yet been prepared, although its 5-carboxylic acid (59) has been obtained[38] by a long synthesis. This acid (59) gives no colour with ferrous salts (contrast pyridine-2-carboxylic acid), it gives a deep violet ferric chloride colour, and it is very easily oxidized to a blue dye. Although the ultraviolet absorption spectrum of the hydroxy acid (**59**) broadly resembles that of the ethoxy acid (**58**), it is likely that the former compound should be represented as the tautomer **60**. Spectral studies[39] have shown conclusively that the ester possesses structure **61**.

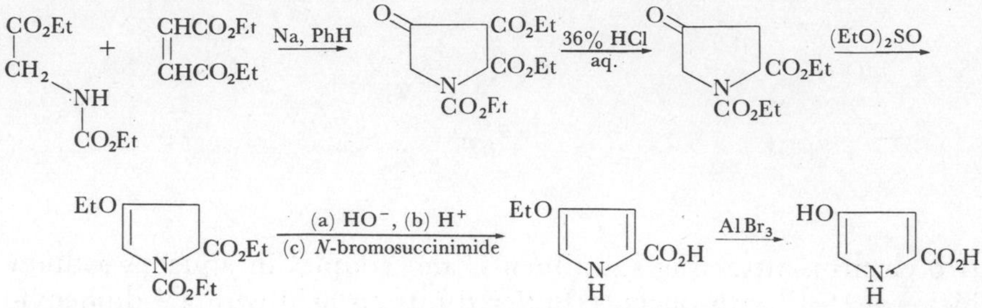

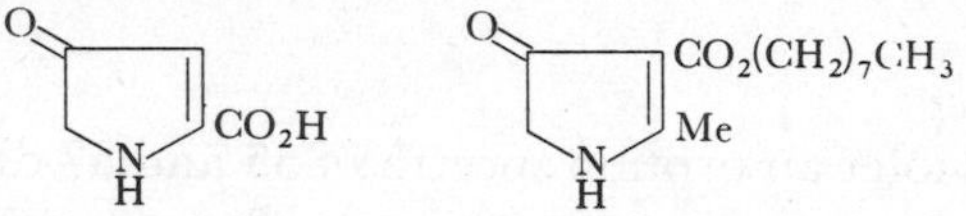

5. *Pyrrole alcohols, aldehydes, ketones, and acids*

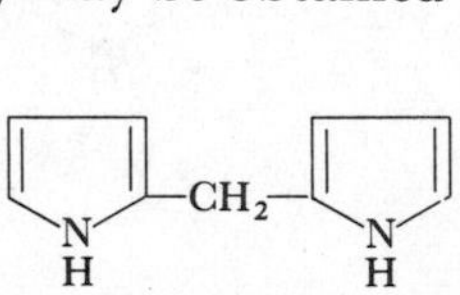

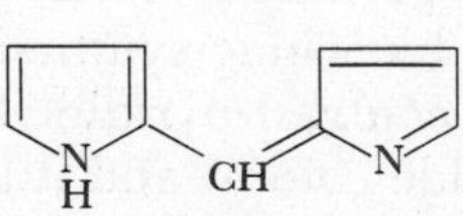

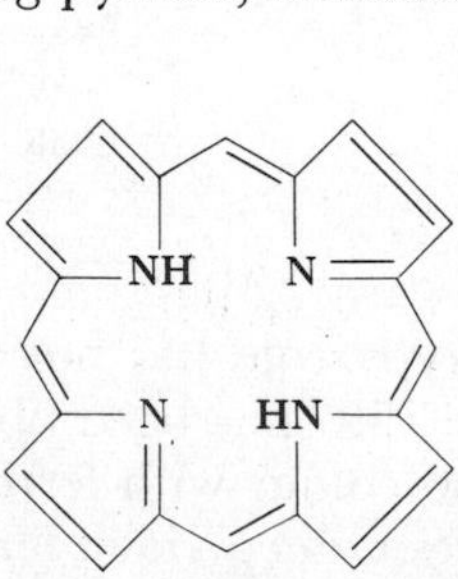

Pyrrole-2-methanol may be obtained by reducing pyrrole-2-carb-aldehyde with sodium borohydride; lithium aluminium hydride can also give 2-methylpyrrole.[40] Several substituted derivatives have been obtained from pyrroles, formaldehyde, and a trace of alkali (p. 70), but usually reaction proceeds further. Alcohols of this type are extremely reactive, and although pyrrole-2-methanol is probably the first product formed from pyrrole and formaldehyde in the presence of acid, the compound usually isolated is the dipyrrylmethane (**62**). This compound is easily oxidized to the methene (**63**). A low yield of porphin (**64**) may be obtained by heating pyrrole, formaldehyde, and pyridine. The pyrrolemethanol **65** has been obtained from the appropriate pyrrole and formaldehyde. On heating it loses formaldehyde, giving the dipyrrylmethane.

65

Pyrrole-2-carbaldehyde is best obtained from pyrrole, phosphorus oxychloride, and dimethylformamide (p. 72), while many substituted pyrrole-2- and -3-carbaldehydes have been obtained from the corresponding pyrroles by the Gattermann reaction (p. 72). The aldehydes have some general properties of aromatic aldehydes. The hydrogen at position 1 is more acidic than that of the parent pyrrole owing to the electron-attracting properties of the carbonyl group, and can be

66a   **66b**

replaced by sodium using sodium ethoxide. Most interesting observations are that pyrrole-2-carbaldehyde[22] and its 1-methyl derivative[41] (like indole-3-carbaldehyde, p. 160) give no Schiff's, Tollen's, or Fehling's reactions and do not undergo the Cannizzaro, benzoin, or (normal) Perkin reactions. These failures can be associated with the recognition of these aldehydes as vinylogous amides, the carbonyl group being deactivated through resonance (**66a** and **66b**) and the molecules being highly polarized.[42] Both these aldehydes, however, give vinylpyrroles[43] with Wittig reagents.[44]

The combination of pyrrole-2-carbaldehydes with pyrroles in the presence of hydrogen bromide, to give dipyrrylmethenes for porphyrin syntheses, has proved most useful. The course of the reaction is not certain, and the route suggested is the formation of a tripyrrylmethane (**67**), which can split in two ways. However, the desired unsymmetrical products have often been obtained, and it is not impossible they are formed directly. Bromination of pyrrole-2-carbaldehyde causes mostly 4-substitution.[45]

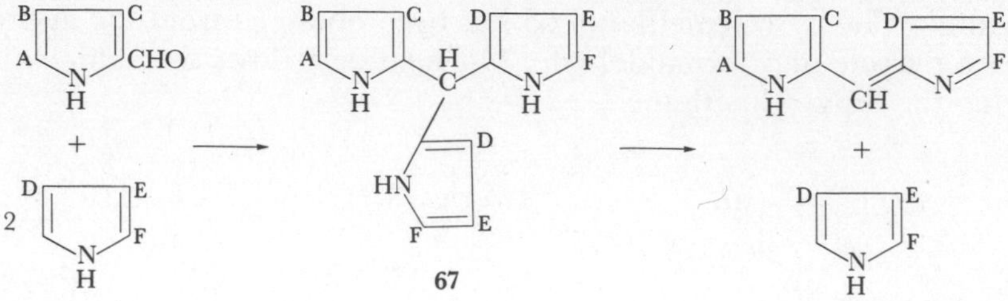

67

Pyrrole ketones may be obtained by a modification of Knorr's synthesis (p. 84) or by acylating a pyrrole directly with acetic anhydride (p. 72); a carboxyl group can be displaced in this second reaction. Pyrrole ketones are stable and undergo standard reactions.

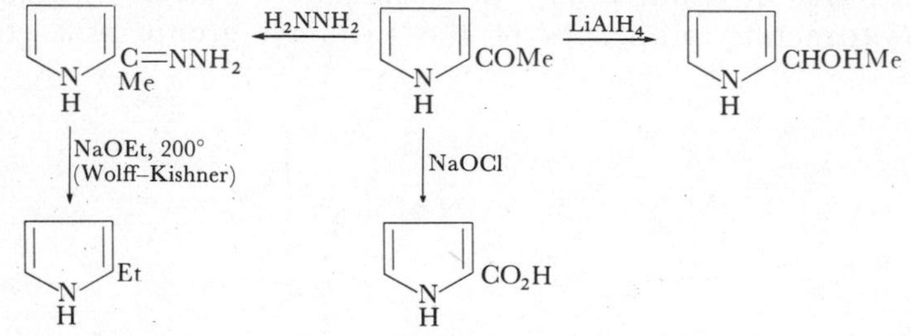

Pyrrolecarboxylic acids (see also pp. 73, 77) are commonly obtained directly by synthesis involving ring closure (pp. 83–86), and less often by the oxidation of alkylpyrroles by fused potassium hydroxide, by carboxylation of metallic derivatives of pyrrole, and from ketones (flow-sheet above). Pyrrole-2-carboxylic acid is best obtained from the aldehyde by oxidation with alkaline silver oxide[46] but has also been obtained from pyrrole itself by direct carboxylation with ammonium carbonate at 120°. This last reaction has been little investigated, but is similar to Kolbe's synthesis of phenolic acids from phenols.

Pyrrolecarboxylic acids, like phenolic acids, are usually decarboxylated readily on heating. This has been of great value in the preparation of alkylpyrroles via Knorr's synthesis. Alkyl groups facilitate and electron-attracting groups hinder the decarboxylation, which usually takes place preferentially at position 2. Pyrrole-2-carboxylic acid on heating with acetic anhydride gives the cyclic compound **68**.

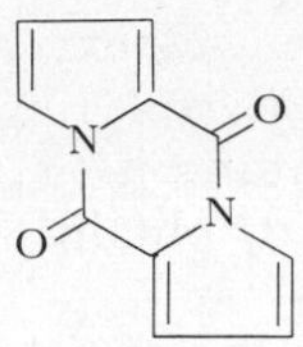

68

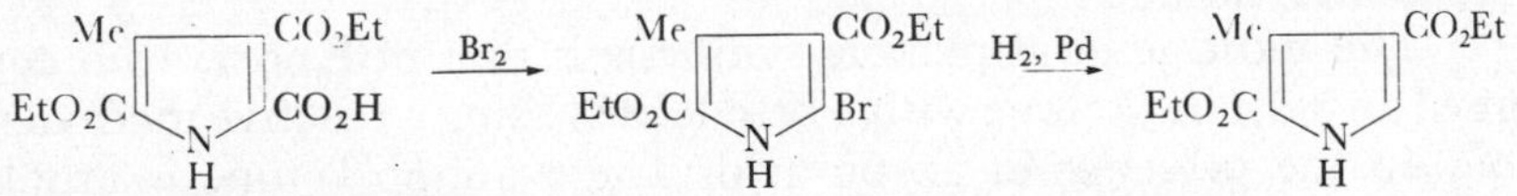

69

Carboxyl groups can often be displaced by incoming substituents. Bromination, for instance, followed by catalytic hydrogenation can be a useful way of removing a carboxyl group when direct decarboxylation fails (e.g. with **69**).

The halogenation of methyl pyrrole-2-carboxylate has been carefully investigated.[47] The highest yield (56%) of 4-substitution was obtained using bromine in acetic acid, while 80% of the 5-chloro compound was isolated after treatment with t-butyl hypochlorite in carbon tetrachloride.

The difference in reactivity at the positions 2 and 3 of the pyrrole ring is again shown up in the hydrolysis of esters. The 2-carboxylic esters are the more rapidly hydrolysed by alkali, and this is illustrated in the synthesis of ethyl pyrrole-3-carboxylate. Many 3-carboxylic

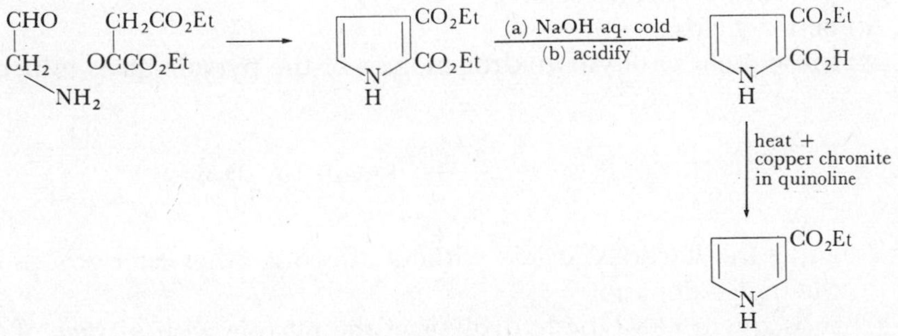

esters are more rapidly attacked by sulphuric acid at 40–60° than the 2-isomers. This may be due to steric effects, as the pyrroles involved usually bear many substituents, but ethyl pyrrole-3-carboxylate, where there is no steric hindrance, is hydrolysed by hot alcoholic potassium hydroxide.

It is noteworthy that while C-ethoxycarbonyl groups inhibit or prevent the hydrogenation of the pyrrole ring, the presence of an N-ethoxycarbonyl group greatly facilitates it (p. 69). This is particularly useful, as the N-carboxylic acid, obtained on hydrolysis, immediately decarboxylates.

E. Synthetic methods

(1) The most general pyrrole synthesis is that of Knorr, who condensed an α-amino ketone with a ketone possessing a reactive methylene group in the presence of acetic acid. The α-amino ketone is usually prepared *in situ* by reducing the corresponding oximino compound with zinc. If the methylene group marked with an asterisk is not sufficiently

$$
\left[
\begin{array}{c}
\text{MeCO} \\
| \\
\text{EtO}_2\text{CCH}_2
\end{array}
\longrightarrow
\begin{array}{c}
\text{MeCO} \\
| \\
\text{EtO}_2\text{CC}=\text{NOH}
\end{array}
\right]
\longrightarrow
\begin{array}{c}
\text{MeCO} \\
| \\
\text{YCHNH}_2
\end{array}
+
\begin{array}{c}
*\text{CH}_2\text{X} \\
| \\
\text{OCMe}
\end{array}
\longrightarrow
$$

reactive the amino ketone self-condenses to a dihydropyrazine (p. 346). The synthesis usually fails or gives very poor results when X = alkyl. Y can be hydrogen, but better results are obtained when it is a COR group, while the methyl groups of the reactants may be replaced by aryl or RCO groups. The synthesis is therefore of very wide application. Recent improvements to the synthesis are (a) to use sodium dithionite as the reducing agent for the isonitroso compound, (b) to use benzyl acetoacetate, and (c) to use t-butyl acetoacetate. The advantages obtained respectively are:

(a) better yields,

(b) subsequent catalytic hydrogenolysis of the pyrrole gives toluene

$$
\text{RCO}_2\text{CH}_2\text{Ph} \xrightarrow{\text{H}_2,\ \text{Pd/C}} \text{RCO}_2\text{H} + \text{PhMe}
$$

and a free carboxylic acid without affecting other ester groups in the molecule, and

(c) subsequent catalytic hydrolysis of the pyrrole with a trace of 4-toluenesulphonic acid at 200° yields butylene and a pyrrole-3- or 4-carboxylic acid, while concurrent decarboxylation occurs if the

$$
\text{RCO}_2\text{Bu-}t \longrightarrow \text{RCO}_2\text{H} + \text{Me}_2\text{C}{=}\text{CH}_2
$$
$$
\searrow \text{RH} + \text{CO}_2
$$

t-butyl ester was at position 2 or 5 leading to a pyrrole unsubstituted at this position. As in (*b*) ethoxycarbonyl groups in the pyrrole are not affected by the procedure.

Treatment of an α-amino ketone with an activated acetylene can give a dihydropyrrole (**70**) which, with acid, dehydrates to the pyrrole.[48] This new synthesis is very similar to that of Knorr, and the dihydropyrrole (**70**) may be a common intermediate.

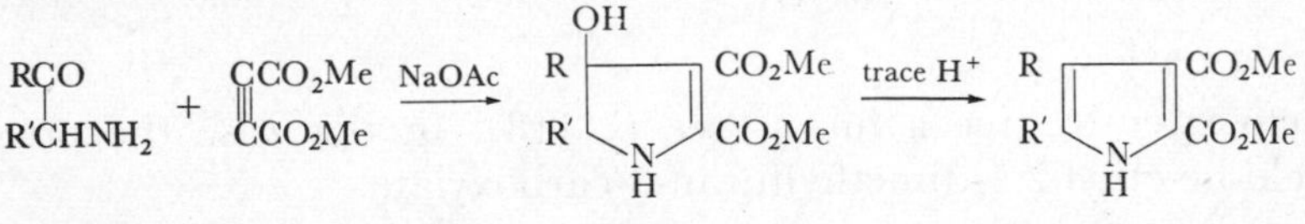

70

(2) The Paal–Knorr synthesis of pyrroles from 1,4-diketones by treating with ammonia or primary amines is an excellent method which is limited by the availability of the diketones. Recently, however, new methods of preparing these diketones from furans have been discovered (p. 99).

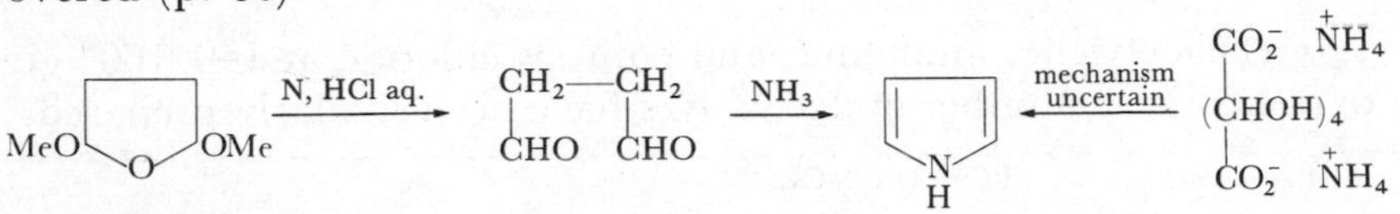

71

Succindialdehyde and ammonia give pyrrole itself, in poor yield; the succindialdehyde, which need not be isolated, can be obtained from the acetal (**23**, p. 99) with dilute hydrochloric acid. Primary amines, however, give much better results, and by using appropriate amines and diketones it is possible to prepare pyrroles with substituents at any position. The first synthesis of pyrrole, the pyrolysis of ammonium mucate, is still the most convenient laboratory preparation for this compound.

(3) A new,[49] probably general, synthesis starts from vinyl ketones. Base-catalysed addition of the glycine derivative and dehydration give the dihydropyrrole. Treatment with sodium ethoxide, at room temperature in some cases, eliminates sodium 4-toluenesulphinate yielding the pyrrole.

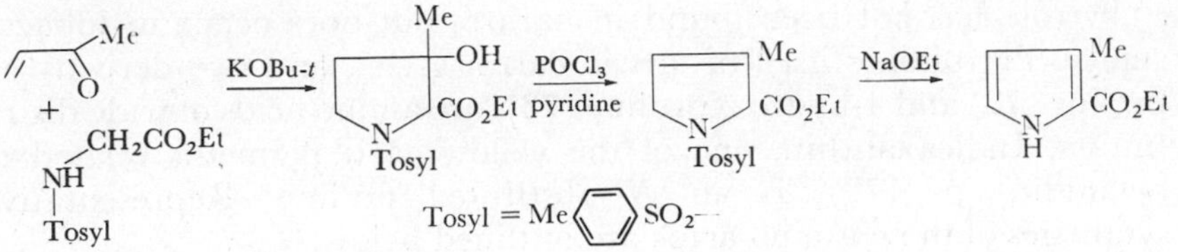

(4) The Hantzsch synthesis is much less generally applicable than that of Knorr, and requires the combination of a β-keto ester with an α-chloro ketone in the presence of ammonia. Ethyl 2-aminocrotonate is almost certainly an intermediate in the example given. A big difficulty is that the chloro ketone can also react in another manner with the

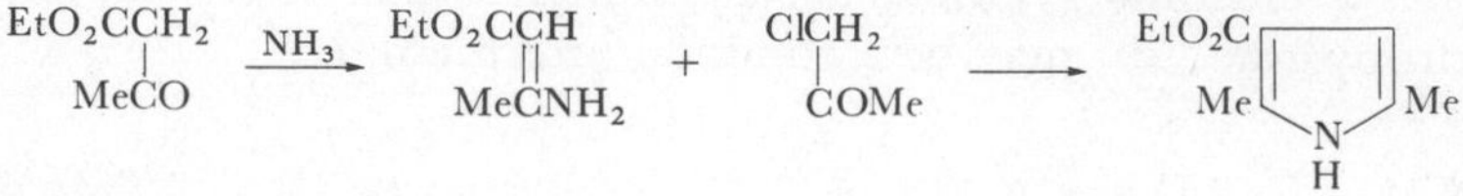

$$EtO_2CCH_2 \xrightarrow{NH_3} EtO_2CCH + ClCH_2 \longrightarrow EtO_2C$$

β-keto ester to give a furan (see p. 118). In this case the product would be ethyl 2,4-dimethylfuran-3-carboxylate.

(5) A new synthesis which may have useful application involves a Diels–Alder reaction.

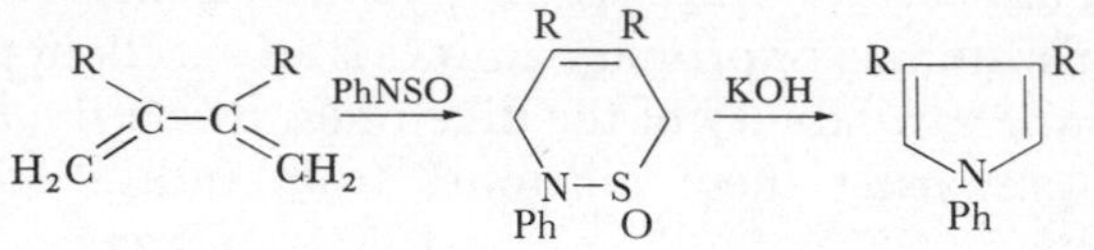

(6) Diacetylene, ammonia, and cuprous chloride at 140–160° give pyrrole, and a number of derivatives have been similarly prepared.[50]

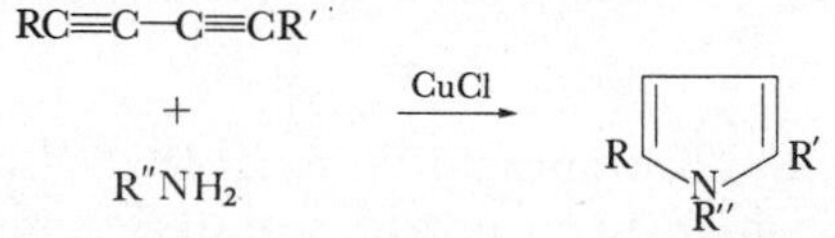

(7) Pyrrole is prepared commercially by passing furan, ammonia, and steam over a heated aluminium oxide catalyst.[51] This type of synthesis has been used for synthesizing isotopically labelled[52] and 1-substituted pyrroles.

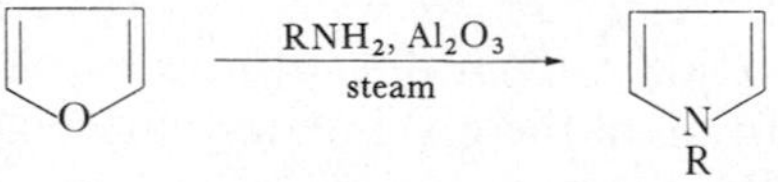

F. Natural occurrence and compounds of special interest

1. *Simple pyrroles*

Pyrrole has not been found in nature, but does occur in tobacco smoke. Pyrrolidine itself occurs in carrot green, and two derivatives, proline (**72**) and 4-hydroxyproline (**73**), are amino acids of wide distribution. Indicaxanthin, one of the yellow cacti pigments related to betanidin (p. 172), is an *N*-substituted proline. Representative syntheses of these amino acids are outlined below.

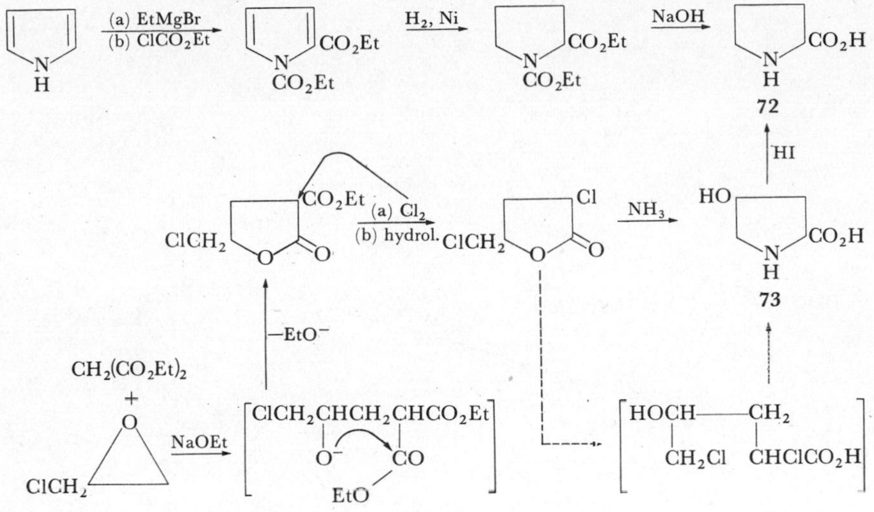

A polymer obtained from 1-vinylpyrrolidone (**74**) with aqueous hydrogen peroxide has been used as a blood-plasma substitute, but dextran sulphate is definitely superior.

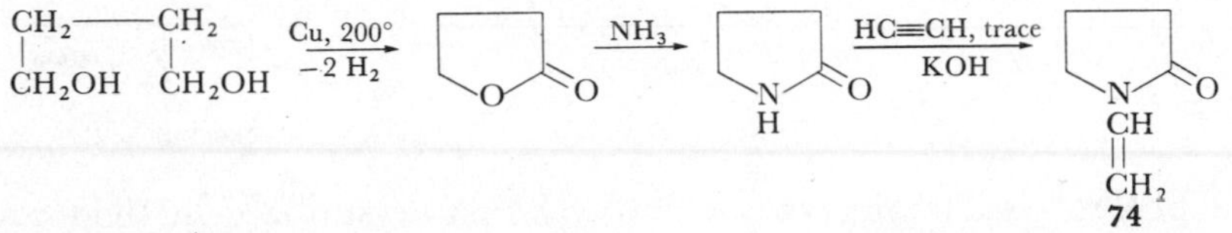

2. The porphyrins[53]

Porphin, the simplest porphyrin, consists of four pyrrole rings linked together by methine bridges and is mentioned briefly on p. 80. A methine bridge is the unsaturated carbon–hydrogen system between each five-membered ring in, for example, protoporphyrin IX (**75**). The rings and substituents on the methine bridges should be labelled as indicated. The porphin system is one of great stability, and calculations have shown that there is a piling up of electrons on the nitrogen atoms.[54] Nuclear magnetic resonance studies show that the ring system can sustain an induced ring current, but that the idea of a single current loop of 18 electrons which would fit Hückel's $(4n + 2)$ π-electron rule is not consistent with all the observed phenomena.[55]

Haemoglobin and chlorophyll are very noteworthy derivatives of porphin, although there are others which will not be considered here.

Haemoglobin is a conjugated protein made up of haem, the porphyrin moiety containing a ferrous atom, and the protein globin. Oxidation of the ferrous atom in haem to the ferric state occurs readily.

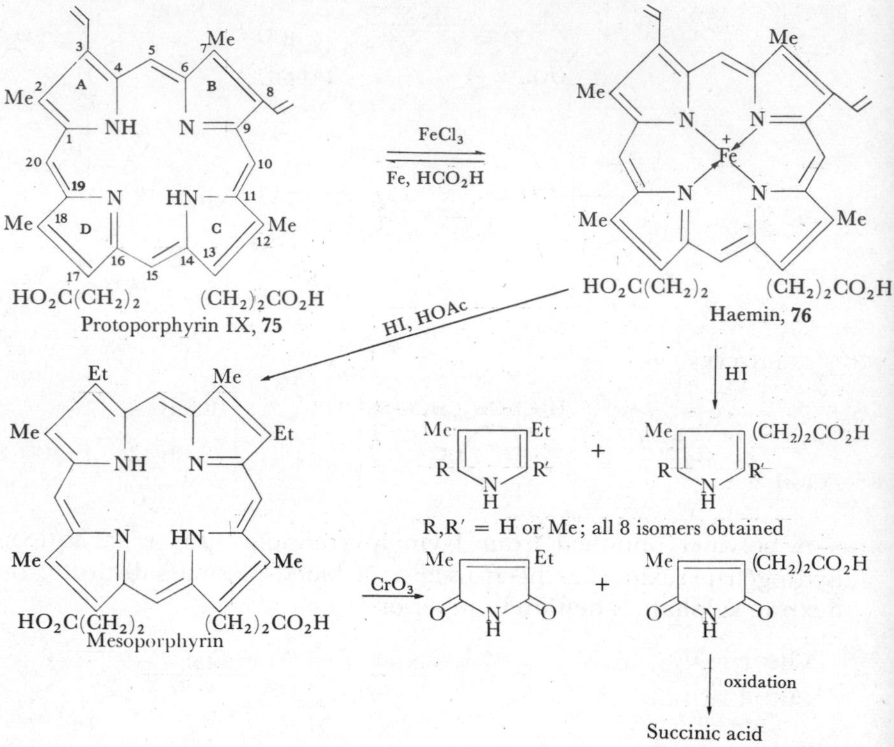

Protoporphyrin IX, 75

$$\xrightleftharpoons[\text{Fe, HCO}_2\text{H}]{\text{FeCl}_3}$$

Haemin, 76

HI, HOAc

Mesoporphyrin

$\xrightarrow{\text{CrO}_3}$

R,R′ = H or Me; all 8 isomers obtained

↓ HI

↓ oxidation

Succinic acid

The product is haemin (76), which was first crystallized in 1853, and it was synthesized by Fischer and Zeile in 1929. Direct removal of the iron gives protoporphyrin IX (75).

The degradation studies outlined above left a number of possibilities for the structure of haemin, and as these could not be resolved by the degradation methods available, Fischer decided to synthesize all the possible structures. His successful sequence, discovered at a comparatively early stage, is shown on the opposite page. Syntheses of porphins and related macrocycles have been reviewed recently.[55]

A great deal of biochemical work, involving the biosynthesis of protoporphyrin from simple intermediates 'labelled' with heavy or radioactive atoms, has been done.[56] It is clear that the biosynthesis of porphobilinogen (77), which is excreted in human urine under certain pathological conditions, proceeds as indicated. Four molecules of porphobilinogen are involved in essentially similar biosyntheses of chlorophylls in plants and of other porphyrins and corrins in bacteria and animals. In the last few years,[56] much effort has been devoted to the study of these biosyntheses but a great deal still remains to be

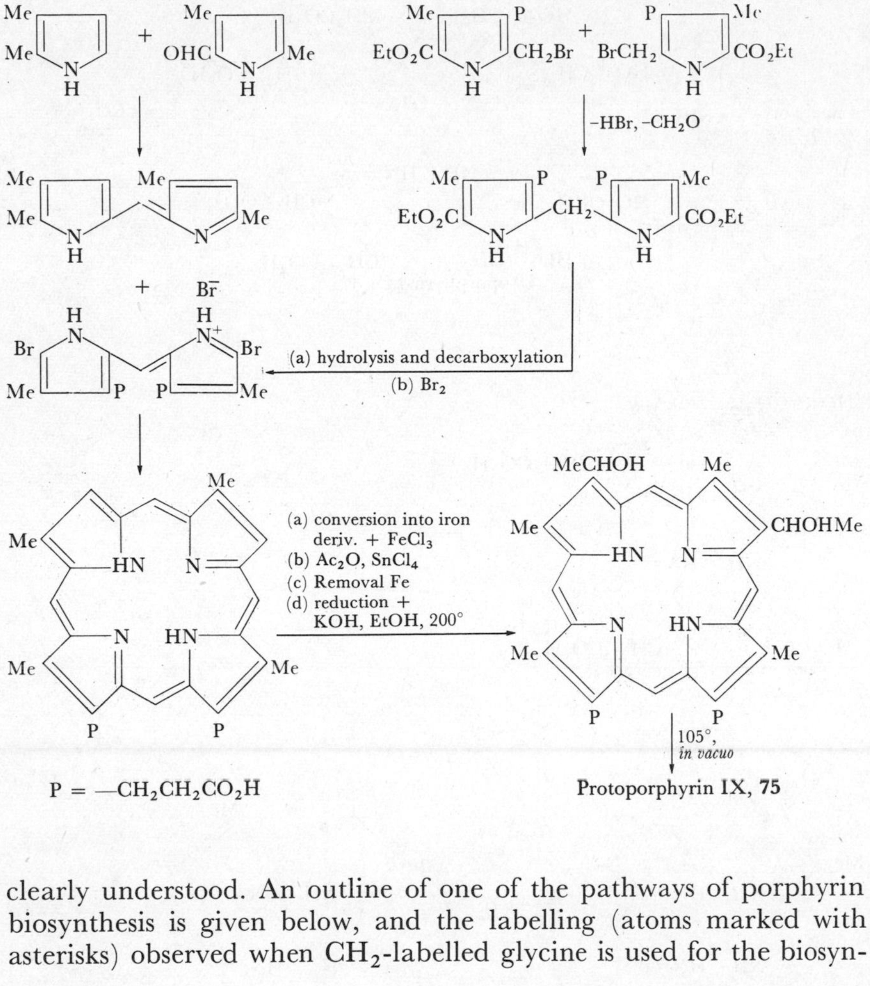

(a) hydrolysis and decarboxylation
(b) Br_2

(a) conversion into iron
    deriv. + $FeCl_3$
(b) Ac_2O, $SnCl_4$
(c) Removal Fe
(d) reduction +
    KOH, EtOH, 200°

$P = -CH_2CH_2CO_2H$

Protoporphyrin IX, **75**

105°,
in vacuo

clearly understood. An outline of one of the pathways of porphyrin biosynthesis is given below, and the labelling (atoms marked with asterisks) observed when CH_2-labelled glycine is used for the biosyn-

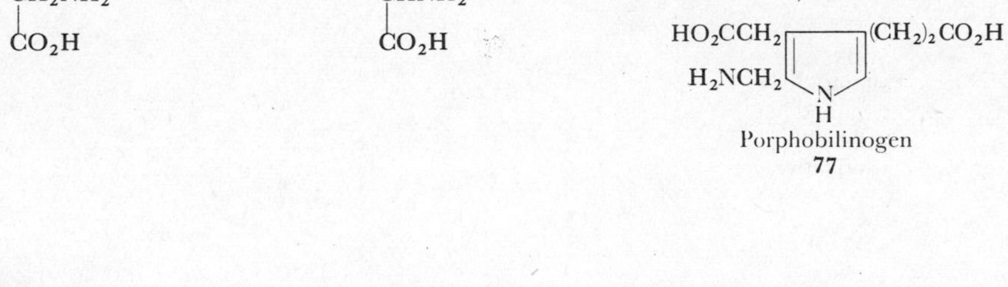

Porphobilinogen
77

4 moles of **77** $\xrightarrow{-4\,NH_3}$

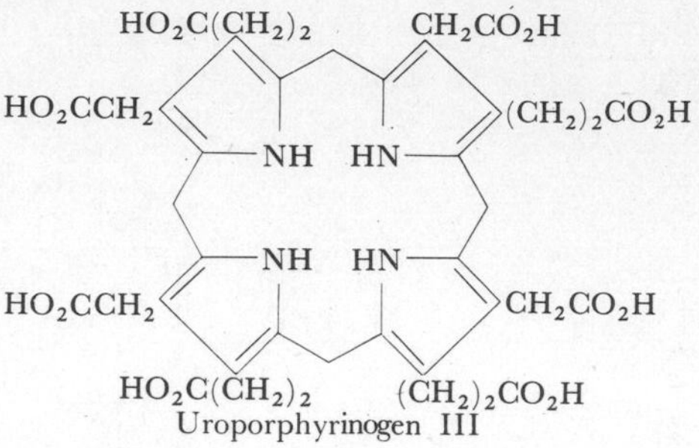
HO₂C(CH₂)₂
CH₂CO₂H
HO₂CCH₂
(CH₂)₂CO₂H
NH HN
NH HN
HO₂CCH₂
CH₂CO₂H
HO₂C(CH₂)₂
(CH₂)₂CO₂H

Uroporphyrinogen III

$\xrightarrow{-4\,CO_2}$

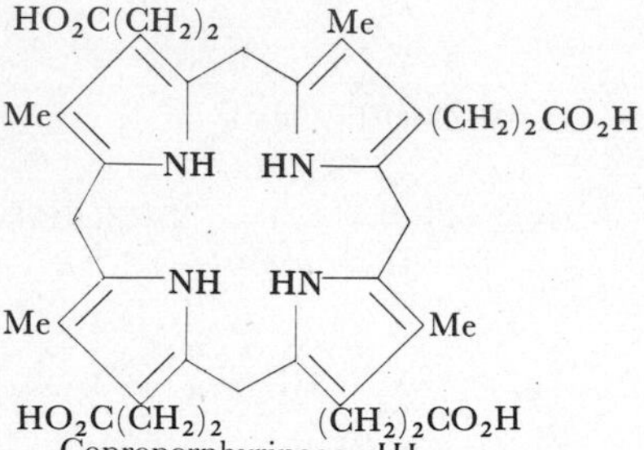
HO₂C(CH₂)₂
Me
Me
(CH₂)₂CO₂H
NH HN
NH HN
Me
Me
HO₂C(CH₂)₂
(CH₂)₂CO₂H

Coproporphyrinogen III

$\xrightarrow{-2\,CO_2,\ -4\,H}$

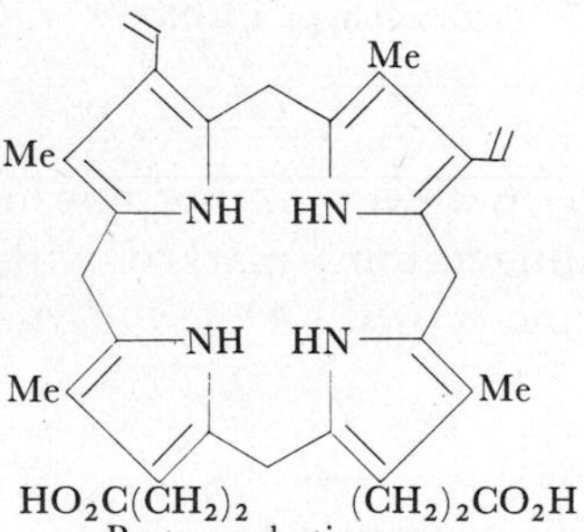
Me
Me
NH HN
NH HN
Me
Me
HO₂C(CH₂)₂
(CH₂)₂CO₂H

Protoporphyrinogen

$\xrightarrow{-6\,H}$

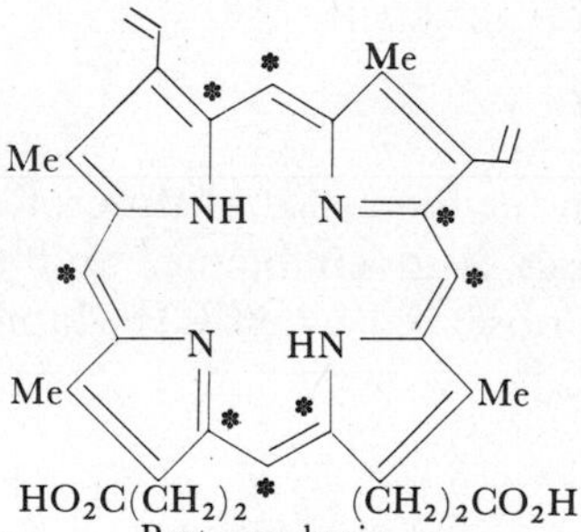
Me
Me
NH N
N HN
Me
Me
HO₂C(CH₂)₂
(CH₂)₂CO₂H

Protoporphyrin

75

$\longrightarrow$

Chlorophylls
and
haemin
derivatives

thesis is shown for protoporphyrin (**75**). One of the most interesting features is that one of the porphobilinogen (**77**) units is 'turned round' with respect to the orientation of the others. A mechanistic scheme accounting for this, and also for the established formation of the corrin system (p. 92) from porphobilinogen,[57] has been put forward.[58]

Chlorophyll[59] was the name originally given to the green colouring matter of the chloroplasts of plants, and it is of major importance in photosynthesis. Stokes in 1818 showed by a spectral examination that chlorophyll was a mixture, and at least 8 chlorophylls are now known. Willstätter, starting in 1906, found that all leaves contained two green pigments, which he named chlorophyll *a* and *b*, that the molecules

$$R = \text{Phytyl} =$$
$$Me_2CH(CH_2)_3CHMe(CH_2)_3CHMe(CH_2)_3CMe{=}CHCH_2{-}$$

contained magnesium, and that the empirical formula of chlorophyll *a* was $C_{55}H_{72}N_4O_5Mg$. The structure of chlorophyll *a* (**78**) has been fairly well established by degradation, and it is a reduced porphyrin. The hydrogen atoms of the reduced pyrrole ring appear to be *trans*. Chlorophyll *a* has been synthesized.[60]

Chlorophyll *b* has the methyl group marked with an asterisk replaced by a carbaldehyde group.

3. Vitamin B_{12}

Cyanocobalamin, or vitamin B_{12},[57] the antipernicious anaemia factor, was first crystallized in 1948, and although much intensive chemical work was carried out in order to determine its structure, comparatively little initial progress was made. The molecule was shown to have the composition $C_{61-64}H_{84-92}O_{13-14}N_{14}PCo$, and on hydrolysis yielded cyanide ion, 1-aminopropan-2-ol, 5–6 moles of ammonia, 5,6-dimethylbenzimidazole-1-α-D-ribofuranoside-3-phosphate and a deep red gum from which a hexabasic acid of unknown constitution was obtained. Although only about 25% of the atoms of this large asymmetric molecule had been assigned to chemically identi-

E

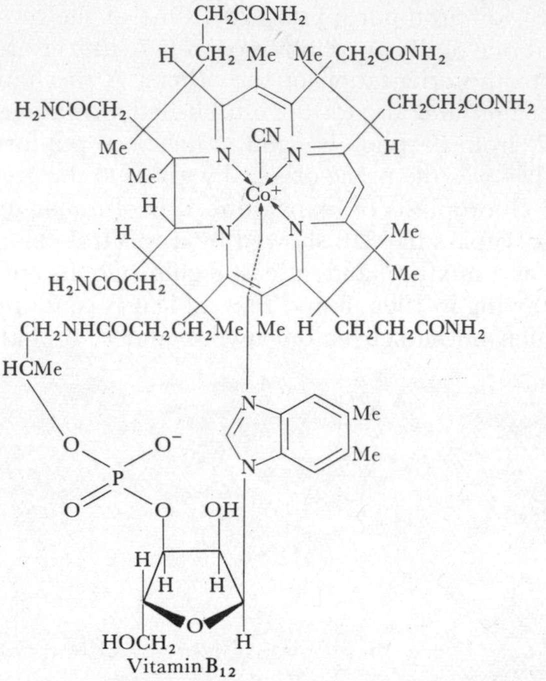

CH_2CONH_2

H CH_2 Me Me CH_2CONH_2

H_2NCOCH_2 $CH_2CH_2CONH_2$

Me   CN   H

Me   N   N

Co^+

H

H   N   N   Me

H_2NCOCH_2 Me

$CH_2NHCOCH_2CH_2$ Me Me H $CH_2CH_2CONH_2$

HCMe

N   Me

O O^- Me

P

N

O   O   OH

H

H   H

HOCH$_2$ O   H

Vitamin B_{12}

fied degradation products, Professor D. Crowfoot Hodgkin and her collaborators, by an extremely brilliant x-ray investigation of the vitamin and its derivatives, succeeded in determining its molecular structure.[61] The molecule of vitamin B_{12} contains a large planar group involving 4 reduced pyrrole rings which resembles a porphyrin. It should be specially noted that it differs from the porphyrin system as it lacks one methine bridge. Recently a number of vitamin B_{12}-like compounds have been isolated in which the 5,6-dimethylbenzimidazole part of the vitamin molecule has been replaced by adenine, 2-methyladenine, or 2-methylhypoxanthine. Corrin, numbered as shown, is the name now given to the ring system from which vitamin B_{12} is derived.

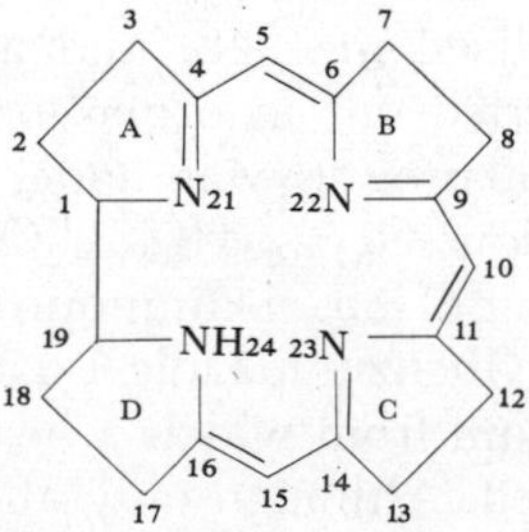

3   5   7

4   6

2   A   B   8

1   N_{21} $_{22}N$ 9

10

19   NH_{24} $_{23}N$ 11

18   D   C   12

16   14

17   15   13

Corrin

2. FURAN

A. Introduction

The earliest furan compound described is pyromucic acid (**1**), usually known as furoic or furan-2-carboxylic acid. It was obtained by Scheele in 1780 by the dry distillation of mucic acid. In 1832 furfural, or furan-2-carbaldehyde (**2**), was obtained by the action of sulphuric acid and manganese dioxide on sugar, but these furans were not related until 1860, when furfural was oxidized to furoic acid with silver oxide. Furan itself was obtained in 1870 by treating barium furoate with soda lime. In 1920 furfural became commercially available, cheaply and in large quantities, from the acid hydrolysis of oat hulls (husks). At this time the outlets for furfural were limited, but its cheapness and availability greatly stimulated the search for uses. Today furfural is a very

| 1 | 2 | 3 | 4 |

valuable raw material, and the source of most furan derivatives. About 25,000 tons a year are produced in the United States.

The positions in the furan ring are usually numbered as in **3**, but in older literature a less convenient lettering system (**4**) is sometimes used. The compound commonly known as furfural (**2**) could therefore be named furan-2-carbaldehyde, or furan α-carbaldehyde. The trivial names of some groups derived from furan are shown.

| 2-Furyl | 3-Furyl | 2-Furfuryl | 2-Furoyl |

B. Physical properties and structure

Furan itself is a colourless liquid, b.p. 31·36°, with a chloroform-like smell. It is only slightly soluble in water, but it is miscible with most organic solvents.

The arrangement of the atoms in the ring was proved by Baeyer in 1877 by the conversion of furfural both into furan and into pimelic acid (**5**), the structure of which had been established earlier.

Calculations using the heat of formation of liquid furan (14·90 kcal/mole[62]) give values between 23·7 and 25·6 kcal/mole for the resonance energy of the molecule. In good agreement molecular-orbital calculations[63] based on the experimentally measured first electronic transition

furan-CHO $\xrightarrow{\text{Ag}_2\text{O}}$ furan-CO_2H $\xrightarrow{-CO_2}$ furan

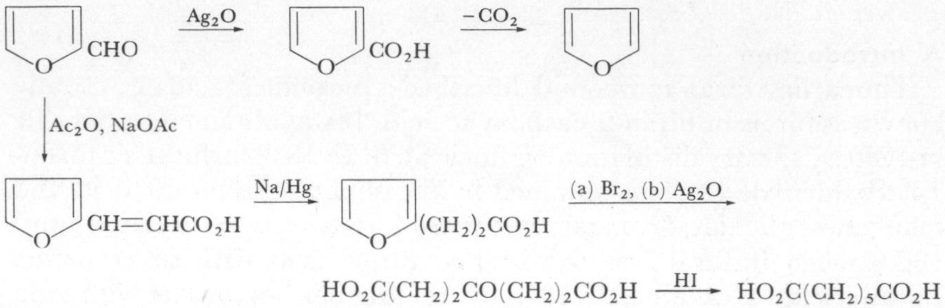

$\downarrow$ Ac$_2$O, NaOAc

furan-CH=CHCO$_2$H $\xrightarrow{\text{Na/Hg}}$ tetrahydrofuran-(CH$_2$)$_2$CO$_2$H $\xrightarrow{\text{(a) Br}_2,\text{ (b) Ag}_2\text{O}}$

$$HO_2C(CH_2)_2CO(CH_2)_2CO_2H \xrightarrow{\text{HI}} HO_2C(CH_2)_5CO_2H$$

5

give a value of 26 kcal/mole. However, calculations based on the heat of hydrogenation of furan give 17 kcal/mole. The discrepancies arise in part from the different methods used in estimating the energy of the 'classical' non-resonating furan. It would appear that the correct value is probably 25 ± 1 kcal/mole, substantially less than that for benzene (36·0 kcal/mole).

Microwave examinations have shown that the furan molecule is planar and have given[64] molecular parameters which agree quite

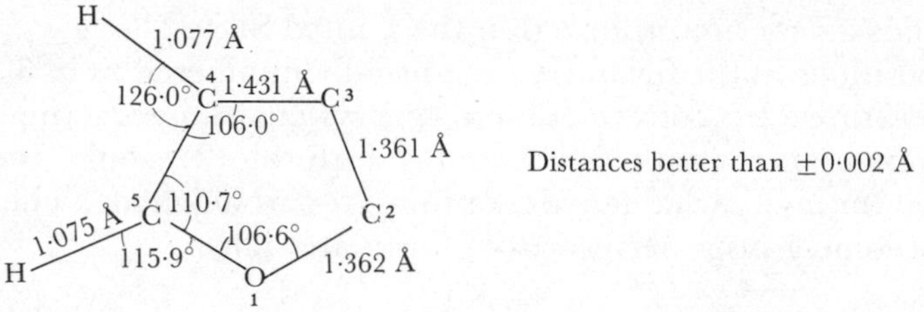

Distances better than ± 0.002 Å

well with those obtained earlier by electron-diffraction methods. The parameters[65] for tetrahydrofuran (**6**) and 2,5-dihydrofuran (**7**), some of which were determined by electron diffraction, are given for com-

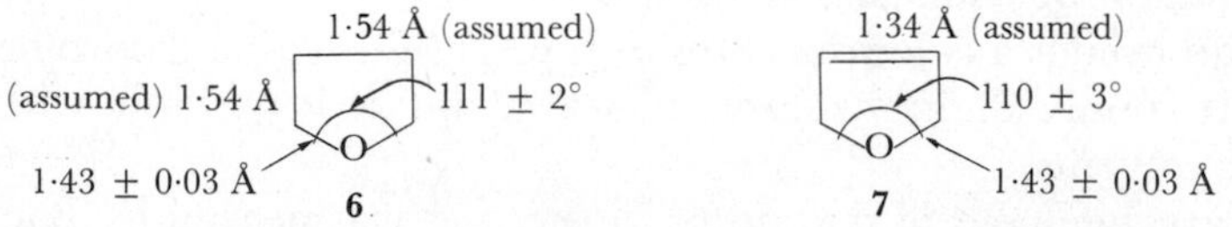

parison. The results show that the carbon–oxygen bonds in furan are shorter than those of the reduced derivatives and also that the carbon–oxygen–carbon angle has contracted slightly in furan. The distance between carbon atoms 3 and 4 of furan is slightly longer than that of the aromatic carbon–carbon bond of benzene (1·40 Å) and that between carbon atoms 2 and 3, and 4 and 5 is very close to the ordinary ethylenic bond length, such as assumed for 2,5-dihydrofuran (**7**). These results show that furan cannot be accurately represented by classical formula **8**, but that it is best considered as a resonance hybrid of which formulae **8a** to **8d** represent the more important hypothetical limiting structures. The furan molecule is far from a regular pentagon in shape, and the bond lengths suggest that structure **8** is the major

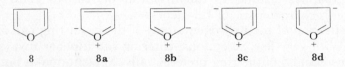

contributor to the resonance hybrid. Of the other resonance structures shown **8a** and **8b** are expected to be the most important for several reasons. The energy required to separate the charges will be lower in these cases than in the other charged structures as the distance involved is less. Structures **8a** and **8b** are completely conjugated, and are therefore more stable than the 'cross conjugated' **8c** and **8d**. However, calculation[63] of the π-electron densities for furan gives the result shown below, the reverse of what might have been expected from the above argument, but the localization energies[63] for electrophilic attack greatly favour substitution at positions 2 and 5.

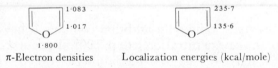

π-Electron densities   Localization energies (kcal/mole)

In order for the furan ring to behave as an aromatic structure it must have six π electrons in the ring. The oxygen atom must therefore provide two electrons for this purpose. The difference between the dipole moments of furan (0·71 D) and tetrahydrofuran (1·68 D) indicates a substantial drift of electrons away from the oxygen atom in furan where this atom is at the positive end of the dipole; in tetrahydrofuran it is at the negative end. As oxygen is more electronegative than nitrogen, it provides these electrons less easily, and in consequence furan is less aromatic than pyrrole.

The physical data therefore suggest that furan itself should behave chemically mainly as a diene ether which possesses unusually great resonance stabilization. This is in fact correct, but it should be specially noted that the introduction of substituents which can interact electronically with the ring system can alter the resonance energy of the final compound sufficiently to change the 'aromatic' and 'aliphatic' chemical characteristics of the ring.

C. Chemical properties

The ring of furan is opened moderately easily by acids, and thus an analogy to the very facile acid hydrolysis of enol ethers is apparent. 2,5-Addition to the double-bond system of the classical formula also occurs readily, leading to dihydrofuran derivatives. This type of addition is characteristic of 1,3-dienes.

Substitution of the hydrogen atoms of the furan ring can also take place. With very few exceptions, entering substituents always attack positions 2 and 5 of the ring preferentially. Substitution at positions 2 and 5 can take place either through addition, leading to a dihydro compound (9) followed by elimination, or by direct displacement, as in

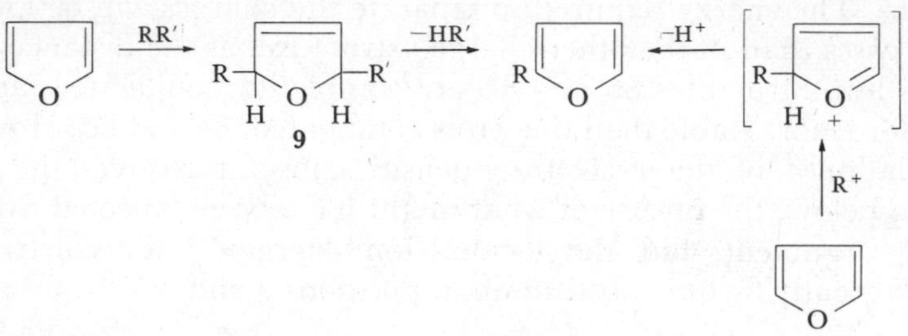

the case of benzene. Where an addition compound has actually been isolated, as in the case of nitration (see p. 100), the course of the reaction is clear, but it may well be that the lability of the intermediate compounds has precluded their easy detection in a number of instances. This could result in a 2,5-addition–elimination sequence leading to a substitution being wrongly considered as a direct substitution. Substitution at positions 3 and 4 cannot involve the sole formation of 2,5-addition compounds as intermediaries. Substitution in these cases must either be direct, as in the case of benzene, or take a perhaps less expected course via the tetrahydrofuran (10). In some cases such intermediate tetrahydrofurans have been detected.

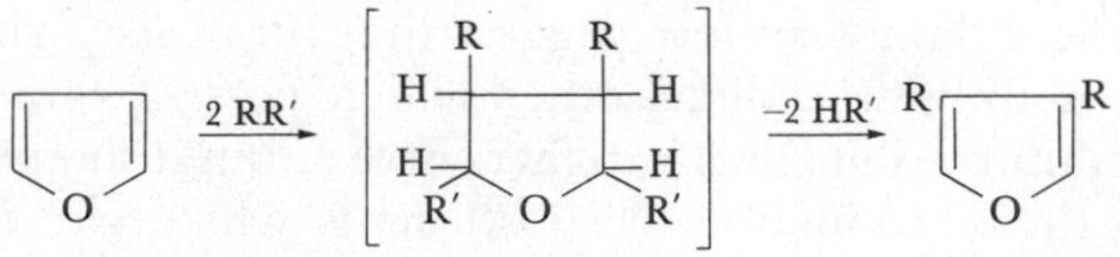

A number of furans may be converted into pyrroles and pyridines. These reactions are discussed on pp. 85, 86 and 229.

The detailed chemical properties of furan will now be considered in three sections.

1. *Furan as an ether*

Enol ethers, in general, are very easily hydrolysed to the corresponding carbonyl compounds by dilute acids. Furan is not nearly so easily hydrolysed, because the initial attack of the proton involves the electrons of the oxygen atom, and these electrons contribute to the six π electrons required for aromaticity. Their withdrawal reduces the resonance energy of the ring and converts the somewhat aromatic furan into

$$\text{11} \qquad\qquad\qquad \text{12}$$

the very much less stabilized cation (probably largely **11**; cf. pyrrole, p. 67). This cation can polymerize, probably like 1,3-dienes, or hydrolyse to succindialdehyde (**12**). The mildest acidic conditions required to effect this hydrolysis are such that polymerization of the cation, or of the derived succindialdehyde, occurs to a major extent.

2. *Addition reactions of furan*

Furan itself is not stable in the presence of air or oxygen, and is usually stabilized by the addition of small quantities of hydroquinone.

$$\text{13}$$

Aerial oxidation takes place by 2,5-addition, leading first to a peroxide (**13**), which has been isolated, and then through a free-radical polymerization to a resin. Hydrogenation of the peroxide gives succindialdehyde. Furan is completely oxidized by potassium permanganate.

Furan behaves as a typical diene in the Diels–Alder reaction. With maleic anhydride it gives the *exo* adduct twice as fast as the less stable *endo* isomer, which quite quickly changes over via dissociation and recombination into the more stable *exo* form.[66] With maleic imide the stereochemistry of the addition can be controlled by the reaction temperature.[67] The maleic anhydride adduct, on boiling with hydrobromic acid, gives phthalic acid. This appears to be a general reaction for this type of compound. Maleic acid behaves[68] like the imide towards furan, and methyl acetylenedicarboxylate adds giving **14**. This last

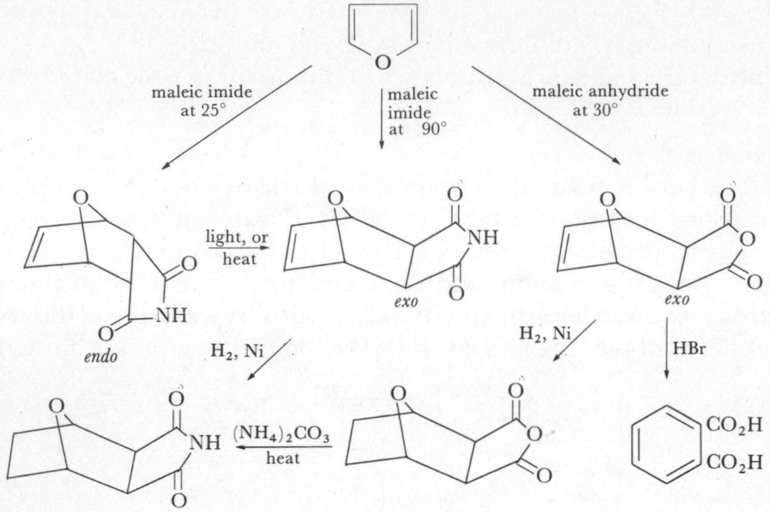

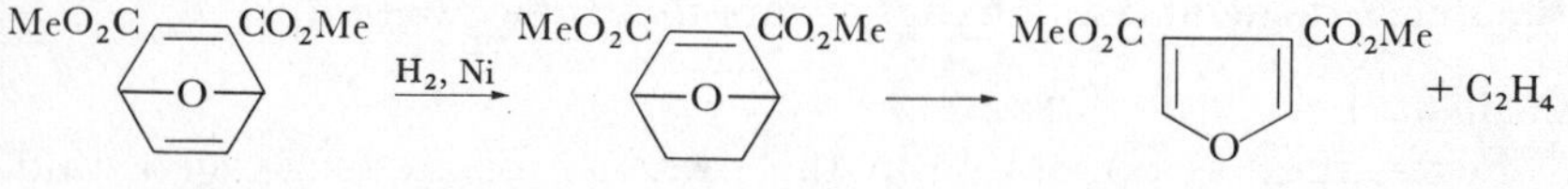

compound on catalytic reduction yields **15**, which on heating undergoes a reverse Diels–Alder reaction, forming methyl furan-3,4-dicarboxylate.

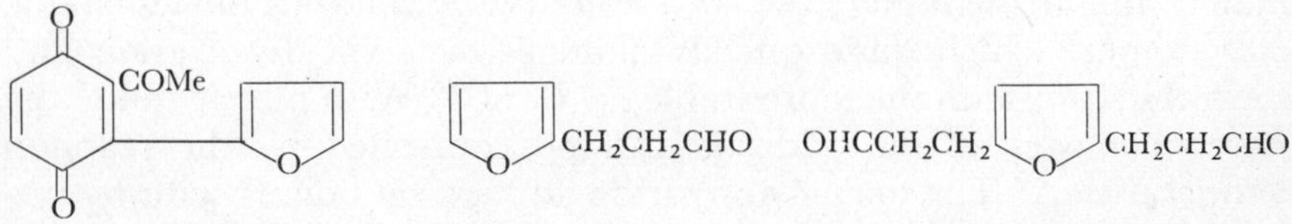

Under certain circumstances furan can behave as a nucleophilic reagent. With 2-acetylquinone[69] it yields **16**, and with acrolein and methyl vinyl ketone in the presence of sulphur dioxide reaction also occurs at position 2 giving, for example, **17** and **18** instead of normal Diels–Alder adducts. This type of behaviour also occurs with pyrroles p.p. 73–74). Furan, however, with ethylene at high temperature and pressure gives a Diels–Alder adduct which has been identified as shown, and it reacts like 1-methylpyrrole with benzyne (p. 69). Furan

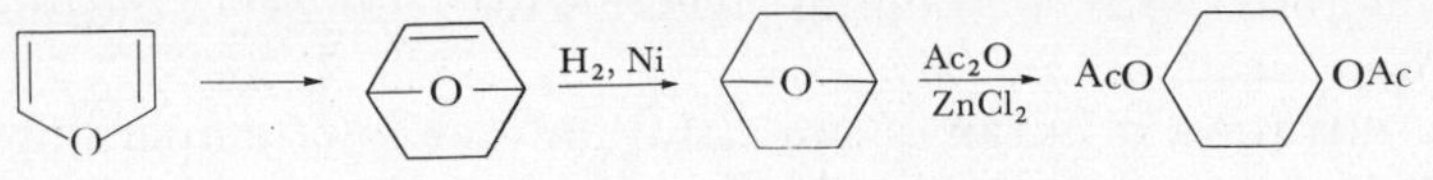

with benzophenone in the presence of light gives **19**,[70] while a similar reaction using dimethylmaleic anhydride with benzophenone present as a sensitizer yields[71] the cyclobutane **20**.

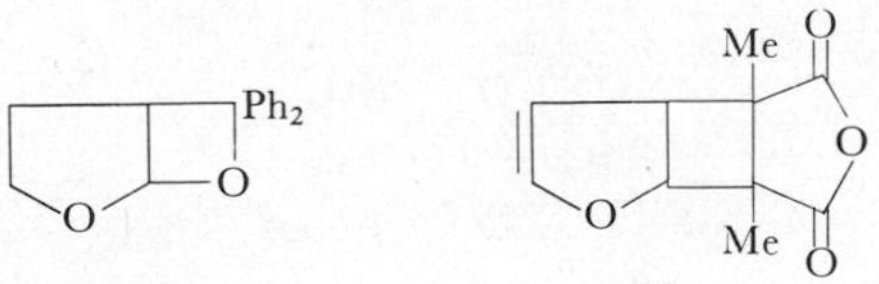

19   20

Furan can be oxidized[72] by bromine in methanol, or electrolytically in methanolic ammonium bromide, to a mixture of *cis*- and *trans*-2,5-dihydro-2,5-dimethoxyfuran (**22**) which has been separated by fractional distillation. Only the electrolytic oxidation is usually successful with furans possessing electron-attracting substituents. The exact mechanisms of these reactions have not been elucidated but clearly involve 2,5-addition. This dihydrodimethoxyfuran (**22**) is a cyclic acetal, and as such is hydrolysed by very dilute acid to maleic aldehyde.

On hydrogenation the dihydro compound (**22**) yields the corresponding tetrahydrofuran (**23**), which on similar hydrolysis with very dilute acid gives succindialdehyde. This is the best available synthesis of this aldehyde. Excellent overall yields are obtained in contrast to those obtained by the direct acid hydrolysis of furan.

In a similar way[72] furan is attacked by lead tetraacetate in a mixture of acetic acid and anhydride, yielding **21**, which has been

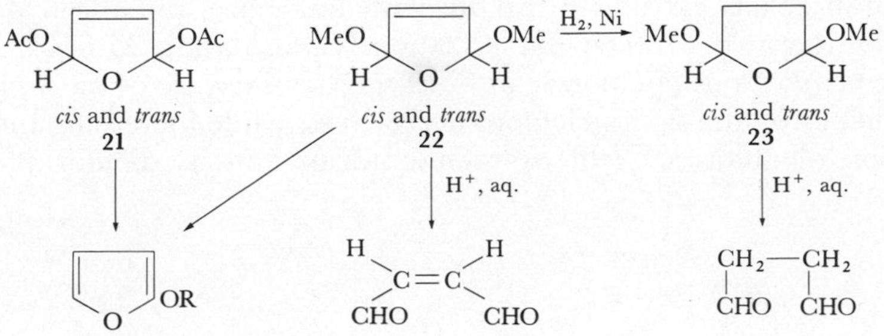

cis and *trans* 21

cis and *trans* 22

cis and *trans* 23

24   R = Me, or Ac

E*

similarly hydrolysed to maleic aldehyde and converted into succindi-aldehyde. Thermal decompositon (acid-catalysed) of the diacetoxy and dimethoxy (**22**) compounds yields derivatives (**24**) of the unknown 2-hydroxyfuran (see p. 108).

The nitration of furan is successful only at low temperatures and under anhydrous conditions. Acetic anhydride and fuming nitric acid are used, and the first product is an addition compound which is probably **25**, as it gives maleic aldehyde with water. The addition

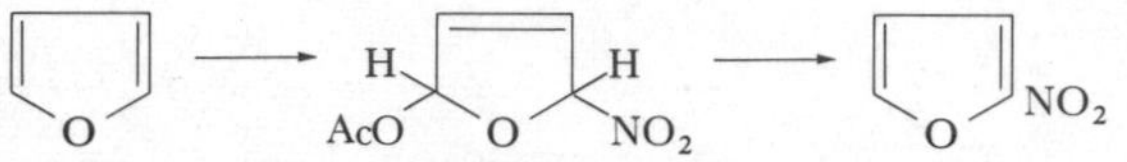

cis and/or *trans*

25

product (**25**) with pyridine gives 2-nitrofuran and not 3-nitrofuran as was once supposed. The structure of the 2-nitrofuran is clearly established, as it has different properties from authentic 3-nitrofuran.

3. *Substitution reactions of furan*

Furan cannot be sulphonated under ordinary conditions, owing to resinification, but with 1-proto-1-pyridinium sulphonate (p. 194)

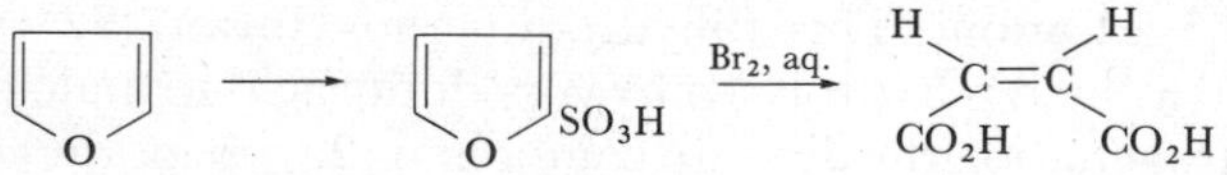

26

in ethylene dichloride, a combination which does not attack toluene, an excellent yield of the 2-sulphonic acid (**26**) is obtained. Oxidation to maleic acid with bromine water proves the position of the entering group, as a similar oxidation of furan-3-sulphonic acid gives sulpho-fumaric acid.

Furan reacts extremely rapidly with halogens, and the hydrogen halide liberated causes polymerization. Chlorination with 1·6 molecular proportions of chlorine at $-40°$ gives a mixture of the 2-chloro, 2,5-dichloro, and 2,3,5-trichloro derivatives, while increasing the proportion of chlorine yields tetrachlorofuran and its dichloride (**27**).

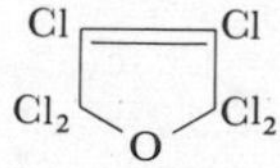

27

2-Bromofuran can be prepared directly in good yield from furan and dioxane dibromide at 0°.[73]

Attempts to alkylate furan by the Friedel–Crafts reaction using alkyl halides with metallic halide catalysis cause extensive resinification, and no simple products have been isolated. This is presumably because of the strongly acidic nature of the catalysts and because alkylfurans are more easily polymerized than furan itself. However, boron trifluoride with 1-methylbut-2-ene gives a mixture of mono- (17%) and dipentylfuran. It should be noted that no hydrogen halide is liberated in this alkylation.

Furan can be acylated very easily by both acid chlorides, or better acid anhydrides, in the presence of stannic chloride, but best results are obtained only when the reaction is carried out in such a manner that contact of the unreacted furan with the acidic catalyst is minimal. Traces of iodine and hydriodic acid can also act as catalysts in the

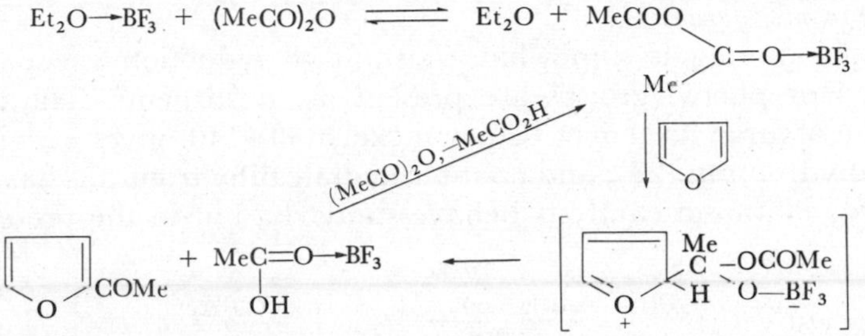

anhydride condensations. Results are much better than in the alkylation of furan, as the acylfurans are relatively stable to acids. One of the best acetylation methods is to treat a mixture of furan and acetic anhydride at 0° with boron trifluoride in ether.[74] The reaction proceeds by attack of the boron trifluoride–acetic anhydride complex on position 2 of the ring.

Furan, in contrast to thiophene, will react with hydrogen cyanide and hydrogen chloride (Gattermann reaction) in the absence of metallic halides. Hydrolysis of the product (28) yields furfural in 35%

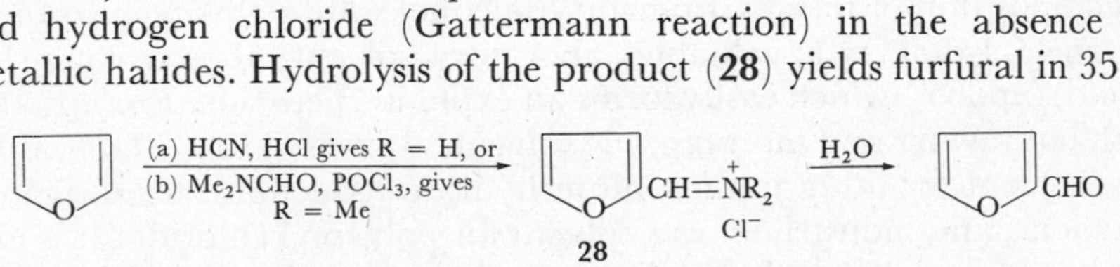

overall yield. Furfural is better obtained from furan by the use of phosphorus oxychloride and dimethylformamide[75] which is so successful in the pyrrole series (p. 72).

The chloromethylation of furan has not been investigated and is unlikely to be successful, as the acid conditions would cause resinification, and furan itself is unchanged by contact with formaldehyde and dimethylamine under the usual Mannich conditions.

Furan reacts with aryldiazonium salts in the presence of alkali, yielding 2-arylfurans. The case of 4-chlorobenzenediazonium chloride is particularly interesting, as some 3-(4-chlorophenyl)furan has been

isolated from the product. This is the first clear case of 3-substitution in furan itself.

D. Derivatives of furan

1. *Some reduced furans*

The furan ring is somewhat resistant to reduction except when carboxyl or phenyl groups are present as substituents. The hydrogenation of furan itself over Raney nickel at 80–140° gives a high yield of tetrahydrofuran (**29**), and no intermediate dihydrofurans have been detected. Platinum catalysts behave similarly, but in the presence of

acetic acid the ring is opened with the production of n-butyl alcohol.

Tetrahydrofuran, which is also obtained industrially by the catalytic decomposition of tetrahydrofurfuryl alcohol (**30**) or by cyclization of butane-1,4-diol, is a valuable laboratory solvent. It is a colourless liquid, b.p. 65°, which easily forms an explosive peroxide. It is miscible with both water and most organic solvents. It is used in the laboratory as a solvent for lithium aluminium hydride reductions, for Grignard reactions, and industrially as a solvent for polyvinyl chloride. It is also used commercially for the production of hexamethylenediamine, which on condensation with adipic acid yields nylon. Another industrial application which was used in Germany during the Second World War is the catalytic vapour-phase dehydration of tetrahydrofuran

$$\text{(diene)} \xleftarrow{-H_2O} \text{(THF)} \xrightarrow{HCl} Cl(CH_2)_4Cl \xrightarrow{NaCN} NC(CH_2)_4CN \xrightarrow{H_2,\ Ni} H_2N(CH_2)_6NH_2$$

to buta-1,3-diene. Tetrahydrofuran is also converted into adipic acid, on an industrial scale, with carbon monoxide and nickel carbonyl. The catalytic oxidation of tetrahydrofuran yields γ-butyrolactone

$$\xrightarrow{\hspace{1cm}} \xrightarrow{\hspace{1cm}} \xrightarrow{H_2O} HO_2C(CH_2)_4CO_2H$$

Adipic acid

(**31**), while chlorination at $-30°$ in the presence of light gives first 2-chloro- and then 2,5-dichloro-tetrahydrofuran.[76] If the chlorination temperature is near $0°$ the 2-chlorotetrahydrofuran loses hydrogen chloride, forming **34**, which then adds more chlorine to give **32**. The chlorine atoms at position 2 in all these compounds are extremely reactive and are readily displaced by nucleophiles such as ethanol, when **33** is obtained from **32**. This cyclic acetal (**33**) with sodium yields 2,3-dihydrofuran (**34**), which on strong heating undergoes an interesting rearrangement to cyclopropanecarbaldehyde. The double bond of

| | | | | $\xrightarrow[\text{vapour}]{400°}$ | CHO | |
| 31 | 32 | 33 | 34 | | | 35 |

2,3-dihydrofuran is very reactive and adds on water, yielding the semi-acetal of 4-hydroxybutan-1-al (**35**). Alcohols, phenols, and acids add similarly. The resulting 'acetals' are easily hydrolysed by dilute acids

$$\underset{\mathbf{32}}{\text{(Cl,Cl)}} \xrightarrow{RMgBr} \text{(Cl,R)} \xrightarrow[\text{Na}]{\text{powdered}} \underset{\text{cis and trans}}{RCH=CHCH_2CH_2OH} \xrightarrow{H_2,\ Pt} R(CH_2)_4OH$$

to their hydroxylic precursors and **35**, and this procedure has been used for protecting hydroxyl groups. The chlorine atom at position 2 of compound **32** also reacts with Grignard reagents, and this is the basis of a very useful synthesis of olefins and a method of chain extension by four carbon atoms. 2,5-Dihydrofuran (**36**) is best obtained by the sequence indicated. The double bond is quite unlike that of 2,3-dihydrofuran and has typical olefinic properties.

$$\underset{H}{\overset{H}{\underset{C}{\overset{C}{|||}}}} \quad \xrightarrow{2\ CH_2O} \quad \underset{CH_2OH}{\overset{CH_2OH}{\underset{C}{\overset{C}{|||}}}} \quad \xrightarrow{H_2,\ Ni}$$

$$\underset{cis}{\overset{H}{\underset{CH_2OH}{C}}=\overset{H}{\underset{CH_2OH}{C}}} \quad \xrightarrow[230\text{–}240°]{Al_2O_3} \quad \textbf{36}$$

$$\underset{trans}{HOCH_2 \diagdown \overset{H}{C} \diagup \quad \diagdown \overset{}{C} \diagup \underset{H}{\quad} \diagup CH_2OH} \quad \xrightarrow[230\text{–}240°]{Al_2O_3} \quad MeCH=CHCHO$$

Tetrahydrofurfuryl alcohol (**37**), obtained from the catalytic hydrogenation of furfural, is another valuable industrial intermediate. The

$$Na^+\ \bar{O}_2C(CH_2)_3CO_2^-\ Na^+ \quad \xrightarrow[NaOH]{molten} \quad \underset{\textbf{37}}{\boxed{}\,CH_2OH} \quad \xrightarrow{270°,\ alumina\ gel}$$

$$\underset{\textbf{38}}{\overset{CH_2-CH_2}{\underset{CH_2OH}{}\ C\equiv CH}}$$

corresponding chloride with sodamide in liquid ammonia yields the acetylene **38**. 3,4-Diphenyltetrahydrofuran is dehydrogenated by sulphur to the furan.[77]

2. Alkyl- and aryl-furans

Many compounds of these types are known, but the majority have been obtained by indirect synthesis. 3-Alkylfurans unsubstituted at the 2- and 5-positions are often difficult to obtain because substitution of the furan ring always takes place preferentially at positions 2 and 5. 3-Methylfuran is now obtained[78] from the commercially available

$$\underset{\textbf{39}}{\overset{Me\underset{\|}{C}CH_2Cl}{\underset{CH_2}{}}} \quad \xrightarrow[\text{(b) CH(OEt)}_3]{\text{(a) Mg, Et}_2O} \quad \overset{Me\underset{\|}{C}CH_2CH(OEt)_2}{\underset{CH_2}{}} \quad \xrightarrow[\text{acid}]{\text{perphthalic}} \quad O \overset{\overset{Me}{|}}{\underset{CH(OEt)_2}{\diagup\!\!\!\diagup CH_2}}$$

$$\Big\downarrow 0{\cdot}1\ \text{N}\ H_2SO_4,\ aq.$$

$$\underset{O}{\boxed{}}CO_2H \quad \xrightarrow[\substack{\text{(b) H}_2,\ \text{Pd/BaSO}_4 \\ \text{(Rosenmund)}}]{\text{(a) SOCl}_2} \quad \underset{O}{\boxed{}}CHO \quad \xrightarrow[\substack{\text{(b) NaOEt,} \\ \text{EtOH, 200°}}]{\text{(a) NH}_2NH_2} \quad Me\underset{O}{\boxed{}}$$

2-methylallyl chloride (**39**). An alternative synthesis involves the preparation and decarboxylation of 3-methylfuran-2-carboxylic acid.[79] 3-Methylfuran is acetylated by acetic anhydride and boron trifluoride etherate,[74] and nitrated in acetic anhydride solution, but only at the 2-position.

In general, the alkylfurans behave like furan itself to most reagents if allowance is made for their increased sensitivity to acids. The electron-donating character of the alkyl groups increases the basicity of the oxygen atom appreciably and the reactivity of the ring to electrophilic reagents. This results, for instance, in sylvan (2-methylfuran) reacting more easily than furan with aqueous acids to give a practical preparation of laevulinic aldehyde, although the by-product **40** is formed[80] and better overall yields can be obtained by the bromine and methanol method (p. 99).

Alkylfurans usually react like the parent compound in the Diels–Alder reaction. A difference, however, occurs in the case of 2-vinylfuran (**41**), which gives a 1:1 adduct with maleic anhydride. This adduct is, however, 3a,4,5,6-tetrahydrobenzofuran-4,5-dicarboxylic anhydride (**42**), showing that of the two diene systems present in 2-vinylfuran the one involving the side-chain is the more active.

Substitution reactions of alkylfurans always involve free 2- or 5-positions, if present, and then the 3- or 4-positions. Oxidation of 2-methylfuran by potassium permanganate proceeds very easily with the production of acetic acid, and 2-methylfuran, unlike furan, undergoes the Mannich reaction at position 5.

2-Methylfuran, available directly from furfural (p. 114), can also be obtained from **43** with hot sodium ethoxide (Wolf–Kishner reaction). In this second synthesis 2-methylene-2,5-dihydrofuran (**44**) is also obtained.[81] This compound (**44**) has a very different ultraviolet absorption spectrum from 2-methylfuran, into which it is converted by a trace of acid. 2-Methylfuran is more reactive than toluene, as with furfural in the presence of a trace of acid it gives a compound which is probably the furfural analogue of **40**. The methyl group also activates

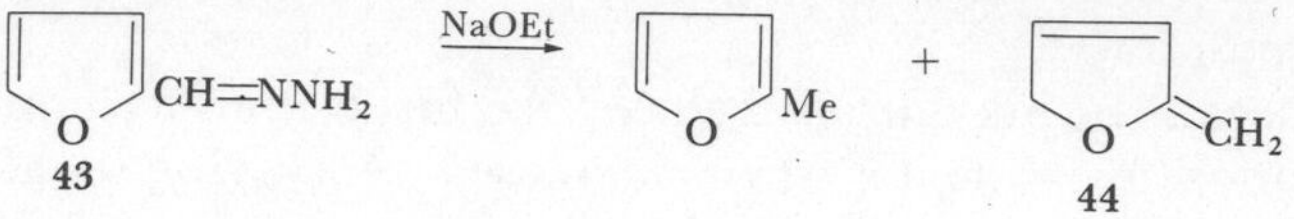

the ring to electrophilic reagents. 2,5-Dimethylfuran is obtained by the cyclization of acetonylacetone.

The oxidation of 2,5-diphenylfuran with nitric and acetic acids opens the ring, yielding *cis*-1,4-diphenylbutene-1,4-dione (**45**) and ozonolysis gives the same ketone, along with some of the aldehyde **46**.[82] As the orientation in the ketone (**45**) is *cis*, it is virtually certain that

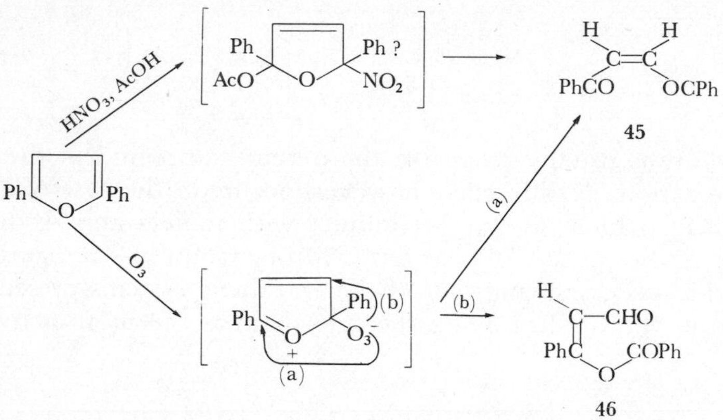

the double bond moves to its final position before the ring opens. This implies that the oxidations proceed via 2,5-addition to the ring.

3. *Halogen derivatives*

The monohalogen derivatives of furan are colourless liquids with a sweet odour, sparingly soluble in water but easily in organic solvents. The 2- and 3-chlorofurans boil at 78° and the 2- and 3-bromofurans at 102° at atmospheric pressure. They discolour and resinify on long standing in the presence of air, and more rapidly with acids. They undergo the Diels–Alder reaction with maleic anhydride, and the products can be converted into phthalic acids.

The halogen–carbon bond is quite stable in these compounds, which do not react with sodium hydroxide or cyanide, or with metallic sodium. 2-Bromofuran does, however, react with sodium methoxide or piperidine, and it gives a Grignard reagent with difficulty. Although 2-iodofuran behaves like iodobenzene with magnesium and gives a Grignard reagent with the usual properties, 3-iodofuran has not been induced to form a Grignard reagent. However with butyllithium at −70° it yields 3-furyllithium[83] which is a useful intermediate for the preparation of 3-substituted furans. Copper is a valuable catalyst for the conversion of 3-iodofuran into 3-methoxy- and 3-cyano-furan with sodium methoxide and cuprous cyanide respectively.[84]

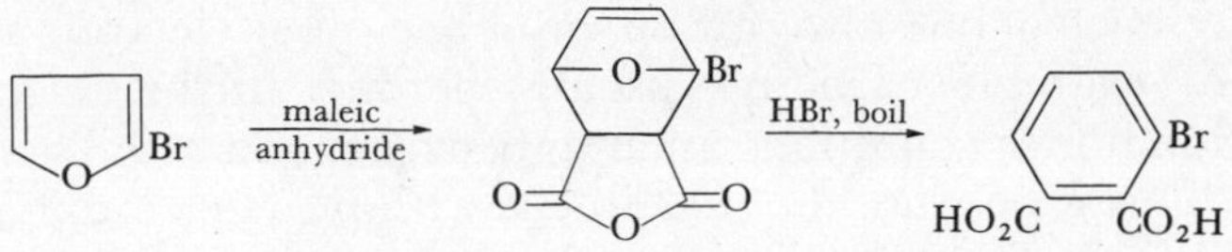

Halogenated furans can sometimes be prepared by direct halogenation (p. 100), but more general synthetic methods are the treatment of furylmercuric salts with halogens and the decarboxylation of halogenated furancarboxylic acids in quinoline. The carboxyl groups of furoic

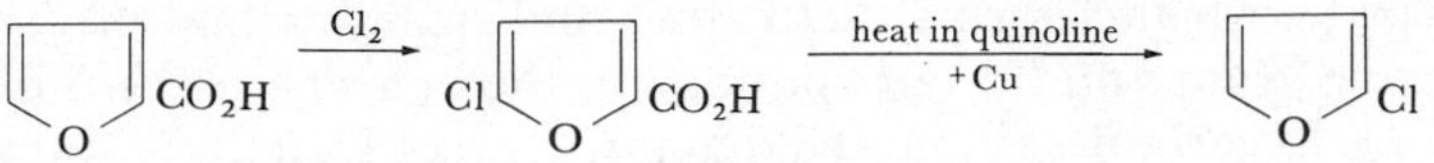

acids can also be replaced by bromine or iodine on treatment with the halogen in aqueous alkali.

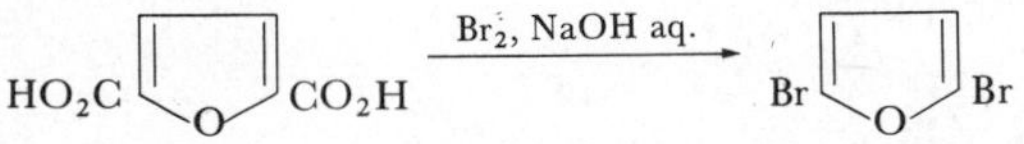

4. Nitrofurans

The 2- and 3-nitrofurans are solids, m.p. 29° and 27° respectively, and the synthesis of 2-nitrofuran has been described (p. 100). 3-Nitrofuran has been obtained as shown. The nitration of furans which do

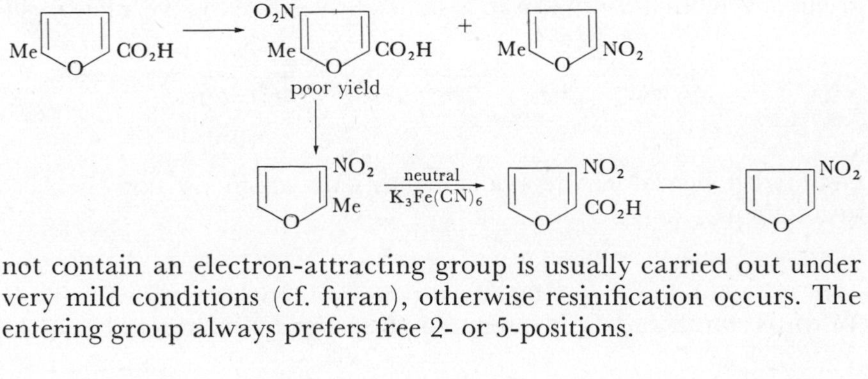

not contain an electron-attracting group is usually carried out under very mild conditions (cf. furan), otherwise resinification occurs. The entering group always prefers free 2- or 5-positions.

The presence of one nitro group, or of one other electron-attracting group, for example carbonyl, usually permits further electrophilic substitution under conditions usual to benzene, and stabilizes the ring to acids. This is because the substituent withdraws electrons from the ring and the resulting deficiency in the aromatic sextet is made up by the oxygen atom. This clearly increases the aromaticity of ring, as its electrons are less localized than before. At the same time the ring, denuded of electrons, is less easily attacked by a proton. 2-Nitrofurans are, however, easily attacked by strong alkalis. The furan ring is opened, presumably through semi-acetal types of intermediates, with the formation of nitrites and a resin.

It is interesting that 3-methylfuran nitrates at position 2, while

furan-3-carbaldehyde yields the 5-nitro derivative. These results are in accord with the normal activating and deactivating effects of the respective groups on the *ortho* position in the benzene series. The effect of the methyl group is so marked that nitration of 3-methyl-2-furoic acid (**47**) also yields 3-methyl-2-nitrofuran (**49**), the carboxyl group

47, R = H
48, R = Et
49
50

being eliminated. This type of elimination also occurs occasionally in the benzene series. The ester (**48**), however, gives **50** on nitration.

5-Bromo-2-nitrofuran, obtained by nitrating 5-bromo-2-furoic acid, has an activated bromine atom (cf. 4-bromonitrobenzene). The methyl group of 2-methyl-5-nitrofuran is sufficiently active to give a low yield

51

of **51** with benzaldehyde under conditions which do not affect 4-nitrotoluene.

5. *Hydroxyfurans*

In spite of a number of claims, it is certain that no simple free 2- or 3-hydroxyfuran has been prepared. Reactions which could lead to these compounds invariably give the tautomeric carbonyl derivatives or their decomposition products.

2-Acetoxy- and 2-methoxy-furan have been prepared by indirect means (p. 99), and **53** has been obtained from **52** as shown. Dilute aqueous acids very easily hydrolyse **53** to diphenyllaevulinic acid. It should be noted that normal phenyl ethers, for example anisole, are completely stable to such mild treatment. The rings of 2-acetoxy- and 2-methoxy-furan also open with 2,4-dinitrophenylhydrazine and acid. The 2,4-dinitrophenylhydrazone of 4-oxobutyric acid is the product.

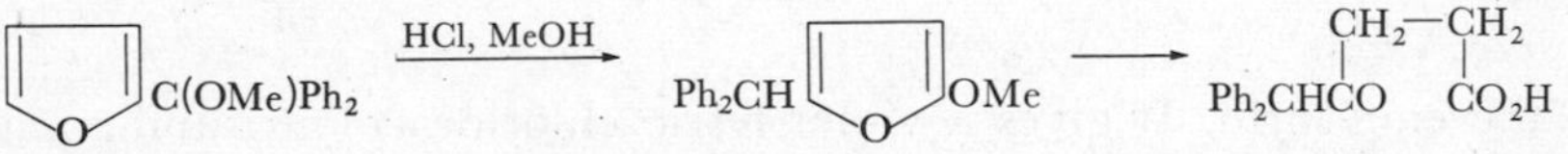

It has not been shown that the unsaturated lactone **54** is an intermediate, but this lactone does react with phenylhydrazine, yielding the phenylhydrazone of 2-formylpropionic acid. The lactone (**54**) is

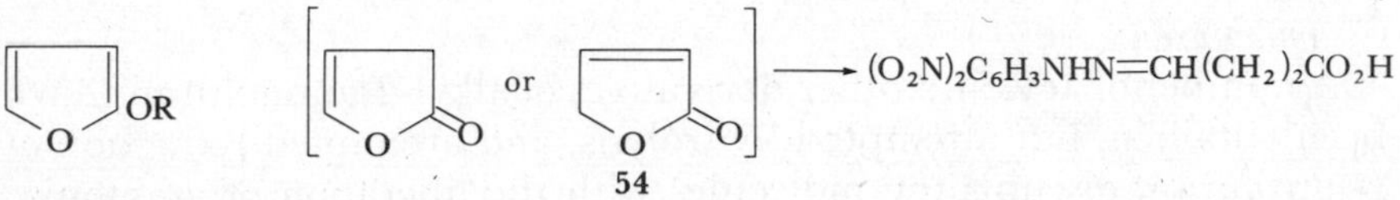

R = Me or Ac

also obtained as a by-product in the preparation of 2-acetoxyfuran. Attempted bromination or chlorination of 2-acetoxyfuran causes the elimination of acetyl halide, and the reaction with lead tetraacetate takes a similar course.

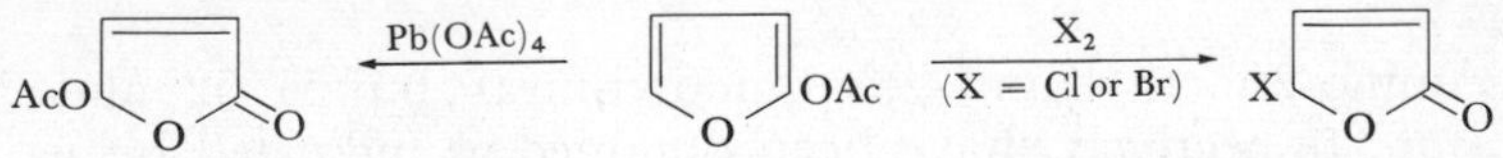

The chemistry of α-angelica lactone (**55**) does not suggest that it exists in equilibrium with the tautomeric 2-hydroxy-5-methylfuran (**56**); only about one-third of a mole of methane is liberated with methylmagnesium iodide. Succinic anhydride (**57**) likewise shows no properties expected of its enol formulation (**58**) and does not give 2,5-dichlorofuran with phosphorus pentachloride.[85]

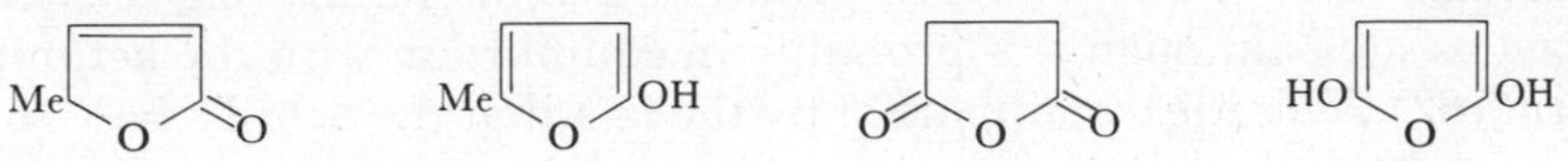

Although some evidence for the existence of 3-hydroxy-2,4,5-tri-phenylfuran has been obtained, all attempts at isolation have yielded the tautomeric furanone (59). In contrast to this, ethyl 3,4-dihydroxy-furan-2,5-dicarboxylate (60), prepared from ethyl oxalate and ethyl diglycollate in the presence of sodium ethoxide, appears to exist only

in the enol form. It gives a violet ferric chloride colour, and mono- and di-O-methyl ethers with methyl sulphate and alkali. Stabilization of the enol structure in this particular case is possible through hydrogen bonding. Compounds such as 59 are vinylogous esters and possess deactivated carbonyl groups which do not usually give reactions of ketones.

6. Aminofurans

A number of acyl and other derivatives of alkyl-2-aminofurans have been obtained, but attempted hydrolysis, and attempted reduction of 2-nitrofuran, disrupts the molecules with the liberation of ammonia. This suggests that tautomerization to the imine is followed by hydro-lysis and polymerization under the reaction conditions.

3-Amino-2-methyl- and -2,5-dimethyl-furan, b.p. 51–52° and 55–56° at 4 mm, respectively, have been obtained as indicated below. The hydrolysis of the formamido derivatives must be carried out under special conditions, and then excellent yields are obtainable. The amines are colourless liquids which smell like pyridine and discolour rapidly on standing in air. They benzoylate normally and give a positive carbylamine reaction. Both amines can be diazotized and coupled with alkaline 2-naphthol, although attempts to replace the diazo group by hydrogen and by the cyano group have failed. It is clear therefore that the amino group of 3-aminofurans (e.g. 61) can react as such although it is probably in equilibrium with the ketimine form (62). This idea is supported by the fact that the Schiff's base (63) cannot be induced to dehydrate, and cleavage of the amine (62,

R = Me) with aqueous alkali gives acetic acid, acetoin, and ammonia.

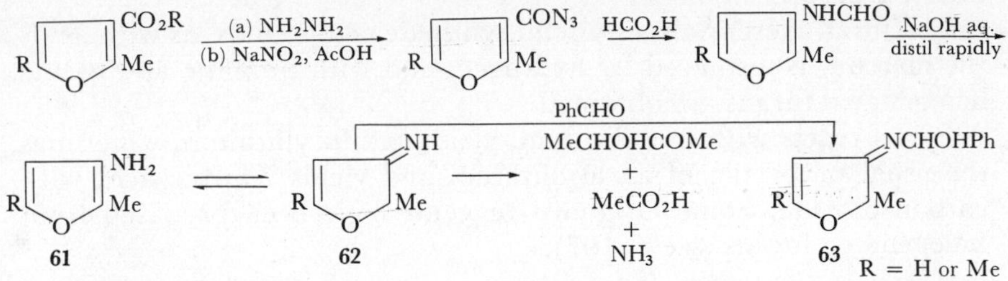

Ethyl 5-amino-2-furoate has been obtained, in contrast to 2-amino-furan, by catalytic or aluminium amalgam reduction of the corresponding nitro compound. Hydrolysis of the amino ester has not been carried out without complete decomposition, although prior acetylation permits a mild hydrolysis to 5-acetamido-2-furoic acid. This can be decarboxylated to 2-acetamidofuran.

7. Metallic compounds of furan

Furan reacts more easily than thiophene with mercuric salts and initially forms 2-furylmercuric derivatives (e.g. **64**). Complete mercuration to 2,3,4,5-furan tetrakismercuriacetate is effected by excess

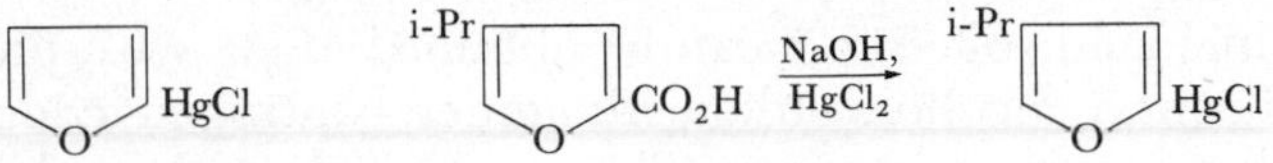

mercuric acetate. Free 2- and 5-positions are more reactive than 3- and 4-positions, but both 3- and 4-positions can be successively substituted in 2,5-dimethylfuran. 2-Furoic acid reacts faster than furan with mercuric chloride, in the presence of sodium hydroxide, and gives furyl-2-mercuric chloride with the elimination of carbon dioxide. Under other conditions 2-furoic acid itself reacts with mercuric acetate,

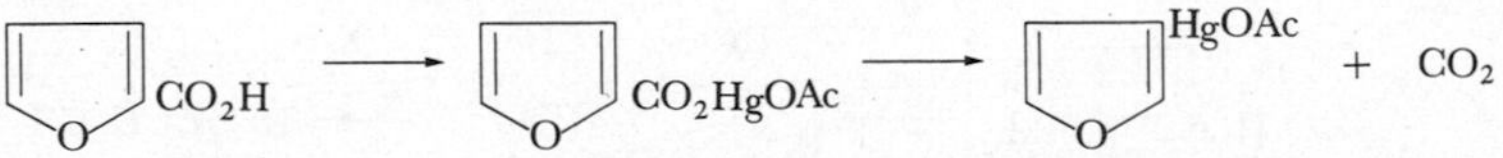

yielding a mixed salt (**65**), which on heating yields furan-3-mercuric acetate (**66**) through a cyclic intermediate.

Although **66** with iodine yields 3-iodofuran, giving a valuable intermediate for the synthesis of 3-substituted furans, it does rearrange with some reagents.[84] Mercuration of furancarboxylic esters usually proceeds normally with the mercuration of the ring and retention of the ester group.

The furan mercurials are useful synthetic compounds, as with acids the mercury is displaced by hydrogen, and with bromine and iodine halogenated furans are obtained.

Furan reacts with butyllithium, yielding 2-furyllithium, which has the usual properties of an aryllithium and yields 2-furoic acid with carbon dioxide. Some Grignard reagents have been prepared from halogenated furans (see p. 107).

8. *Furfuryl alcohol*

This compound is a colourless liquid, b.p. 170°, miscible with water and most organic solvents. It is obtained commercially by the catalytic hydrogenation of furfural and is stored in the absence of air and traces of acids to reduce resinification. It becomes immiscible with water on polymerization and has some uses in the plastics industry. Furfuryl alcohol behaves as a primary alcohol and a reactive furan. For example, it reduces aqueous permanganate in the cold, and it behaves like furan towards bromine and methanol. The ring is reduced on catalytic hydrogenation. Furfuryl alcohol can be used for synthesis in basic or neutral solution, but in acidic media it is very difficult to control the nature of the product.

Laevulinic acid (62–64%) can be obtained along with polymer by treating furfuryl alcohol with acids under controlled conditions so as to reduce resin formation. The most likely mechanism of the internal oxidation–reduction is shown, although other possibilities have not been definitely excluded. This type of rearrangement and

ring opening is quite general for furfuryl alcohols with a free 2- or 5-position. It also occurs with most furan derivatives with a vinyl side-chain which can be hydrated to the furfuryl alcohol. Both **67** and **68**, which can be obtained from furfural and nitromethane under different conditions, yield the same product (**69**) with aqueous hydrochloric

[structure 67] CH=CHNO$_2$ [structure 68] CHOHCH$_2$NO$_2$ HO$_2$C(CH$_2$)$_2$CO(CH$_2$)$_2$NO$_2$

67   68   69

acid. 2-Furylacrylic acid and furfurylideneacetone behave similarly. 5-Hydroxymethylfurfural (**70**), obtained from hexoses with acids, yields laevulinic and formic acids on acid hydrolysis. The mechanism of this reaction is not certain, but it does not proceed through the initial formation of furfuryl alcohol and formic acid. The tracer study illustrated shows that the aldehyde group is the source of the formic acid.

HOCH$_2$ [structure] ^{14}CHO $\longrightarrow$ CH$_3$CO(CH$_2$)$_2$CO$_2$H + H^{14}CO$_2$H

70

Furfuryl alcohol is converted into the very reactive furfuryl chloride by thionyl chloride with ethereal pyridine at low temperatures. Furfuryl chloride is even more reactive than benzyl chloride, and attempts to form a Grignard reagent have yielded only *sym*-2-difurylethane. The chloride can be used as an alkyl halide in acetoacetic ester, and many other syntheses when these are carried out in organic solvents; the expected products ensue. However, furfuryl chloride and aqueous potassium cyanide yield largely 5-methyl-2-furonitrile with some 2-furylacetonitrile. This may be due to an extended allylic rearrangement which can be compared with the acid ring opening of furfuryl alcohol. 2-Furylacetonitrile is made from furfuryltrimethyl-

[structure] CH$_2$Cl $\xrightarrow{-Cl^-}$ [[structure] $\overset{+}{C}$H$_2$ $\longrightarrow$ $\overset{+}{[structure]}$Me] $\xrightarrow{NC^-}$ NC[structure]Me

ammonium iodide and sodium cyanide.

9. *Furan aldehydes and ketones*

Furfural (furan-2-carbaldehyde), b.p. 161·7°, is a colourless liquid when freshly distilled and possesses an aromatic pungent odour. It is somewhat soluble in water (8% at 20°) and is miscible with most common organic solvents, including aromatic hydrocarbons. It is only slightly soluble in saturated aliphatic hydrocarbons at ordinary temperatures, and shows a remarkable power of extracting unsaturated hydrocarbons from mixtures with related saturated materials. This property enables otherwise very difficult separations of similar boiling materials to be effected, and about half the furfural produced is used for such separations in the vegetable oil and petroleum industries. Furfural reacts, like formaldehyde, with phenols to form resins, and these have industrial applications. The catalytic reduction of furfural on an industrial scale can lead to furfuryl alcohol or tetrahydrofurfuryl alcohol using nickel catalysts, and to 2-methylfuran using copper chromite.

Furfural has many reactions similar to those of benzaldehyde, but there are important differences which will be noted. It behaves like benzaldehyde towards the following reagents and gives the expected products: sodium bisulphite, hydrazine and its derivatives, Grignard reagents, alkylzincs, chloro esters in the Reformatsky reaction, activated methylene groups in the Perkin (p. 94),[86] Claisen, Knoevenagel, and aldol condensations, ammonia, orthoformic ester and ammonium chloride (giving the acetal), acetic anhydride and stannous chloride (giving the diacetate, p. 115), hydrogen over nickel (giving furfuryl alcohol), alkaline permanganate (giving 2-furoic acid), etc. Like benzaldehyde, furfural undergoes the benzoin reaction with potassium cyanide and the Cannizzaro reaction with potassium hydroxide. The yields in both these reactions are, however, poor owing to the formation of unidentified coloured by-products. Alkaline oxidation converts furfural into 2-furoic acid, but aqueous acidic reagents usually cause ring rupture, with the formation of derivatives of maleic dialdehyde.

Furfural is much more stable to acidic reagents than furan because of the electron-attracting aldehyde group. Substitution in the ring, as in the case of furan, takes place at the unsubstituted 5-position with one exception discussed below. The ring is much more active than that

Furoin

of benzaldehyde and can be easily nitrated, brominated,[87] acylated and alkylated (Friedel–Crafts), etc.

Furfural on treatment with aluminium chloride and isopropyl chloride indisputably yields 4-isopropylfurfural, the structure of which has been carefully proved.[88] No 5-isopropylfurfural was detected in the reaction product. This is very unexpected and is perhaps the only recorded case of a substituent entering the furan ring entirely at a 3- or 4-position when there is a free 5-position available. The reaction does

not proceed via substitution at the 5-position followed by rearrangement, as 5-isopropylfurfural is stable to aluminium chloride under the
alkylation conditions.

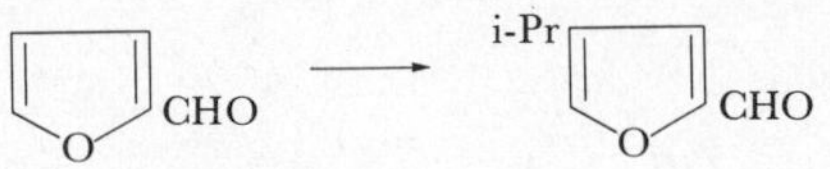

Furfural itself does not react with maleic anhydride, in common with
furans possessing electron-attracting substituents. It behaves like
furan, however, after conversion[89] into the diacetate (**71**) when the

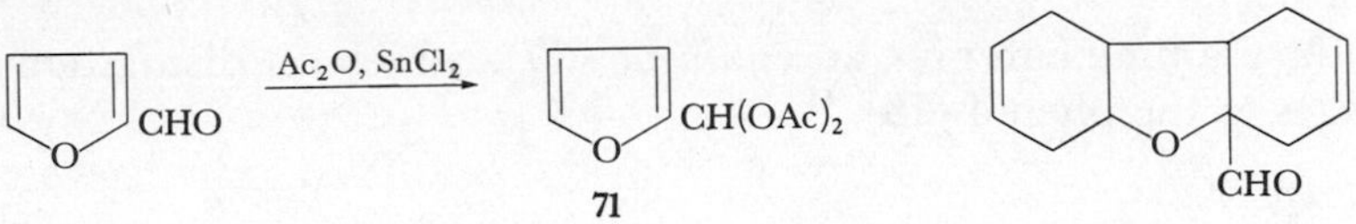

71

72

electron-attracting properties of the aldehyde group are neutralized.
The diacetate also reacts like furan towards bromine and methanol (cf.
p. 99). Furfural itself can, however, react as a dienophile; with two
moles of butadiene, **72** is formed.

Furfural reacts with many aliphatic and aromatic amines to form the
expected anils, for example **73** is formed from aniline and furfural
alone. However, if the furfural is treated with aniline hydrochloride
the ring is opened, yielding the purple glutaconic aldehyde derivative
74 which dyes red on cotton, wool, and silk. This derivative can
be converted into a pyridine (**75**). Furan-3-carbaldehyde has been

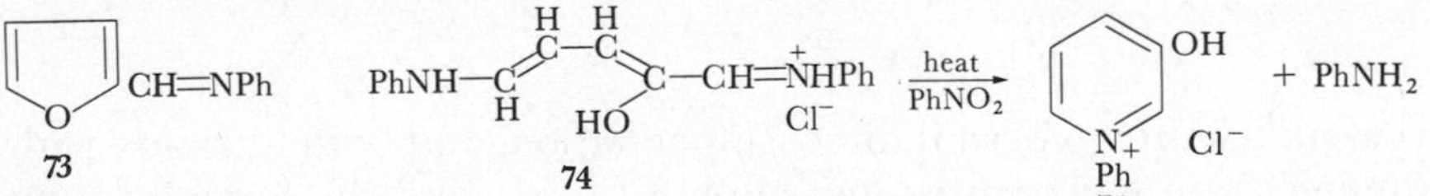

73

74

75

obtained from the catalytic hydrogenation of 3-furoyl chloride. It
does not give a colour with aniline under acidic conditions.

2-Furyl methyl ketone is obtainable from furan by acetylation, and
from 2-furoic acid derivatives by standard methods. 2-Furyl phenyl
ketone can be prepared from benzene and 2-furoyl chloride and
aluminium chloride. Like furfural, both ketones react with aniline
hydrochloride, and electrophilic substituents enter position 5. Many
types of 2-furyl ketones yield pyridines (**76**) on heating with ammonia
and ammonium chloride (p. 229).[90] Replacing the ammonia by a

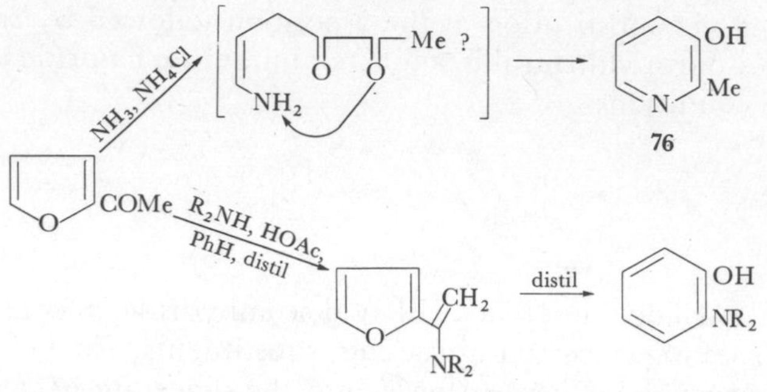

secondary amine can give an enamine (**77**), which on distillation re-arranges to the phenol (**78**).[91]

10. *Furoic acids*

2-Furoic acid is a colourless crystalline solid of m.p. 133° which sublimes easily and is sparingly soluble in water. It is very stable at room temperatures in contrast to many other furan derivatives, and is a stronger acid than benzoic acid. Furoic acid is obtainable in excellent yield by the oxidation of furfural by oxygen in the presence of alkali and a cuprous oxide–silver oxide catalyst.[92] 2-Furoyl chloride can be prepared with thionyl chloride and, like benzoyl chloride, is only slowly hydrolysed by water. It has the expected reactions with amines, alcohols, etc.

The electron-attracting carboxyl group of 2-furoic acid stabilizes the

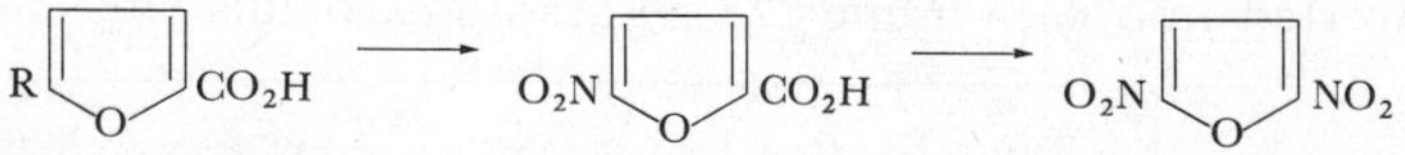

R = H or CO_2H

ring sufficiently to permit direct sulphonation, and both nitration with fuming nitric acid or nitric and sulphuric acids, and chloromethylation take place at position 5.[93] The nitration of 2-furoic acid, or of furan-2,5-dicarboxylic acid, yields first 5-nitro-2-furoic acid and then 2,5-dinitrofuran. This type of decarboxylation with the simultaneous introduction of a nitro group or halogen atom (p. 107) is common with furans and a similar decarboxylation can occur with mercuric chloride (see p. 111). Furoic esters do not decarboxylate on nitration, and in contrast to benzoic esters can be used in the Friedel–Crafts reaction. 5-Bromo-2-furoic acid, along with some 2,3,4,5-tetrabromotetrahydrofuroic acid,[94] can be obtained from 2-furoic acid with bromine but hot aqueous bromine causes decomposition to 'mucobromic acid' (**79**).

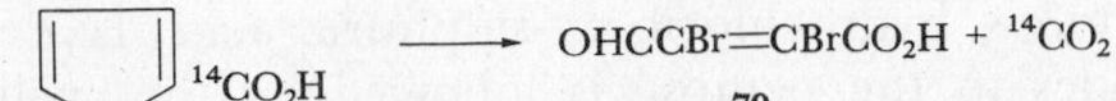

$$OHCCBr=CBrCO_2H + {}^{14}CO_2$$
79

$${}^{14}CO_2H$$

The carboxyl group of the furoic acid has been shown by tracer studies to give rise to the carbon dioxide.

The decarboxylation of furoic acids by heat proceeds readily, 2-carboxyl groups being lost preferentially. The rather inaccessible 3-furoic acid can be made by selectively decarboxylating furan-2,3-, -2,4-, or -3,4-dicarboxylic acid. Neither 2-furoic acid nor its methyl esters undergo the Diels–Alder reaction with maleic anhydride.

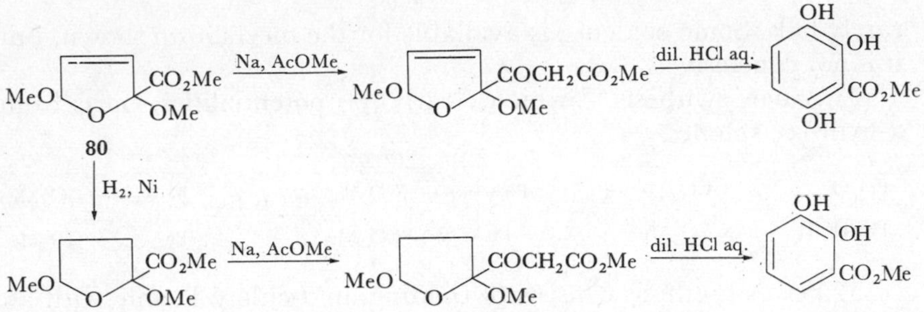

Methyl furoate is not affected by bromine and methanol, but electrolytic oxidation in methanolic ammonium bromide yields **80**. This ester may be converted into some comparatively inaccessible benzoic acids as shown.[95]

E. Synthetic methods

(1) Furan itself is best prepared in the laboratory by the decarboxylation of furoic acid in quinoline with a copper catalyst.[92] Industrially it

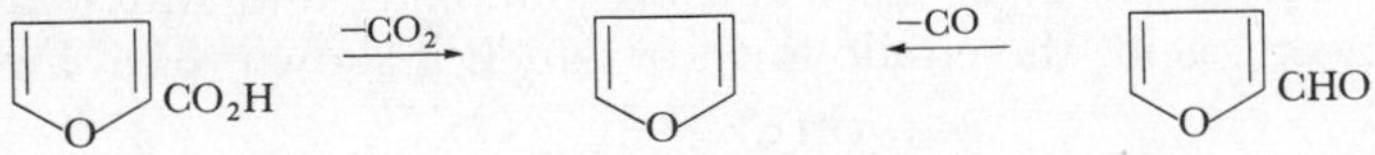

is obtained by the catalytic decomposition of furfural in steam (90% yield).

(2) Furfural is obtained commercially by the steam distillation of oat hulls (husks) and other naturally available material containing pentose

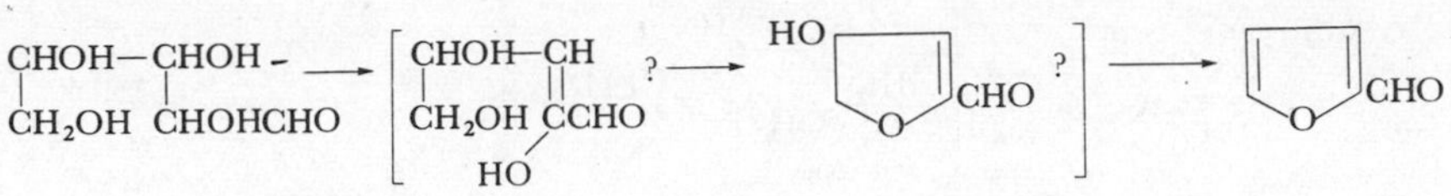

residues in 1–3 N hydrochloric or sulphuric acid. Hydrolysis of the polysaccharides to the pentose is followed by the cyclization. The mechanism of the reaction is not clearly understood, although there is some evidence to support the sequence shown. A similar decomposition of hexoses yields 5-hydroxymethylfurfural.

(3) The cyclodehydration of 1,4-diketones by acidic reagents, including sulphuric acid, zinc chloride, acetic anhydride, and phosphorus pentoxide, is a very general reaction for the synthesis of furans and

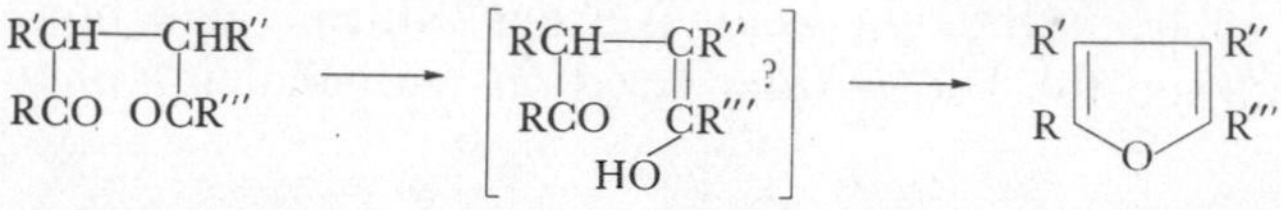

rarely fails. Some evidence is available for the mechanism shown, but it is not conclusive.

(4) A new synthesis,[48] which clearly has potentialities, starts from α-hydroxy ketones.

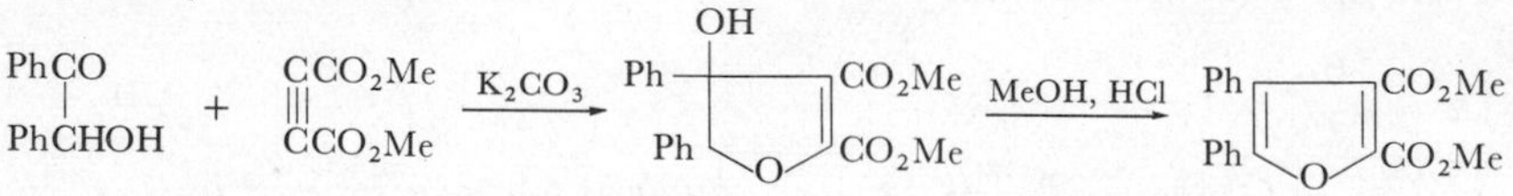

(5) Feist's synthesis consists of treating an α-chloro ketone with an acetoacetic ester derivative in the presence of pyridine. Ammonia has been used instead of pyridine, but then some pyrrole is formed (p. 86) if the reactants are heated.

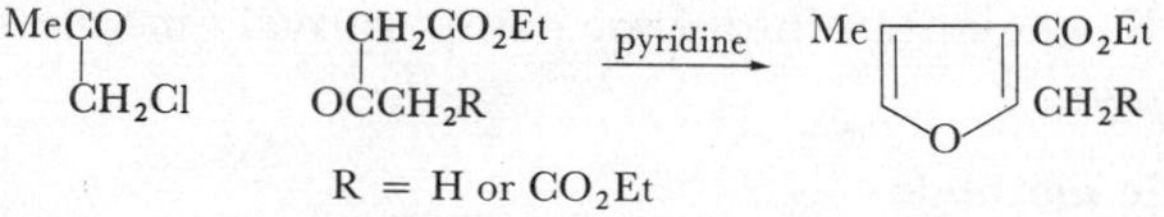

$$R = H \text{ or } CO_2Et$$

(6) Furans can be obtained from certain 2-pyrones. Coumalic acid is obtained from malic acid with sulphuric acid. The malic acid, as a typical α-hydroxy acid, loses carbon monoxide and water and gives formylacetic acid, the enolic form of which is shown (81). Two moles

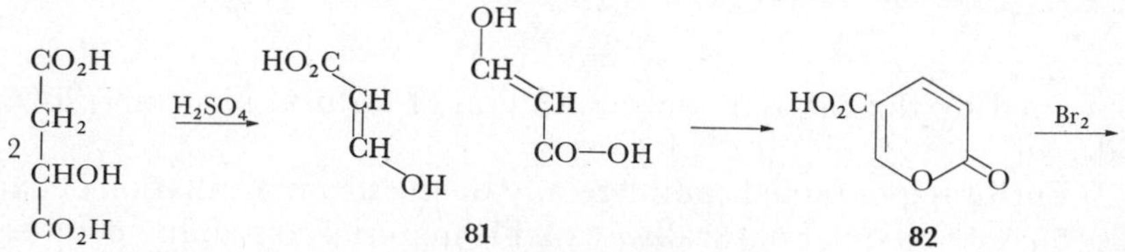

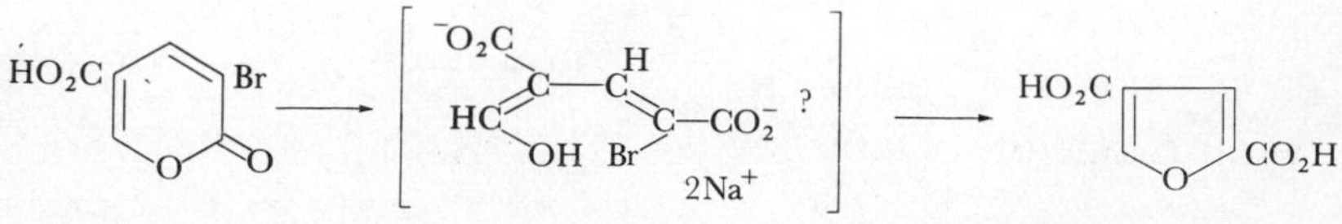

condense to coumalic acid (**82**), which is then brominated. Decomposition of the bromo compound with alkali yields furan-2,4-dicarboxylic acid.

F. Natural occurrence and compounds of special interest

Furan and sylvan (2-methylfuran) have been found in low-boiling wood oils. Furfuryl mercaptan (**83**) has a very disagreeable odour, but at very low concentrations its odour strongly resembles that of roasted coffee. It is a constituent of the oil from roasted coffee. A number of

furans occur naturally, examples being **84**, which has been isolated from *Perilla frutescens*, and **85**, which has been obtained from sweet potatoes infected with *Ceratostomella fimbriata*.[96]

Furfural is the furan of greatest interest, and its chemistry has been discussed earlier. 'Furacin', or 5-nitrofurfural semicarbazone (**86**), is a useful antibacterial.

3. THIOPHENE

A. Introduction

The discovery of thiophene by Victor Meyer in 1882 was due to the substitution by an assistant of pure benzene, prepared from calcium benzoate, for the coal-tar benzene which was normally used in his lecture demonstration. On treating the pure benzene with isatin and concentrated sulphuric acid, the 'indophenine test', which was supposed at that time to be specific for aromatic compounds, the expected blue colour which was normally formed with coal-tar benzene did not develop. Victor Meyer soon came to the correct conclusion that coal-tar benzene contained an impurity responsible for the colour reaction. He found that the impurity was sulphonated more easily than benzene and that the product formed a crystalline lead salt. Purification of this, followed by desulphonation, yielded crude thiophene. Victor Meyer recognized its aromatic character, as the dibromothiophene obtained on bromination, like bromobenzene, could neither be dehydrobrominated with alcoholic potash nor easily reduced like aliphatic compounds with the replacement of the bromine atoms by hydrogen. He then synthesized thiophene by heating sodium succinate with phosphorus trisulphide, a method which was widely used until the synthesis from butane and sulphur was put on a commercial basis. There are comparatively few commercial outlets for thiophene at present, although it is used as a constituent of some copolymers and in the synthesis of some drugs.

Like pyrrole and furan, the atoms of the thiophene ring can be numbered (**1**) or lettered (**2**), but this second system is almost obsolete.

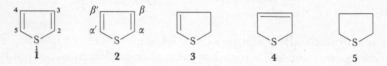

The trivial names of 2-thiolene, 3-thiolene, and thiolane have been proposed for 2,3- (**3**) and 2,5-dihydrothiophene (**4**), and for tetrahydrothiophene (**5**) respectively, but as these trivial names have not been generally accepted, the systematic names will be used here. The trivial names for some groups derived from thiophene are shown.

2-Thienyl	3-Thenyl	2-Thenoyl	3-Thenal, or 3-Thenylidene

B. Physical properties and structure

Thiophene is a colourless liquid, b.p. 84·1° and f.p. −38·3°, which has an odour very similar to that of benzene. It is slightly denser (d_4^{25} 1·058) than water, with which it is immiscible, but it is miscible with most organic solvents.

Victor Meyer showed the arrangement of the atoms in the ring by

$$Na^+\ \bar{O}_2C\ \underset{CH_2-CH_2}{}\ CO_2^-\ Na^+ \xrightarrow{P_2S_3} \quad \xleftarrow{P_2S_3} \quad \underset{CHO\ \ CHO}{CH_2-CH_2}$$

25–30%
yield

two syntheses and proposed the same formula as is current today. The dimensions of the thiophene molecule have been determined with certainty by a study of the microwave spectrum;[97] no *a priori* assumptions had to be made in the calculation, and the results are in excellent agreement with those of earlier electron-diffraction studies. The carbon–sulphur–carbon angle is less than 105°, as might be expected by analogy with other compounds,[98] and is effectively the same as the bond angle in hydrogen sulphide ($\overset{..}{9}2\cdot1 \pm 0\cdot2$°). The carbon–sulphur distance is less than the normal single bond carbon–sulphur

H
1·081 Å
123·3° ₄C —— 1·423 Å —— C₃
112·4°
1·370 Å
⁵C 111·5° C₂
1·078 Å 119·9° 92·2° 1·714 Å
H S
1

distance, which is 1·82 Å. This information suggests that the molecule is not well represented by the classical structure (1), and that it is in a state of resonance to which other structures contribute. In agreement with this the resonance energy of thiophene, calculated from combustion data (the heat of formation, liquid, is 19·52 kcal/mole), is 29–31 kcal/mole, and calculated by molecular–orbital methods based on the observed first electronic transition,[63] is 34 kcal/mole. Although this is less than that of benzene (36 kcal/mole), it is higher than that of furan or pyrrole. This order of resonance energies is in agreement with the fact that sulphur is less electronegative than oxygen or nitrogen and is therefore more ready to release electrons into the ring to form

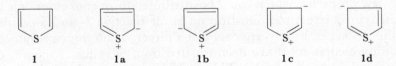

1   1a   1b   1c   1d

the sextet of π electrons required for aromaticity. The major contributing resonance structures are 1 to 1d.

Schomaker and Pauling suggested in 1939 that the sulphur–carbon bonds in thiophene did not consist of pure p orbitals, but that some of the 3d orbitals of the sulphur atom were used. This idea has been extended by Longuet-Higgins, who calculated the carbon–sulphur distance as 1·73 Å by the molecular-orbital method. This is in excellent agreement with experiment. It has subsequently been shown that the bond angle of hydrogen sulphide can also be accounted for on the basis of roughly equal (ca. 15%) s and d contributions to the p bonding

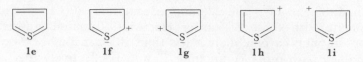

1e   1f   1g   1h   1i

orbitals. It therefore appears that the additional structures 1e to 1i contribute to the resonance form of thiophene. Electrophilic attack on the molecule takes place easily and very predominantly at positions 2 and 5. This is in accord with the idea that the localization energies, and not the π-electron densities, for thiophene[63] control the position of electrophilic attack, as for furan (p. 95). A most interesting recent

1·81
π-Electron densities   Localization energies (kcal/mole)

observation[99] is that thiophene can be alkylated on the sulphur atom (p.123). This supports the idea that the resonance structures with a negative charge on the sulphur atom, 1f to 1i, have significance. The difference between the dipole moments of thiophene (0·52 D) and tetrahydrothiophene (1·87 D) is exactly the same as the corresponding difference from the furan series, and is discussed later (p.143).

C. Chemical properties

Thiophene resembles benzene, rather than furan or pyrrole, in many of its reactions, but it is much more reactive and less stable. It has very few properties which could be attributed to an enol ether or a 1,3-diene type of structure. Substitution at the reactive 2- and 5-positions of the molecule usually appears to be direct, as no intermediate 2,5-addition compounds have been isolated from nitration reactions, etc. (contrast furan and pyrrole). Thiophene is reported to form an ozonide. On autoxidation in the presence of light thiophene is broken down to oxalic and sulphuric acids. The ring is also disrupted to hydrogen sulphide and other products in the presence of alumina at 200°. Fluorination in the gas phase gives sulphur hexafluoride and fluorocarbons.

1. Addition reactions

Thiophene is stable to aqueous, but not to anhydrous, mineral acids. The ring is opened to some extent on boiling with 100% orthophosphoric acid, while 100% sulphuric acid, hydrogen fluoride, and stannic and ferric chlorides cause polymerization to dark amorphous solids. Under milder conditions orthophosphoric acid gives a trimer (6) and a pentamer of unknown constitution. The structure of the trimer is based on the results of hydrogenation, and desulphurization, over a cobalt–molybdate on alumina catalyst at 360–370°. A colourless oil was obtained which contained 20% of 5-methylundecane (7) and no dodecane. If the methylundecane is not a rearrangement product, then structure 6 is correct, although, perhaps surprisingly, it is not analogous to that of the pyrrole trimer (p. 68). When aluminium chloride is dropped into thiophene it is instantly coated with amorphous polymer. Aluminium chloride is therefore a poor catalyst for Friedel–Crafts reactions involving thiophene, and when benzene is used in such reactions it should be thiophene free for best results.

$$Me(CH_2)_5 CHMe(CH_2)_3 Me$$

6   7

Thiophene, with either trimethyloxonium borofluoride or methyl iodide and silver perchlorate in inert solvents, gives the 1-methyl-thiophenium cation (8) which was isolated as the hexafluorophosphate.[99] Its structure was proved as outlined. Both the ultraviolet absorption and nuclear magnetic resonance spectra of the ion, which is not decomposed by water, suggest strongly that it should possess aromatic properties, but chemical data is not yet available.

$$\bar{P}F_6 \quad H_2, Pd \qquad PF_6 \quad (a)\ MeI,\ (b)\ NaPF_6$$

8

The direct oxidation of thiophene probably yields first the 1-oxide and then the 1,1-dioxide which polymerize *in situ*. The 1-oxide (10) has been obtained[100] in solution by treating the *trans*-tetrahydrothiophene (9) with cold sodium methoxide or *t*-butoxide. All attempts to isolate it gave a dimer, but reduction to thiophene confirms its structure.

$$\xrightarrow{\text{NaOMe}} \qquad \xrightarrow{\text{NaBH}_4}$$

9   10

F

Thiophene 1,1-dioxide (**13**) has also been synthesized by the indirect route[101] outlined below. It has not been isolated in a pure

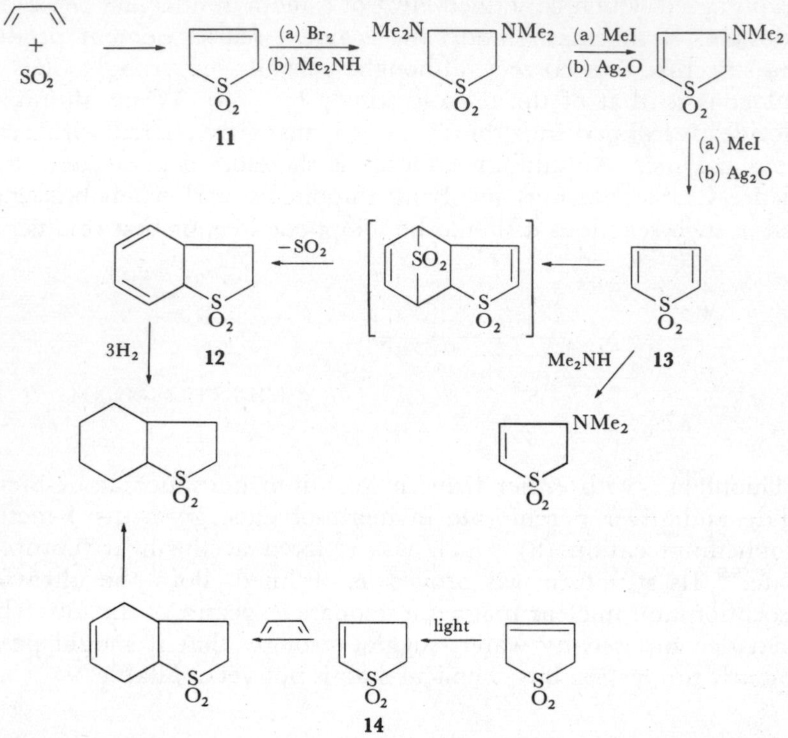

condition, as it reacts rapidly with itself, with the loss of sulphur dioxide yielding **12**, probably through the intermediary of an adduct of the Diels–Alder type, as shown.

The dioxide (**13**) can be extracted from water by chloroform, and its ultraviolet absorption spectrum closely resembles those of the 1-oxide **10** and cyclopentadiene but not those of compounds **11** and **14**. Cyclopentadiene also forms a dimer (**15**) readily. These observations, and the Michael addition reaction shown, suggest that the thiophene oxides are not aromatic in character and do not possess six π electrons. It appears that in these compounds the resonance energy of the rings are not sufficient to cause the sulphur atom to expand its octet. 2,3-Diphenylthiophene, in contrast to thiophene, is oxidized by peroxy acids to an isolable stable 1,1-dioxide[102] which on heating gives a dimer of analogous structure to **12**.

15   16   17   18

Although thiophene does not react with maleic anhydride under typical Diels–Alder conditions in the presence of light, it combines[70] with dimethylmaleic anhydride sensitized by benzophenone in exactly the same way as furan (p. 99). The thermal decomposition of ethyl azidoformate (N_3CO_2Et) in thiophene gives 21% of the pyrrole (17), some sulphur and other products.[103] This suggests that 2,5-addition of the nitrene ($=NCO_2Et$), leading to an intermediate (16), may occur followed by extrusion of sulphur.

The reduction of thiophene gives a number of products according to the conditions (see pp. 127–128), and at 40° with chlorine a maximum of 13% of 2,3,4,5-tetrachlorotetrahydrothiophene (18), along with 2-chloro- and 2,5-dichloro-thiophene, is obtained. Two of the six possible geometric isomers of 18 have been characterized. Further substitution of 18 is possible, and octachlorotetrahydrothiophene can be obtained from thiophene and chlorine in the presence of iodine.

2. Substitution reactions

Thiophene, while much more reactive than benzene, is much more stable than pyrrole or furan to acids. This enables it to undergo many substitution reactions under comparatively mild conditions. There is a great tendency for the attacking group to enter 2- or 5-positions in preference to 3- or 4-positions, although there are some notable exceptions in substituted derivatives. There is a much larger tendency for existing substituents to be displaced by incoming groups than in the benzene series.

The sulphonation of thiophene, a reaction used widely for its separation from benzene, occurs readily with 95% sulphuric acid at 30°. The product is largely the 2-sulphonic acid (69–76%), and better yields (86%) are claimed if 1-proto-1-pyridinium sulphonate (pp. 71, 194) is used.[104] Some thiophene-3-sulphonic acid is also formed, and further reaction leads to disulphonic acids. Desulphonation of the acids with superheated steam gives back thiophene.

Thiophene reacts with isatin in sulphuric acid to give a deep blue colour, due to the formation of indophenine. This reaction is used for the detection of thiophene in coal-tar distillates, and is

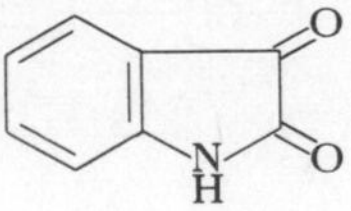

Isatin 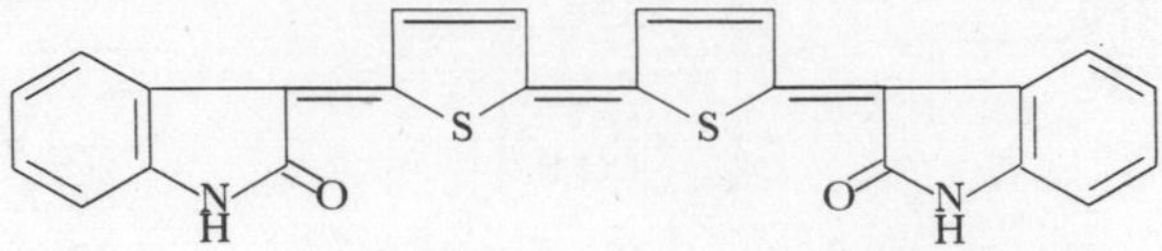   Indophenine

sensitive to 0·025%. This colour reaction is positive for some substituted thiophenes but has not been systematically investigated.

TABLE 1. Chlorothiophenes from the chlorination of thiophene (2100 g)

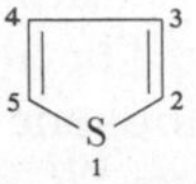

Derivative	Amount (g)	% yield based on chlorine
2-Chloro-	1055	36·8
3-Chloro-	3·3	0·1
2,3-Dichloro-	63	3·3
2,4-Dichloro-	64	3·3
2,5-Dichloro-	519	27·1
3,4-Dichloro-	113	5·9
2,3,4-Trichloro-	120	7·3
2,3,5-Trichloro-	2·5	0·2

The chlorination of thiophene proceeds very rapidly even in the dark at $-30°$ and gives substitution as well as addition products. The substitution products obtained from 25 moles each of thiophene and chlorine after dehydrochlorination with mixed sodium–potassium hydroxide are listed in Table 1. The alkali dehydrochlorinates tetra-chlorotetrahydrothiophene to a mixture of the 2,4- (44%), 2,5- (2%), and 3,4-dichlorothiophenes (56%). The chlorination of thiophene with sulphuryl chloride also gives 2-chlorothiophene (43%).

Bromine reacts rapidly with thiophene, but addition products have not been characterized. Treatment of the product with alkali gives largely 2,5-dibromothiophene. Refluxing thiophene with N-bromo-succinimide is the best preparative method for 2-bromothiophene (77% yield). The direct iodination of thiophene in the presence of mercuric oxide also gives an excellent yield of 2-iodothiophene.

Attempts to nitrate thiophene under conditions normal for the benzene series invariably result in the destruction of the ring, but nitration at $10°$ in acetic acid–acetic anhydride gives over 80% of the 2-nitro compound; a little of the 3-nitro isomer is also formed. Only a weak secondary isotope effect was observed[105] in the nitration of 2-^{3}H-thiophene with benzoyl nitrate in methyl cyanide solution at $-2°$, so that the loss of the proton (or ^{3}H$^+$) is not rate determining as is also the case for benzene.

The direct alkylation of thiophene with olefins in the presence of catalysts such as phosphoric acid, boron trifluoride, or 80% sulphuric acid has been investigated only comparatively recently. Ethylene fails to react under the conditions used, propylene reacts slowly, and iso-butylene rapidly. It is interesting that both the 2- and 3-positions are attacked to about the same extent by the very reactive, and therefore relatively unselective, cations derived from the olefins. In contrast to this the acylation of thiophene by acyl halides, or anhydrides in the presence of stannic chloride or phosphoric acid, which cause less polymerization than aluminium chloride, gives exclusively 2- or 5-acylthiophenes when these positions are free. Acylation may also be effected by merely boiling thiophene, a carboxylic acid, and phosphorus pentoxide in benzene.

The chloromethylation of thiophene proceeds very easily, yielding 2-chloromethylthiophene at $10°$ and the 2,5-bis derivative at $50°$.

$$\underset{19}{\text{[thiophene]}{-}CH_2N{=}CH_2 \cdot HCl} \xrightarrow{MeOH} \underset{20}{\text{[thiophene]}{-}CH_2\overset{+}{N}H_3 \ \ Cl^-} \ + \ CH_2(OMe)_2$$

Thiophene is reactive enough to combine with formaldehyde and ammonium chloride, in a type of Mannich reaction, to give 19. With methanol, 19 yields thenylamine hydrochloride (20). Thiophene is very easily mercurated (see p. 133).

Phenyl radicals, obtained through the decomposition of phenyl-azotriphenylmethane, with thiophene give a mixture of the 2- (63%) and 3-phenylthiophenes (37%). If benzoyl peroxide is used as the radical source, 2-phenylthiophene (23%) and 2,2'-bithienyl (59%) are the major products.[106]

D. Derivatives of thiophene

1. Some reduced thiophenes

Thiophene is reduced by sodium in a mixture of methanol and liquid ammonia at $-40°$ to a mixture of compounds.[107] In contrast to thiophene, but like tetrahydrothiophene, both dihydro compounds

2,3-Dihydrothiophene, 2,5-Dihydrothiophene,
b.p. 112° b.p. 122°

form methiodides. 2,5-Dihydrothiophene is quite stable, and with hydrogen peroxide gives the 1,1-dioxide, which has also been obtained from butadiene and sulphur dioxide (p. 124, **11**). 2,3-Dihydrothiophene is very reactive and polymerizes on standing. On oxidation with hydrogen peroxide it also gives a 1,1-dioxide, and this last compound has been obtained from 2,5-dihydrothiophene 1,1-dioxide by irradiation with ultraviolet light p. 124.

Tetrahydrothiophene (**21**), sometimes known as thiolane, is a colourless liquid, b.p. 121·1°, with a slightly puckered ring and can be obtained as indicated. In contrast to thiirane and thietane, it is not affected by butyllithium,[108] and it has the typical properties of an aliphatic sulphide. On oxidation with hydrogen peroxide it gives the 1,1-dioxide, and it reacts with methyl iodide, forming the sulphonium iodide. Tetrahydrothiophene can be dehydrogenated to thiophene

(32%) with platinized charcoal.

Catalytic hydrogenation of thiophene under most conditions usually removes the sulphur atom, and butane is the major product. Nickel

catalysts are rapidly poisoned by thiophene, although Raney nickel is useful for desulphurizations (see pp. 47, 56, 138, 328, 336, and 337).[109] The desulphurization of certain thiophenes to the corresponding butanes by boiling with Raney nickel has also been used as a synthetic procedure for long-chain compounds.[110] Hydrogenation in the presence of molybdenum disulphide, or over a very large excess of palladium on charcoal, does, however, reduce thiophene to tetrahydrothiophene.

2. *Alkyl- and aryl-thiophenes*

Many alkylthiophenes have been obtained by cyclization of the appropriate succinic or laevulinic acids, and the Wolf–Kishner reduction (cf. p. 82) of acylthiophenes has been widely applied. The direct alkylation of thiophene by olefins is mentioned on p. 127, and thiophene in the presence of zinc chloride will combine with benzyl alcohol, giving **22** and **23**, and with benzaldehyde giving **24**. 2-Vinylthiophene

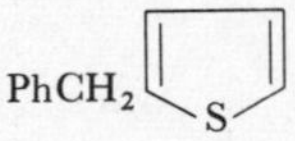

has been obtained by two methods, and behaves like 2-vinylfuran towards maleic anhydride[111] and quinone.[112]

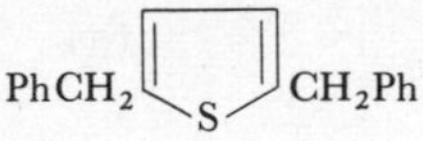

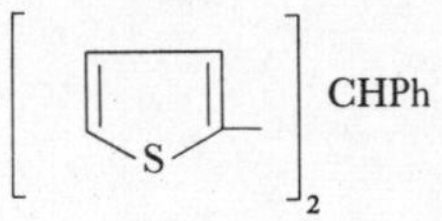

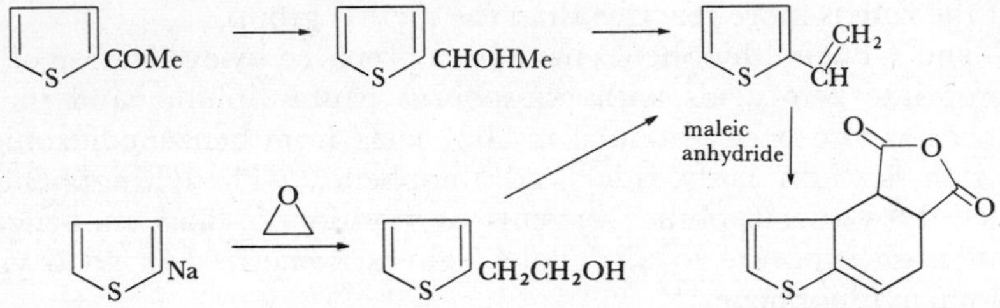

Alkylthiophenes are very easily substituted, and substituents enter positions 2 or 5 first when possible. In the case of 3-methylthiophene substitution could occur at either the 2- or 5-position. Except in the case of metallation, most substituents enter the 2-position predominantly, showing that the major effect of the methyl group is at this position (Table 2).

TABLE 2. Isomer formation in the monosubstitution of 3-methylthiophene

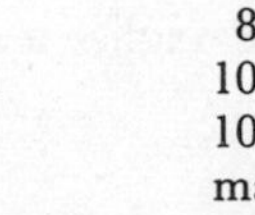

Reaction	Isomer ratio	
	2-	5-
Acylation	80%	20%
Aminomethylation	100%	0%
Halogenation	100%	0%
Nitration	major	minor
Metallation	0%	100%

Elemental bromine usually substitutes all the available ring positions before attacking the side chain, whatever the conditions, but side-chain bromination does occur first if *N*-bromosuccinimide is used in the presence of peroxides. The direct oxidation of methylthiophenes gives very poor yields of thiophenecarboxylic acids, methyl groups at

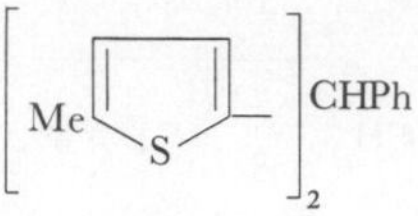

$$\left[\text{Me}\underset{S}{\bigsqcup}\right]_2 \text{CHPh}$$

25

position 2 being attacked preferentially. 2-Methylthiophene combines with benzaldehyde in the presence of zinc chloride to give **25**, showing that the ring is more reactive than the methyl group.

2- and 3-Phenylthiophenes have been prepared by cyclization of the appropriate keto acids with phosphorus pentasulphide, and the 2-isomer has also been obtained in 20% yield from benzenediazonium chloride, sodium hydroxide, and thiophene. 2-Phenylthiophene is attacked by electrophilic reagents at position 5, and in benzene solution on exposure to ultraviolet light is isomerized in good yield to 3-phenylthiophene.[113]

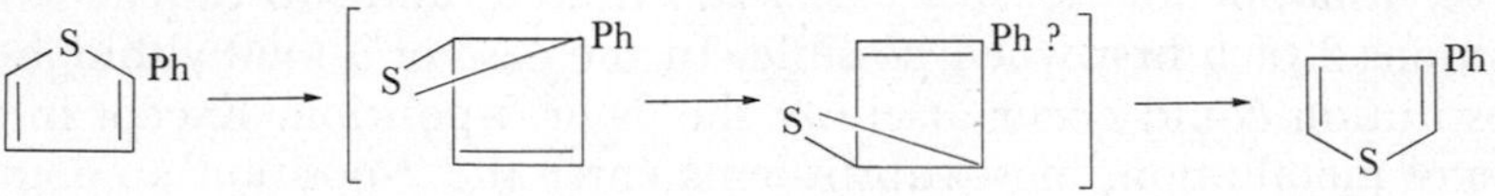

Tetraphenylthiophene (thionessal, **26**) was the first thiophene obtained by synthesis and is easily prepared from stilbene and sulphur. It boils without decomposition at 460°. Vigorous oxidation breaks the

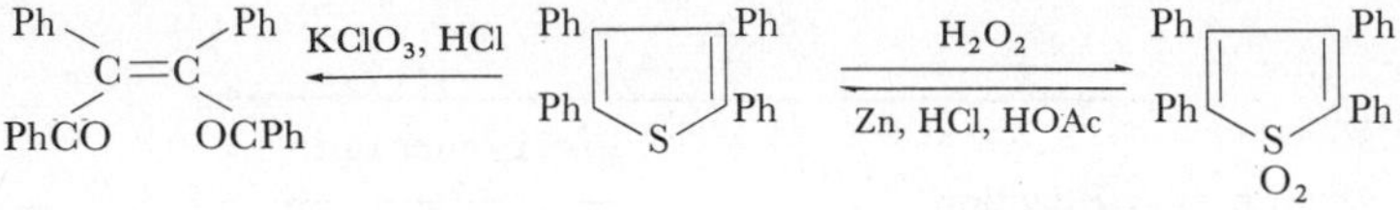

26   27

ring, while hydrogen peroxide yields a stable 1,1-dioxide (**27**),[114] in contrast to thiophene itself.

3. *Halogenated thiophenes*

2-Chlorothiophene is a colourless liquid, b.p. 128°. It is reported not to form a Grignard reagent, but with sodium in benzene 2-thienyl sodium (**28**) is formed. It is remarkable that if the reaction is carried out in ether 2-chloro-, 2-bromo-, and 2-iodo-thiophene yield the 5-(2-halothienyl)sodium (e.g. **29**). 2-Chlorothiophene undergoes the

Na, or Na/Hg
in PhH, 70°

Na, or Na/Hg,
in Et$_2$O

28   29

usual substitution reactions of thiophene, but more slowly.

Although 3-bromo- and 3-iodo-thiophene[115] do not react with magnesium under ether they will do so in the presence of reacting methyl iodide, and the 2-isomers form Grignard reagents under the usual conditions. 2-Bromothiophene is converted into thiophene-2-carboxylic acid by aqueous–alcoholic potassium cuprocyanide at 200°, and is reduced by sodium amalgam to thiophene. Bromine atoms are also easily displaced by chlorine atoms, or by nitro groups, for example 30

$\xrightarrow{\text{HNO}_3}$

30   31

gives 31. The oxidation of tetrabromothiophene by nitric acid is said to give dibromomaleic acid, and reduction with zinc and acetic acid yields 3,4-dibromothiophene.[116]

4. Nitrothiophenes

2- and 3-Nitrothiophene are pale yellow solids of m.p. 46·5° and 78–79° respectively. 2-Nitrothiophene is obtained by the nitration of thiophene in acetic anhydride, and 3-nitrothiophene is best prepared indirectly through nitration of thiophene-2-sulphonic acid,

$\xrightarrow{\text{HNO}_3}$ ⎡   ⎤ +   (a) H$_2$SO$_4$
10%   90%   (b) steam distil

or better the sulphonyl chloride. These last two nitrations are specially noteworthy, as in very few other instances in the thiophene series does a substituent enter position 4 predominantly when position 5 is unsubstituted. Nitration of 2-nitrothiophene gives 56% of 2,4- and 44% of 2,5-dinitrothiophene,[117] while the nitration of 3-nitrothiophene is reported to give 2,4-dinitrothiophene.

$\xrightarrow{\text{HNO}_3,\ \text{Ac}_2\text{O}}$ $\xrightarrow{\text{HNO}_3,\ \text{H}_2\text{SO}_4}$

The nitration of 2-chlorothiophene eventually gives 2-chloro-3,5-dinitrothiophene.[118] The chlorine atom of this compound is much more

F*

easily displaced by anionic reagents (e.g. $^-$OH) than that of chloro-2,4-dinitrobenzene, and has been displaced by hydroxyl, alkoxyl, and amino groups.

5. *Aminothiophenes*

2-Nitrothiophene on reduction with tin and alcoholic hydrogen chloride yields 2-aminothiophene stannichloride, from which the base is obtained by treatment with alkali in an inert atmosphere. Attempted degradation[119] of thiophene-2-carboxyamide by the Hofmann method gives only thiophene-2-carboxylic acid. 2-Aminothiophene, b.p. 77–79° at 11 mm, very rapidly decomposes in air, but is stable in an inert atmosphere or as salts. In contradiction to earlier statements, it is now reported[120] to form 2-thienyldiazonium chloride with nitrous acid at 0°, and that this diazonium salt couples normally with 2-naphthol. Aminothiophenes containing electron-attracting groups, such as ester groups, can be easily diazotized and coupled. 2-Aminothiophene is sulphonated at position 5. 2-Acetamidothiophene (**32**), in contrast to the less reactive acetanilide, couples with

4-nitrobenzenediazonium chloride in acetic acid, and the attack takes place at position 5.

3-Aminothiophene has been obtained both by the reduction of 3-nitrothiophene and by the Hofmann degradation of thiophene-3-carboxyamide.[119] It decomposes more readily than 2-aminothiophene, and its salts also polymerize. However, with acetic anhydride and benzoyl chloride it gives stable acyl derivatives. The 'instability' of the aminothiophenes is probably due both to their tending to tautomerize to reactive products, and to the very great ring activation produced by the electron-donating characteristics of the amino group.

6. *Hydroxythiophenes*

Both 2- and 3-hydroxythiophenes have been obtained from the thienylmagnesium bromides, either by treatment with oxygen or by successive reaction with butyl borate and hydrogen peroxide.[121] Both are soluble in alkali, give deep red ferric chloride colours, couple with benzenediazonium chloride, and decompose on standing at room temperature. 3-Hydroxythiophene[122] is a pale yellow liquid, b.p. 39–40° at 0·01 mm. Its infrared absorption spectrum in liquid film suggests that approximately equal amounts of bonded hydroxyl and unsaturated carbonyl groups are present. The compound is therefore best considered as a tautomeric mixture of **33** and **34**. Nuclear magnetic resonance studies[123] show that 2-hydroxythiophene exists almost

exclusively as **35**. 2-Methoxythiophene is a colourless liquid, b.p. 153–155°, and has been obtained both from 2-iodothiophene, sodium methoxide, and cupric oxide[124] and from 2-hydroxythiophene with methyl sulphate and alkali.

7. *Metallic derivatives of thiophene*

The mercuration of thiophenes under various conditions has been widely studied. Thiophene reacts with mercuric chloride in the presence of some sodium acetate to give mono (**36**) and bis (**37**) derivatives. This reaction can be used for removing thiophene from

benzene, and reaction proceeds, very slowly if at all, in the presence of carbonyl, nitro, or other electron-attracting groups. Steam distillation in the presence of hydrochloric acid decomposes the mercurichlorides to the parent thiophenes. Thiophene combines with mercuric acetate, giving **38** or **39** according to the conditions, and if the 2- and 5-positions are blocked the 3,4-bismercuriacetate is formed; carboxyl groups are displaced in this reaction with the elimination of carbon dioxide. Unlike the chloride, mercuric acetate attacks 2- and 3-nitrothiophenes, forming **40** and **41** respectively. Treatment of **39** with iodine in potassium iodide gives **42**. This type of replacement of mercury by halogen is typical. Most of the mercury derivatives of thiophenes have melting points suitable for characterization purposes.

The Grignard reagents derived from thiophene have the usual reactions and are mentioned on pp. 130–131. However, lithium and
sodium derivatives of thiophene are often more convenient than the
Grignard reagents, as they can be prepared without using a halogenated
thiophene. Butyllithium and thiophene yield 2-thienyllithium, while
surprisingly, sodium amalgam and 2-halothiophenes in ether yield 2-
halo-5-thienyl sodium (see p. 130). The thienylsodiums undergo
typical Grignard-type reactions with carbon dioxide, carbon disulphide, aldehydes, ketones, ethylene oxide, etc.

8. *Thiophene alcohols, aldehydes, ketones, and acids*

2-Thenyl alcohol (**43**) is a colourless liquid, b.p. 207° In the presence
of acids it polymerizes, like furfuryl alcohol, forming resins. It can be
obtained by several general methods, including the treatment of
2-thienylmagnesium iodide with formaldehyde. 2-Thenyl chloride is
obtained from the alcohol with thionyl chloride in the usual way, and,

in contrast to furfuryl chloride, gives a Grignard derivative. Treatment
of this (**44**) with water gives the expected 2-methylthiophene, but
carbonation yields a mixture of **45** and **46** in 1:2 ratio;[125] 3-thenyl-
magnesium bromide on carbonation similarly yields a 2:3 mixture of
3-thienylacetic acid and 3-methylthiophene-2-carboxylic acid.[126]
Benzylmagnesium chloride also behaves anomalously in some circumstances, for instance with formaldehyde, 2-methylbenzyl alcohol is
formed.

Thiophene-2-carbaldehyde, b.p. 198°, resembles benzaldehyde
greatly in smell and chemical behaviour. It also undergoes typical
Cannizzaro and benzoin reactions. 2,2′-Thenoin (**47**) can be oxidized to
2,2′-thenil (**48**), which with alkali yields 2,2′-thenilic acid (**49**).

Thiophene-2-carbaldehyde is best obtained from thiophene with dimethylformamide (cf. pp. 72 and 101) and phosphorus oxychloride.[127] Nitration in sulphuric acid gives the 4-derivative, while bromination of the aldehyde or nitration of its diacetate in acetic anhydride occurs at position 5.[128]

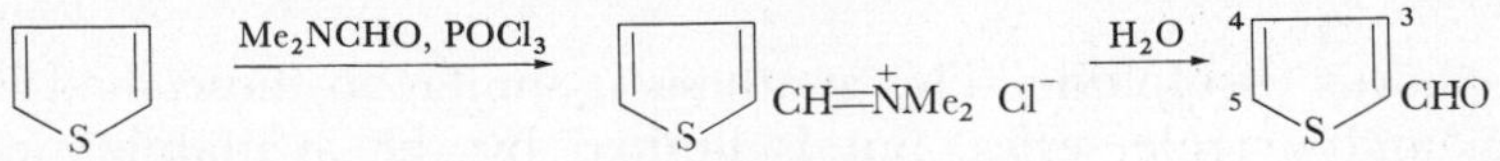

2-Acetylthiophene, or 2-thienyl methyl ketone, b.p. 214°, is very similar to acetophenone in colour, odour, and chemical properties. On nitration it yields a mixture of the 5- and 4-nitro derivatives, the former being present in greater proportion. 2-Acetylthiophene is best prepared in the laboratory from thiophene, acetic anhydride, and 85% orthophosphoric acid.

Thiophene-2-carboxylic acid, m.p. 129–130°, greatly resembles benzoic acid in most of its properties, although it is a stronger acid ($K \approx 3 \cdot 2 \times 10^{-4}$). It is, however, nitrated much more easily, and the product consists mostly of the 5-nitro derivative. This shows that

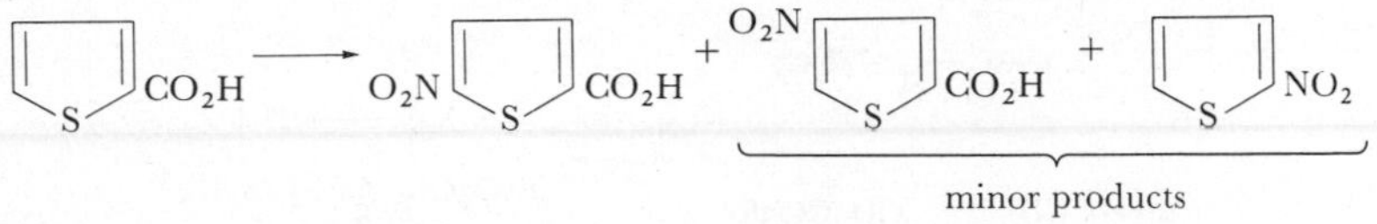

minor products

the directing effect of the carboxyl group does not overcome that of the ring. Thiophenecarboxylic acids can be decarboxylated by boiling with copper in quinoline, or by displacement of the carboxyl by a mercuriacetate group and subsequent removal of the mercury.

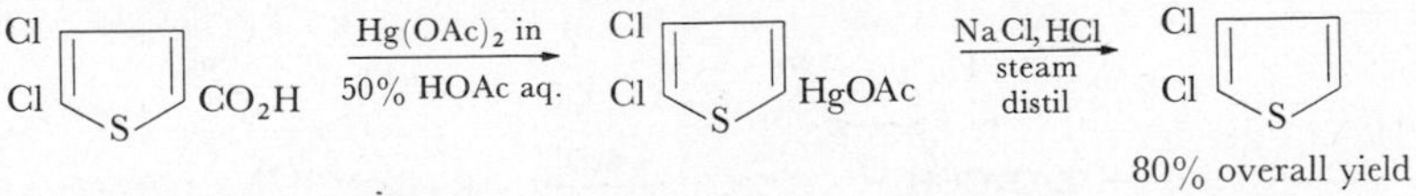

80% overall yield

E. Synthetic methods[129]

(1) Thiophene can be prepared in the laboratory by distilling sodium succinate with phosphorus trisulphide. This method was first used by

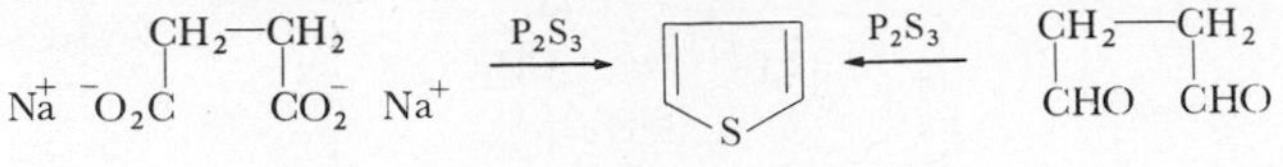

Victor Meyer. By replacing the sodium succinate by salts of keto acids, such as laevulinic acid, alkyl- and aryl-thiophenes may be obtained. A variation of this synthesis is to heat a 1,4-dialdehyde or diketone with

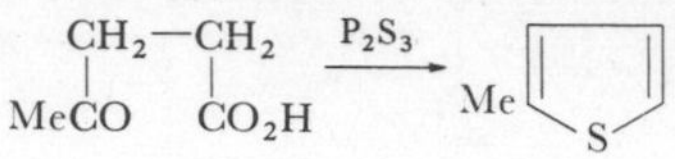

phosphorus trisulphide. This synthesis is similar to those used in the furan and pyrrole series, but is limited by the availability of the intermediates.

(2) Thiophene is available commercially from the continuous cyclization of butane, butene, or butadiene with sulphur. The contact time is about 2 seconds at 566°, and the redistilled product has a purity of 99%. It contains traces of carbon disulphide and benzene. This method can be applied to other hydrocarbons, for instance to isoprene (2-

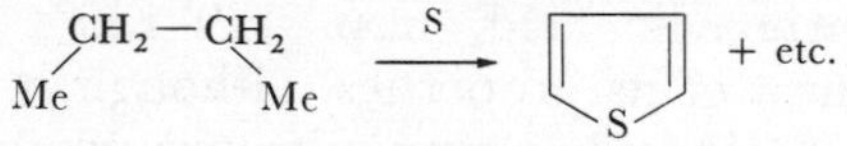

methylbutadiene), which yields 3-methylthiophene.

(3) A very general synthesis is that of Hinsberg. X and Y can be

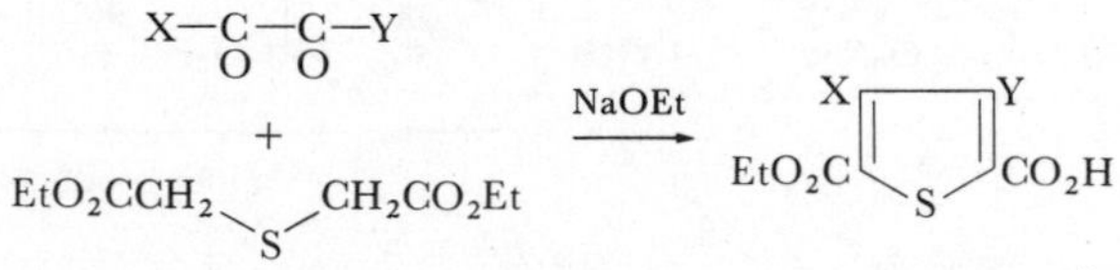

hydrogen, alkyl, aryl, hydroxyl, methoxyl, or carboxyl. It is notable that oxalic acid undergoes the reaction. A mechanism for the synthesis, which is consistent both with ^{18}O tracer studies and the formation of a half-ester as the final product, has been put forward.[130]

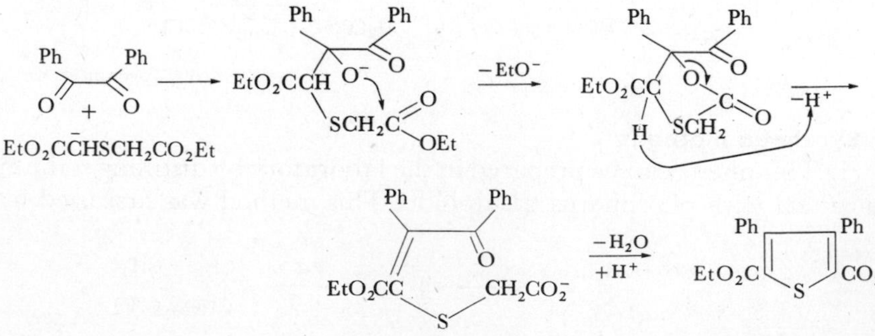

(4) A new synthesis, which has general application, starts with vinyl ketones or the related B-dialkylamino ketones.[131]

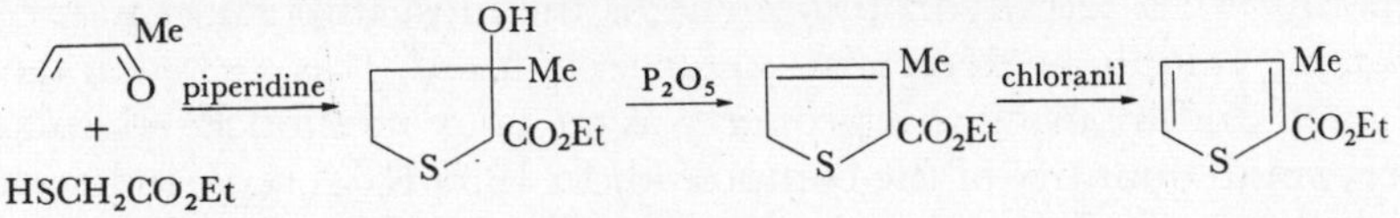

(5) Diacetylenes combine with hydrogen sulphide under weakly basic conditions to give thiophenes.[132] The substituents R and R' can be hydrogen, alkyl, aryl, carboxyl, or substituted ethinyl. This synthesis seems to be limited only by the availability of the diacetylene, and may be the route by which thiophenes are formed in plants.

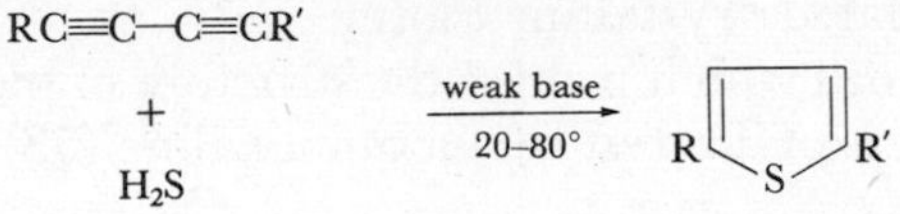

50–85% yield

(6) Acetylene combines with sulphur, yielding thiophene, but better results are obtained with methyl acetylenedicarboxylate.

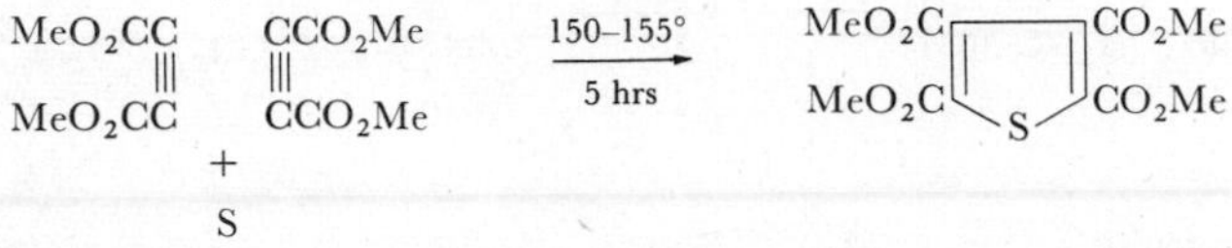

(7) A rather unusual synthesis of 2,4-diphenylthiophene has been reported.[133]

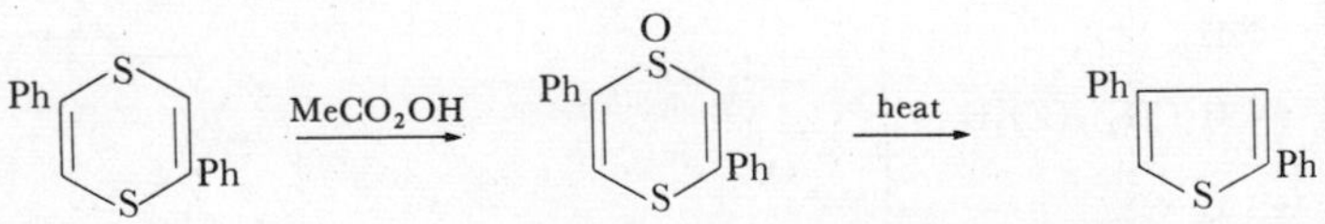

F. Natural occurrence and compounds of special interest

There is no evidence that thiophene, or tetrahydrothiophene, occur as such in nature, although they are constituents of coal tar and shale oil. All the possible methylthiophenes have also been isolated from the same sources. α,α-Terthienyl (50) has been isolated from the flowers of the Indian marigold. It is not impossible that it could have been formed from a polyacetylene.[134] Another thiophene (51), isolated from

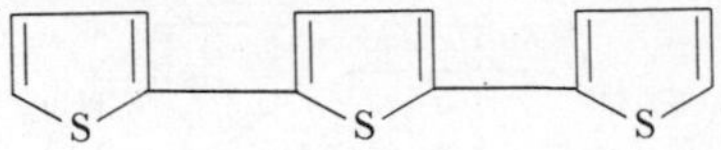

50

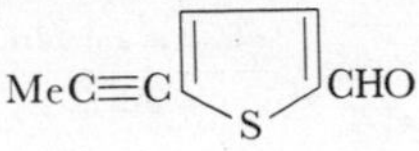

51

Daedalea juniperina cultures, is interesting in that it contains an acety-lene link.[135]

Biotin(**54**), a tetrahydrothiophene, is the most important naturally occurring thiophene derivative so far recognized. It is a growth factor for yeast, and by using this property as an assay method Kögl isolated a very small quantity of the compound. In 1936 Kögl reported finding a richer source of the material in egg yolk, and from 250 kg of dried duck egg yolks he isolated 1·1 mg of biotin methyl ester. Coenzyme R, a well-recognized growth factor for several species of legume nodule bacteria (*Rhizobium* sp.), was shown to be identical with biotin in 1940, and a little later that year biotin was also shown to be identical with a growth factor required by man and present in liver. From this source du Vigneaud isolated crystalline biotin.

The degradations which proved the structure of biotin are shown in the flow-sheet. It is of interest that a quinoxaline (**53**) is obtained from

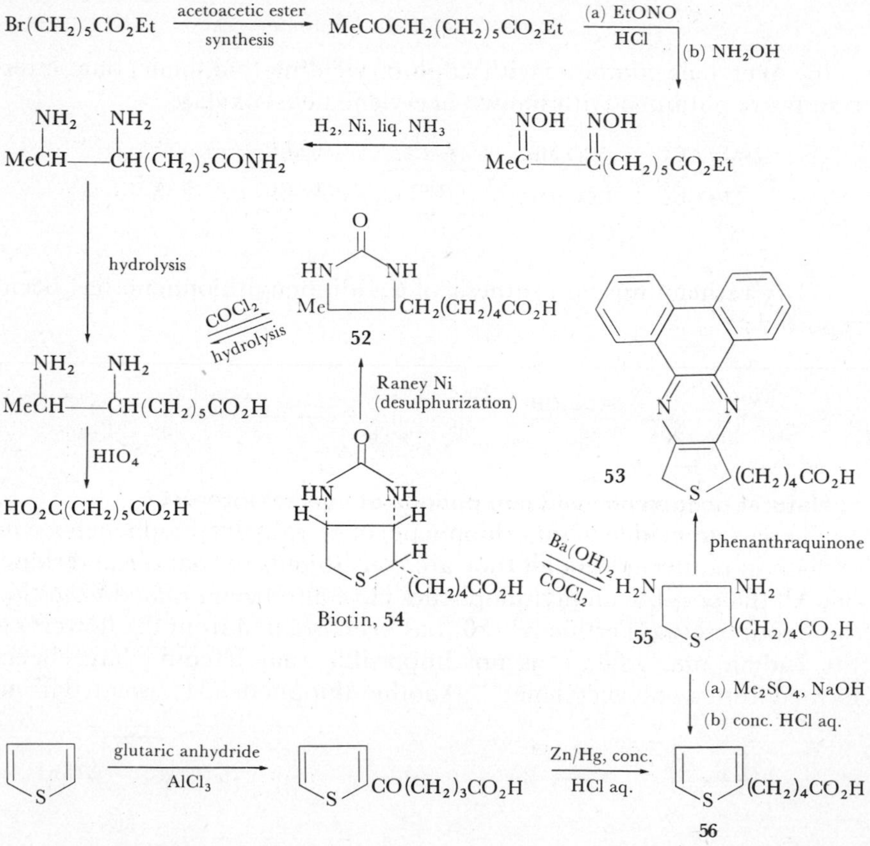

the diamine (**55**) and phenanthraquinone instead of the expected di-
hydroquinoxaline. The Raney nickel desulphurization of biotin (**54**) to

Glutaric anhydride   H$_2$NCHCO$_2$H   H$_2$NCHCO$_2$H

| CH$_2$ + $\xrightarrow{\text{NaOH}}$ CH$_2$ CH$_2$CO$_2$H

MeOH   SH   ClCH$_2$CO$_2$H   S

MeO$_2$C(CH$_2$)$_3$CO$_2$H   **57**

SOCl$_2$

(a) benzoylate
(b) esterify + MeOH
(c) MeOH, MeONa

MeO$_2$C(CH$_2$)$_3$COCl

Rosenmund hydrogenation
H$_2$, Pd/BaSO$_4$/S   PhCONH ⌐───┐ O $\xleftarrow{\text{AcOH, HCl}}$ PhCONH ⌐───┐ O

MeO$_2$C(CH$_2$)$_3$CHO   S   S   CO$_2$Me

58

piperidine
acetate

PhCONH ⌐───┐ O $\xrightarrow{\text{NH}_2\text{OH}}$ PhCONH ⌐───┐ NOH

S   CH(CH$_2$)$_3$CO$_2$Me   S   CH(CH$_2$)$_3$CO$_2$Me

Zn, Ac$_2$O, AcOH   **59**

products
separated

PhCONH ⌐───┐ NHAc   PhCONH ⌐───┐ NHAc

S   (CH$_2$)$_4$CO$_2$Me   S   CH(CH$_2$)$_3$CO$_2$Me

60   **61**

Pd/C, H$_2$ several stages

PhCONH ⌐───┐ NHAc

S   (CH$_2$)$_4$CO$_2$Me

The two racemates formed were separated   ($\pm$)-allobiotin (rings *trans*)
and individually treated successively with   ($\pm$)-epiallobiotin (rings *trans*)
(a) BaOH aq., 140°, and (b) COCl$_2$

O   O

HN   NH   HN   NH

H─   ─H   H─   ─H

H

S   (CH$_2$)$_4$CO$_2$H   S   (CH$_2$)$_4$CO$_2$H

($\pm$)-Biotin (rings and side chain *cis*)   ($\pm$)-Allobiotin (rings *trans*)

desthiobiotin (52) is a characteristic reaction of thiophenes (p. 128), and the modified Hofmann exhaustive methylation of 55, which gives 56, is worthy of note.

Biotin has 3 asymmetric carbon atoms, and so 8 optically active forms (4 racemates) of the molecule can exist. All of these have been obtained by synthesis. Only one of the optically active forms, that which is identical with natural (+)-biotin is biologically active. In confirmation of deductions from chemical studies x-ray examinations[136] have shown that the ring junction is *cis*, that the orientation of the side chain in respect to it is also *cis*, and that the absolute configuration is as shown.

Three quite similar syntheses of biotin have been effected, but only that of the Merck group will be outlined. L-Cysteine (57) was the starting material, but racemization took place at the cyclization stage, which gave 58. The next point of interest is the reduction of the oxime (59) as two isomeric products were formed, separated, and their structures elucidated. Both of these compounds were treated similarly, although the sequence is only shown on the chart for the one which gave biotin. On hydrogenation both gave two racemates, all of which were subjected to the reactions indicated. (±)-Biotin (rings *cis*) and (±)-allobiotin (rings *trans*) were obtained from 60, while 61 gave (±)-allobiotin and (±)-epiallobiotin (rings *trans*). The fourth racemate (±)-epibiotin, which is isomeric with (±)-biotin at position 2, has been obtained by another synthesis. Biotin acts as a coenzyme in carboxylation and decarboxylation *in vivo*, the 1'-carboxylic acid (62) being the intermediate compound.[137] Biotin is also involved in the synthesis of long-chain fatty acids.

Biocytin, ε-N-biotyllysine (63), has been obtained from yeast and by synthesis. It is as active as biotin in promoting the growth of some

62

63

organisms, but not all. The function of biocytin in cell metabolism is not yet clear.[138]

4. A SUMMARY COMPARISON OF THE AROMATIC PROPERTIES OF PYRROLE, FURAN, AND THIOPHENE

The meaning of the term 'aromatic' is in practice determined by common usage and is extremely difficult to define precisely in a generally acceptable way. Sir Robert Robinson's statement, that aromatic compounds show reduced unsaturation and a tendency to retain the type, gives an indication as to how aromatic compounds may be expected to *behave* in chemical reactions, and it is from this standpoint the present discussion will start.

In the Diels–Alder reaction furan generally behaves as a normal diene, pyrrole does not behave as a normal diene but undergoes addition reactions of the Michael type, while thiophene does not react; thiophene does however copolymerize with maleic anhydride in the presence of peroxide catalysts. Exceptions are of course known, with the substituted heterocycles and with extremely reactive dieneophiles. With aqueous mineral acid the same order of reactivity is shown as furan readily polymerizes, pyrrole forms recognizable salts which then polymerize, while thiophene is inert.

Furan forms 2,5-addition compounds readily, and compounds of this sort are often isolable intermediates in reactions leading, eventually, to substituted furans. It is even likely that these addition compounds are formed in most reactions which introduce substitutents at position 2 or 5 of the furan ring. Intermediate 2,5-addition compounds have so far not been detected in the electrophilic substitution of pyrrole, and it is known that the nitration of thiophene is essentially similar to that of benzene.

Very few direct comparisons of reactivity have been made between furan, pyrrole, and thiophene, but all are much more reactive than benzene to electrophilic reagents. The nitration of 1 gives 2, showing that the furan ring is the more reactive under these conditions. The

photolysis[139] of ethyl diazoacetate in furan and thiophene gives, presumably via the formation of ethoxycarbonylcarbene (3), the compounds 4 (X = O or S). Treatment with methanolic hydrogen chloride, in the case of the thiophene derivative, reforms the aromatic ring yielding 5, but in the furan series the aldehyde 6 is obtained.

One can conclude that, from the point of view of *behaviour* in chemical reactions, aromaticity increases in the order furan, pyrrole, and thiophene. Although not long ago this gradation was related, more or less satisfactorily, to the resonance energies and the bond lengths of these heterocycles, new and much more accurate data makes these older correlations unsatisfactory.

In the last few years the shapes of furan, pyrrole, and thiophene have been determined with great accuracy, with the surprising result that these compounds are very much more similar than might have been imagined from a consideration of earlier structural information. A noticeable gradation in bond lengths is not shown. The percentage contraction in length of the bond between the heteroatom and the adjacent carbon atom, as compared with the corresponding length in saturated aliphatic analogues, is remarkably constant (Table 3).

TABLE 3. Comparison of bond lengths in furan, pyrrole, and thiophene

| Hetero-atom | Bond length (Å) | | | | % contraction of X—C in heterocycle |
| | in ring | | | X—C saturated | |
	c	b	a		
N	1·429	1·371	1·383	1·47	5·9
O	1·431	1·361	1·362	1·43	4·8
S	1·423	1·370	1·714	1·82	5·8

Although the resonance energy for pyrrole is somewhat uncertain it must be of the same order of those of furan and thiophene, which numerically approach that of benzene (36·0 kcal/mole). If the resonance energies of these compounds are divided by the number of atoms constituting the rings, and contributing to the π-electron sextet, one finds the surprising result that, *per atom*, thiophene is at least as stabilized as benzene and the other compounds only somewhat less (Table 4); again there is no clear cut gradation as was once thought to be the case.

TABLE 4. Resonance energies and dipole moments of furan, pyrrole, and thiophene

	Resonance energy (kcal/mole)		λ_{max} (Å) ε_{max}		Dipole moment (D)	Dipole moment of tetrahydro derivative (D)
	A	B				
Furan	23·7–25·6	26	2500	1	0·71	1·68
Pyrrole	21–24	24·7	2400	300	1·84	1·57
Thiophene	29–31	34	2310	8000	0·52	1·87

A. From heats of combustion.   B. From molecular-orbital calculations.

Two of the six π electrons required for the aromaticity[140] of these heterocycles must come from the heteroatom. According to resonance theory this means that the charged structures **7a** to **7d**, as well as the uncharged structure **7**, are contributors to the resonance hybrid. The extent of electron release will depend both on the polarizability and on

X = O, NH, or S

the electronegativity of the heteroatom. The electronegativities do decrease regularly from oxygen through nitrogen to sulphur. However the dipole moment differences between furan and thiophene (heteroatoms positive) and their corresponding tetrahydro derivatives (heteroatoms negative) are the *same* (Table 4); a similar comparison for pyrrole and tetrahydropyrrole is difficult to make for pyrrole associates and the direction of the dipole for tetrahydropyrrole is not in the plane of the ring. It is therefore likely, on the dipole moment data, that for both furan and thiophene the charged contributors **7a** to **7d** are of similar importance in the hybrid. Structures **7a** to **7d** can in fact only make small contributions because of the low values of the dipole moments of the three heterocycles.

Attempts have been made to calculate and to estimate, from observed data, the magnitude of the ring current induced in these heterocycles by an applied magnetic field. The only certain conclusion, as yet, is that the magnitude of the induced current for all these heterocycles is less than that for benzene.[141]

Calculations of the π-electron densities at the 2 and 3 positions show that for furan and thiophene it is the highest at the 3 position, but for pyrrole it is highest at position 2. The localization energies for electrophilic substitution are however for all three heterocycles lowest at position 2.

A comparison of the acid-dissociation constants (Table 5) of these

TABLE 5. Acid-dissociation constants

Acid	$K \times 10^5$	Acid	$K \times 10^5$
Pyrrole-2-carboxylic	4·0	Thiophene-2-carboxylic	32
Pyrrole-3-carboxylic	1·0	Thiophene-3-carboxylic	7·8
Furan-2-carboxylic	70	Benzoic	6·3

three heterocycles is interesting. Pyrrole-2-carboxylic acid and thiophene-2-carboxylic are about four times as strong as the corresponding 3-carboxylic acids; the data for furan-3-carboxylic acid is not yet available. For the pyrrole-2-carboxylic acid this would not be expected on the basis of the higher π-electron density at position 2, but is consistent with the lower localization energy for nucleophilic attack at position 2; intramolecular hydrogen bonding, not possible in the 3-carboxylic acid, could also account for the difference in acidity.[142] The apparent low acidic strengths of the pyrrole acids may be due to the weakly basic properties of the pyrrole ring, which although very weak are nevertheless much more pronounced than those of furan and thiophene. The much greater strength of furan-2-carboxylic acid, as compared with thiophene-2-carboxylic acid, is noteworthy and can be associated with the greater inductive effect of oxygen as compared with sulphur.

TABLE 6. Ionization potentials and electronegativities

	M_D		Ionization potentials (eV)		Electro-negativities[143]
Furan	18·43	H_2O	12·56	O	3·50
Pyrrole	21·7	NH_3	11·2	N	3·07
Thiophene	24·36	H_2S	10·42	S	2·44
				C	2·50

The increasing polarizability of oxygen, nitrogen, and sulphur atoms attached to single bonds is indicated by the ionization potentials for water, ammonia, and hydrogen sulphide (Table 6). The molar refractivity (M_D) for furan,[144] pyrrole,[145] and thiophene[146] increase in this order, which is therefore the order of increasing polarizability for these compounds. The increasing 'aromatic character' of the series furan (which possesses the least), pyrrole and thiophene (which closely resembles benzene), as indicated by chemical reactions, can therefore be related both to the polarizability of the heteroatom (by the attacking reagent), and to the electronegativity of the heteroatom.

5. HETEROCYCLIC ANALOGUES WITH OTHER HETEROATOMS

A. Selenium

A selenium analogue (1) of benzofuran has been obtained,[147] but has been little investigated; the selenium analogue of furan, selenole, is not yet known.

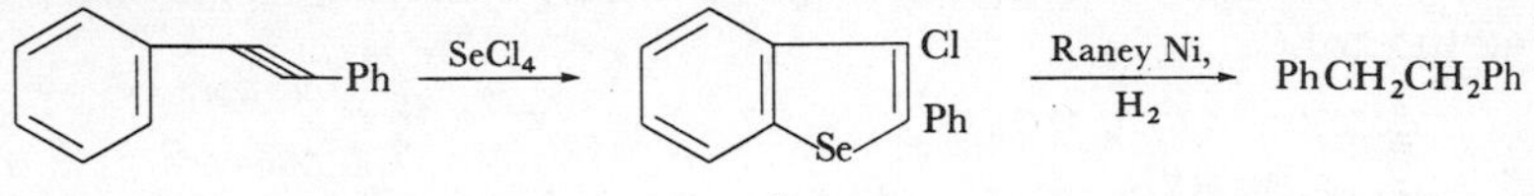

B. Phosphorus

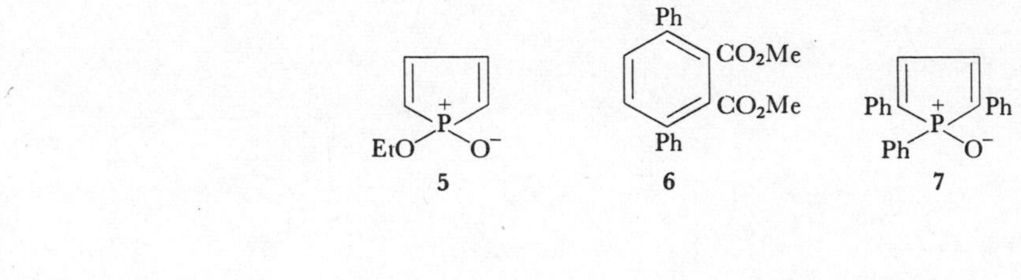

The phosphorus analogue of pyrrole, phosphole (2), is of special interest concerning the degree of aromaticity it might show, but until recently only saturated derivatives of this ring system had been synthesized. 1,2,5-Triphenylphosphole (4) is available[148] in 50–65% yield from 1,4-diphenylbutadiene and phenylphosphonous dichloride; presumably a Diels–Alder adduct (3) is first formed and loses hydrogen chloride. It is a bright yellow compound, m.p. 187–9°, absorbing at much longer wavelengths in the ultraviolet than 1,2,5-triphenyl-pyrrole, which suggests that the phosphole has less aromatic character. It has less diene character than the oxide (7), for although it reacts with dimethyl acetylenedicarboxylate with the loss of phosphorus giving **6**, it does not react with maleic anhydride under conditions where the oxide gives a normal Diels–Alder adduct across the 2,5-positions.

The ultraviolet absorption spectrum of the 1-ethoxyphosphole 1-oxide[149] (**5**) is very like that of thiophene 1,1-dioxide (see p.   ), and gives a normal Diels–Alder adduct across the 2,5-positions with cyclopentadiene.

Triphenylphosphine combines easily with both dimethyl acetylenedicarboxylate[150] and dicyanoacetylene[151] to give the 1,1,1-triphenylpholes (e.g. **8**). This ester, the structure of which has been established from its nuclear magnetic resonance spectrum, isomerizes on standing to the diene (**9**). The rearrangement is assisted by methanol.

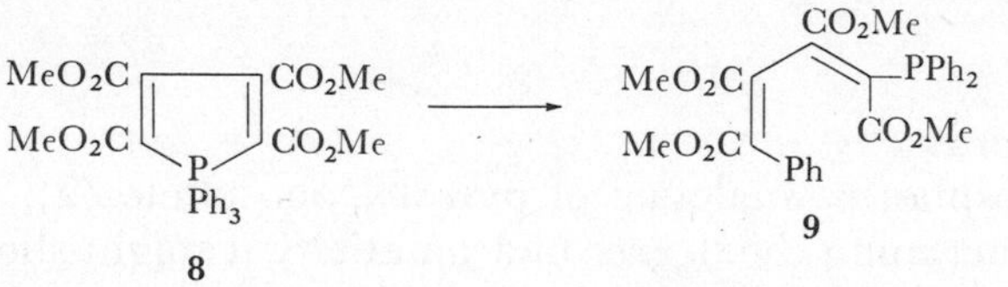

C. Boron

A borole derivative (**10**) has been obtained,[152] but has been little examined.

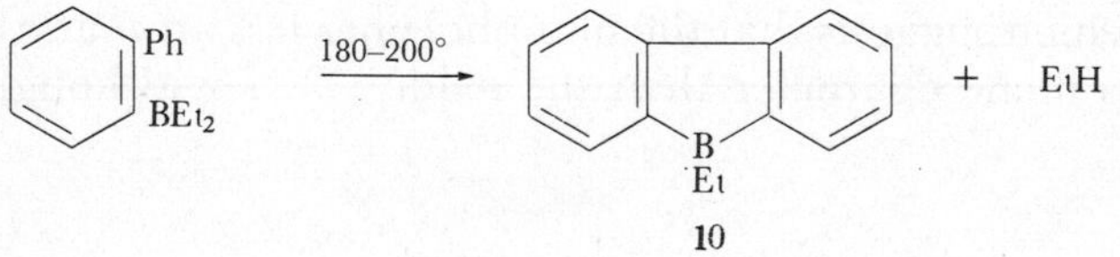

D. Aluminium

The first derivative of aluminole, a benzaluminole (**11**), which has been synthesized, readily loses aluminium.[153]

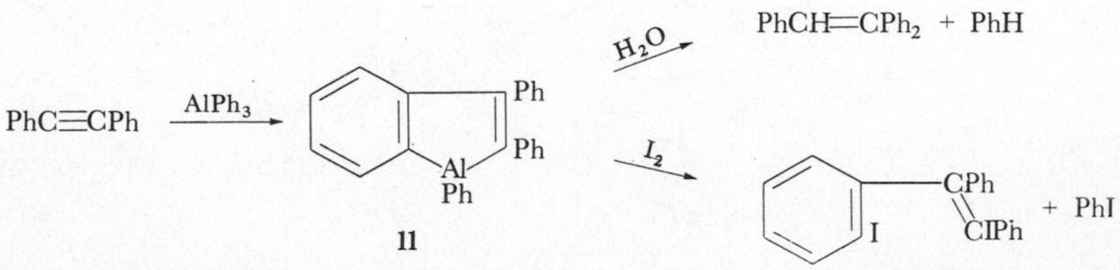

GENERAL BIBLIOGRAPHY

PYRROLE

Taylor and Baker, *Sidgwick's Organic Chemistry of Nitrogen,* Oxford University Press, 1942.
Corwin in *Heterocyclic Compounds,* Vol. I, ed. Elderfield, Wiley, New York, 1950.
Baltazzi and Krimen, *Chem. Rev., 63,* 511 (1963).

FURAN

Dunlop and Peters, *The Furans,* Am. Chem. Soc. Monograph No. 119, Reinhold, New York, 1953.
Dean, *Naturally Occurring Oxygen Ring Compounds,* Butterworths, London 1963.
Elderfield and Dodd in *Heterocyclic Compounds,* ed. Elderfield, Vol. I, Wiley, New York, 1950.
Jones and Taylor, *Quart. Rev. (London),* 4, 195 (1950).
Dunlop, *Furfural from Agricultural Sources,* Royal Institute of Chemistry Lectures, No. 4, 1956.
Topsom, *Rev. Pure Appl. Chem.,* 14, 127 (1964).

THIOPHENE

Hartough, *Thiophene and Its Derivatives,* Interscience, New York, 1952.
Hartough and Meisel, *Compounds with Condensed Thiophene Rings,* Interscience, New York, 1954.
Blicke in *Heterocyclic Compounds,* Vol. I, ed. Elderfield, Wiley, New York, 1950.
Gronowitz, *Advan. Heterocyclic Chem.,* 1, 1 (1963).

REFERENCES

1. Badger, Harris, Jones and Sasse, *J. Chem. Soc.,* 4329 (1962).
2. Simonetta, *J. Chim. Phys.,* 49, 68 (1952).
3. Wilcox and Goldstein, *J. Chem. Phys.,* 20, 1656 (1952).
4. Bak, Christensen, Hansen, and Rastrup-Andersen, *J. Chem. Phys.,* 24, 720 (1956); compare Cumpter, *Trans. Faraday Soc.,* 54, 1266 (1958).
5. Gomel and Lumbroso, *Bull. Soc. Chim. France,* 2200 (1962).
6. Longuet-Higgins and Coulson, *Trans. Faraday Soc.,* 43, 87 (1947); but see Brown, *Australian J. Chem.,* 8, 100 (1955).
6a. Re and Scarpati, *Rend. Accad. Sci. Fis. Mat. (Soc. Naz. Sci., Napoli),* 31, 88 (1964).
7. Lord and Miller, *J. Chem. Phys.,* 10, 328 (1942).
8. Bennett, Gale, and Stevenson, *J. Chem. Soc.,* 1518 (1965).
9. Wibaut and Gulje, *Proc. Konikl. Ned. Akad. Wetenschap, Ser. B,* 54, 330 (1951).
10. Currell and Zechmeister, *J. Am. Chem. Soc.,* 80, 205 (1958).
11. Whipple, Chiang, and Hinman, *J. Am. Chem. Soc.,* 85, 26 (1963).
12. Smith, *Advan. Heterocyclic Chem.,* 2, 287 (1963).
13. de Mayo and Reid, *Chem. Ind. (London),* 1576 (1962).
13a. Mandell and Blanchard, *J. Am. Chem. Soc.,* 79, 6198 (1957).
14. Wittig and Reichel, *Chem. Ber.,* 96, 2851 (1963), and earlier papers; Wolthuis, Vander Jagt, Mels, and Boer, *J. Org. Chem.,* 30, 190 (1965).
15. Treibs and Kolm, *Ann.,* 606, 166 (1957).
16. Treibs and Fritz, *Ann.,* 611, 162 (1958).
17. Treibs and Zimmer-Galler, *Ann.,* 664, 140 (1963).
18. Hobbs, McMillan, Papadopulos, and VanderWerf, *J. Am. Chem. Soc.,* 84, 43 (1962).
19. Reddy, *Chem. Ind. (London),* 1426 (1965).
20. Anderson and Hoplins, *Can. J. Chem.,* 42, 1279 (1964).
21. Skell and Bean, *J. Am. Chem. Soc.,* 84, 4660 (1962).
22. Morgan and Morrey, *Tetrahedron,* 22, 57 (1966), and papers cited therein.
23. Silverstein, Ryskiewicz, Willard, and Koehler, *J. Org. Chem.,* 20 668 (1955); see also Smith, *J. Chem. Soc.,* 3842 (1954).
24. Jones and Laslett, *Australian J. Chem.,* 17, 1056 (1964).
25. Kirmse, *Progr. Org. Chem.,* 6, 164 (1964).
26. Closs and Schwartz, *J. Org. Chem.,* 26, 2609 (1961).
27. Fuhlhage and VanderWerf, *J. Am. Chem. Soc.,* 80, 6249 (1958).
28. Bonnett, Clark, Giddey, and Todd, *J. Chem. Soc.,* 2087 (1959).

29. Evans, *J. Am. Chem. Soc.*, **73**, 5230 (1951).
30. Burckhalter and Short, *J. Org. Chem.*, **23**, 1278 (1958).
31. Tschamler and Voetter, *Monatsh.*, **83**, 302 (1952).
32. Private suggestion by Dr. M. J. T. Robinson.
33. Herz, *J. Org. Chem.*, **22**, 1260 (1957).
34. Grob and Utzinger, *Helv. Chim. Acta*, **37**, 1256 (1954).
35. Tedder and Webster, *J. Chem. Soc.*, 3270 (1960).
36. Tedder and Webster, *J. Chem. Soc.*, 1638 (1962).
37. Grob and Ankli, *Helv. Chim. Acta*, **32**, 2010, 2023 (1949).
38. Kuhn and Osswald, *Chem. Ber.*, **89**, 1423 (1956).
39. Atkinson and Bullock, *Can. J. Chem.*, **41**, 625 (1963).
40. Hinman and Theodoropulos, *J. Org. Chem.*, **28**, 3058 (1963).
41. Herz and Brash, *J. Org. Chem.*, **23**, 1513 (1958).
42. Khan and Morgan, *J. Chem. Soc.*, 2579 (1964).
43. Jones and Lindner, *Australian J. Chem.*, **18**, 875 (1965).
44. Trippett, *Quart. Rev. (London)*, **17**, 406 (1963).
45. Anderson and Shu-Fan Lee, *Can. J. Chem.*, **43**, 409 (1965).
46. Hodge and Rickards, *J. Chem. Soc.*, 2543 (1963).
47. Hodge and Rickards, *J. Chem. Soc.*, 459 (1965).
48. Henrickson, Rees and Templeton, *J. Am. Chem. Soc.*, **86**, 107 (1964).
49. Terry, Jackson, Kenner, and Kornis, *J. Chem. Soc.*, 4389 (1965).
50. Schulte, Reisch, and Walker, *Chem. Ber.*, **98**, 98 (1965).
51. DuPont, *U.S. Pat.*, 2,600,289.
52. Bak, Pedersen, and Sørensen, *Acta Chem. Scand.*, **18**, 275 (1964).
53. Corwin in *Organic Chemistry*, Vol. II, 2nd edition, ed. Gilman, Wiley, New York, 1943, p. 1260.
54. Longuet-Higgins, Rector, and Platt, *J. Chem. Phys.*, **18**, 1174 (1950).
55. Caughey and Koski, *Biochemistry*, **1**, 923 (1962).
55a. Harris, Johnson, and Kay, *Quart. Rev. (London)*, **20**, 211 (1966).
56. Lascelles, *Tetrapyrrole Synthesis and its Regulation*, Benjamin, New York, 1964.
57. Lester Smith, *Vitamin B_{12}*, 3rd edition, Methuen, London, 1965.
58. Mathewson and Corwin, *J. Am. Chem. Soc.*, **83**, 135 (1961).
59. Steele in *Organic Chemistry*, Vol. II, 2nd edition, ed. Gilman, Wiley, New York, 1943, p. 1293; Linstead, Eisner, Ficken and Johns, 'Recent work on naturally occurring heterocyclic compounds', *Chem. Soc. Special Publ.* No. 3, 83 (1955).
60. Woodward *et al.*, *J. Am. Chem. Soc.*, **82**, 3850 (1960).
61. D. Crowfoot Hodgkin *et al.*, *Proc. Roy. Soc. Ser. A*, **242**, 228 (1957).
62. Guthrie, Waddington *et al.*, *J. Am. Chem. Soc.*, **74**, 4662 (1952).
63. Sappenfield and Kreevoy, *Tetrahedron*, **19**, Suppl 2, 157 (1963).
64. Bak, Christensen, Dixon, Hansen-Nygaard, Andersen, and Schöttlander, *J. Mol. Spectroscopy*, **9**, 124 (1962).
65. Beach, *J. Chem. Phys.*, **9**, 54 (1941).
66. Anet, *Tetrahedron Letters*, 1219 (1962).
67. Kwart and Burchuk, *J. Am. Chem. Soc.*, **74**, 3094 (1952).
68. Berson and Swidler, *J. Am. Chem. Soc.*, **75**, 1721 (1953).
69. Eugster and Bosshard, *Helv. Chim. Acta*, **46**, 815 (1963).
70. Schenck, Hartmann, and Steinmetz, *Chem. Ber.*, **96**, 498 (1963).
71. Schenck, Hartmann, Mannsfield, Metzner, and Krauch, *Chem. Ber.*, **95**, 1642 (1962).
72. Elming, *Advan. Org. Chem.*, **2**, 67 (1960).
73. Terent'ev, Belen'kii and Yanovskaya, through *Chem. Abstr.*, **49**, 12327d (1955).
74. Finan and Fothergill, *J. Chem. Soc.*, 2723 (1963).
75. Traynelis, Miskel, and Sowa, *J. Org. Chem.*, **22**, 1269 (1957).
76. Kratochvil and Hort, *Coll. Czech. Chem. Commun.*, **27**, 52 (1962); Gross, *Chem. Ber.*, **95**, 83 (1962).
77. Farnum and Burr, *J. Org. Chem.*, **28**, 1387 (1963).
78. Cornforth, *J. Chem. Soc.*, 1310, (1958).

79. Burness, *Org. Synth.*, **39**, 46 (1959).
80. Eftax and Dunlop, *J. Org. Chem.*, **30**, 1317 (1965).
81. Rice, *J. Am. Chem. Soc.*, **74**, 3193 (1952).
82. White, Colomb, and Bailey, *J. Org. Chem.*, **30**, 481 (1965).
83. Gronowitz and Sörlin, *Acta Chem. Scand.*, **15**, 1419 (1961).
84. Gronowitz and Sörlin, *Arkiv Kemi*, **19**, 515 (1963).
85. Wheland, *Advanced Organic Chemistry*, Wiley, New York, 1949, p. 646.
86. *Org. Syn.*, Coll. Vol. III, 425 (1955).
87. Nazarova, through *Chem. Abstr.*, **49**, 6214f (1955).
88. Gilman, Calloway and Burtner, *J. Am. Chem. Soc.*, **57**, 906 (1935).
89. *Org. Syn.*, **33**, 39 (1953).
90. Leditschke, *Chem. Ber.*, **86**, 123 (1953).
91. Birkoffer and Daum, *Chem. Ber.*, **95**, 183 (1962).
92. Cloke and Pilgrim, *J. Am. Chem. Soc.*, **61**, 2667 (1939).
93. Moldenhauer *et al.*, *Ann.*, **580**, 169 (1953).
94. Mabry, *J. Org. Chem.*, **28**, 1699 (1963).
95. Clauson-Kaas and Nedenskov, *Acta Chem. Scand.*, **9**, 27 (1955).
96. Bose, *J. Indian Chem. Soc.*, **37**, 653 (1960).
97. Bak, Christensen, Hansen-Nygaard, and Rastrup-Andersen, *J. Mol. Spectr.*, **7**, 58 (1961).
98. Abrahams, *Quart. Rev. (London)*, **10**, 407 (1956).
99. Brumlik, Kosak, and Pitcher, *J. Am. Chem. Soc.*, **86**, 5360 (1964).
100. Procházka, *Coll. Czech. Chem. Commun.*, **30**, 1158 (1965).
101. Bailey and Cummins, *J. Am. Chem. Soc.*, **76**, 1932, 1940 (1954).
102. Overberger and Whelan, *J. Org. Chem.*, **26**, 4328 (1961).
103. Hafner and Kaiser, *Tetrahedron Letters*, 2185 (1964).
104. Terent'ev and Kadatskii, through *Chem. Abstr.*, **48**, 3339 (1954).
105. Östman, *Arkiv Kemi*, **19**, 499 (1963).
106. Griffen and Martin, *Chem. Commun.*, 154 (1965).
107. Birch and McAllan, *J. Chem. Soc.*, 2556 (1951).
108. Bordwell, Andersen and Pitt, *J. Am. Chem. Soc.*, **76**, 1082 (1954).
109. Hauptmann and Walter, *Chem. Rev.*, **62**, 347 (1962); Pettit and van Tamelen, *Org. Reactions*, **12**, 356 (1962).
110. Crombie, *Ann. Rept. Chem. Soc.*, **52**, 309 (1955).
111. Scully and Brown, *J. Am. Chem. Soc.*, **75**, 6329 (1953).
112. Davies and Porter, *J. Chem. Soc.*, 4958 (1957).
113. Wynberg and van Dreil, *J. Am. Chem. Soc.*, **87**, 3998 (1965).
114. Bordwell and McKellin, *J. Am. Chem. Soc.*, **73**, 2251 (1951).
115. Gronowitz, *Arkiv Kemi*, **7**, 267 (1954).
116. Gronowitz, *Acta Chem. Scand.*, **13**, 1045 (1959).
117. Östman, *Arkiv Kemi*, **19**, 527 (1963).
118. Hurd and Kreuz, *J. Am. Chem. Soc.*, **74**, 2965 (1952).
119. Campaigne and Monroe, *J. Am. Chem. Soc.*, **76**, 2447 (1954).
120. Putokhin and Yakovlev, through *Chem. Abstr.*, **49**, 12431 (1955).
121. Hörnfeldt and Gronowitz, *Acta Chem. Scand.*, **16**, 789 (1962).
122. Ford and Mackay, *J. Chem. Soc.*, 4985 (1956).
123. Hörnfeldt and Gronowitz, *Arkiv Kemi*, **21**, 239 (1963).
124. Sicé, *J. Am. Chem. Soc.*, **75**, 3697 (1953).
125. Campaigne and Collins, *J. Heterocyclic Chem.*, **2**, 136 (1965).
126. Campaigne and Yokley, *J. Org. Chem.*, **28**, 914 (1963).
127. Campaigne and Archer, *J. Am. Chem. Soc.*, **75**, 989 (1953).
128. Buu-Hoï and Lavit, *J. Chem. Soc.*, 1721 (1958); Gronowitz, *Arkiv Kemi*, **13**, 295 (1958).
129. Wolf and Folkers, *Org. Reactions*, **6**, 410 (1951).
130. Wynberg and Kooreman, *J. Am. Chem. Soc.*, **87**, 1739 (1965).
131. Tilak, Desai, and Gupte, *Tetrahedron Letters*, 1609 (1964); *Private communication from Professor B. D. Tilak.*
132. Schulte, Reisch, and Hörnei, *Chem. Ber.*, **95**, 1943 (1962).

133. Szmant and Alfonso, *J. Am. Chem. Soc.*, **79**, 205 (1957).
134. Challenger, *Sci. Progr. (London)*, **41**, 593 (1953).
135. Birkinshaw and Chaplen, *Biochem. J.*, **60**, 255 (1955).
136. Traub, *Nature*, **178**, 649 (1956); Trotter and Hamilton, *Biochemistry*, **5**, 713 (1966).
137. Knappe, Biederbick, and Brümmer, *Angew. Chem.*, **74**, 432 (1962).
138. Lascelles, *Ann. Rept. Chem. Soc.*, **49**, 256 (1952).
139. Schenck and Steinmetz, *Ann.*, **668**, 19 (1963).
140. Armit and Robinson, *J. Chem. Soc.*, **127**, 1604 (1925).
141. Davies, *Chem. Commun.*, 258 (1965).
142. Khan and Morgan, *Tetrahedron*, **21**, 2197 (1965).
143. Allred and Rochow, *J. Inorg. Nuclear Chem.*, **5**, 264, 269 (1958).
144. Smyth and Walls, *J. Am. Chem. Soc.*, **54**, 3230 (1932).
145. Kofod, Sutton, and Jackson, *J. Chem. Soc.*, 1467 (1952).
146. Keswani and Freiser, *J. Am. Chem. Soc.*, **71**, 218 (1949).
147. Riley, Flato, and McIntyre, *J. Org. Chem.*, **28**, 1138 (1963).
148. Campbell, Cookson, Hocking, and Hughes, *J. Chem. Soc.*, 2184 (1965).
149. Usher and Westheimer, *J. Am. Chem. Soc.*, **86**, 4732 (1964).
150. Hendrickson, Spenger, and Sims, *Tetrahedron*, **19**, 707 (1963).
151. Reddy and Weiss, *J. Org. Chem.*, **28**, 1822 (1963).
152. Köster and Benedikt, *Angew. Chem.*, **75**, 419 (1963).
153. Eisch and Kaska, *J. Am. Chem. Soc.*, **84**, 1501 (1962).

CHAPTER IV

FUSED RING SYSTEMS INVOLVING PYRROLE, FURAN, AND THIOPHENE RINGS

A benzene ring may be fused on to the carbon atoms of each of these three heterocyclic compounds in two different positions. Six possible

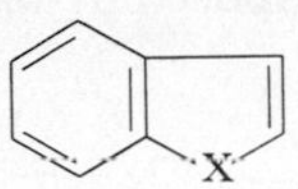

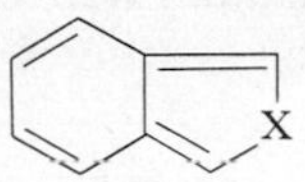

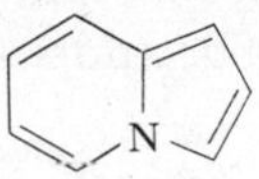

Indole	X = NH	Isoindole
Benzofuran	X = O	Isobenzofuran
Thianaphthene	X = S	Isothianaphthene

Indolizine

structures emerge, and derivatives of all are known. In the case of pyrrole where the heteroatom is trivalent yet another structure can be written, that of indolizine. Of these seven ring systems that of indole requires most attention.

1. INDOLE

A. Introduction

Indole was first prepared in 1866, by heating oxindole with zinc dust, and in recent years it has become commercially available. The indole ring system is found in many naturally occurring compounds of great chemical and biochemical interest. Three specific simple examples are the essential amino acid tryptophan, the dyestuff indigo, and the plant growth hormone indole-3-acetic acid.

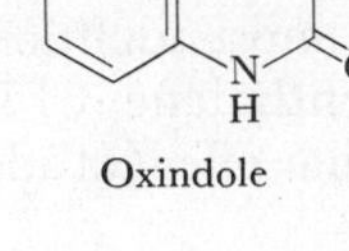

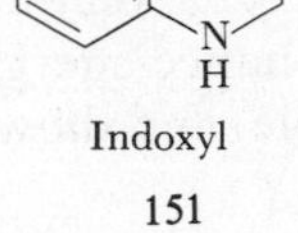

| | 3H-Indolenine | 2H-Indolenine |

| Oxindole | Indoxyl | Isatin |

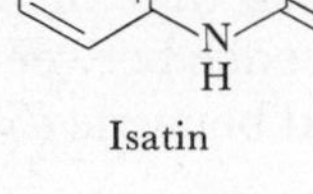

The positions of the indole ring are usually numbered as shown(**1**) although occasionally α- and β- are used to indicate the 2- and 3-positions respectively as in the case of pyrrole. Derivatives of both indolenines have been prepared, and the common names for some important indoles are shown.

B. Physical properties and structure

Indole is a colourless crystalline solid, m.p. 52°, which boils with some decomposition at 254°. It is remarkably volatile and is easily soluble in most organic solvents. It may be crystallized from water and is sparingly soluble in the cold. When pure it has a pleasant but very persistent smell, and it is used as a perfume base.

The formula of indole, as usually written (**1**), was proposed by Baeyer in 1869, and was based on the syntheses outlined.

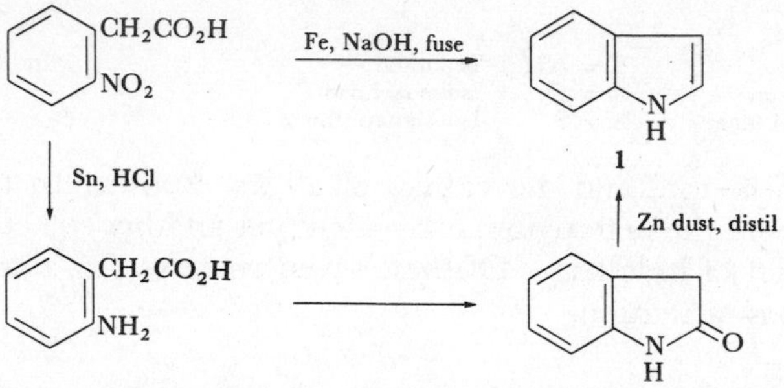

The molecular dimensions of indole have not yet been determined. The π-electron densities at the various atoms in the ring have been calculated by molecular-orbital methods. The results show, in conformity with experiment, that the 3-position is the most susceptible to electrophilic reagents and is much more reactive than benzene in this respect.

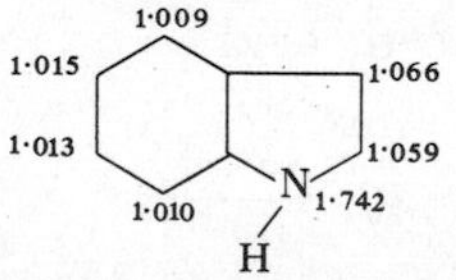

π-Electron densities calculated
by the molecular-orbital method

The resonance energy of indole, calculated from its heat of combustion, is 47–49 kcal/mole. The increase in resonance energy (ca. 23 kcal/mole) over that of pyrrole (23–27 kcal/mole) is almost identical to the difference between the resonance energies of naphthalene (61 kcal/mole) and benzene (36 kcal/mole) and shows the similar effect of adding the additional ring. Of the resonance structures which can be written for indole (compare pyrrole), the uncharged structure **1** is probably the most important, as it involves full conjugation in both rings; the benzene ring can, of course, be written in its other Kekulé form (**1a**). Of the ionic structures possible only those with a negative charge in the

nitrogen-containing ring will be considered. Only one structure (**1b**), involving an *ortho*-quinonoid benzene ring, can provide a negative charge at position 2. In the case where the negative charge is at position 3 the benzene ring can have all the uncharged resonance forms possible for benzene itself; two are shown (**1c** and **1d**). It therefore appears, in agreement with the molecular-orbital calculation, that one effect of fusing the benzene and pyrrole rings is to alter the position of greatest reactivity to electrophilic reagents of the pyrrole ring from position 2 to position 3. This is, of course, on the assumption that the contributions of ionic forms to the resonance hybrid are of similar importance, as in the case of pyrrole itself, and the chemical reactions of indole support this contention. The status of the indolenine tautomers of indole corresponds exactly to the pyrrole analogy. Although both tautomers of 2-ethoxyindole are known (p. 162) there is no evidence which suggests that indole itself tautomerizes to a detectable extent, and the formation of indolenines (p. 157; cf. pyrrolenines, p. 65) requires only the addition of the electrophilic reagent at the very reactive 2- or 3-position of the indole ring, followed in some cases by the subsequent expulsion of a proton from position 1, and not the prior tautomerization of the original indole to an indolenine.

C. Chemical properties

The chemical properties of indole are, in general, quite similar to those of pyrrole if allowance is made for the marked stabilizing influence of the benzene ring and its effect in directing electrophilic reagents to position 3. Indole, like pyrrole, gives a red colour with a pine splint dipped in hydrochloric acid, and a positive Ehrlich reaction (see p. 155).

1. *The direct oxidation of indole*

The nitrogen-containing ring of many substituted indoles can be opened by the action of peroxy acids and ozone, and is also opened enzymatically *in vivo*. In the case of indole itself (**1**) some oxidation to 2-formamidobenzaldehyde (**2**) takes place, but the major product is indigo (p. 170).

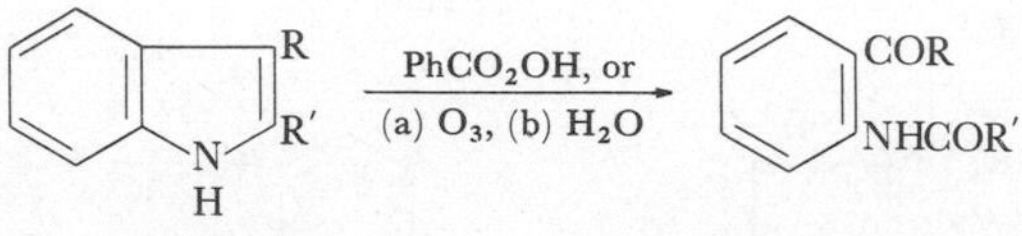

1, R=R′=H   2, R=R′=H

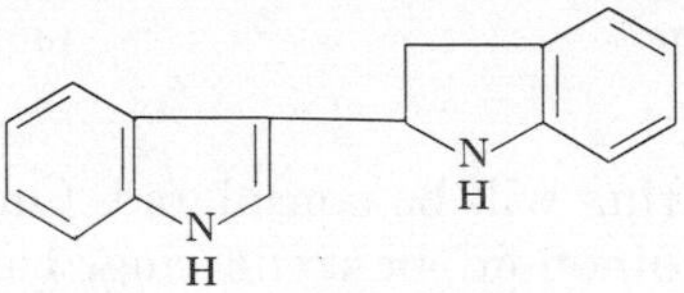

Indole dimer

2. *Addition reactions*

Indole, like pyrrole, is a very weak base, and it is polymerized similarly by acids unless electron-attracting substituents are present. From the polymerization of indole itself a crystalline dimer[1] and a trimer have been isolated. The structure of the dimer, which may be compared with pyrrole trimer (p. 67), is shown above. Indoles in strongly acid solution accept[2] a proton at position 3. Deuterium exchange, under these conditions,[3] occurs most rapidly at position 1, then at position 3 and occasionally also at position 2.

Indole itself is reduced to 2,3-dihydroindole, or indoline (**3**) by zinc or tin and hydrochloric acid, electrolytic reduction, and by controlled hydrogenation over copper or nickel catalysts, but the reduction of derivatives can be difficult. More powerful hydrogenation yields octa-hydroindole (**4**) and finally 2-ethylcyclohexylamine (**5**). 2,3-Dihydro-

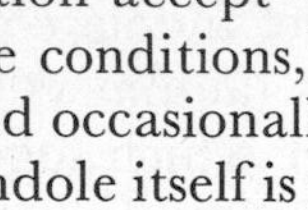

3 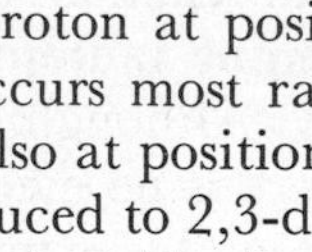   4 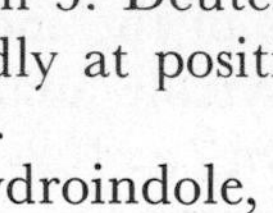   5 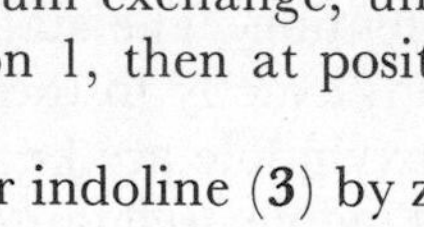   6

indole is a colourless liquid, b.p. 230°, and on catalytic dehydrogenation or oxidation with silver sulphate yields indole. It has the typical properties of an aromatic–aliphatic secondary amine.

Indole also adds sodium bisulphite, forming **6**, which acetylates on the nitrogen atom.[4] Electrophilic substitution, such as nitration, now takes place successively at positions 5 and 7. Subsequent treatment with sodium hydroxide splits out the substituents in the 5-membered ring and gives a useful synthesis of substituted indoles.

3. *Substitution reactions*

The hydrogen at position 1 of indole is appreciably acidic (cf. pyrrole, p. 69) and can be displaced by metallic sodium, or potassium hydroxide at 125–130°, or by Grignard reagents. The sodium salt with methyl iodide gives mainly 1-methylindole with small amounts of 2- and 3-methylindole. Treating the Grignard derivative, which is largely ionic,[5] with a variety of reagents usually, but not always, gives the corresponding 3-substituted indoles. This can be compared with similar reactions, but at position 2, in the pyrrole series (p. 71).

In general, the direct electrophilic substitution of indoles yields 3-derivatives. If this position is blocked the substituent enters position 2, otherwise the benzene ring.

Ehrlich discovered that indoles on treatment with hydrochloric acid and 4-dimethylaminobenzaldehyde give red to violet colours, a test which still bears his name. The colour does not develop if the indole has substituents at both 2- and 3-positions. The product from the reaction of 2-methylindole and the aldehyde is a 3-indolenine (**7**) which has been isolated[6] as the perchlorate; a similar 2-indolenine is obtainable from 3-methylindole. The colour is associated with the fact that, as in the aminotriphenylmethane dyes, the positive charge is not restricted to the nitrogen atom of the indole ring, as in **7**, but can also be written on the other nitrogen atom (**7a**). The compound is best considered as a resonance hybrid. Similar red-purple compounds are

G

formed in the pyrrole series where attack occurs at position 2 of the ring.[7]

7   7a

The attempted nitration of indole under ordinary acidic conditions leads to decomposition of the ring system. 3-Nitroindole can, however, be obtained from indole, sodium ethoxide, and ethyl nitrate (cf. 2-nitropyrrole, p. 72). The sulphonation of indole with 1-proto-1-pyridinium sulphonate (p. 194) is claimed to yield the 1-sulphonic acid at 50° and the 2-sulphonic acid at 120°. This is surprising, as the 3-sulphonic acid might be expected. Indole can be directly halogenated in good yield by bromine in pyridine,[8] and also by iodine and by sulphuryl chloride. 1-Acylindoles can also be directly halogenated. In all these cases the 3-halogenated indole is formed. Further substitution to 2,3-dichloroindole can take place with sulphuryl chloride. Indole can be mercurated by mercuric acetate to a bis-mercuriacetate which is either the 1,3- or 3,3-derivative.[9]

Indole is attacked at position 3 by oxalyl chloride, ethyl diazoacetate, formaldehyde and dimethylamine (Mannich reaction), and propio-

	R
8,	$COCOCl$
9,	CH_2CO_2Et
10,	CH_2NMe_2
11,	$CH_2CH_2CO_2H$

H   12   H   13

lactone with the respective formation of **8–11**. α-Acetamidoacrylic acid (**12**) also reacts at position 3, through a Michael type of addition, yielding acetyltryptophan (**13**).[10] Indole is attacked by acetic anhydride (cf. pyrrole, p. 72) at 180–200°, giving 1-acetylindole with some 1,3-diacetylindole. At higher temperatures the second compound is the main product, and it is easily hydrolysed by dilute alkali to 3-acetylindole.

A kinetic study[11] of the reaction of 4-nitrobenzenediazonium chloride with indole and its 3-deuterium derivative has shown that there is a slow attack of the diazonium cation on the neutral indole molecule at position 3, followed by a rapid expulsion of a proton or deuteron. This substitution therefore proceeds by the same mechanism invoked in the nitration of benzene.

Treatment of indole with methyl iodide converts it successively into the 2-methyl and 2,3-dimethyl derivatives followed by **14** and **15**. It is not possible to stop the methylation efficiently until ionic products are formed. It is particularly interesting that compounds **14** and **15** nitrate at position 5 in 88% and 77% yield respectively.[12] This is the first example of a positively charged group directly attached to a benzene ring directing an attacking nitronium cation to the *para* position.

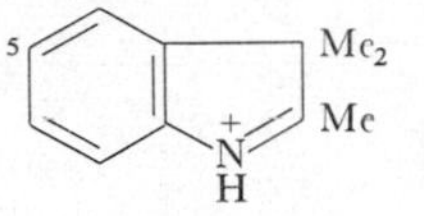

14 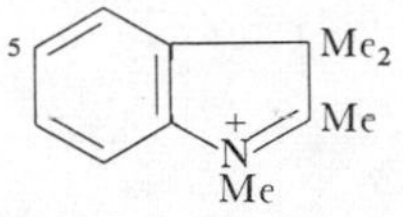   15

1,1-Dimethylindolium hydroxide (**17**), convertible into the perchlorate, has been obtained indirectly from isatin.[13] Reduction with

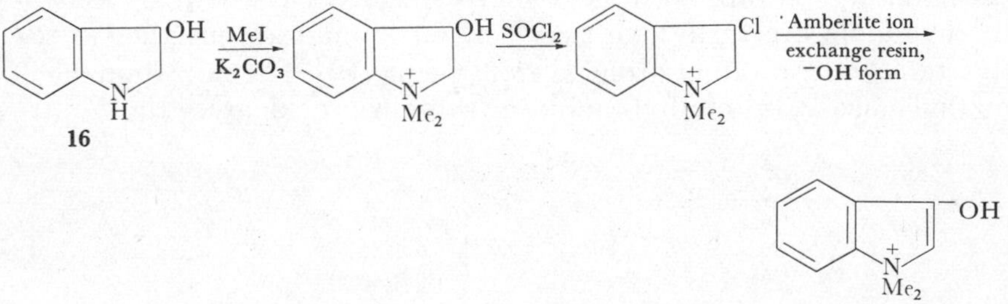

17

lithium aluminium hydride gave the alcohol (**16**) which was treated as indicated. The hydroxide (**17**) possessed an ultraviolet absorption spectrum very similar to those of styrene and indene. It was remarkably easily demethylated to 1-methylindole, standing for one hour with a solution of sodium hydroxide at room temperature being sufficient.

The alkylation of indoles with sodium alkoxides at high temperatures proceeds only at position 3. The mechanism of this substitution is probably the same as that of a similar substitution in the pyrrole series (p. 76).

Indole with benzyl radicals gives[14] small amounts of 1- (1·67%) and 3-benzylindole (2·15%).

D. Derivatives of indole

In general, substituents attached to the carbocyclic and heterocyclic rings of indole have properties normal to the corresponding benzene and pyrrole derivatives respectively.

1. *Alkyl, aryl, and related indoles*

Alkylindoles can be prepared by direct synthesis or by the direct or indirect alkylation of indole. 3-Methylindole (skatole) is the major odoriferous constituent of human faeces. It is also a valuable perfume base, and can be obtained by Fischer's synthesis (p. 167). 2-Methyl-indole can also be obtained by Fischer's synthesis and is converted into a carbazole (**18**) on heating with methyl vinyl ketone.[15] This shows that

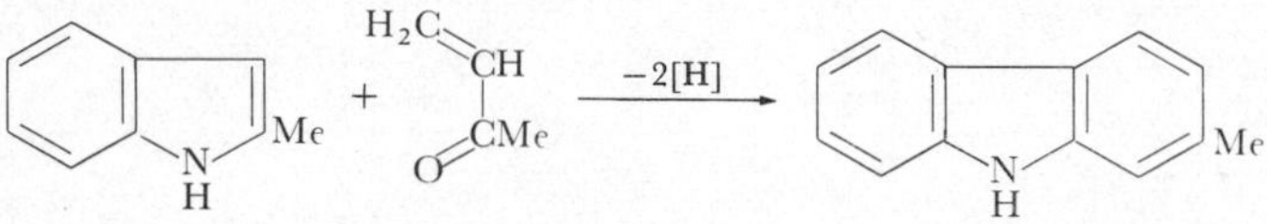

the 2-methyl group must be somewhat activated. Both 2- and 3-methylindole are easily oxidized[16] by ferric chloride in ether to red dyestuffs, one product from skatole being **19**. The nitration of 2-methyl- and 2,3-dimethyl-indole in sulphuric acid gives the 5-nitro

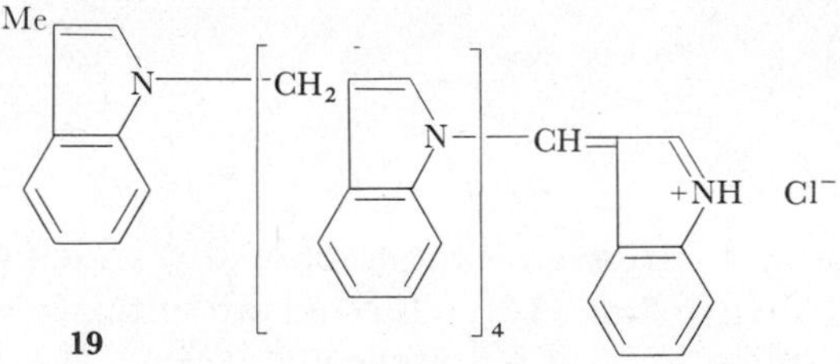

derivatives. Presumably the 3-protonated indoles are actually nitrated, for, 2,3-diphenylindole under these conditions yields 5-nitro-(3-*p*-nitrophenyl)-2-phenylindole but with copper nitrate in acetic acid gives 6-nitro-2,3-diphenylindole.[17]

3-Methyl-2-phenylindole (**20**) is of interest in that, like many other

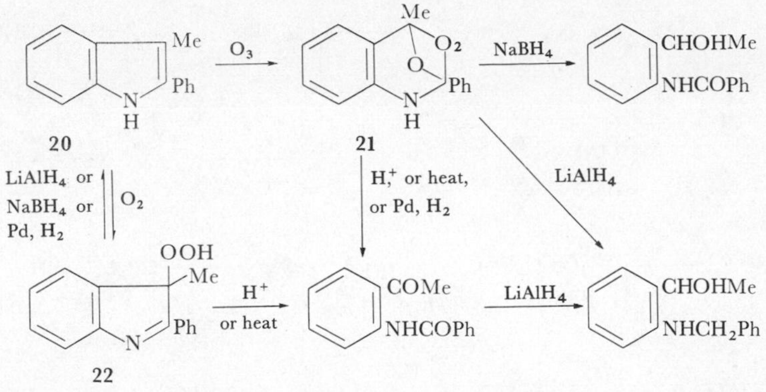

2-arylindoles, it gives a stable ozonide (**21**) and on autoxidation in boiling benzene–ligroin it yields[18] a hydroperoxide (**22**). The degradations of these compounds are shown.

2,3-Dimethylindole on bromination in aqueous media yields much 2-hydroxymethyl-3-methylindole (**23**). The reaction scheme[19] below accounts for this, and other similar transformations are known in the indole series.

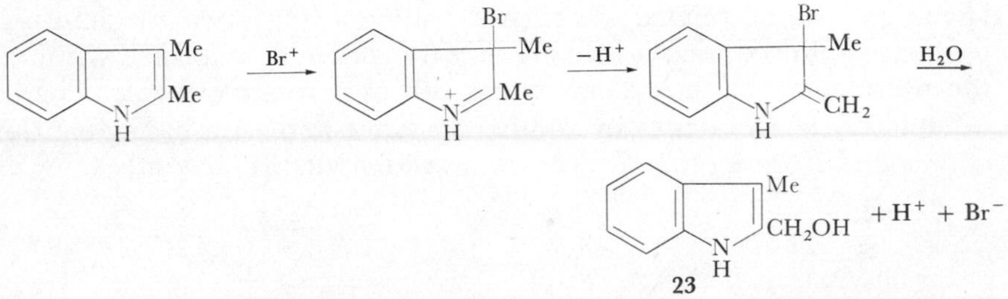

Gramine (**24**), obtained from indole with formaldehyde and dimethylamine by the Mannich reaction, forms a crystalline methiodide (**25**). The aliphatic amino groups of **24** and **25** can be displaced by suitable reagents as though they were halogen atoms. Syntheses of 3-indoleacetonitrile (**26**) and of tryptophan (**27**) are outlined. The nitrile is found in cabbages and other plants and on hydrolysis yields indole-3-acetic acid. This last is a plant growth hormone known as auxin, and it is also found in human urine.

Indole-3-carbaldehyde (**29**) is best obtained from indole using the N-dimethylformamide–phosphorus oxychloride technique so successful with pyrrole (p. 72). It can also be obtained, along with 3-chloroquinoline, from indole, chloroform, and alkali. This synthesis may proceed through the conversion of chloroform into dichlorocarbene which then combines with the indole anion (**28**) (cf. pyrrole, p. 73). Investigations of related reactions[20] suggest that two mechanistic paths are followed, and it is likely that the aldehyde is formed without the intermediacy of the cyclopropane (**30**). A derivative of an analogue of **30** has been isolated[21] in another instance and with base gave the corresponding quinoline. Indole-3-carbaldehyde (**31**) has only some of

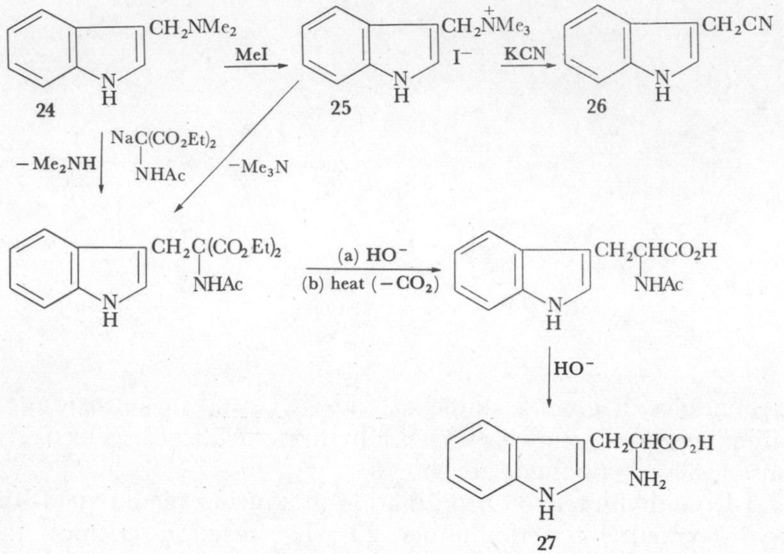

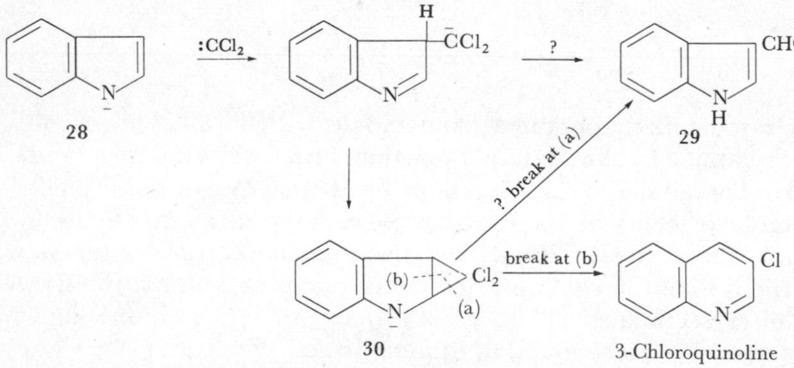

the properties of an aromatic aldehyde. Its low solubility in ether and its ultraviolet absorption spectrum show that the molecule is very zwitterionic in character, and it can be considered as a 'vinylogous amide'. The conclusion that structure **31a** is an important contributor to the resonance hybrid which represents the aldehyde is confirmed by recent infrared absorption spectrum studies.[22] It also agrees with the experimental observation[23] that a cyanohydrin is not formed from the aldehyde and hydrogen cyanide. Indole-3-carbaldehyde does not react under the ordinary conditions of the Cannizzaro reaction, although

$$
\begin{array}{ccc}
\text{31} & \longleftrightarrow & \text{31a}
\end{array}
$$

$$
\begin{array}{ccc}
\text{32} & \longleftrightarrow & \text{32a}
\end{array}
$$

1-methylindole-3-carbaldehyde undergoes the reaction normally. It therefore appears that the hydrogen atom at position 1 of indole-3-carbaldehyde is connected with the failure, and its removal under the strongly alkaline conditions would leave the resonant anion (**32–32a**) which could conceivably be too stable to undergo further transformation. Indole-3-carbaldehydes, perhaps for similar reasons, do not undergo the benzoin reaction.

Many indolecarboxylic acids have been prepared by Fischer's synthesis (p. 167). The 3-carboxylic acid, along with a small proportion of the 2-isomer, can also be obtained by heating the Grignard or potassium derivative of indole with carbon dioxide. Decarboxylation of these acids also occurs readily, the 3-carboxyl group being the more labile.

2. *Oxindole*

Oxindole (**33**) is a colourless solid, m.p. 126–127°, and has been obtained in a variety of ways, including the reduction of isatin and of 2-nitrophenylacetic acid. The most generally useful systhesis is outlined on the next page.

Oxindole under normal conditions is probably best represented as **33** owing to the resemblance of its ultraviolet absorption spectrum to those of its 1-methyl and 1,3,3-trimethyl derivatives. This conclusion is supported by infrared absorption spectrum studies.[24] Nevertheless, two moles of methane are evolved with methylmagnesium iodide. This is almost certainly due to a direct attack of the Grignard reagent on **33** giving the resonant dianion **34**. It is not necessary to postulate tautomerization of **33** to **35** before reaction with the Grignard reagent.

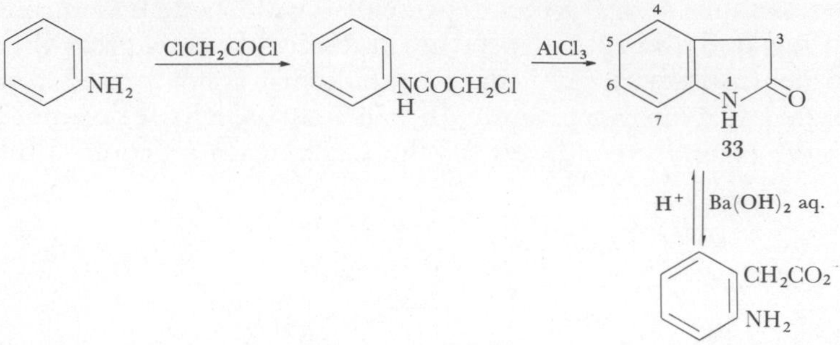

This is because conversion of **33** into **35** would involve the ionization of a proton from position 3, and Grignard reagents react with protons irrespective of their sources. The heterocyclic ring of oxindole is opened by barium hydroxide at 150°, giving barium 2-aminophenylacetate, but immediately closes again on acidification. Oxindole is nitrated at position 5, and possesses a reactive methylene group at position 3 which condenses with aldehydes, ketones, etc., in the usual way. It is weakly basic and forms a water-soluble hydrochloride. It also forms sodium and silver salts which with methyl iodide usually give *N*- and *O*-alkyl derivatives, respectively.

2-Ethoxyoxindole (**36**), obtained from oxindole with triethyloxonium fluoborate, possesses an N–H absorption band in the infrared. It is particularly interesting[25] as on sublimation it gives the isomeric indolenine (**37**), which shows no N–H absorption. Both compounds gave the same nuclear magnetic resonance spectrum in carbon tetrachloride where equilibrium is established. The ratio of **36**:**37** is about 1:1·5.

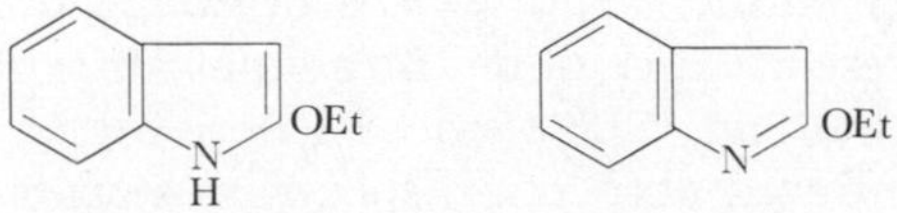

The oxidation of indoles by *N*-bromosuccinimide, or bromine, can lead to oxindoles and occasionally rearrangements occur as in the example given below.[26] An ester shift is not common.

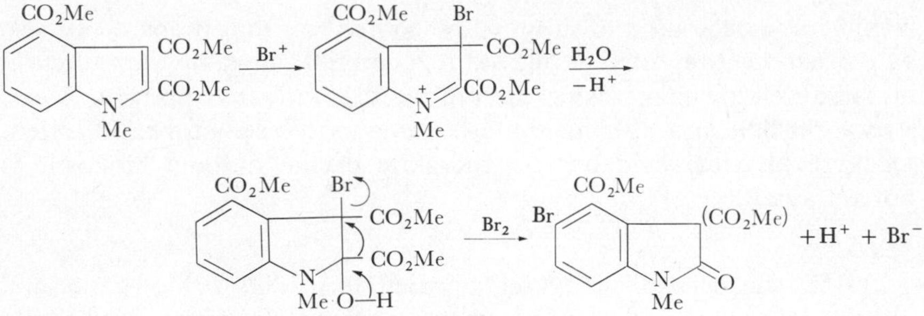

3. *Indoxyl*

Indoxyl (**38–39**) is an unstable yellow compound, m.p. 85°, which is very easily oxidized to the dyestuff indigo; the synthesis of indoxyl is considered with that of this dyestuff on p. 172.

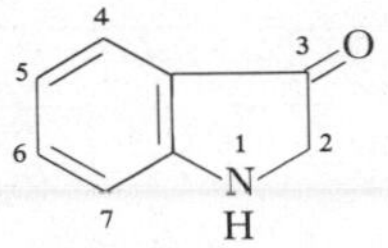

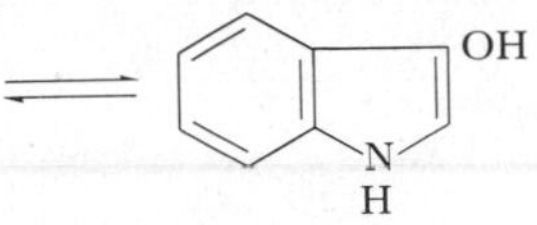

Indoxyl is soluble in alkali, gives a red ferric chloride colour, and is resinified by concentrated hydrochloric acid. This suggests it is in fact 3-hydroxyindole (**39**), and it does give indole on distillation with zinc dust. Indoxyl occurs as salts of the *O*-sulphate in human urine. Methylation of indoxyl with sodium carbonate and methyl sulphate gives 3-methoxyindole, but if methyl iodide is used 2,2-dimethylindoxyl is the product. Indoxyl also reacts at position 2 with benzenediazonium chloride, nitrous acid, nitrosobenzene, and many aldehydes and ketones in the presence of acetic acid. The product in the case of benzaldehyde is **40**, and compounds of this type are called indogenides. These last

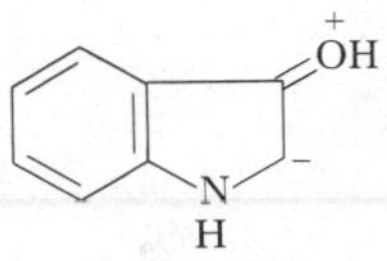

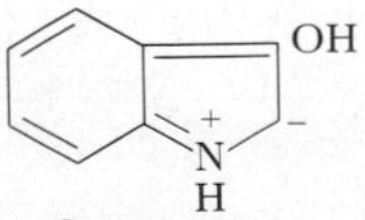

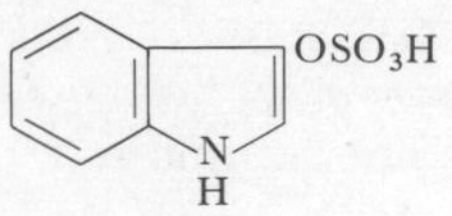

Indoxyl sulphate 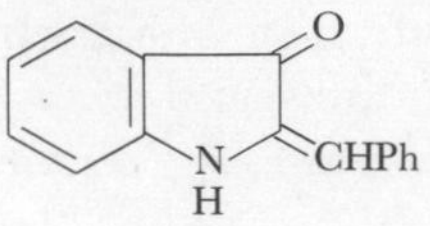   40

results have been used to support the contention that indoxyl can also be correctly represented as **38**, but it is equally plausible that reaction of the aldehyde takes place directly at the activated position 2 (see structures **39a** and **39b**) of the 3-hydroxyindole structure (**39**) cited. Decisive physical evidence on the state of the indoxyl molecule is not yet available.[27]

4. *Isatin*

Isatin (**41**) crystallizes in red needles, m.p. 200–201°. It was first obtained by the oxidation of indigo, and has been synthesized by many methods. The most widely used synthesis starts from aniline, and a useful synthesis of 1-substituted isatins involves oxalyl chloride.

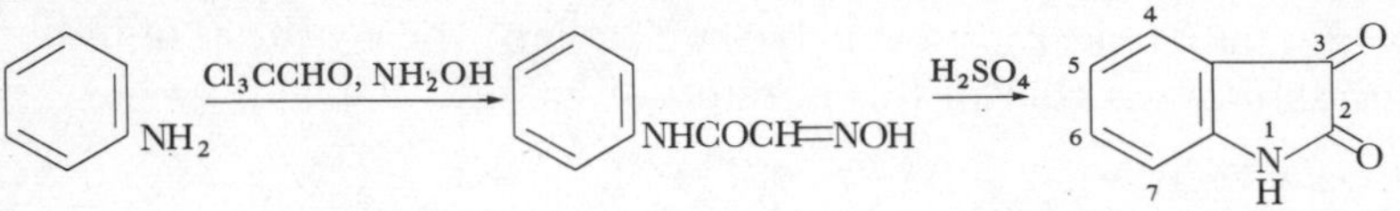

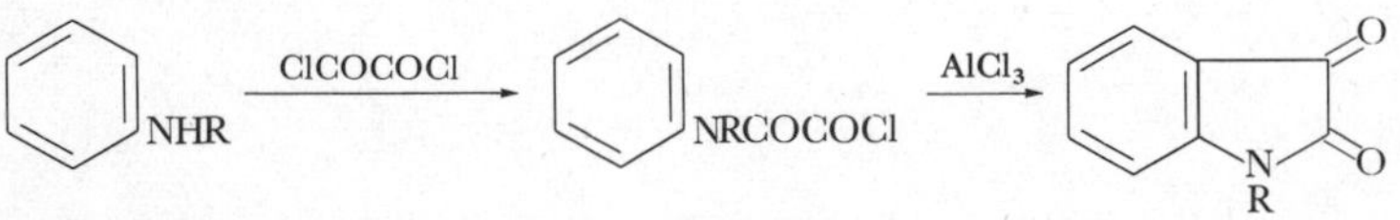

The structure of crystalline isatin has been determined by an x-ray examination which shows that it is predominantly in the lactam form. In solution, however, several ionic and molecular species can be present, depending on the hydrogen ion concentration, but the infrared absorption spectrum of a chloroform solution shows that under these conditions only the lactam form is present.[28]

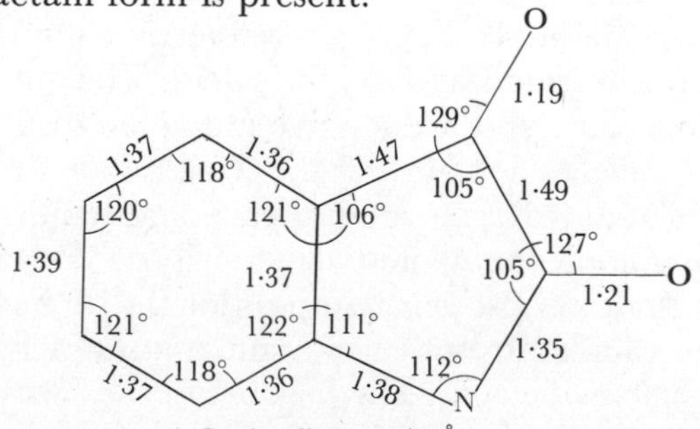

Isatin, distances in Å

Isatin is basic enough to dissolve in concentrated hydrochloric acid, and it forms a stable perchlorate. It also has an acidic hydrogen and forms sodium and silver salts. The alkylation of these gives 1-alkyl and 2-alkoxy derivatives respectively. The anion derived from isatin is

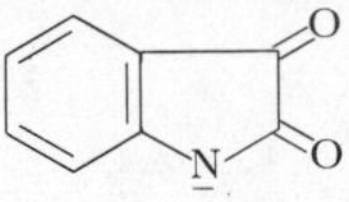

42 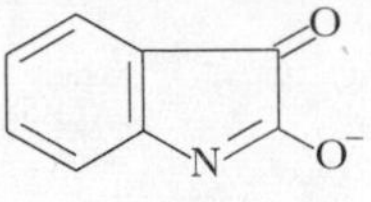   42a 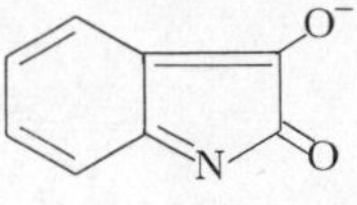   42b

therefore best represented as a resonance hybrid of **42** and **42a** with a very small contribution from the *ortho*-quinonoid **42b**.

The two carbonyl groups of isatin have widely differing properties. The one at position 3 is ketonic and undergoes typical reactions of ketones. For instance, with hydroxylamine it gives **43**, with acetone **44** or **45** is formed according to the conditions, and it undergoes the Reformatsky reaction normally. The indophenine reaction, which

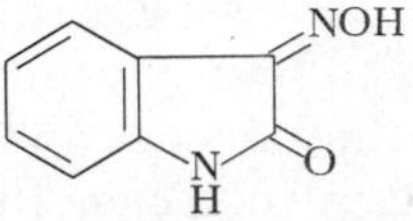

43 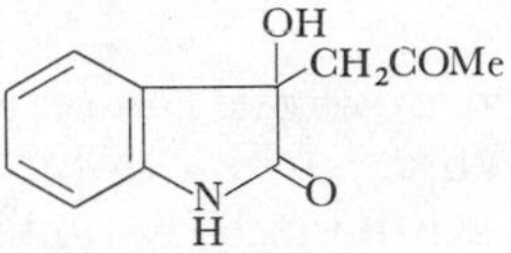   44 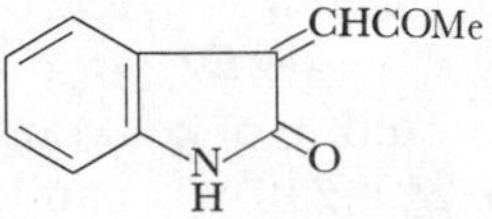   45

also involves condensation at position 3, is discussed on p. 125. Reduction by sodium dithionite or sodium amalgam in alkali gives dioxindole (**46**), while the amalgam in acid yields the expected pinacol, isatide (**47**). Dioxindole on further reduction with tin and hydrochloric acid gives oxindole itself. The carbonyl group at position 2 of isatin is similar to that of an amide in properties, and aqueous alkali opens

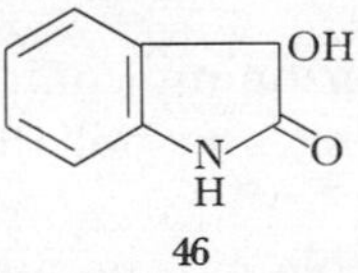

46 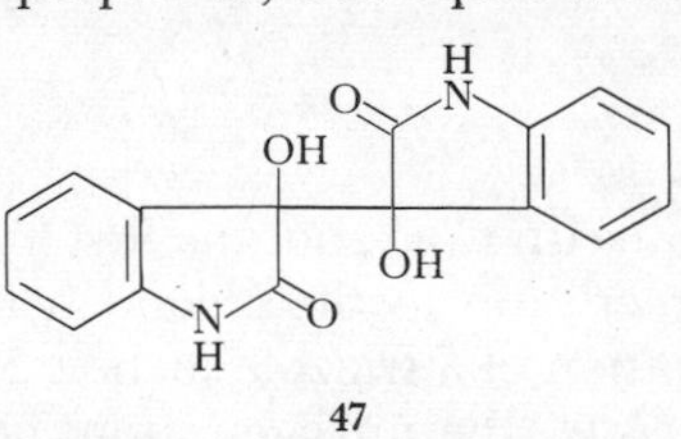   47

the ring to give sodium isatinate (**48**). Acidification immediately precipitates isatin. Sodium isatinate condenses with suitable ketones,

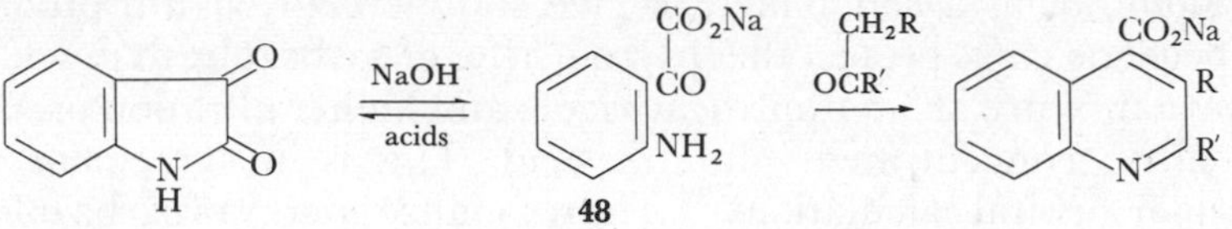

48

forming quinoline-4-carboxylic acids. This reaction has very general application and is named after its discoverer, Pfitzinger.

The oxidation of isatin with chromic acid gives isatoic anhydride (**49**), which is hydrolysed to anthranilic acid by dilute acid.

Anthranilic acid can also be obtained by direct oxidation.

1-Methylisatin 3-thiosemicarbazone appears to be an extremely valuable prophylactic agent against smallpox, and this is the first example of the prophylaxis of a virus disease by a synthetic chemical.[29]

5. *Carbazole*

Carbazole (**52**), or dibenzopyrrole, can be isolated from the anthracene fraction of coal tar. When pure it exhibits no fluorescence and has m.p. 245–246°. It can be synthesized by boiling 2-nitrodiphenyl with triethyl phosphite,[30] by the dehydrogenation of 1,2,3,4-tetrahydrocarbazole obtained via the Fischer indole synthesis from cyclohexanone phenylhydrazone, and from 2-aminodiphenylamine (**50**, R = H) as shown. When a substituent is present (e.g. **50**, R = alkyl) the

synthesis can still work, but the first formed diazonium compound may cyclize directly on to the second benzene ring and not through the prior formation of a triazole such as **51**.

Like pyrrole, the nitrogen atom of carbazole can be alkylated by alkyl halides in the presence of sodamide, and vinylated by acetylene in the presence of sodium hydroxide. N-Vinylcarbazole can be polymerized alone, or as a copolymer, to give commercially useful products. The benzene rings protect the 'pyrrole' ring of carbazole, so much that it gives a mixture of 3,6-dinitrocarbazole and higher nitration products with nitric–concentrated sulphuric acid. This is in agreement with molecular-orbital calculations.[31] The resonance energy of carbazole (74

1·002

1·017

1·004

N
H   1·015

π-Electron densities

kcal/mole) is only slightly greater than that of biphenyl (71 kcal/mole) or of two benzene molecules (2 × 36 kcal/mole).

E. Synthetic methods

A large number of methods of indole synthesis are available (see both books listed in the general bibliography, p. 186), but only the more important will be mentioned here.

(1) The most widely used synthesis of indole derivatives is due to Fischer,[32] and consists of heating ketone or aldehyde phenylhydrazones with anhydrous zinc chloride, boron trifluoride, polyphosphoric acid, or other acid catalysts. It should be particular noted that indole itself cannot be obtained from acetaldehyde phenylhydrazone by this

Me₂C

^{15}N ⟶ Me + ^{15}NH₃

N
H
53

method, although the synthesis is otherwise very general and can also be applied to the preparation of 1-alkyl- or 1-aryl-indoles. Indole has, however, been obtained by the decarboxylation of indole-2-carboxylic acid, prepared by cyclizing pyruvic acid phenylhydrazone. The mechanism of Fischer's synthesis has been the subject of much discussion, but that proposed by Robinson and Robinson is generally accepted. The position of the nitrogen atom which is eliminated has been established by tracer studies, but the way in which the hydrogen atoms move is not certain. It may be that the addition of a proton to the more basic nitrogen of **54** is the significant step, and that the sequence shown is

53 ⟶   H₂C
        CMe   H⁺   H₂C
      N—N   CMe
      H H   N—N⁺
                     H H₂

      54   55

H CH₂
   CMe −H⁺   Me   −NH₃   Me
N NH₂   N NH₂   N
H +   H   H

      56   57

followed. In particular cases intermediates analogous to structures **54**, **56**,[33] and **57**[34] have been detected.

Another possibility is the addition of protons to both nitrogen atoms of **54** followed by a 'benzidine' type of rearrangement to the indole. One difficulty, however, is that indoles can be obtained in good yield by heating suitable phenylhydrazones in an inert solvent, such as tetralin in the absence of acid, and even in the presence of a trace of alkali.[35] It is not impossible, however, that indole formation occurs by a different mechanism under these different conditions.

The Japp–Klingemann reaction provides a useful route to some of the phenylhydrazones required for the Fischer synthesis. This involves the attack of a diazonium salt on a β-keto acid or ester, under basic conditions.

$$MeCOCH(CH_2Ph)CO_2^- Na^+ \xrightarrow{PhN_2^+ Cl^-} MeCOC(CH_2Ph)=NNHPh + CO_2$$

$$MeCOCH(CH_2Ph)CO_2Et \xrightarrow{PhN_2^+ Cl^-} PhNHN=C(CH_2Ph)CO_2Et + MeCO_2H$$

The carboxyl or the acyl group of the β-keto compound is respectively eliminated with the formation of the hydrazone.

(2) The best modification of the Madelung synthesis involves the cyclization of a 2-acylaminotoluene with potassium *t*-butoxide. Indole

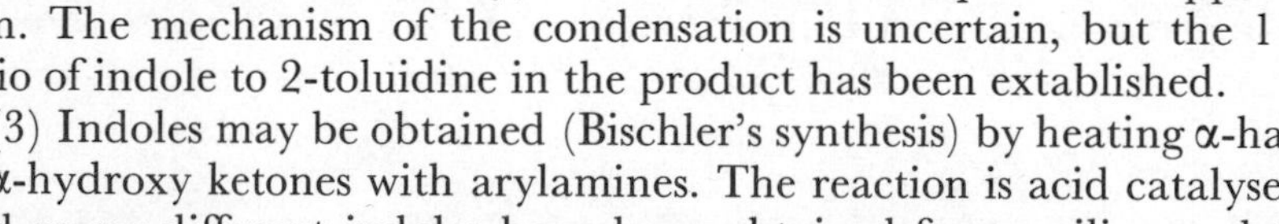

itself can be made in this way, and the reaction has quite wide application. The mechanism of the condensation is uncertain, but the 1:1 ratio of indole to 2-toluidine in the product has been extablished.

(3) Indoles may be obtained (Bischler's synthesis) by heating α-halo of α-hydroxy ketones with arylamines. The reaction is acid catalysed, and many different indoles have been obtained from aniline and *N*-methylaniline.

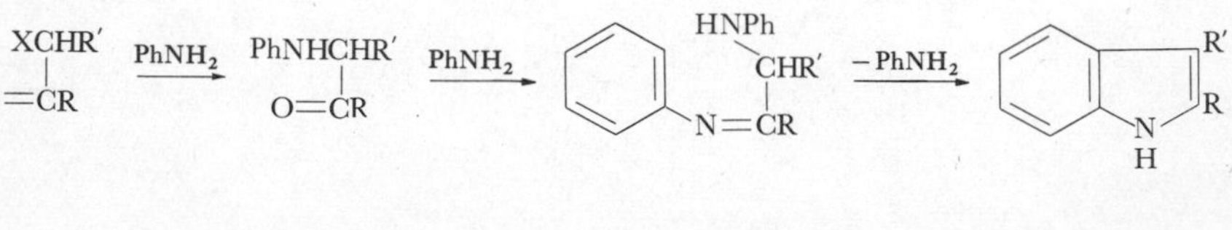

(4) The Reissert synthesis gives good results, but has been used less.

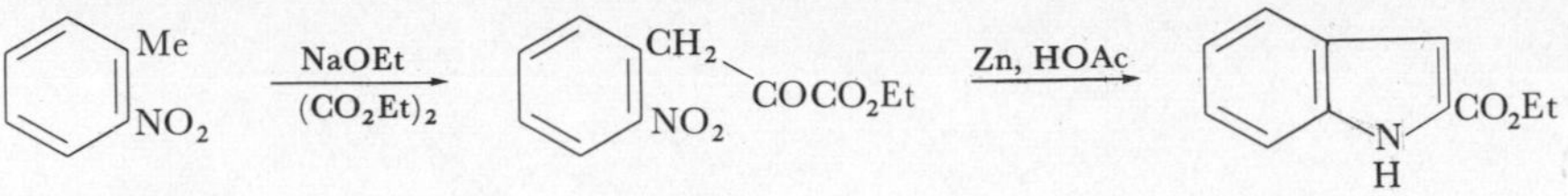

F. Natural occurrence and compounds of special interest

Indole itself occurs free in jasmines, orange blossoms, citrus fruit, etc. It is formed by the decomposition of tryptophan residues in proteins.

1. *Tryptophan*

L-Tryptophan (**59**) is a very widely distributed naturally occurring

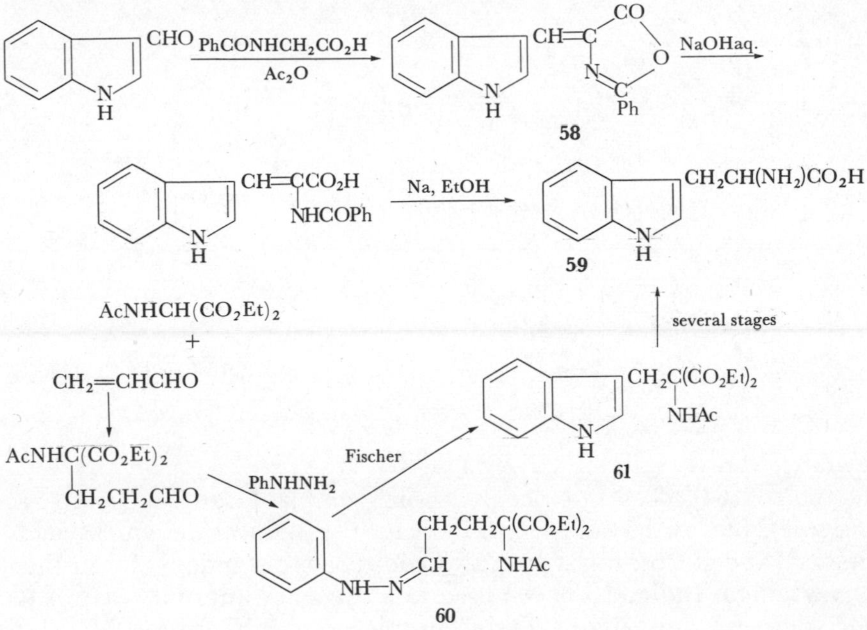

amino acid essential to man and many living organisms. It has been synthesized from indole-3-carbaldehyde through the oxazolone (**58**), from gramine (see p. 160), and by the cyclization of the phenyl-hydrazone **60**. This is achieved by Fischer's method, and the product (**61**) is one of the intermediates of the gramine synthesis and is similarly converted into tryptophan (p. 160). Another very convenient synthesis is from indole (p. 156). Resolution can be achieved by separating the brucine salts of acetyltryptophan.

The biosynthesis of tryptophan by a mould, *Neurospora crassa*, occurs by condensation of serine (**62**) with indole, and it has been shown

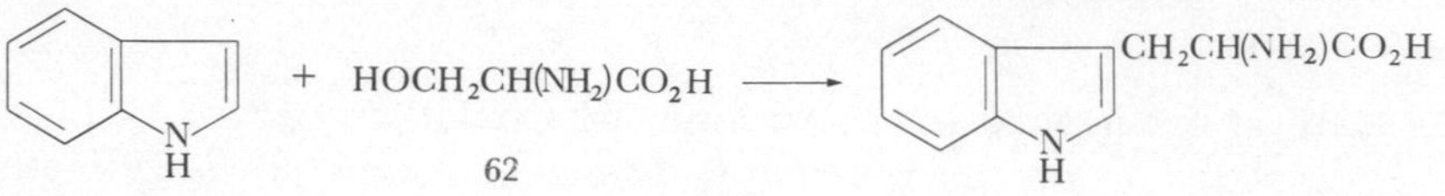

that anthranilic acid can be converted into indole microbiologically.[36] A possible chemical sequence is outlined, and the path of the aromatic carboxyl group has been followed by using a radioactive carbon atom.

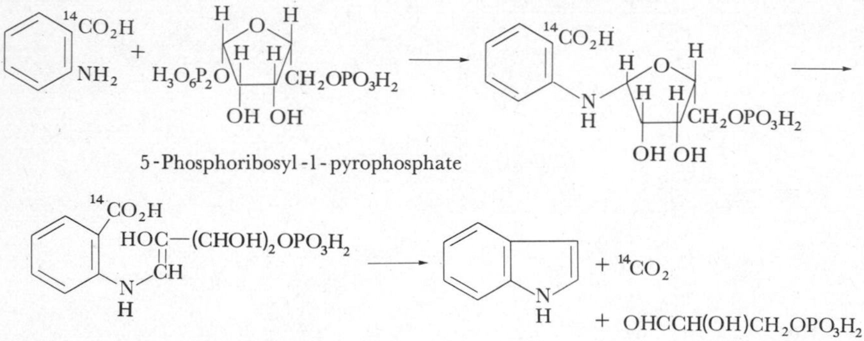

5-Phosphoribosyl-1-pyrophosphate

2. *Indigo*

Indigo (**64**) does not occur as such in plant sources (*Indigofera tinctoria*), but as the compound indican, the β-glucoside which yields indoxyl and glucose on hydrolysis. Oxidation of the indoxyl by air then gives indigo. Indigo has been used as a dye since antiquity, as has its 6,6′-dibromo derivative ('Tyrian purple') obtained from a Mediterranean mollusc. These bromine atoms are presumably introduced before the indigo system is synthesized in the snail, as the bromination of indigo itself yields the 5,5′-dibromo derivative. The *cis* structure for indigo (**63**) was put forward by Baeyer partly on the basis of its oxidation to isatin by nitric acid, chromic acid, and by other reagents. Robinson pointed out that the rings were more likely to be *trans* to each other, and this has been confirmed by x-ray measurements. Indigo is best considered as a resonance hybrid to which structures such as **64a** contribute; it is unlikely therefore that *cis*-indigo will

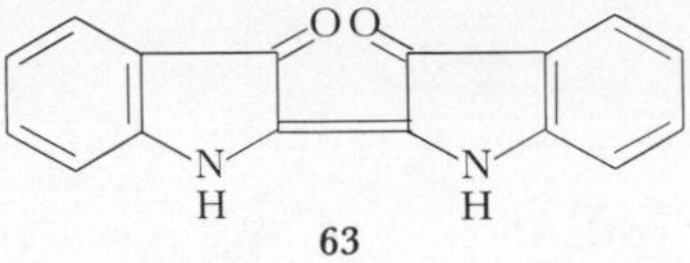

63 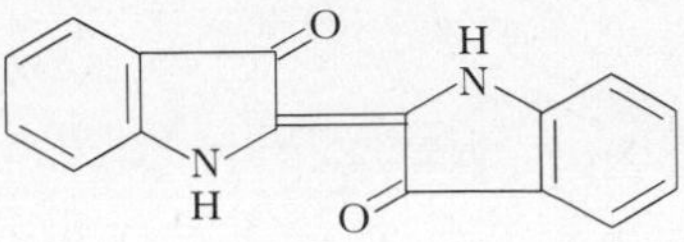   64

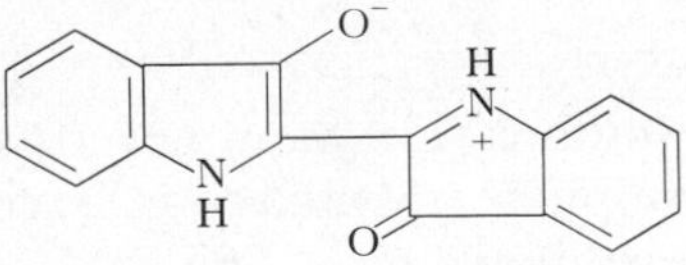

64a

have a separate existence, for if it did the resonance form corresponding to **64a** would have a big tendency to twist about the central single bond and decrease the distance between the opposite charges.

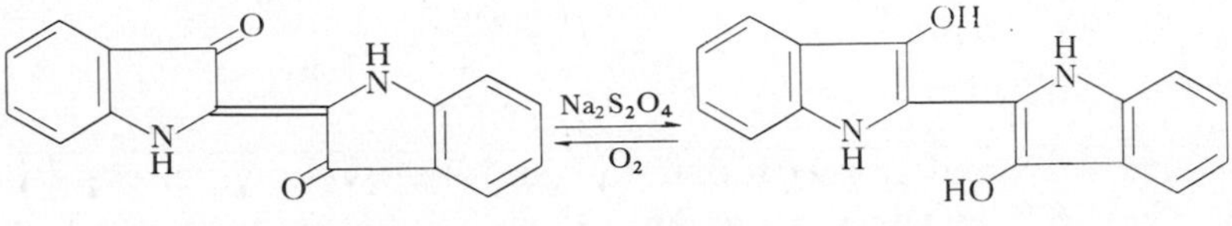

65

For dyeing purposes indigo is reduced to the yellow leucoindigo (**65**) by sodium hydrosulphite. The fabric is treated with a solution of leucoindigo in aqueous sodium carbonate, and then the indigo is regenerated by aerial oxidation.

Indigo was first synthesized by Baeyer. The second commercial synthesis, due to Heumann, is outlined below.

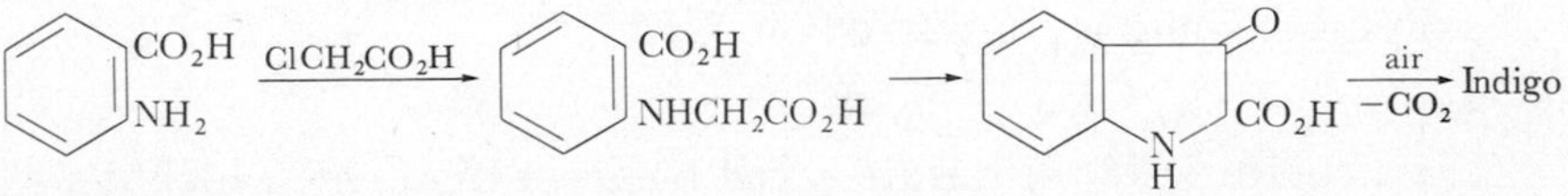

The crucial stage is the cyclization, and in recent years it has been found that phenylglycine itself can be cyclized to indoxyl at 120° by a mixture of sodamide and sodium and potassium hydroxides. The first sequence shown is used commercially, and the others have been investigated from this point of view. The indoxyl is oxidized to indigo by air under alkaline conditions. The Sandmeyer synthesis of indigo from aniline and carbon disulphide was used commercially for a short period. Another synthesis is mentioned on p. 265.

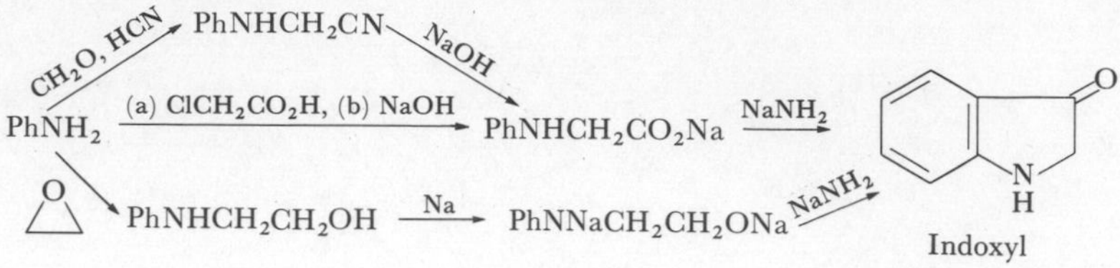

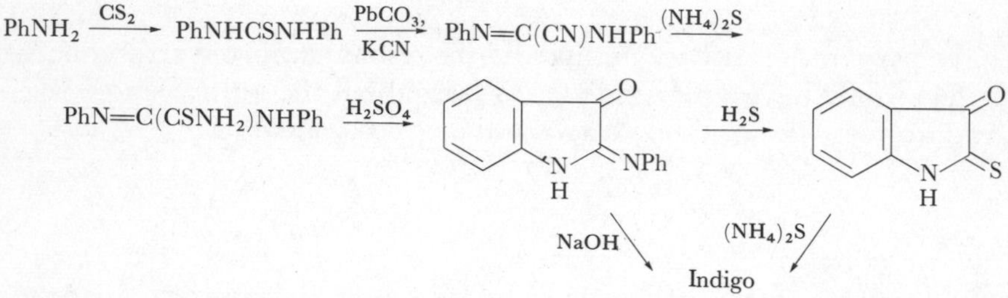

Isatin will condense with oxindole and indoxyl to give respectively isoindigo (**67**) and indirubin (**66**). These compounds are deep red in

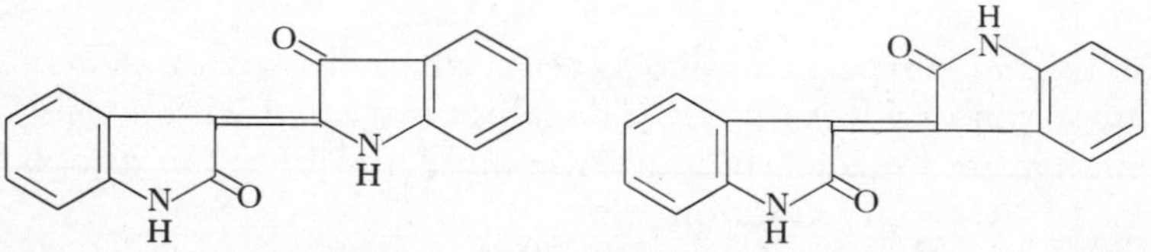

66	**67**

colour but are not of value as dyestuffs. Thioindigo is derived from thianaphthene and is considered on p. 185.

3. *Betanin*

The structure (**68**) of this deep red beetroot pigment, which defied investigators for many years, has now been elucidated[37] through the use of modern chromatographic and spectral techniques. Scission of the glucose residue yields betanidin (**69**), which is obtained along with its epimer at $C_{(15)}$, isobetanidin. Treating betanidin with *S*-proline and base gave indicaxanthin (**70**), a yellow pigment present in certain cacti.[38]

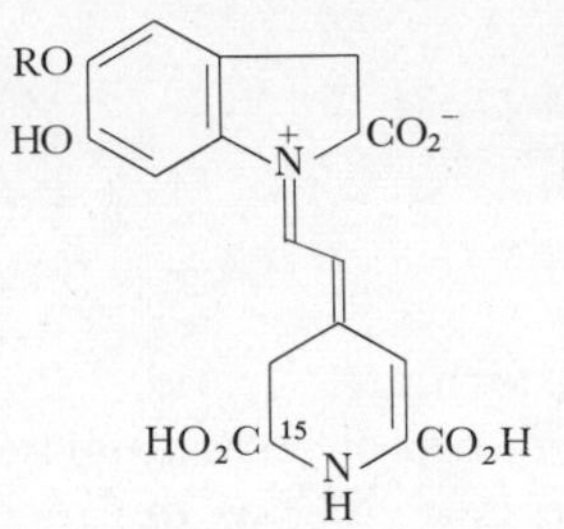

68, R = 1-β-glucopyranoside   **70**
69, R = H

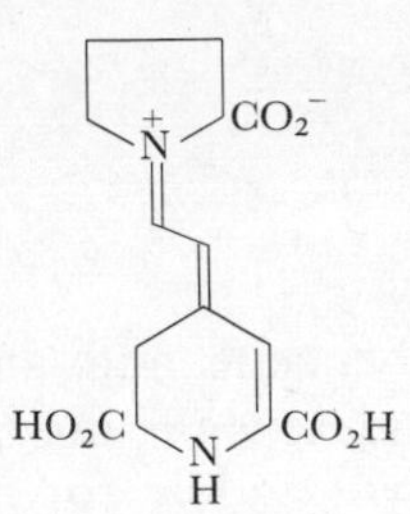

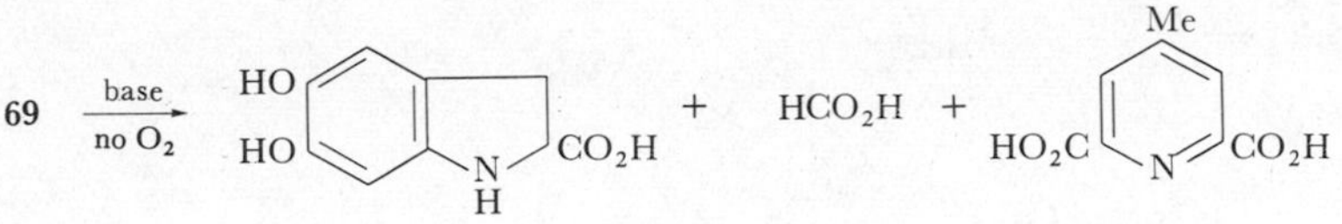

2. ISOINDOLES

Isoindole (**1**) has been prepared[30a] in solution and isolated as the maleic anhydride adduct (cf. **7**). The more important charged resonance structures are expected to be **1a** and **1b** in conformity with molecular-orbital calculations,[31] and tautomerism involving iso-indolenine (**2**) also anticipated.

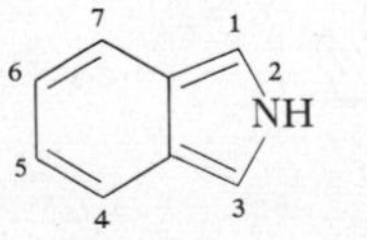

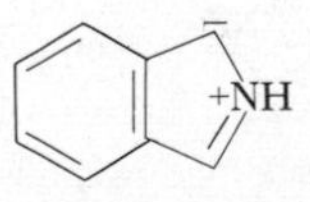

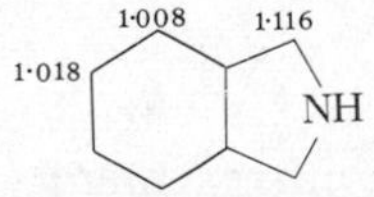

π-Electron densities of isoindole

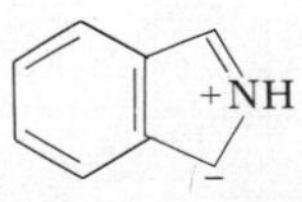

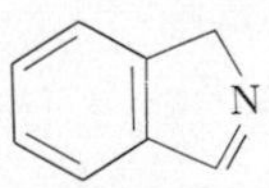

1-Phenylisoindole has been synthesized[39] and exists as a tautomeric mixture of **3** with 9% of **4** in deuterochloroform solution. The third possible tautomer was not detected. It gave a blue colour with Ehrlich's reagent and resinified with acid or on exposure to air, reactions typical of isoindoles. 1,3-Diphenylisoindole is readily available from 1,2-

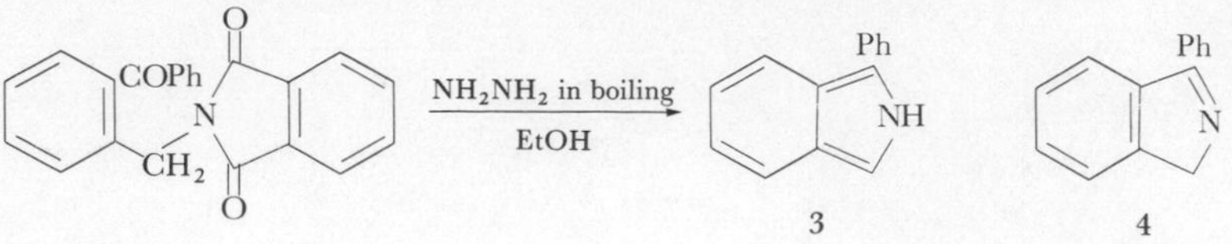

dibenzoylbenzene and ammonium formate,[40] and 1,2-diphenyldi-hydroisoindole is the product of a remarkable rearrangement (p. 15).

2-Methylisoindole (6) has been prepared[41] as outlined, and is a colourless crystalline solid, m.p. 90–91°, which does not react with methyl iodide. On catalytic hydrogenation it gives 2-methyl-1,3-

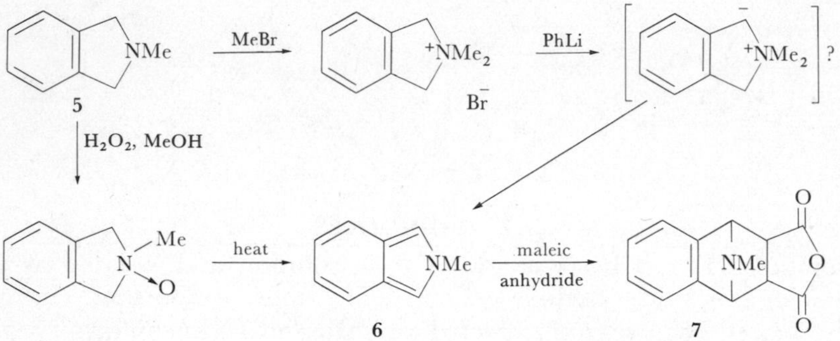

dihydroisoindole (5) and with maleic anhydride the adduct 7 is

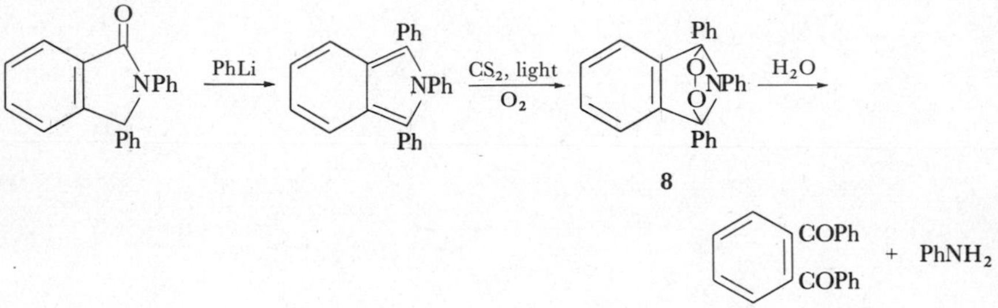

formed. In a similar way triphenylisoindole forms a peroxide (8) which breaks down on treatment with water.[42]

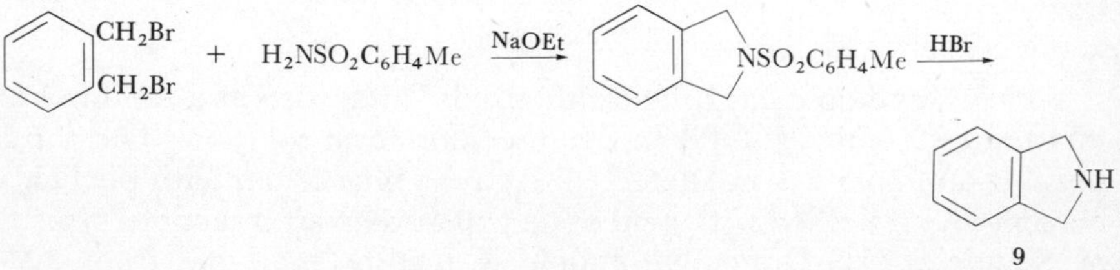

Dihydroisoindole (**9**) is easily prepared.[43] It has the properties of a typical secondary amine.

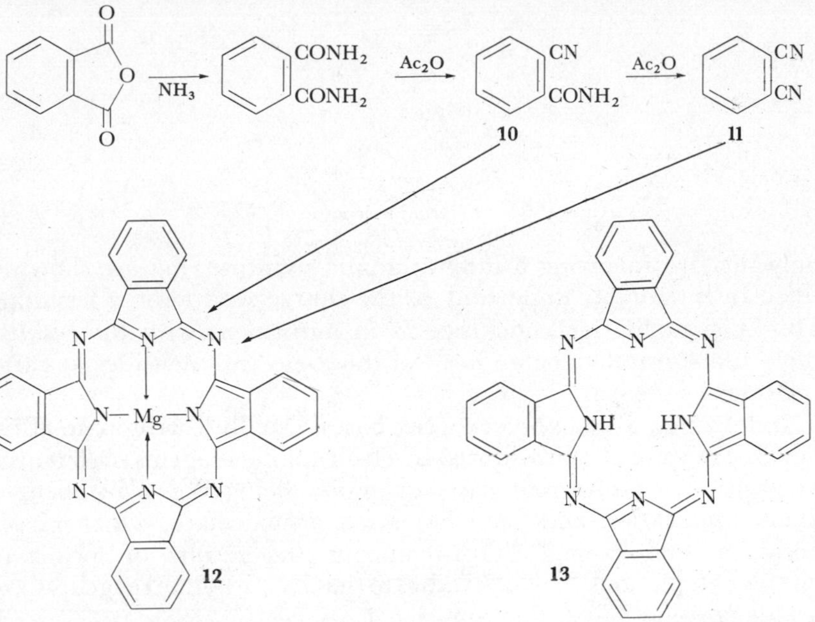

The phthalocyanines are by far the most valuable derivatives of isoindole and are extremely stable blue dyestuffs. Phthalocyanin itself (**13**) can be obtained by heating phthalonitrile (**11**) or 2-cyano-benzamide (**10**) with magnesium oxide. The bright blue magnesium derivative (**12**) is formed and is converted into free phthalocyanin (**13**) by concentrated sulphuric acid at $-3°$. The phthalocyanin ring system is very similar to that of porphyrin and is remarkably stable. It is, however, broken down by hot concentrated sulphuric acid to phthalimide and phthalic acid. A number of metal derivatives of phthalocyanin are known, and of these copper phthalocyanin is particularly stable and can be sublimed unchanged at ca. 580° *in vacuo*. It is unaffected by boiling hydrochloric acid or molten potassium hydroxide and is precipitated unchanged from its sulphuric acid solution by water.

3. INDOLIZINE AND CYCLAZINE

Indolizine (**1**), previously called pyrrocoline, is isoelectronic with indole. A number of charged resonance structures can be written, but

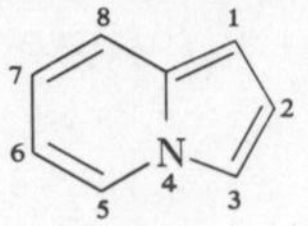

1 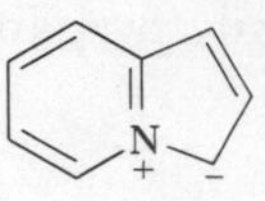   1a 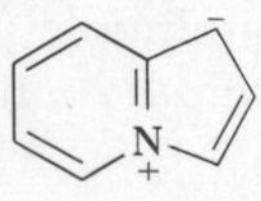   1b

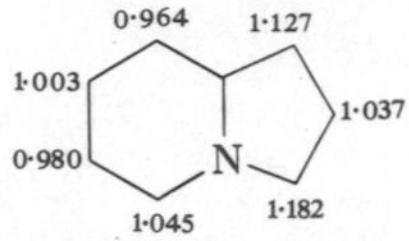

π -Electron densities

only the two involving a fully aromatic pyridine ring are shown. Of these **1a** is the more important, as the charge separation is less than in **1b**. This qualitative conclusion is in agreement with the results of molecular-orbital calculations[44] of the π-electron densities at various positions in the ring.

Indolizines, although very weak bases, usually[45] protonate at position 3. They are also substituted by electrophilic reagents preferentially at position 3 with great ease, examples being the 4-nitrobenzenediazonium cation and even hot ethyl acetoacetate, which gives 3-acetoacetylindolizine.[46] This confirms the results of localization energy calculations,[47] which indicate that electrophilic reagents should attack position 3 first, then position 1.

Indolizine is a colourless solid, m.p. 74°, with a blue fluorescence and an odour resembling naphthalene. It can be synthesized[48] from **2** in 35% overall yield. Another synthesis starts from 2-methylpyridine, and this type of cyclization has been used widely for the preparation of indolizines.[49] Indolizine-1- and -3-carboxylic acids decarboxylate just above their melting points.

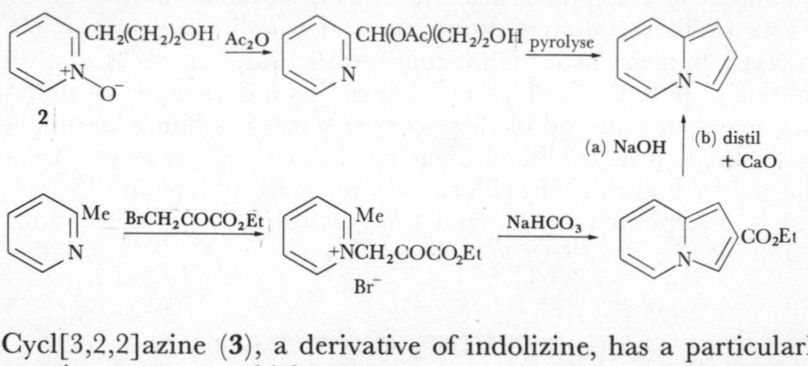

Cycl[3,2,2]azine (**3**), a derivative of indolizine, has a particularly interesting structure which possesses ten π-electrons and conforms to Hückel's rule. It was first prepared[50] as outlined, and is a stable yellow aromatic compound of m.p. 64°. It protonates,[51,52] nitrates, and acetylates under Friedel–Crafts conditions[53] at position 1 in accordance with the results of localization-energy calculations.[50] Nuclear magnetic resonance studies show that the molecule can sustain a large ring current.[52,54]

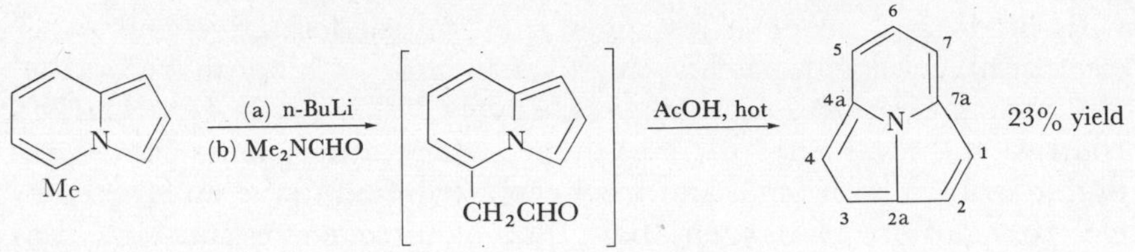

4. BENZOFURAN

A. General properties

Benzofuran (**1**), sometimes called coumarone, is a colourless liquid b.p. 173° which may be isolated from coal tar. Its structure has not been investigated in detail, but it has aromatic properties and is best treated as a resonance hybrid to which **1** is the major contributor; minor contributions are made by charged structures such as **1a** and **1b**. Benzofuran is much more stable to chemical attack than furan.

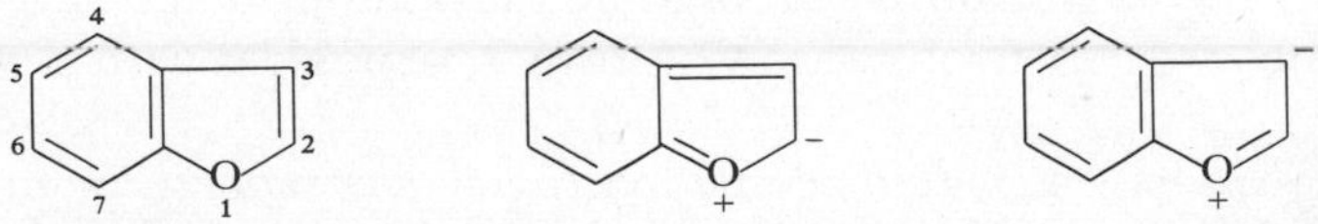

The heterocyclic ring of benzofuran is much less easily opened than that of furan, but it can be split by the two routes outlined. Although

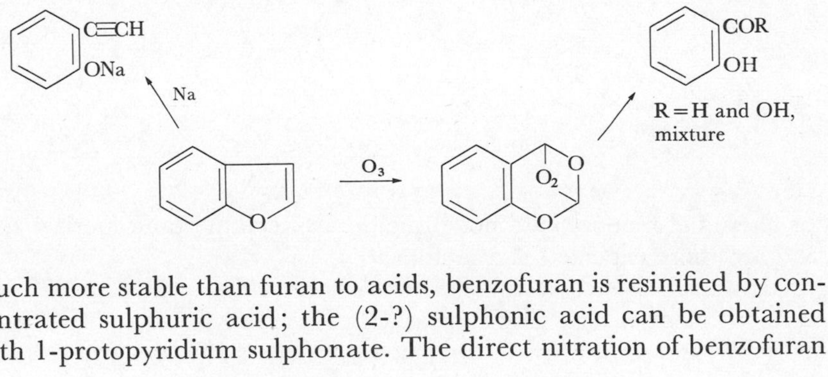

much more stable than furan to acids, benzofuran is resinified by concentrated sulphuric acid; the (2-?) sulphonic acid can be obtained with 1-protopyridium sulphonate. The direct nitration of benzofuran with nitric and acetic acids gives the 2-nitro derivative and other electrophilic reagents, such as acetic anhydride with boron trifluoride, also attack position 2 virtually exclusively.[55] This is in very marked contrast to indole and thianaphthene, where attack takes place predominantly at position 3, and has been attributed to the much greater electronegativity of oxygen than that of nitrogen or sulphur. Proceeding further, and rather naively, if the electrons of the oxygen atom did not take part in the reaction with the electrophilic reagent, then the benzofuran could be treated as styrene. The formation of addition pro-

X = Cl or Br   2

ducts, as occurs readily with bromine and chlorine, is then expected and the addition of the electrophilic nitronium cation would occur at the position, in this case position 2, which would give the more stabilized cation (**2**). Why the electronegativity of the oxygen should be the controlling factor, if in fact it is so, in the case of benzofuran is not clear, but it may be that the bonding of the oxygen in the heterocyclic ring is not comparable as regards resonance to the bonding of the oxygen atom of anisole. Some benzofurans even form 2,3-epoxides with perbenzoic acid.[56]

Benzofuran is easily reduced by hydrogen over palladium, or sodium and alcohol to the 2,3-dihydro derivative, which is also known as coumaran. Coumaran behaves as a typical aryl alkyl ether and is dehydrogenated by sulphur to benzofuran.

Coumaran-2-one (**3**) is the lactone of 2-hydroxyphenylacetic acid.

3   4

Its chemical reactions do not indicate appreciable tautomerism to **4**, and are those expected of a lactone.

Coumaran-3-one is a stable colourless crystalline solid, m.p. 97°. The same problems of structure arise as with 3-hydroxyfuran and two tautomeric (**5** and **7**) and a number of resonance structures are possible.

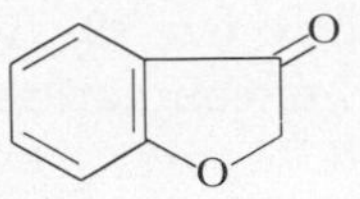

Coumaran-3-one appears to exist entirely in the keto form (5) according to bromine titration, and it is a strong reducing agent. The carbonyl group behaves normally towards hydroxylamine, and the methylene group is sufficiently reactive to condense with benzaldehyde in the presence of hydrochloric acid. Coumaran-3-one with methyl sulphate and acetic anhydride gives 3-methoxy- and 3-acetoxy-benzofuran, respectively. This does not provide evidence for the tautomerization of 5 to 7 as the conjugate anion (6) and cation (8) are the same for both of these structures and are probably the reacting species.

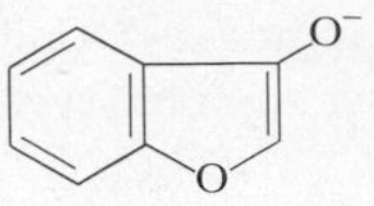

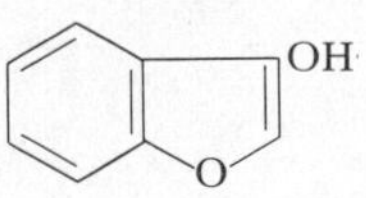

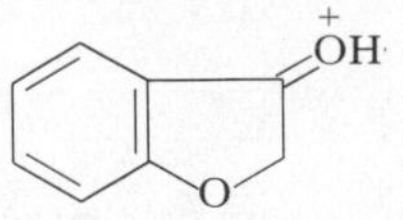

B. Synthetic methods

(1) A useful laboratory synthesis starts with coumarin, and is generally applicable.

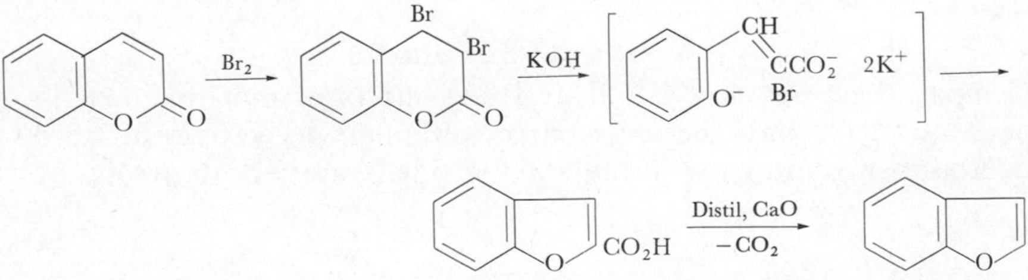

(2) An internal Claisen reaction may be used to bring about ring closure. When the sodium derivative of ethyl salicylate is used the

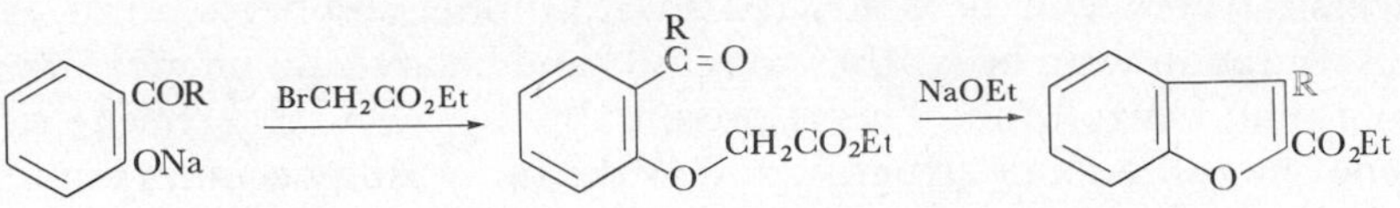

product is ethyl coumaran-3-one-2-carboxylate (**9**), which can be decarboxylated giving the best synthesis[57] of coumaran-3-one (**10**).

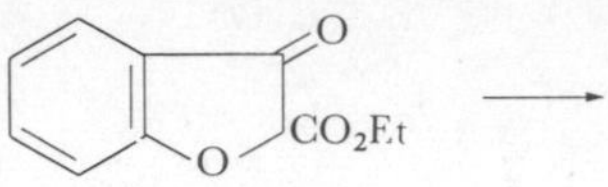

5.   DIBENZOFURAN

Dibenzofuran, or diphenylene oxide (**1**), is made in 20% yield by the pyrolysis of phenol over lead oxide. It is very much more stable to acids than benzofuran, it is very resistant to ether-cleaving agents, and with chlorosulphonic acid it yields the 2-sulphonic acid followed by the 2,8-disulphonic acid. Halogenation also takes place at these positions.

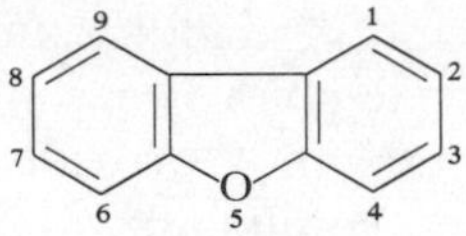

Nitration in acetic anhydride[58] gives a mixture of the 1-, 2-, and 3-nitro derivatives in $1:2:2$ ratio. The free radical $\cdot CH_2CO_2H$ attacks the 1-, 2-, 3-, and 4-positions in 53, 0, 15, and 32% ratio, respectively,[59] in agreement with localization-energy calculations.[59] Reaction with butyllithium occurs at position 4, giving the 4-lithium derivative.

6.   ISOBENZOFURANS

Comparatively few alkyl and aryl derivatives of the unknown isobenzofuran (**1**) have been prepared, although derivatives of 1,3-dihydroisobenzofuran (e.g. phthalic anhydride, **3**) are very numerous. The

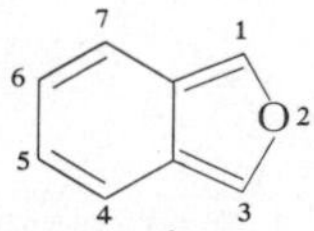

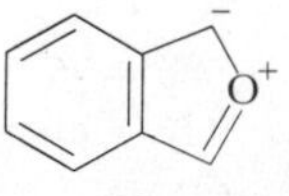

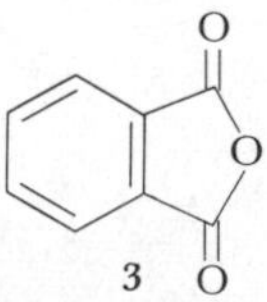

discussion here will be restricted to 1,3-diphenylisobenzofuran (**4**). This compound can be synthesized easily and behaves much more like a furan than benzofuran. This is presumably because the benzene ring cannot have a Kekulé structure unless the furan ring becomes ionic in character due to a high proportion of charged resonance forms such as

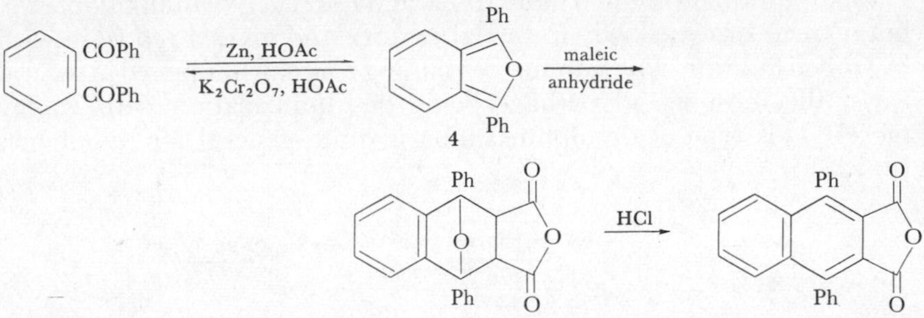

2. The ring is therefore easily opened and reacts easily with dienophiles.

7.   THIANAPHTHENE AND RELATED COMPOUNDS

A. Physical properties and structure

Thianaphthene (**1**), also known as benzothiophene, was first obtained by a difficult synthesis in 1893, and in 1902 it was isolated from coal tar. It is the major sulphur-containing impurity in technical naphthalene.

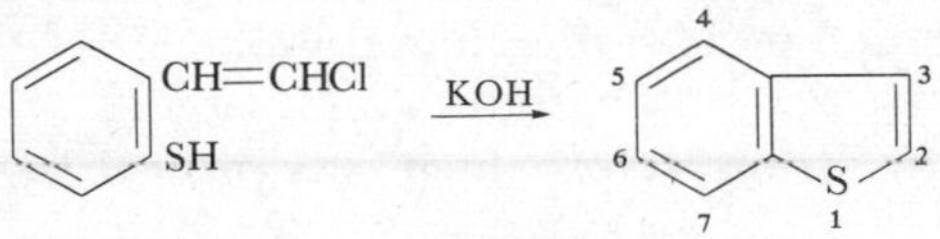

Thianaphthene itself has little commercial value, but derivatives in the form of thioindigo dyes have great value and have been much investigated.

Thianaphthene is a colourless solid, m.p. 32°, b.p. 220–221°, and has a dipole moment of 0·62 D. Its structure has not been investigated by physical means, but chemical properties indicate that it is best represented as a resonance hybrid of **1** and the charged structures **1a**, **1b**, and **1c** in order of decreasing importance.

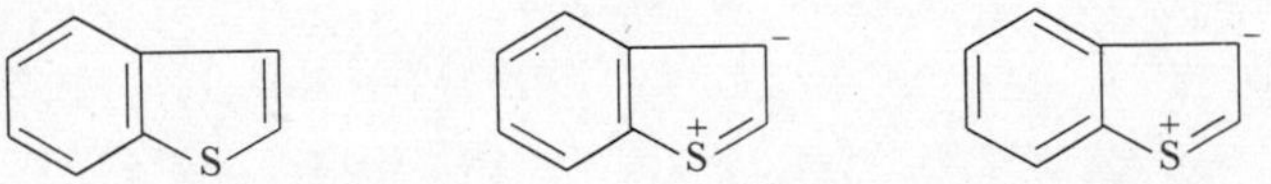

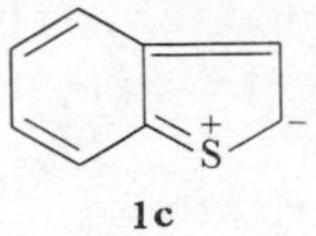

B. Chemical properties and derivatives

Thianaphthene is much more stable and less reactive than thiophene, but it turns brown slowly in the laboratory and gives a red resin with hydrogen fluoride. The sulphur-containing ring can be opened in several ways, the most useful perhaps being desulphurization with Raney nickel. This type of desulphurization is quite general for thiophenes (p. 128).

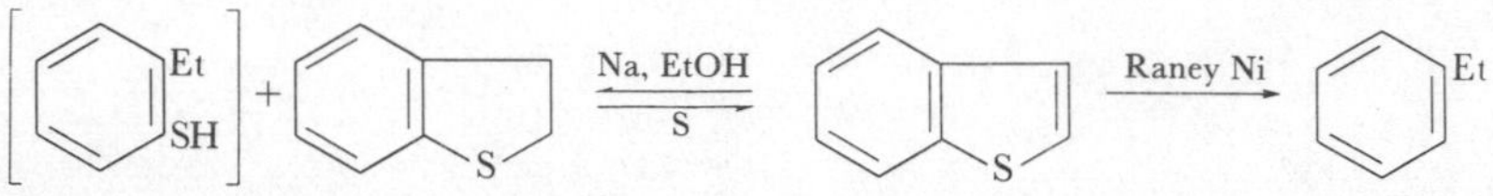

Thianaphthene does not react with methyl iodide, but with hydrogen peroxide (30%) in refluxing acetic acid yields a 1,1-dioxide, or sulphone (2).

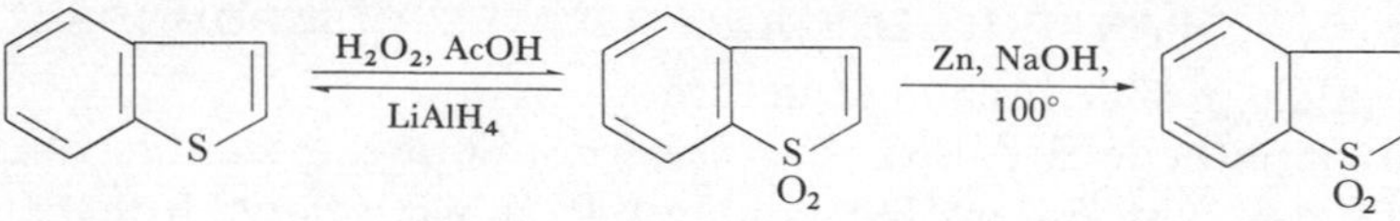

2

This dioxide is much more stable than thiophene 1,1-dioxide. It undergoes a Diels–Alder reaction with itself only at 220°. Sulphur dioxide is lost, giving 3, the structure of which was proved by conversion to 4.

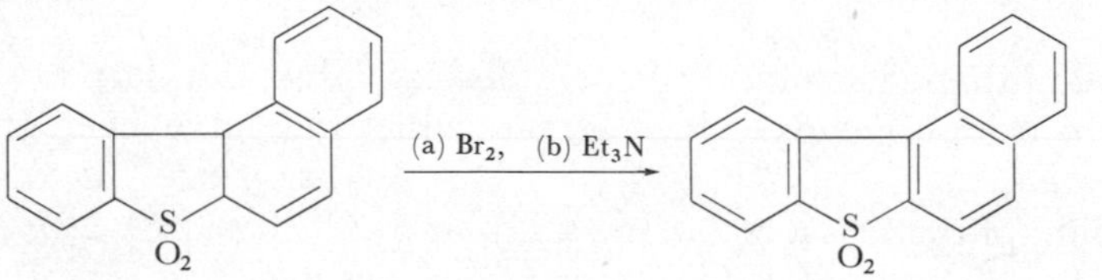

3

(a) Br$_2$,   (b) Et$_3$N

4

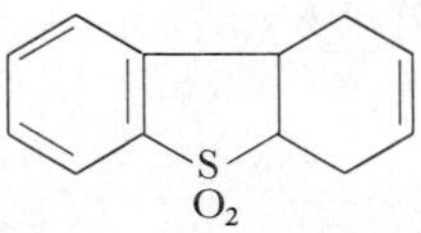

5

Thianaphthene 1,1-dioxide also yields 5 with butadiene. The 2,3-double bond of the 1,1-dioxide (2) has the very interesting property of adding thiophenol in different directions according to whether ionic or free radical catalysis is employed.[60] The nitration of thianaphthene 1,1-dioxide gives the 6-nitro derivative.

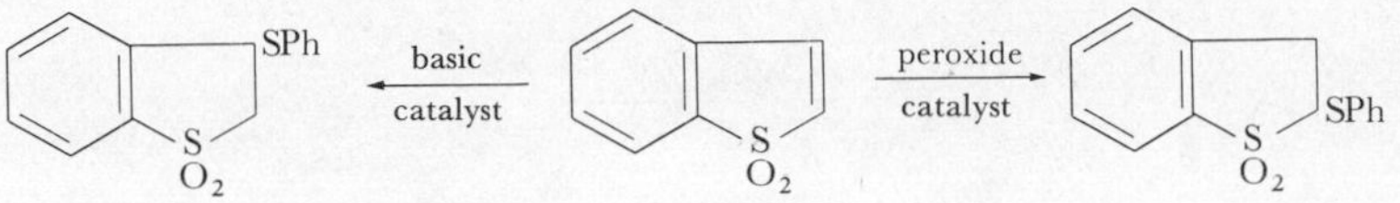

2

The sulphonation, bromination (with *N*-bromosuccinimide), chloro-methylation, acylation (Friedel–Crafts), and nitration of thianaphthene take place predominantly at position 3. 3-Nitrothianaphthene cannot be isolated from the last reaction in good yield, as it self-condenses to a dimer. 3-Aminothianaphthene, obtained from the 3-nitro compound by reduction, is not stable enough to be isolated in the pure state, and is usually prepared as a derivative. The isopropylation of thianaphthene, remarkably enough, takes place[61] mostly at position 2.

The direct metallation of thianaphthene with sodium, or butyl-lithium, takes place at position 2, and carbonation gives thianaphthene-

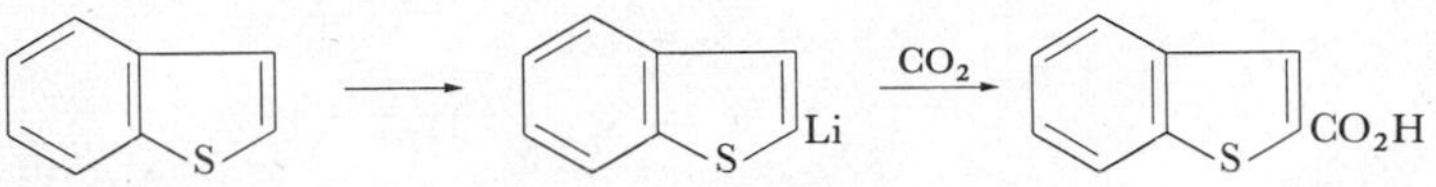

6

2-carboxylic acid (6). Thianaphthene, like benzene, reacts with ethyl diazoacetate.[62]

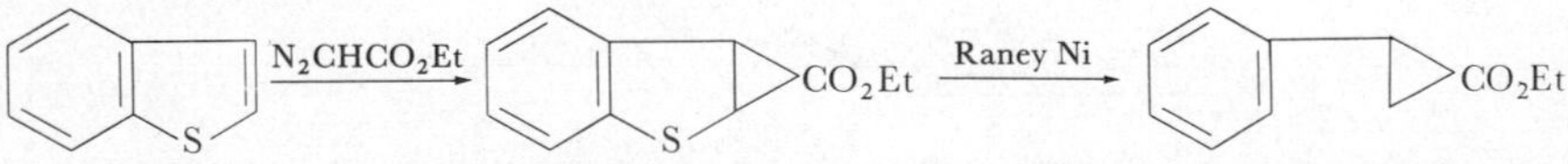

5-Hydroxythianaphthene is of special interest, as on bromination[63] it yields 7. By analogy with 2-naphthol, bromination only at position 4

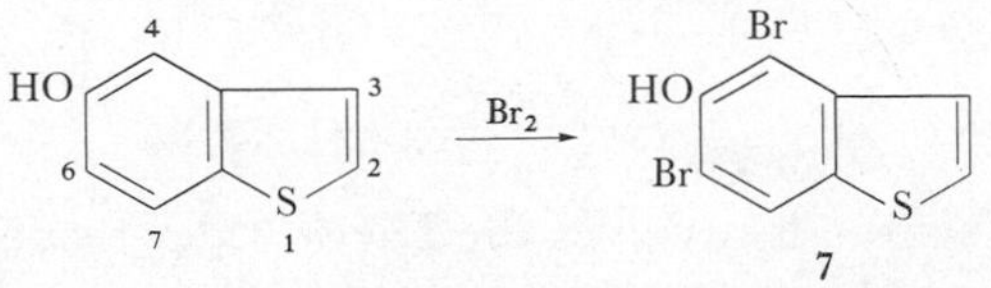

7

would be expected, and the result shows the lesser effect of fusing a thiophene ring, in comparison with a benzene ring, on to the phenol system.

Dibenzothiophene (8) can be obtained[65] from diphenyl, and has m.p. 99–100°. Oxidation with hydrogen peroxide in acetic acid first gives the 5-oxide, followed by the 5,5-dioxide. Both these compounds are reduced to dibenzothiophene by lithium aluminium hydride. Electrophilic reagents attack positions 2 and 8 of dibenzothiophene as might be expected, and metallation usually takes place at position 4. Phenyl radicals, from benzoyl peroxide, attack positions 1, 2, 3, and 4 in approximately 3 : 1 : 2 : 3 ratio.[64]

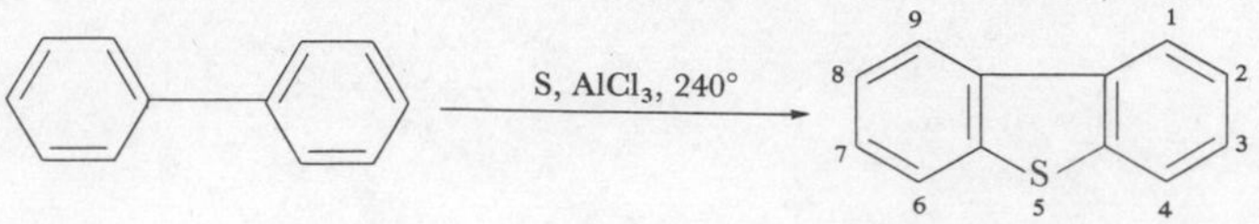

C. Synthetic methods[65]

(1) Thianaphthene is available commercially and is possibly prepared from ethylbenzene in the vapour phase. It can also be obtained in 71% yield from thiophenol and acetylene at 600–650°.

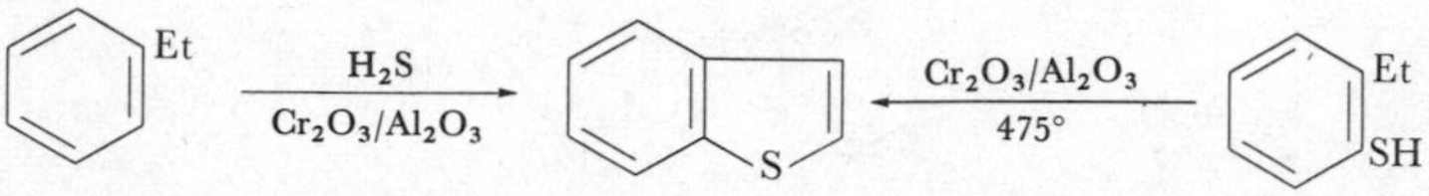

(2) The best method[65] of synthesising thianaphthenes is shown; other routes similar to those for benzofurans (p. 179 (2)) have been used.

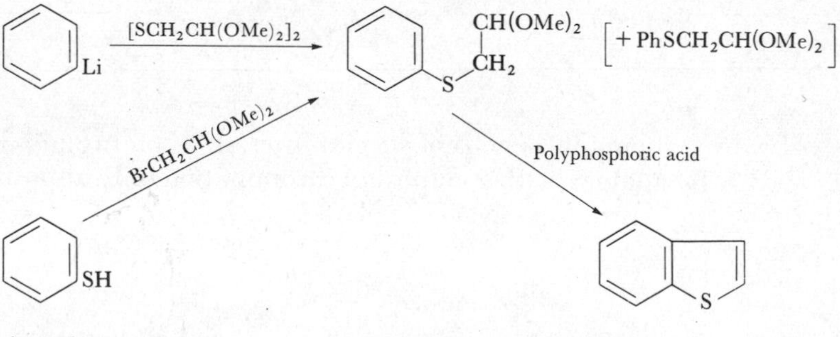

(3) Another synthesis involves the Diels–Alder reaction.

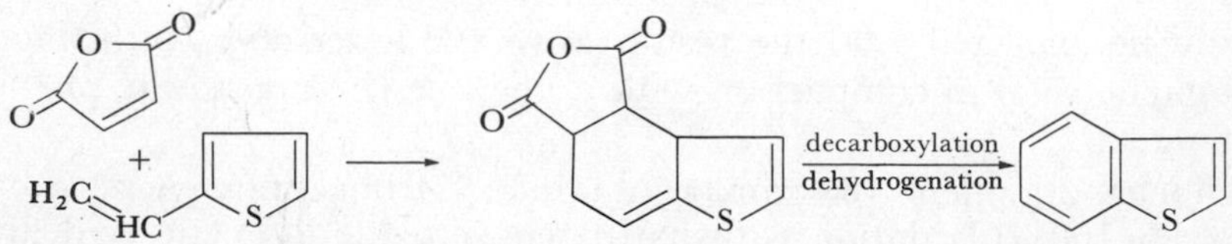

D. Isothianaphthene

Benzo[c]thiophene (**9**), or isothianaphthene, has an odour like that of naphthalene and is stable at $-30°$ under nitrogen for only one day. With maleic anhydride it gives the expected adduct (**10**), which is desulphurized to a naphthalene (**11**) by sodium hydroxide.[66]

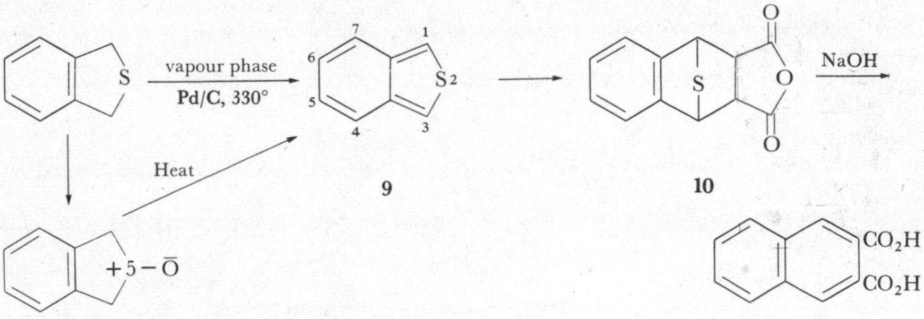

E. Compounds of special interest

Thioindigo (**13**), which has been shown by x-ray measurements to have the *trans* structure, is of special interest as many of its derivatives are valuable fast dyestuffs varying in colour from yellow-orange to violet-black. Two and a half million pounds of thioindigo dyes were sold in the United States in 1958. For a full discussion of the immense amount of work on this subject the reader is referred to Hartough and Meisel's monograph on condensed thiophenes (see general bibliography).

Thioindigo itself is obtainable by the mild oxidation of the sulphur analogue of indoxyl (**12**), sometimes called 3-hydroxythianaphthene.

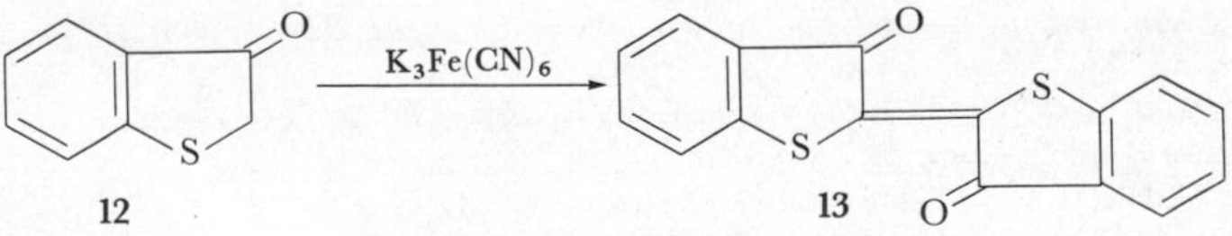

Asymmetrical thioindigos can also be made (X = O or NH, or S when the two benzene rings have different substituents), as can analogues of

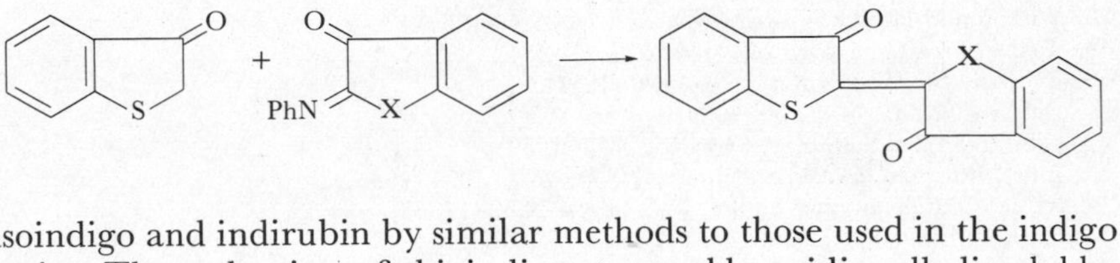

isoindigo and indirubin by similar methods to those used in the indigo series. The reduction of thioindigos to weakly acidic, alkali soluble, colourless dihydro compounds by sodium hydrosulphite in the dyeing vat, followed by aerial oxidation on the fibre, constitutes the dyeing process, as in the case of indigo dyes.

GENERAL BIBLIOGRAPHY

INDOLE

Sumpter and Miller, *Heterocyclic Compounds with Indole and Carbazole Systems*, Interscience, New York, 1954.

Julian, Meyer, and Printy, in *Heterocyclic Compounds*, Vol. III, ed. Elderfield, Wiley, New York, 1952.

ISOINDOLE

Elderfield and Dodd, in *Heterocyclic Compounds*, Vol. III, ed. Elderfield, Wiley, New York, 1952.

Moser and Thomas, *Phthalocyanine Compounds*, Am. Chem. Soc. Monograph No. 157, Reinhold, New York, 1963.

INDOLIZINE

Mosby, *Heterocyclic Compounds with Bridgehead Nitrogen Atoms*, Interscience, New York, Part 1 (1961) and Part 2 (1962).

BENZOFURANS

Elderfield and Meyer, Elderfield and Parham, in *Heterocyclic Compounds*, Vol. II, ed. Elderfield, Wiley, New York, 1951.

BENZOTHIOPHENES

Hartough and Meisel, *Compounds with Condensed Thiophene Rings*, Interscience, New York, 1954.

REFERENCES

1. Smith, *Advan. Heterocyclic Chem.*, **2**, 287 (1963).
2. Hinman and Lang, *J. Am. Chem. Soc.*, **86**, 3796 (1964) and papers therein cited.
3. Challis and Long, *J. Am. Chem. Soc.*, **85**, 2524 (1963).
4. Thesing, Semler, and Mohr, *Chem. Ber.*, **95**, 2205 (1962).
5. Reinecke, Johnson, and Sebastian, *Tetrahedron Letters*, 1183 (1963).
6. Dobeneck and Prietzel, *Z. Physiol. Chem.*, **299**, 214 (1955).
7. Morgan and Schunior, *J. Org. Chem.*, **27**, 3696 (1962).
8. Piers, Meimaroglou, Jardine, and Brown, *Can. J. Chem.*, **41**, 2399 (1963).
9. Kirby and Shah, *Chem. Commun.*, 381 (1965).
10. Snyder and MacDonald, *J. Am. Chem. Soc.*, **77**, 1257 (1955).
11. Binks and Ridd, *J. Chem. Soc.*, 2398 (1957).
12. Brown and Katritzky, *Tetrahedron Letters*, 803 (1964).
13. Hinman and Lang, *J. Org. Chem.*, **29**, 1449 (1964).
14. Hutton and Waters, *J. Chem. Soc.*, 4253 (1965).
15. Szmuszkovicz, *J. Am. Chem. Soc.*, **79**, 2819 (1957).
16. von Dobeneck and Lehnerer, *Chem. Ber.*, **90**, 161 (1957).
17. Da Settimo and Saettone, *Tetrahedron*, **21**, 823 (1965).
18. Witkop and Patrick, *J. Am. Chem. Soc.*, **74**, 3855 (1952).
19. Taylor, *Proc. Chem. Soc.*, 247 (1962).
20. Rees and Smithen, *J. Chem. Soc.*, 928 (1964).
21. Dobbs, *Chem. Commun.*, 56 (1965).
22. O'Sullivan and Sadler, *J. Chem. Soc.*, 877 (1959).
23. Ames, Bowman, Evans, and Jones, *J. Chem. Soc.*, 1984 (1956).
24. Kellie, O'Sullivan, and Sadler, *J. Chem. Soc.*, 3809 (1956).
25. Harley-Mason and Leeney, *Proc. Chem. Soc.*, 368 (1964).
26. Acheson and Snaith, *Proc. Chem. Soc.*, 344 (1963); *J. Chem. Soc.*, 3229 (1964).

27. Holt, Kellie, O'Sullivan, and Sadler, *J. Chem. Soc.*, 1217 (1958).
28. O'Sullivan and Sadler, *J. Chem. Soc.*, 2202 (1956).
29. Bauer, St. Vincent, Kempe, and Downie, *Lancet*, **ii**, 494 (1963).
30. Cadogan and Cameron-Wood, *Proc. Chem. Soc.*, 361 (1962).
30a. Kreher and Seubert, *Z. Naturforsch;* **20b**, 75 (1965).
31. Longuet-Higgins and Coulson, *Trans. Faraday Soc.*, **43**, 87 (1947).
32. Robinson, *Chem. Rev.*, **63**, 373 (1963).
33. Southwick, McGrew, Engel, Milliman, and Owellen, *J. Org. Chem.*, **28**, 3058 (1963).
34. Carlin, Magistro, and Mains, *J. Am. Chem. Soc.*, **86**, 5300 (1964); Robinson and Brown, *Can. J. Chem.*, **42**, 1940 (1964).
35. Fitzpatrick and Hiser, *J. Org. Chem.*, **22**, 1703 (1957).
36. Yanofsky, *J. Biol. Chem.*, **223**, 171 (1956).
37. Wilcox, Wyler, Mabry, and Dreiding, *Helv. Chim. Acta*, **48**, 252 (1965).
38. Wyler, Wilcox, and Dreiding, *Helv. Chim. Acta*, **48**, 361 (1965).
39. Veber and Lwowski, *J. Am. Chem. Soc.*, **86**, 4152 (1964).
40. Emmett, Veber, and Lwowski, *Chem. Commun.*, 272 (1965).
41. Thesing, Schäfer, and Melchior, *Ann.*, **671**, 119 (1964).
42. Theilacker and Schmidt, *Ann.*, **605**, 43 (1957).
43. Bornstein, Lashua, and Boisselle, *J. Org. Chem.*, **22**, 1255 (1957).
44. Galbraith, Small, Barnes, and Boekelheide, *J. Am. Chem. Soc.*, **83**, 453 (1961).
45. Armarego, *J. Chem. Soc.*, 1226 (1961); Fraser and Reid, *J. Chem. Soc.*, 1421 (1963).
46. Steponov and Grineva, *Zh. Obshch. Khim.*, **32**, 1529 (1962).
47. Boekelheide and Small, *J. Am. Chem. Soc.*, **83**, 462 (1961).
48. Boekelheide and Feely, *J. Org. Chem.*, **22**, 589 (1957).
49. Bragg and Wibberley, *J. Chem. Soc.*, 3277 (1963).
50. Windgassen, Saunders, and Boekelheide, *J. Am. Chem. Soc.*, **81**, 1459 (1959).
51. Gerson, Heilbronner, and Zimmermann, *Helv. Chim. Acta*, **46**, 1940 (1963).
52. Boekelheide, Gerson, Heilbronner, and Meuche, *Helv. Chim. Acta*, **46**, 1951 (1963).
53. Boekelheide and Small, *J. Am. Chem. Soc.*, **83**, 462 (1961).
54. Jackman, Porter, and Underwood, *Australian J. Chem.*, **18**, 1221 (1965).
55. Farrar and Levine, *J. Am. Chem. Soc.*, **72**, 4433 (1950).
56. Bisagni and Royer, *Bull. Soc. Chim. France*, 925 (1962).
57. Schroeder, Corcoran, Holden, and Mulligen, *J. Org. Chem.*, **27**, 586 (1962).
58. Dewar and Urch, *J. Chem. Soc.*, 345 (1957).
59. Southwick, Munsell, and Barktus, *J. Am. Chem. Soc.*, **83**, 1358 (1961).
60. Bordwell, Chapman, and McKellin, *J. Am. Chem. Soc.*, **76**, 3637 (1954).
61. Bedell, Spaeth, and Bobbitt, *J. Org. Chem.*, **27**, 2026 (1962).
62. Badger, Christie, Rodda, and Pryke, *J. Chem. Soc.,* 1179 (1958).
63. Martin-Smith and Gates, *J. Am. Chem. Soc.*, **78**, 6177 (1956).
64. McCall, Neale, and Rawlings, *J. Chem. Soc.*, 5288 (1962).
65. B. D. Tilak, *Tetrahedron*, **9**, 76 (1960).
66. Mayer, Kleinert, Richter, and Gewald, *Angew. Chem.*, **74**, 118 (1962). B. D. Tilak, H. S. Desai and S. S. Gepta, *Tetrahedron Letters*, 1956 (1966).

H

CHAPTER V

HETEROCYCLIC ANALOGUES OF BENZENE WITH ONE HETEROATOM

The most important ring system of this class, that of pyridine, can be derived theoretically from benzene by the replacement of a carbon and a hydrogen atom by one of nitrogen. This change leaves the aromatic structure of the ring essentially unaltered. A similar replacement of

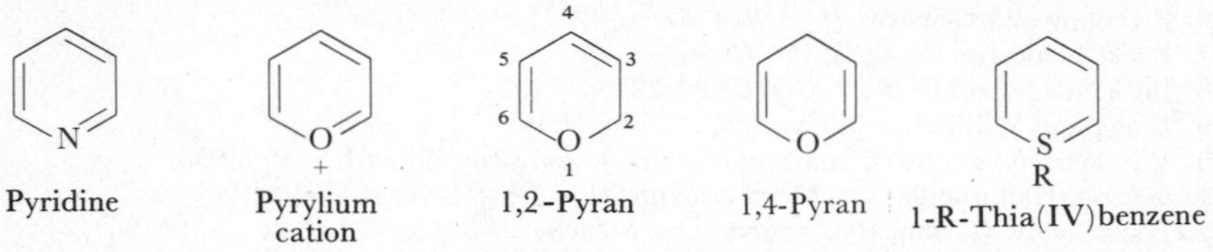

| Pyridine | Pyrylium cation | 1,2-Pyran | 1,4-Pyran | 1-R-Thia(IV)benzene |

carbon and hydrogen atoms by one of oxygen cannot be envisaged because of valency considerations unless the oxygen atom subsequently bears a positive charge. This is the case with the pyrylium cation, which has aromatic properties reminiscent of those of certain benzenes. Reduction of the pyrylium cation could lead to the non-aromatic 1,2- and 1,4-pyrans, and derivatives of both are known. Sulphur analogues of the pyrylium salts and pyrans, which are called thiapyrylium salts and thiapyrans, respectively, and some unstable tetravalent sulphur-containing compounds, the thia(IV)benzenes, have been prepared recently.

1. PYRIDINE

A. Introduction

Pyridine was discovered by Anderson in 1849, and he isolated this base in a pure state from bone oil. Anderson also obtained pure picoline (methylpyridine) and lutidine (dimethylpyridine) from the same source. These pyridines do not occur free in bones, but are formed thermally during the distillation.

Compounds containing the pyridine ring are widely distributed in nature. Certain of them, examples being vitamin B_6 and the nicotinamide adenine dinucleotide phosphates, are of the greatest biochemical importance. The pyridine ring also features in the structures of many drugs, dyes, and alkaloids.

Pyridine is an aromatic compound which is very similar to benzene in general structure. The asymmetry of the ring, however, greatly increases the number of structural isomers possible in comparison with the benzene series; there is only one monomethylbenzene, but there are three monomethylpyridines. Pyridine has nineteen possible methyl substitution products, whereas benzene gives rise to only twelve. Pyridine is also a tertiary base and has many properties characteristic of such compounds.

Because of the difficulty of introducing substituents directly into the pyridine ring, although pyridine itself is available in quantity, many syntheses involving the building of the ring have been developed. Most of the substituted pyridines have been obtained in this way, although recently discovered substitution reactions may alter the position somewhat. This situation is in direct contrast to that of the benzene series, where interest in syntheses of the ring has long been lacking owing to the ease with which substitutions and transformations of existing substituents may be carried out.

The positions of substituents round the pyridine ring are numbered (**1**) or occasionally lettered (**2**). The cation derived from pyridine is called pyridinium, and hexahydropyridine is usually known as

piperidine. A comparatively large number of pyridines possess trivial names.

B. Physical properties and structure

Pyridine is a very hygroscopic colourless liquid, f.p. $-42°$, b.p. $115°$, with a characteristic and somewhat unpleasant smell. It is miscible with most organic solvents and with water. Drying is best effected with potassium hydroxide or barium oxide, as pyridine reacts with sodium (p. 198). Pyridine is a very powerful solvent for many types of organic compounds, and it will often dissolve salts to give conducting solutions.

The cyclic structure usually written for pyridine (**1**) was suggested in

1869 by Körner, and the arrangement of the atoms was confirmed by a synthesis from pentamethylenediamine.

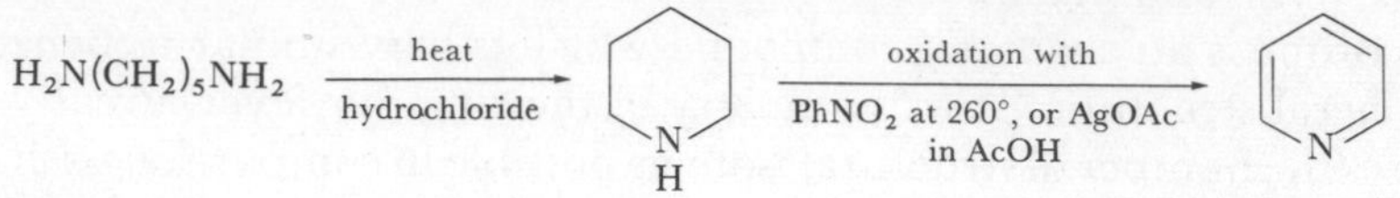

$H_2N(CH_2)_5NH_2$
heat
hydrochloride
N
H
oxidation with
$PhNO_2$ at 260°, or AgOAc
in AcOH
N

The literature contains a number of values for the resonance energy of pyridine, but the most reliable result, based on 1963 combustion data,[1] is 31·9 ± 2·0 kcal/mole. This is slightly less than the accepted value for benzene (36 kcal/mole).

The dimensions of the pyridine molecule have been calculated from microwave measurements.[2] The pure sp^2 hybridization of the electrons of the carbon atoms which is present in benzene is slightly disturbed, as

H
1·075 Å
H
1·080 Å
118·1°
1·400 ± 0·005 Å
118·6°
1·390 ± 0·005 Å
124·0°
1·085 Å
116·7°
1·340 ± 0·005 Å
H
N

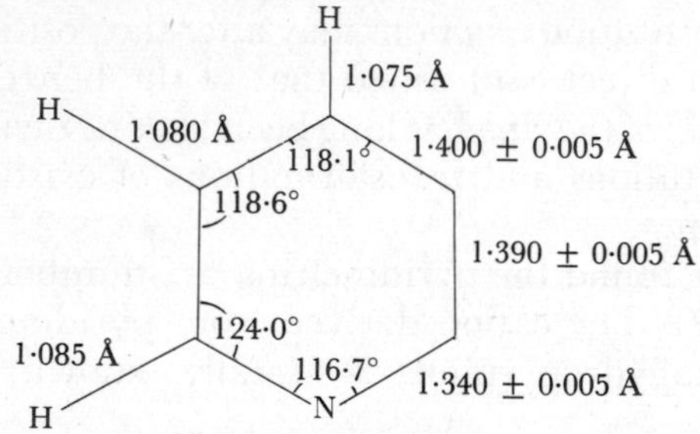

Dimensions of pyridine

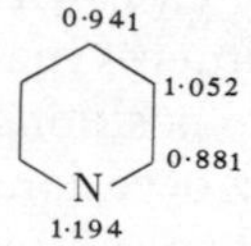

0·941
1·052
0·881
N
1·194

π-Electron densities

the bond angles are not exactly 120°. A comparison of the carbon–carbon bond lengths of benzene, pyridine, and pyrrole shows that all the carbon–carbon bonds in the first two compounds are in the 1·39–1·40 Å region. In pyrrole the carbon–carbon bonds show a much larger alternation in length (p. 64), which indicates less resonance than in pyridine or benzene. As the pyridine ring is not quite symmetrical, although planar, it is reasonable that the resonance energy of pyridine is of the same order but a little less than that of benzene.

In accordance with the physical picture, which indicates no fixation of double bonds in the pyridine molecule, the ozonolysis of 2,3-dimethylpyridine gives a mixture of ammonia, glyoxal, methylglyoxal, and diacetyl.

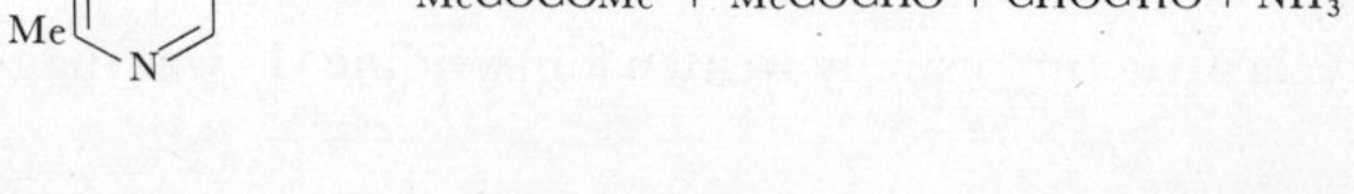

Me
Me
N
O_3
MeCOCOMe + MeCOCHO + CHOCHO + NH_3

The π-electron densities at the various positions of the pyridine ring have been calculated by a self-consistent field method[3] and show that there is a considerable drift of electrons from the ring towards the nitrogen atom. This is in accord with the dipole moment of pyridine (2·20 D), the negative pole of which is at the nitrogen atom.

From all these data it is clear that an alternation of double and single bonds, as suggested by formula **1**, is not actually the case in pyridine. A resonance hybrid of the Kekulé formulae (**1**, **1a**), which suffices to

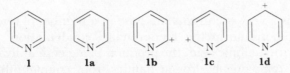

describe the structure in the case of benzene, is inadequate, as the build-up of electrons on the nitrogen atom is not taken into consideration. This can be done by including contributions from the charged structures **1b**–**1d** to the resonance hybrid, and then the chemical properties of pyridine can be adequately accounted for. Of the charged structures those involving the least charge separation should be favoured. This is in agreement with the preferential attack of nucleophilic reagents at position 2 of the ring and with the electron-density calculations[3] (p. 190) which also suggest correctly, as do localization-energy calculations,[4] that electrophilic attack should occur preferentially at position 3 for the uncharged pyridine molecule (see p. 196). In spite of the importance of charged and other structures to the resonance picture of pyridine, it is normally convenient to represent pyridine, like benzene, by the Kekulé structure (**1**).

C. Chemical properties

Pyridine is a very stable compound with a great deal of aromatic character. In many properties it greatly resembles benzene. At the same time it contains a tertiary nitrogen atom which possesses many properties of a typical tertiary amine. Pyridine is a weak monoacid base and forms stable salts with strong acids. It can even be used as a solvent for some chromic acid oxidations. It should be particularly noted that reactions taking place under strongly acid conditions may involve the pyridinium cation, while comparable reactions in the benzene series involve the benzene molecule. This is a major difference and is discussed shortly in greater detail.

1. *Addition and ring-opening reactions*

Pyridine ($K_b = 2\cdot3 \times 10^{-9}$) is a much weaker base than ammonia

$(K_b = 1\cdot8 \times 10^{-5})$ or trimethylamine $(K_b = 6\cdot5 \times 10^{-4})$. However, it forms stable salts with many acids, and most of these salts are easily soluble in water. Notable exceptions to this are the mercurichloride $(PyHClHgCl_2)$, chloroaurate $(PyHAuCl_4)$, and the chloroplatinate $(Py_2H_2PtCl_6)$. The formation of salts involves the lone pair of electrons on the nitrogen atom. In contrast to the case of pyrrole, this lone pair is not needed to make up the aromatic sextet of electrons, and so in the pyridine series salt formation does not destroy the aromatic properties of the ring.

Pyridine is a very useful solvent–base in a number of reactions. It is used with piperidine in the Knoevenagel condensation of aromatic aldehydes with malonic acid, the products being cinnamic acids. It can be used for removing hydrogen halides from compounds under anhydrous conditions. It is also useful in the acylation of phenols, alcohols, and amines by acid chlorides, acid anhydrides, and mixed anhydrides. The acid derivative combines with the pyridine to give a quaternary salt (e.g. **2**), a number of which have been isolated in the case of acid chlorides. This salt then reacts with the hydroxyl or amino group yielding the acyl derivative; the liberated acid is taken up as the

pyridine salt (**3**). Quaternary salts such as **2** are immediately decomposed by water to pyridine hydrochloride and the organic acid, but with ethyl cyanoacetate[5] the ring can open yielding **4**.

Pyridine is easily converted into quaternary salts by treatment with reagents such as methyl sulphate or methyl iodide. 1-Methylpyridinium iodide (**5**) is a colourless hygroscopic solid easily soluble in water, and it behaves as a strong electrolyte in aqueous solution. In conformity with its ionic properties it is virtually insoluble in ether or hydrocarbon solvents. On heating to about 300° this methiodide rearranges to a mixture of 2- and 4-methylpyridinium iodides. The electrical conductivity of aqueous solutions of 1-methylpyridinium iodide (5) shows that the compound is, apparently, completely ionized, although these solutions do not accurately obey Beer's law as regards absorption in the ultraviolet region. This is considered[6] to support the supposition that a small amount of the pseudo-iodide, structurally analogous to 7, is present in equilibrium. As the addition of sodium hydroxide does not alter the electrical conductivity (allowing for the presence of the additional ions) of solutions of 1-methylpyridinium iodide (5), it is clear that the resulting hydroxide (6) is also completely ionized within the limitations of the experiment. The amount of unionized hydroxide (7) at equilibrium under these conditions must be small, and this conclusion is supported by the observation that the ultraviolet absorption spectrum of the methiodide (5) is unchanged by the addition of alkali. If an appreciable change from the ionic aromatic species (6) to the non-aromatic non-ionized pseudo-hydroxide (7) occurred the spectrum would alter. The oxidation of 1-methylpyridinium hydroxide (6) by alkaline potassium ferricyanide does, however, give 1-methyl-2-pyridone (8) in good yield. As oxidations with ferricyanide ions usually proceed by the abstraction of hydrogen and not by the addition of oxygen, a case can be made for the supposition that a small proportion of the pseudo-hydroxide (7) is in equilibrium with the ionic hydroxide (6) in aqueous solution.

The cyanide ion also attacks 1-methylpyridinium salts at position 2 yielding compounds structurally analogous to 7. However, rearrangement to the thermodynamically more stable 4-cyano-1,4-dihydro-1-methylpyridines can subsequently take place.[6a]

1-Methylpyridinium iodide slowly evolves methylamine with boiling aqueous sodium hydroxide, but the other products of this decomposition have not been identified. When the group attached to the nitrogen atom is strongly electron attracting, the ring is comparatively easily opened by nucleophilic reagents. 2,4-Dinitrophenylpyridinium chloride (9) is a colourless crystalline solid which is formed from pyridine and 2,4-dinitrochlorobenzene at 100°; this reaction is reversed at 200°. With water at 150° the chloride yields pyridine hydrochloride and 2,4-dinitrophenol, but with cold aqueous alkali a deep red compound (10) is formed. The red compound, on successive treatment with dilute acid and aniline, yields 2,4-dinitroaniline and glutaconic aldehyde dianil (**11**). Azulene can be obtained from **9** as indicated. The overall yield from pyridine is 60%. 1-Cyanopyridinium bromide (**12**), obtained from pyridine and cyanogen bromide, behaves like **9** towards aqueous aniline, while 1-protopyridinium sulphonate (**13**), sometimes called pyridine–sulphur trioxide complex, gives the sodium salt of glutaconic aldehyde (**14**, enol form) and sodium sulphamate with aqueous alkali. **13** is a useful mild sulphonating agent, and is obtained from its constituents in an inert solvent, such as methylene chloride.

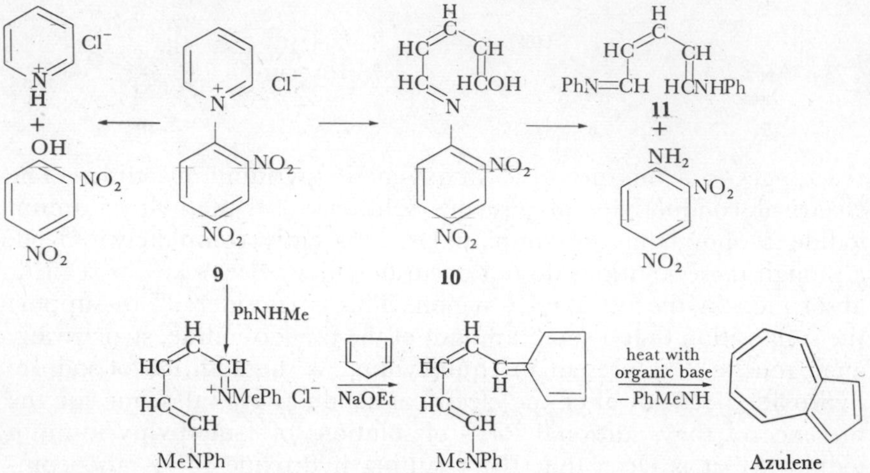

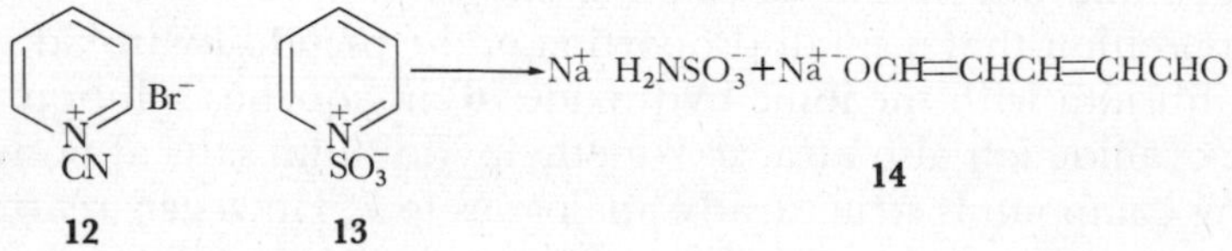

Pyridine is oxidized easily to the *N*- or 1-oxide by 30% aqueous hydrogen peroxide in acetic acid. Pyridine 1-oxide has some very interesting properties which are discussed later (pp. 207–211).

The infrared absorption spectra of solutions of iodine in pyridine suggests[7] that 1-iodopyridinium iodide (**15**) is obtained. If similar compounds are formed with bromine and chlorine, the catalytic effect of pyridine on halogenations such as the bromination of benzene is understandable. The pyridinium cation could be a more ready source of positive halogen than the halogen molecule itself.

Pyridine is easily reduced to hexahydropyridine, or piperidine (**16**), by a variery of methods, including hydrogen over Raney nickel,

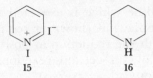

15   16

rhodium at 60°, palladium charcoal with acetic acid[8] at 80°, Raney nickel, or by sodium and absolute alcohol, by electrolytic reduction and by lithium aluminium hydride under forcing conditions. Intermediate reduction products, although looked for, have been obtained in poor yield only from the sodium–ethanol reduction. 1,4-Dihydropyridine has, however, been obtained by the reduction of pyridine with trimethylsilane.[9] It is extremely sensitive to air.

Substituted di- and tetra-hydropyridines are known. Pyridine does not undergo a normal Diels–Alder reaction and gives complex products with ketene[10] and dimethyl acetylenedicarboxylate (p. 278);[11] some other addition reactions are mentioned on pp. 197 and 198.

The pyridine is cleaved by ultrasonic waves giving acetylene and hydrogen cyanide,[12] and it is slowly opened by ultraviolet light, giving glutaconic aldehyde derivatives. These are yellow and account for the colour of old samples of pyridines.

2. Substitution reactions

Molecular-orbital calculations (p. 190) show that the π-electron density at position 3 of the pyridine ring is higher than that at positions 2 or 4. This is a consequence of nitrogen being more electronegative than carbon, and the nitrogen atom therefore causes a drift of electrons in its direction. This drift denudes the 2- and 4-positions of electrons by a resonance interaction (**17**), and the effect is very strong. It can be compared with the similar drift of electrons from the 2- and 4-positions of the ring in nitrobenzene (**18**). There is also the inductive effect of the

17   18

H*

nitrogen atom in pyridine which is expected to reduce the electron density at position 3 somewhat (however see p. 190), although very little in comparison with the reduction at positions 2 and 4. This has been detected chemically in certain reactions of 3-methylpyridine (p. 206) and of 3-bromopyridine (p. 213).

A general comparison of the reactions of pyridine and nitrobenzene is often made. The analogy is helpful if not pressed too hard, and is satisfactory for nucleophilic substitutions. Under acid conditions or attack by electrophilic reagents the two compounds are not strictly comparable. Pyridine is first attacked at its most electronegative position, at the nitrogen atom, to give a pyridinium cation (**19**). Here the positive charge is actually on the ring, and it has been shown experimentally[13] that it is this sort of cation (e.g. **19**) which is actually attacked by the electrophilic reagent. The positive charge greatly accentuates the electronegative properties of the nitrogen atom in withdrawing electrons from the ring, and so attack on the cation,

19

if it takes place appreciably, does so very slowly and at position 3. Nitrobenzene, in contrast to pyridine, is such an extremely weak base that it can be considered 'non-basic' under most conditions. Even if the nitro group does accept a cation to some extent under the forcing conditions of nitration, there will still be a substantial equilibrium concentration of uncharged nitrobenzene present, and this will be the species nitrated.

An assessment of the electrophilic reactivity of the pyridine ring, as opposed to the situation where the nitrogen carries a positively charged atom or group, has been made[14] from a consideration of the rates of pyrolysis of a series of acetates (**20**). The transition state (**21**) is stabilized, or destabilized, by the nature of the aromatic ring (R).

20   **21**

The observed rates for phenyl, and the three pyridyl groups were:

and this gives the order of relative abilities of these aromatic groups to stabilize an adjacent carbonium ion.

The Friedel–Crafts reaction fails with pyridine. 3-Nitropyridine (4·5%) and some 2-nitropyridine (0·5%) is obtained under optimum conditions from pyridine, 100% sulphuric acid, and sodium and potassium nitrates at 300°. At 450° only 2-nitropyridine (2%) is obtained (cf. bromination at 500°). Pyridine with nitronium borofluoride yields 1-nitropyridinium borofluoride.[15]

Sulphonation of pyridine in the presence of mercuric sulphate proceeds at 230° to give the 3-sulphonic acid (70% yield). The mercuration of pyridine appears to be an electrophilic substitution and is comparatively easy.

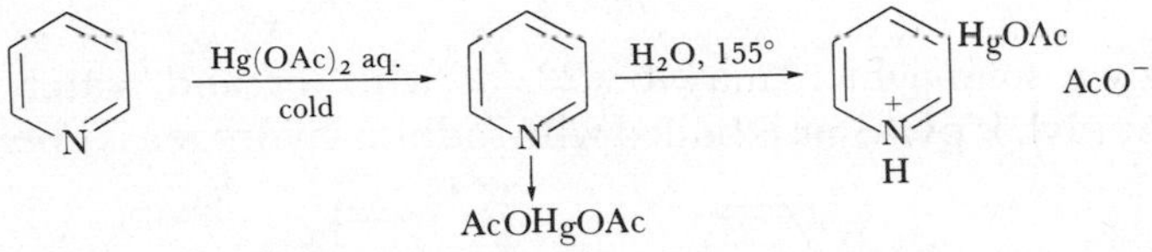

Halogenation of pyridine with excess aluminium,[16] sulphur, or thionyl chlorides[17] gives the 3- and 3,5-derivatives in fair yield. Bromination in concentrated sulphuric acid[18] or in the vapour phase[19] at about 300° gives 3-bromo- and 3,5-dibromo-pyridine. In the vapour at ca. 500°, substitution appears to proceed through a radical mechanism, and the products are the 2-bromo- (48%) and 2,6-dibromo-pyridines. Similar results are obtained on chlorination. Pyridine reacts with thionyl chloride to form 1-(4-pyridyl)pyridinium chloride (22) in good yield. This product is of special interest, as on hydrolysis with water or ammonia it gives 4-pyridone or 4-amino-pyridine respectively.

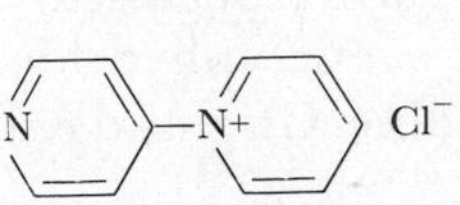

22

The reaction of pyridine at 105° with benzoyl peroxide, lead tetra-benzoate, phenyliodosobenzoate, or N-nitrosoacetanilide, all of which

act as a source of phenyl radicals, gives[20] in every case a mixture of
2-phenyl- (55%), 3-phenyl- (31%), and 4-phenyl-pyridine (14%).
Localization-energy calculations for free-radical attack on pyridine
account well for these results if the correct parameters are used.[20a]
A corresponding decomposition of N-nitrosoacetanilide in the presence
of nitrobenzene shows that attack of the phenyl radical on the nitrobenzene occurs mostly at the 2- (60–70%) and 4- (30–40%) positions
with up to 10% at position 3. The situation is therefore rather different
from that of pyridine.

Nucleophilic attack takes place easily at the 2- and 4-positions of
pyridine. The former position is usually favoured in accordance with
density calculations (p. 190). Both sodamide and potassium hydroxide
attack at position 2; further reaction with sodamide gives 2,6-di-
aminopyridine. Pyridine reacts with sodium in the cold to give a

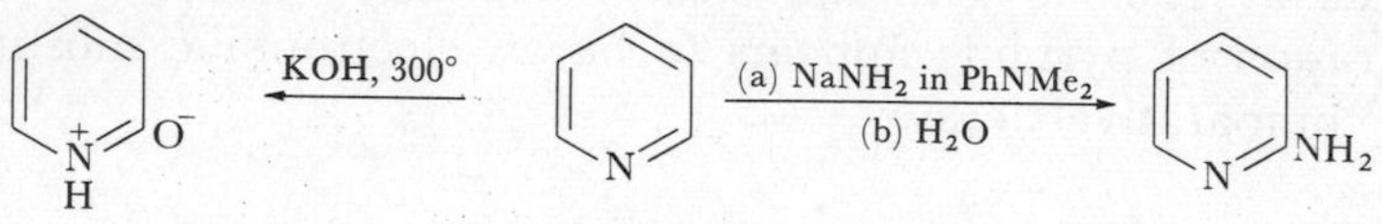

dark brown solid which may be **23**, as with air and water it gives
4,4'-dipyridyl. If pyridine is boiled with sodium, hydrogen is liberated,[21]

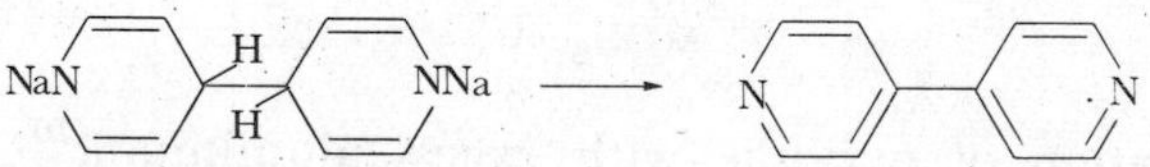

and subsequent treatment with bromine gives a mixture of dipyridyls.
2,2'-Dipyridyl along with some 2-(2-pyridyl)pyrrole is formed

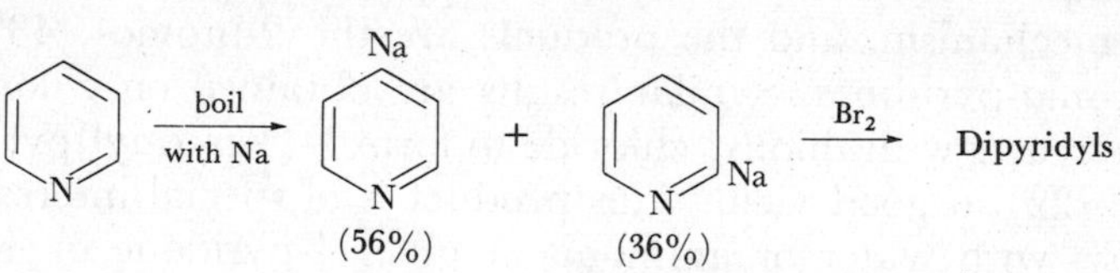

when pyridine is boiled with degassed Raney nickel.[22] Pyridine
also reacts with zinc and acetic anhydride to give **24**, which can be
converted into 4-ethylpyridine. Grignard reagents (at 150°) and phenyl-

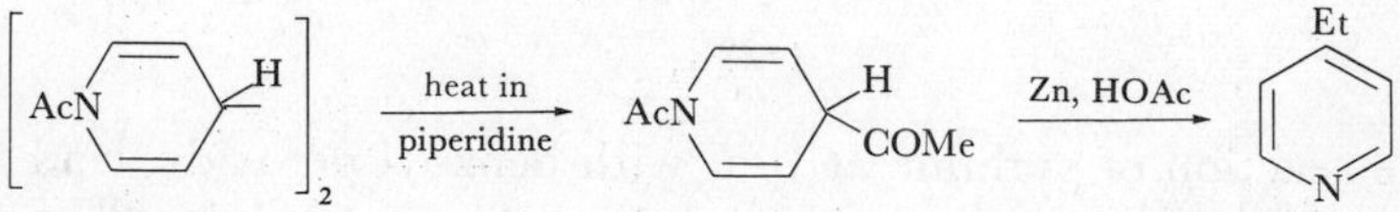

lithium react with pyridine usually at position 2, but sometimes 4-substituted pyridines are major products. N,N-Dimethylbenzamide and

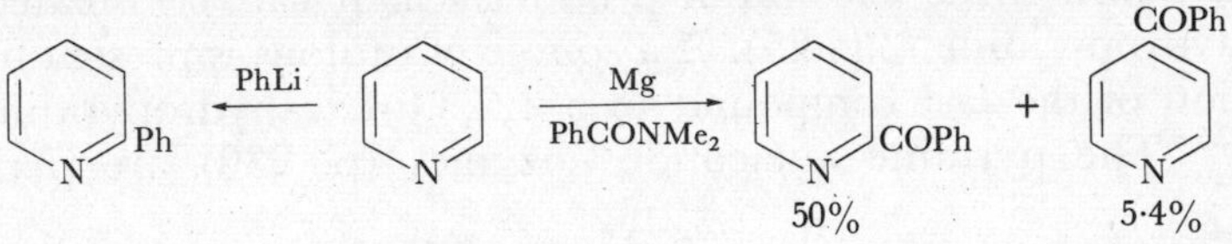

amalgamated magnesium behave in a similar way.[23] This last reaction promises useful application.

D. Derivatives of pyridine
1. *Reduced pyridines*

As compounds such as 2-pyridone, which can be regarded as a dihydropyridine (1,2-dihydro-2-oxopyridine) or less correctly as a pyridine (2-hydroxypyridine), are dealt with elsewhere, comparatively few simple dihydropyridines remain for consideration. The reduction of pyridine itself theoretically could give three possible dihydro compounds, but so far only one has been obtained (p. 195) without doubt from any reduction. The sodium–ethanol–liquid ammonia reduction of 2-methylpyridine appears to give dihydropyridines as the first stage, for treatment of the product with acids gives cyclohexenone. A few highly substituted dihydropyridines unsubstituted on the

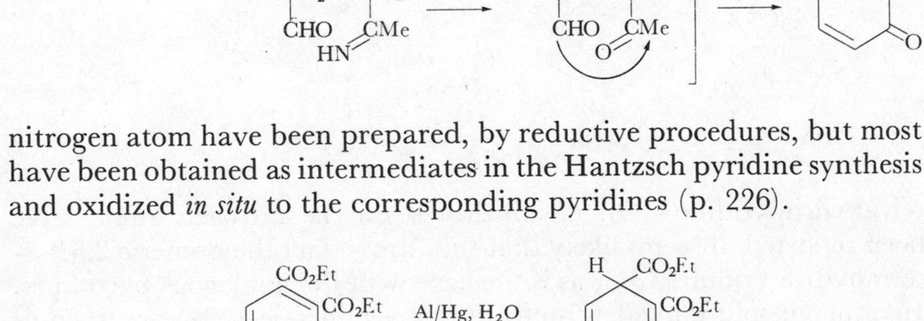

nitrogen atom have been prepared, by reductive procedures, but most have been obtained as intermediates in the Hantzsch pyridine synthesis and oxidized *in situ* to the corresponding pyridines (p. 226).

The reduction of 1-alkyl- or 1-aryl-pyridinium salts by sodium dithionite[24] yields the corresponding 1,4-dihydropyridines, but using sodium borohydride the initial product which can be isolated is a 1,2-dihydropyridine (e.g. 25). If a source of protons is present further reduction of the last compound to a 1,2,3,6-tetrahydropyridine can occur.[25] The pyridine–nucleotide enzymes (p. 230) are pyridines

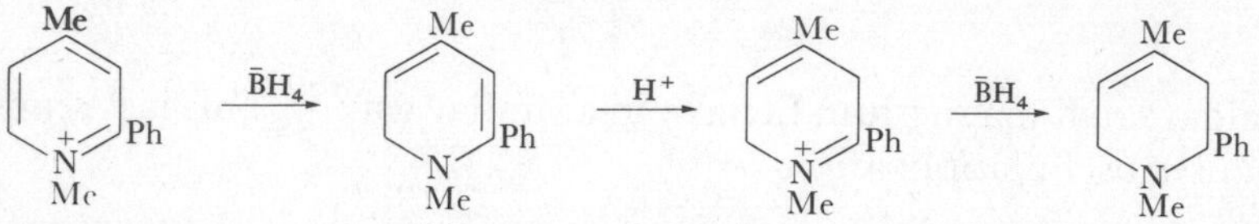

which are involved in oxidation–reduction *in vivo* through reversible conversion into their 1,4-dihydro derivatives. The electrolytic reduction of the pyridinium cation (26) gives a remarkably stable free radical (27) which distils *in vacuo* as an emerald-green oil. It is very sensitive to oxygen, and magnetic measurements suggest that the oil contains 60–100% of the radical.[26]

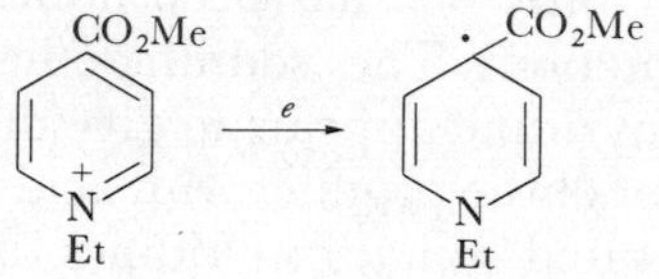

1,2,3,6-Tetrahydropyridine (29) has been obtained in very poor yield from the sodium and ethanol reduction of pyridine and by the dehydrobromination of 4-bromopiperidine. It adds bromine rapidly and reacts with two moles of methyl iodide, giving the quaternary iodide. A derivative (28) is present in betel nut. Although derivatives of 1,2,3,4-

tetrahydropyridine (30), unsubstituted on the nitrogen atom, have been reported, it seems likely that they are in fact the isomeric 2,3,4,5-tetrahydropyridines (31), as is the case with the analogous pyrrolines. In aqueous solution 2,3,4,5-tetrahydropyridines (e.g. 32) are in equilibrium with the corresponding carbinolamines and amino ketones, and benzoylation gives the *N*-benzoylamino ketone.

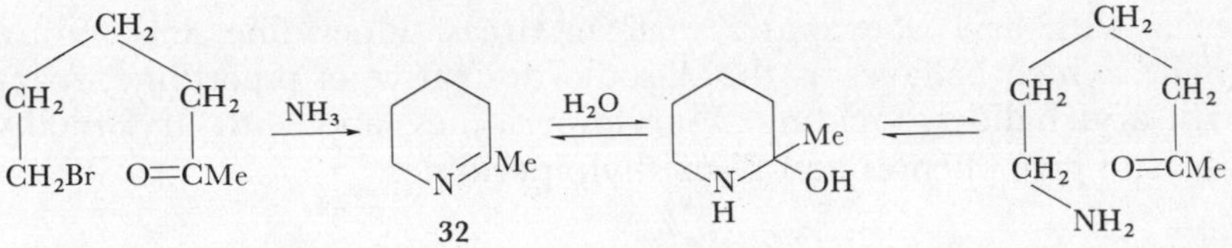

Piperidine or hexahydropyridine is obtained commerically by the hydrogenation of pyridine over nickel at about 200°. It is a colourless liquid, b.p. 106°, dipole moment 1.17 ± 0.01 D, which is miscible with water and has an amine-like smell. It is a slightly stronger base ($K_b = 1.6 \times 10^{-3}$) than diethylamine ($K_b = 1.2 \times 10^{-3}$), possibly because the ethyl groups can adopt a conformation which interferes with

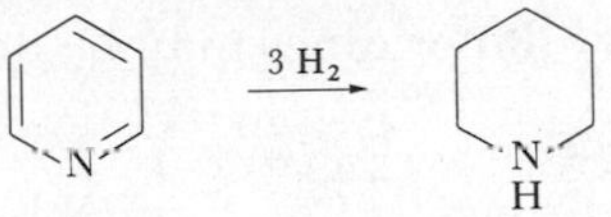

the approach of the proton. Such interference is not possible in piperidine itself because the ring is not sufficiently flexible. Piperidine fumes

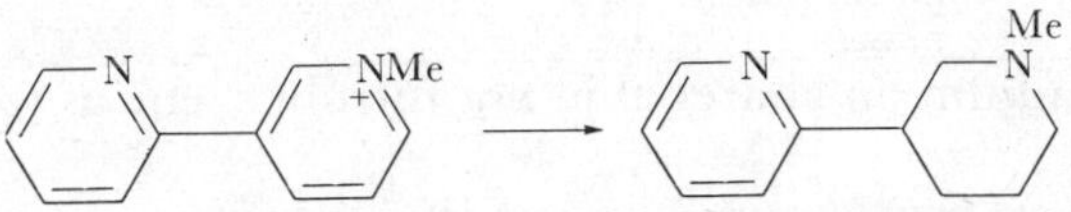

in air with the formation of the carbonate. N-Alkyl- and N-aryl-piperidines can be obtained by the reduction or hydrogenation of the N-substituted pyridinium salts. As 33 with formic acid and potassium formate, an interesting reducing combination, yields 34, it appears that the pyridinium cation is more easily reduced than pyridine itself.[27]. The mechanism of this reduction is probably similar to that of the borohydride reductions discussed on the previous page. A number of substituted piperidines have been obtained by the cyclization of the appropriate dihalogen compounds, or of the halogenated amines.

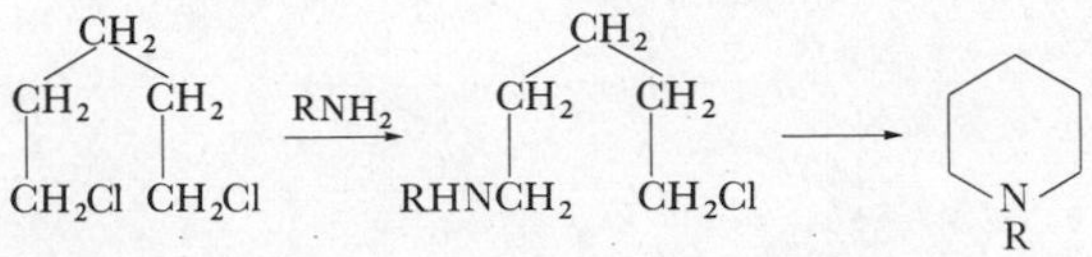

Piperidine has many of the properties of a typical aliphatic secondary amine. It forms salts, nitroso, acyl, alkyl, and aryl derivatives and reacts with aryl isocyanates to form ureas. Piperidine and sodium amide, which behaves as the *N*-sodio derivative of piperidine, reacts with aryl halides, yielding *N*-arylpiperidines, and with aryl methyl ethers to give phenols and *N*-methylpiperidine.

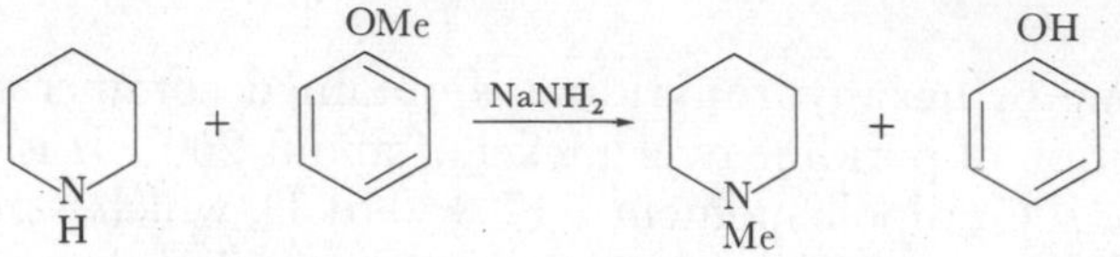

The oxidation of piperidine by benzoyl peroxide or by hydrogen peroxide gives the hydroxylamine derivatives **35** or **36**, respectively. The hydroxy compound (**36**) may tautomerize, and derivatives of both tautomers are known.[28] Piperidines may be dehydrogenated to pyri-

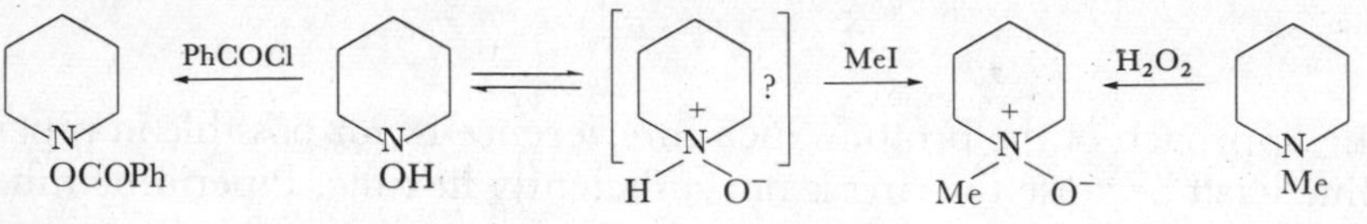

dines by palladium on charcoal in hot nitrobenzene as well as by other reagents.

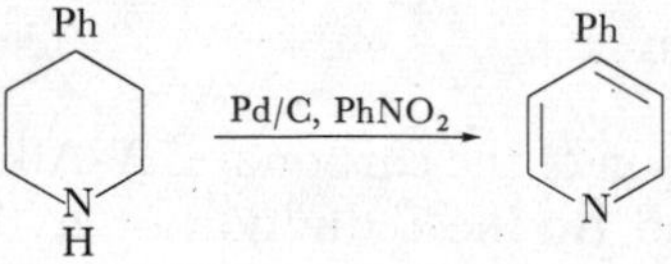

The piperidine, and similar rings, occur widely in natural products. The 'Hofmann exhaustive methylation' procedure has been very much used with such naturally occurring bases to provide structural information, and in the case of piperidine it opens the ring. The aromatic pyridine ring is not opened by this method. The base is first

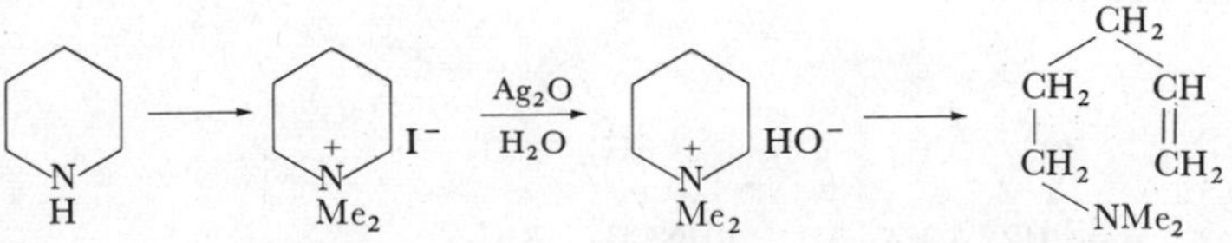

fully methylated to the quaternary iodide (**37**), which is then converted into the hydroxide (**38**). Dry distillation of the hydroxide causes ring scission with the elimination of water, giving **39**. The whole sequence is repeated as often as necessary to remove the nitrogen atom from the rest of the molecule. In the case above one additional sequence is necessary and the conjugated penta-1,3-diene (**40**) is the product.

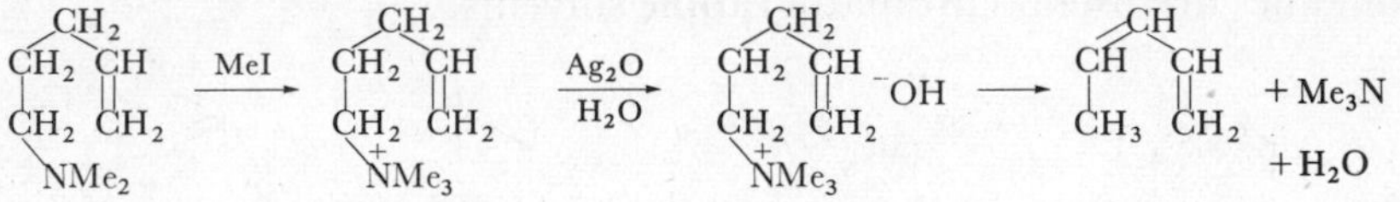

40

It is not known whether the penta-1,3-diene is formed directly or if the unconjugated penta-1,4-diene is first formed and then isomerizes. Two methylation and decomposition sequences are necessary to remove the nitrogen atom from piperidine, as two nitrogen–carbon bonds must be broken. Three applications of the reaction are needed to remove the nitrogen atom from quinolizidine (**41**).

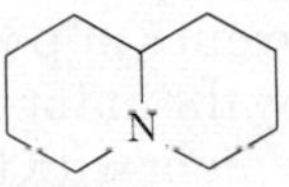

41

Two other methods of opening the piperidine ring were developed by von Braun. In the first of these piperidine is benzoylated and the product (**42**) treated with phosphorus pentachloride. This is a convenient

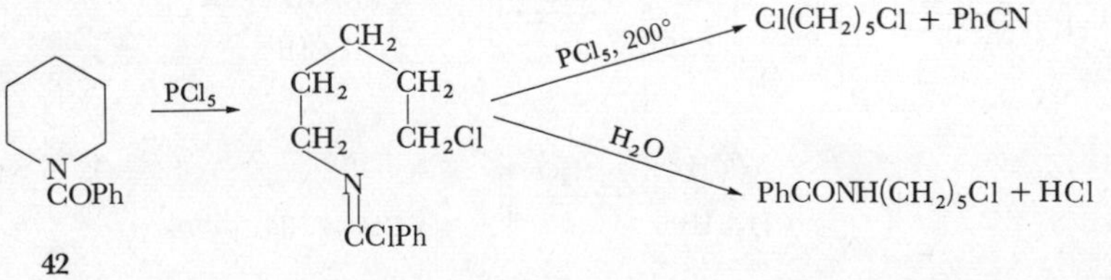

42

method of making 1,5-dichloropentane. In the second method[29], N-alkyl- or N-aryl-piperidines are quaternized with cyanogen bromide and the quaternary salt (**43**) hydrolysed by 48% aqueous hydrobromic acid.

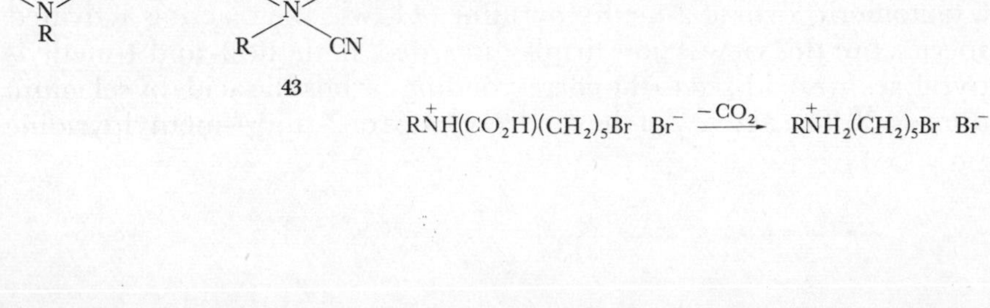

43

$$\overset{+}{R}NH(CO_2H)(CH_2)_5Br \ Br^- \xrightarrow{-CO_2} \overset{+}{R}NH_2(CH_2)_5Br \ Br^-$$

2. *Alkylpyridines*

Many of these compounds, like pyridine itself, are obtained from coal tar. The monomethylpyridines are sometimes called picolines, dimethylpyridines lutidines, and trimethylpyridines collidines. The collidines are useful chromatographic solvents.

2 - or α -	3 - or β -	4 - or γ-	2,4-	2,4,6-
	Picoline		Lutidine	Collidine

The chemical properties of the three methylpyridines as representative examples of the alkylpyridines will be considered in some detail. Although the electron-donating characteristic of the methyl group does activate the pyridine ring appreciably towards electrophilic attack, the electron-attracting property of the pyridine ring on the methyl groups is much more striking. Methyl groups at positions 2 and 4 of the pyridine ring are denuded of electrons by the inductive and resonance effect of the nitrogen atom in general agreement with the molecular-orbital calculations on pyridine (p. 190). A proton is easily lost from these activated methyl groups under suitable conditions, and in consequence, for instance, condensation takes place between 2-methylpyridine and benz-

Stilbazole

44

aldehyde in the presence of acetic anhydride or zinc chloride. Treatment of 2-methylpyridine with phenyllithium or sodamide in liquid ammonia converts it into the corresponding metal derivatives, which give the typical reactions of such compounds. 4-Methylpyridine undergoes an exactly comparable series of reactions. It was at one time thought that a tautomeric form of 2-methylpyridine (**44**) was the reacting activated species, but this view is now firmly discarded. Both the 2- and 4-methylpyridines are oxidized to the corresponding carboxylic acids by selenium dioxide.[30] The activity of the methyl groups of 2- and 4-methylpyridine is increased by converting the compounds into quaternary salts, for example with methyl iodide, and is not lost when the compounds are converted into their 1-oxides (p. 207). The positive charge on the nitrogen atom augments its electrophilic properties.

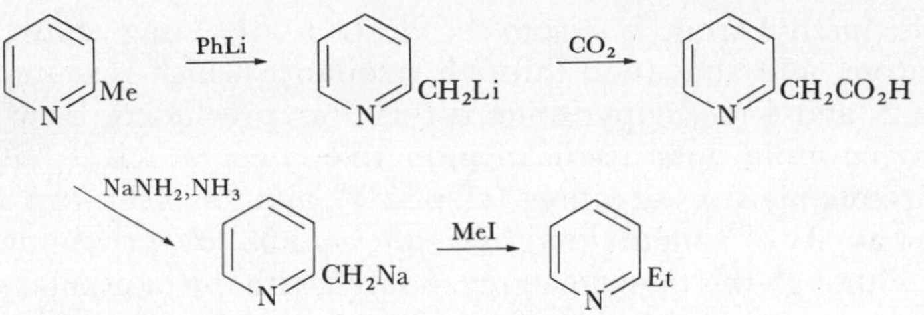

2-Vinylpyridine is made commercially as shown below. It can be

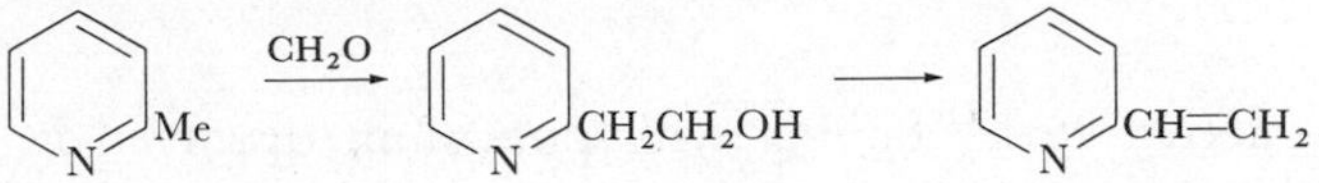

polymerized like styrene, and its methylene group is sufficiently electrophilic to react with nucleophilic reagents as indicated. 4-Vinylpyridine

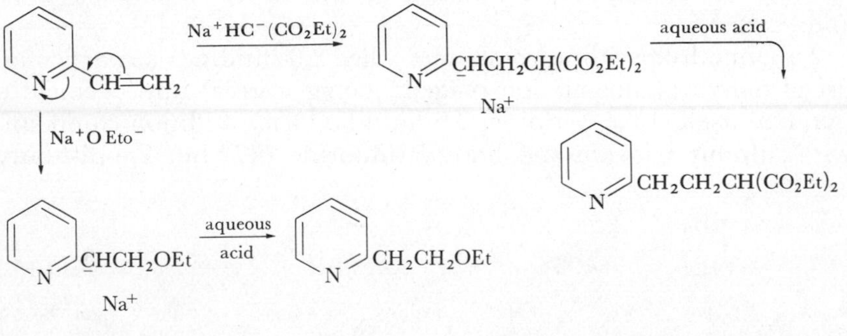

is similar in preparation and properties. These additions may be compared with the Michael reaction, one example of which is given.

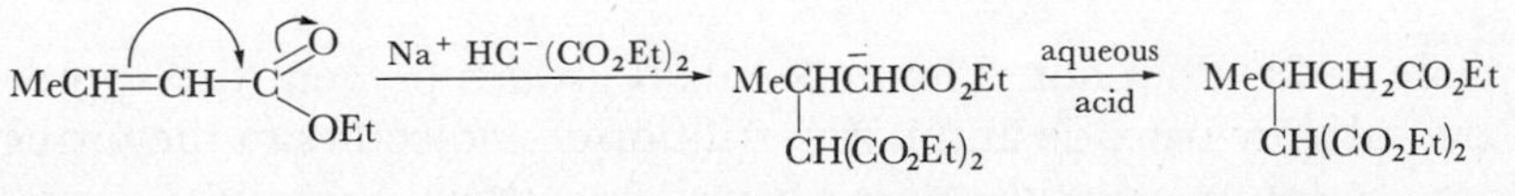

Until recently the methyl group of 3-methylpyridine was thought to possess none of the activity well known in its isomers. It is in fact comparatively unreactive and does not react with benzaldehyde in acetic anhydride or with selenium dioxide.[30]. It is also unreactive to phenyllithium, which gives 3-methyl-2-phenylpyridine.[31] These results are expected, as the methyl group is *meta* to the electron-attracting centre, the nitrogen atom, and activation through resonance which is so important in the 2- and 4-methylpyridines is therefore precluded. However, the nitrogen atom does assert an inductive effect which is not dependent on resonance considerations (cf. p. 213), and this is shown up by the greater basicity of 3-methylpyridine ($pK_a = 5·68$) over pyridine ($pK_a = 5·17$), although this does not agree too well with the molecular-orbital picture (p. 190). 3-Methylpyridine does in fact react with sodamide in liquid ammonia to give the ion (45), which with methyl chloride or iodide yields 3-ethylpyridine.[32] The racemization of the

45

optically active 46 by boiling with potassium dissolved in triethyl-methanol supports the contention that an ion such as 45 can be formed. Further treatment of 3-ethylpyridine gives successively 3-isopropylpyridine and 3-*t*-butylpyridine. It appears that the order of reactivity of the picoline methyl groups in this reaction is $2 > 3$ and $4 > 2$.[33]

2,6-Dimethylpyridine (sometimes called 2,6-lutidine) is a particularly useful dehydrohalogenation reagent, being a great improvement on pyridine itself. Like pyridine, 2,6-lutidine forms addition compounds with sulphur trioxide and boron trifluoride (47) but 2,6-di-*t*-butyl-

46   47   48   49

pyridine (48) does not. The bulky alkyl groups prevent the approach of the sulphur trioxide and boron trifluoride molecules to the nitrogen atom. Sulphur trioxide does, however, attack the ring, giving a sulphonic acid which is the 3-derivative (49). Di-*t*-butylpyridine ($pK_a = 3·58$) forms salts with protonic acids, but it is a much weaker base than pyridine itself ($pK_a = 4·38$, also in 50% EtOH).

The chlorination of 2-methylpyridine gives first 2-trichloromethyl-pyridine. The ring is then attacked successively at the 5- and 3-positions.

The halogenation of 4-methylpyridine gives tars containing ionic halogen, and the bromination of 3-methylpyridine hydrochloride gives 3-bromomethylpyridine. The methylpyridine 1-oxides are discussed with pyridine 1-oxide (below).

3. *Arylpyridines*

The phenylpyridines are of particular interest in connexion with their oxidation and reduction, as this gives information about the comparative reactivity, but not necessarily of the aromaticity, of the two rings. 2-Phenylpyridine is easily obtained from pyridine and phenyllithium, and 4-phenylpyridine by the synthesis outlined.[34] The

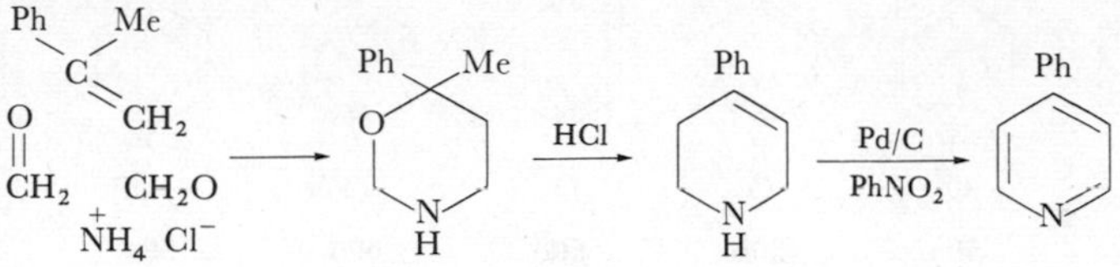

hydrogenation of 2- and 3-phenylpyridines over platinum oxide (Adams) catalyst gives the corresponding phenylpiperidines. In general, the hydrogenation of a pyridine proceeds more easily than that of the corresponding benzene. The phenylpyridines all give

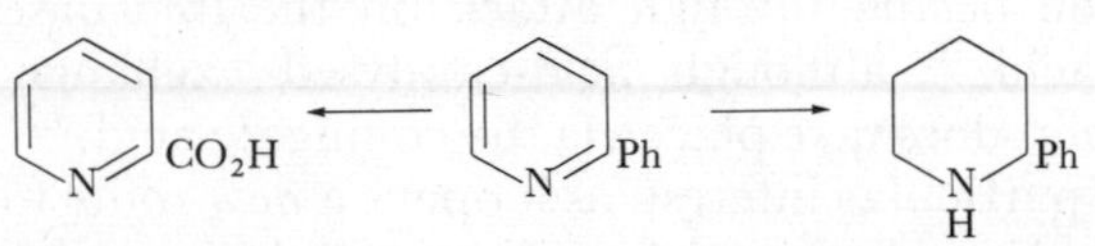

pyridinecarboxylic acids on oxidation with potassium permanganate, indicating the greater stability of the pyridine ring under these conditions.

4. *Pyridine 1-oxide, or pyridine N-oxide*

This compound (50) is easily prepared by the oxidation of pyridine in glacial acetic acid by 30% aqueous hydrogen peroxide at 70–80°. It forms water-soluble colourless crystals, m.p. 66°, and has attracted much interest in recent years owing to the diverse reactions it can undergo.[35] It is a much weaker base than pyridine, but does form some salts.

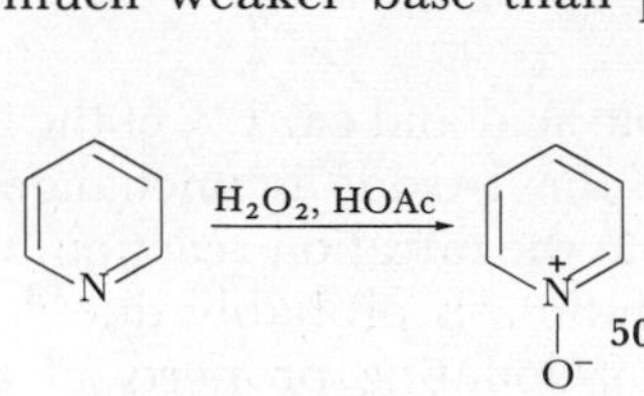

As the dipole moment (4·24 D) of pyridine 1-oxide is lower than that calculated from the moments of pyridine and the trimethylamine oxide, Ochiai concluded that the resonance structures **50a–50c** must be important, and predicted that nitration should take place at positions 2 or 4. Later dipole moment studies with a series of pyridine 1-oxides substituted at position 4 have shown that the oxygen atom can either release or accept electrons according to the substituent. The resonance structures **50d**, **50e**, and **50f** must therefore make appropriate contributions to the resonance hybrid, and it can therefore be understood why the oxide undergoes many types of reaction. Experiment showed that

50   50a   50b   50c   50d   50e   50f

Ochiai's prediction was correct and that in nitric–sulphuric acids at 100° 4-nitropyridine 1-oxide is by far the major product; at 150° some 2-nitropyridine (7·6%) is also obtained, presumably through de-oxygenation of the corresponding N-oxide which would be formed first. Nitration occurs through attack on the free base, not on the conjugated acid,[36] although acid-catalysed exchange of the ring hydrogen atoms does take place via the conjugate acid.[37] The nitration reaction is of particular interest, as it opens a new route to the synthesis of 4-substituted pyridines from pyridines unsubstituted at this position. Pyridine 1-oxide rather surprisingly does not sulphonate at all readily. The mildest condition effecting reaction, sulphuric acid containing 20% of sulphur trioxide and mercuric sulphate at 220–240°, gives

51

40–45% of the 3-sulphonic acid and ca. 1% of the 2- and ca. 2% of the 4-isomers;[38] ca. 40% of the 1-oxide is unchanged. The remarkable change in orientation from the nitration reaction, which is also carried out in sulphuric acid solution, is probably due[39] to the formation of **51**, in which the electron-donating property of the oxygen atom is suppressed. Bromine and silver sulphate, a source of bromonium ions, in 90% sulphuric acid gives a mixture of the 2- and 4-bromo-pyridine 1-oxides in 1:2 ratio[40] and may be compared with the nitration reaction above. However bromination in fuming sulphuric acid, when the species being attacked is probably **51**, gives 3-bromopyridine 1-oxide as the main product.[41] With mercuric acetate in acetic acid the 1-oxide mercurates[42] at position 2 and then 6, but some attack also occurs at position 3. Phenyl radicals, obtained from diazoamino-benzene at 181°, phenylate pyridine 1-oxide at positions 2-, 3-, and 4- in 9·9:1:3·9 ratio.[43] This ratio is similar to that obtained in the phenylation of nitrobenzene (p. 198).

The reduction of pyridine 1-oxides is more difficult than that of most tertiary amine oxides, probably because of the resonance interaction. They are not usually reduced by sulphurous acid, but hydrogenation or reaction with phosphorus trichloride is generally effective.

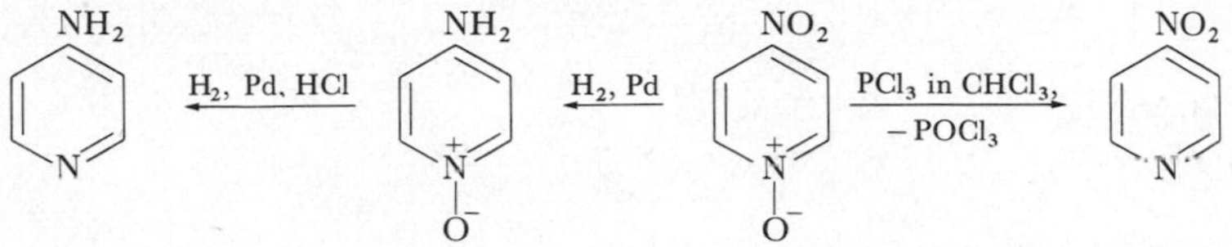

Pyridine 1-oxide with phenylmagnesium bromide gives 1,2-dihydro-1-hydroxy-2-phenylpyridine (**52**) which is soluble in 10% aqueous sodium hydroxide but not in 10% aqueous sodium carbonate or dilute hydrochloric acid. It is easily converted into 2-phenylpyridine.[44]

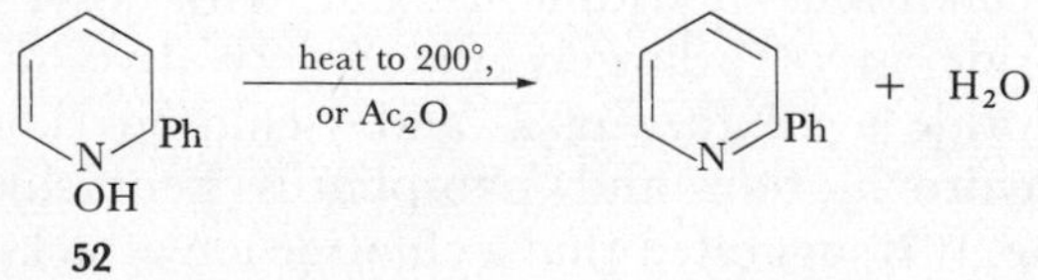

Pyridine 1-oxide can be alkylated on the oxygen atom by methyl iodide. Hydrolysis of the product with alkali yields pyridine and

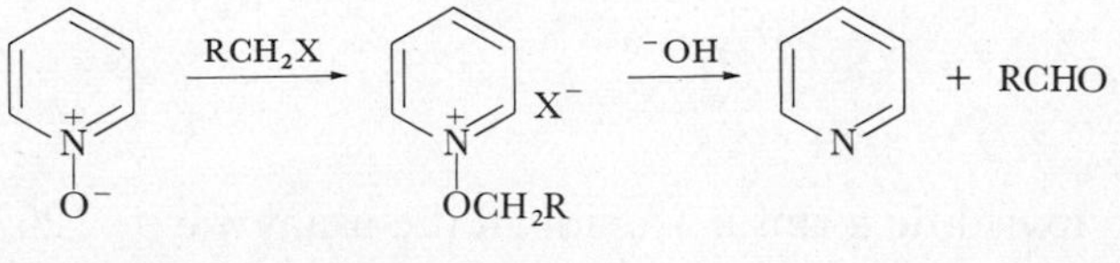

X = Cl, Br, or I; R = H or Ph

formaldehyde, and aromatic aldehydes can be obtained in excellent yield by this method.[45] Cyclic quaternary salts decompose similarly.[46]

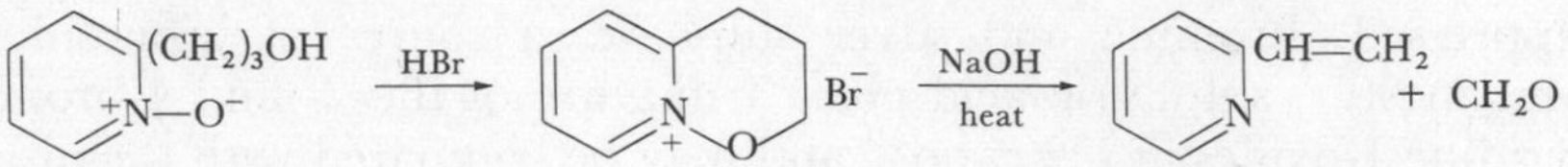

1-Methoxy-2-methylpyridinium methosulphate, obtained from the appropriate 1-oxide and methyl sulphate, with sodium cyanide yields 2-cyano-6-methylpyridine.[47] This type of reaction has valuable potentialities, and is probably similar in mechanism to the much better known conversion of pyridine 1-oxide into 2-pyridone by acetic anhydride. The first stage of the last reaction is almost certainly the formation of 53, as the corresponding perchlorate is formed from the same reactants in the presence of perchloric acid.[48] One or two other intermediates, 55 and possibly also 54, are formed as hydrogenation of the reaction mixture yields 56 while 2-pyridone is not reduced

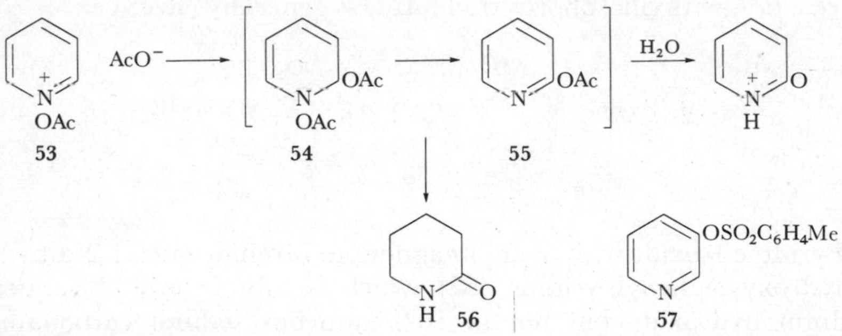

under these conditions. Pyridine 1-oxide with tosyl (4-toluenesul-phonyl) chloride gives[49] largely the 3-derivative (57), and with sulphuryl chloride a mixture of 2- and 4-chloropyridines is formed. The oxide hydrochloride and phosphorus pentachloride give 4-chloropyridine. It is suggested that a chloride ion attacks the 4-position in the last reaction.

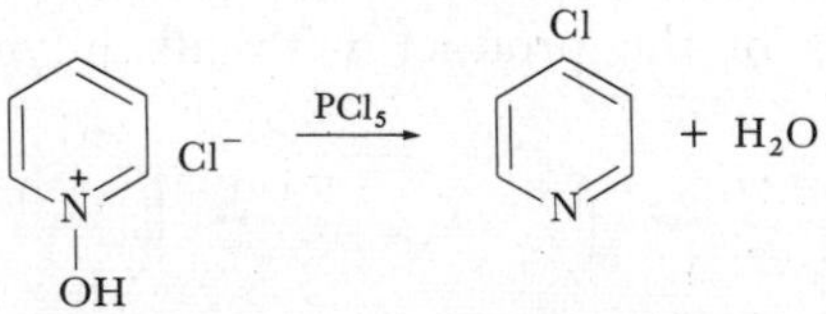

2-Methylpyridine forms a 1-oxide in the usual way (p. 207), and on treatment with acetic anhydride a mixture of 64 along with 3- and 5-acetoxy-2-methylpyridines (67 : 15 : 18 ratio, respectively), containing a small amount of the pyridone (63), is formed.[50] The reaction appears to proceed through the formation of 59, which then first gives[51] the anhydro base (**60**). This decomposes to the free-radical pair (**61**), retained in a solvent cage, and leads to **64**. Tracer studies show that there is 50% incorporation of oxygen in **64** when ^{18}O-labelled acetic anhydride is used.[52] Partial dissociation of the radical pair (**61**) and attack of the acetoxyl radical at other positions of the pyridine ring, accounts well for the minor products formed. 4-Methylpyridine

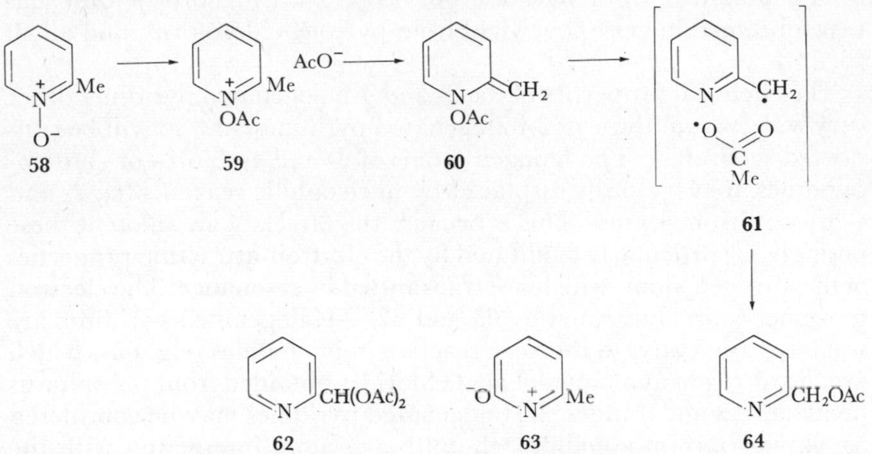

l-oxide in a similar way with acetic anhydride yields 4-acetoxy-methylpyridine and some 3-acetoxy-4-methylpyridine. Tracer studies[53] show that the reaction does not proceed in exactly the same way as for 2-methylpyridine 1-oxide, but that the acetoxy anion appears to attack the anhydro base analogous to **60**.

Conversion of 2-acetoxymethylpyridine into the 1-oxide and treatment with acetic anhydride gives a useful preparation of pyridine-2-carbaldehyde diacetate (**62**). The methyl groups of 2- and 4-methyl-pyridine 1-oxide are activated (p. 205).

5. *Halogenated pyridines*

2- and 4-Chloropyridine can be obtained in the laboratory by heating the corresponding pyridone with phosphorus oxychloride or pentachloride, a reaction reminiscent of the conversion of amides into iminochlorides (**66**) by phosphorus pentachloride. This method is the most convenient for 4-chloro- and 4-bromo-pyridines, while the 2-substituted isomers are often more readily available from 2-amino-pyridine (p. 215). 1-Methyl-2-pyridone loses its methyl group with phosphorus pentachloride, and some 2,5-dichloropyridine is also formed. 3-Hydroxypyridine does not react with any of the phosphorus halides, and has not been converted directly into a 3-halogenated pyridine. 3-Bromo- and 3-chloro-pyridine can be prepared from 3-aminopyridine by ordinary diazotization sequences. 3-Bromopyridine is also obtained from pyridine (p. 197), and 3-chloropyridine has been obtained in very poor yield from pyrrole, chloroform, and alkali (p. 73).

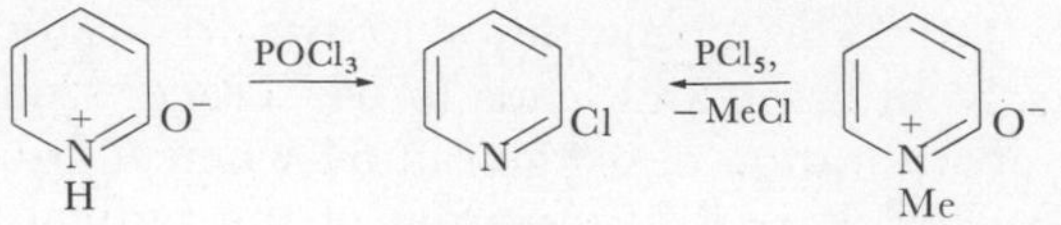

The chemical properties of the 2- and 4-halogenated pyridines differ very widely from those of 3-halogenated pyridines, and so will be considered separately. The halogen atoms of 2- and 4-chloro- or -bromo-pyridines are very easily displaced by nucleophilic reagents (cf. 2- and 4-bromonitrobenzene). This is because the attack of an anion at these positions is particularly facilitated by the electron-attracting properties of the nitrogen atom, which are transmitted by resonance. The electron movements are illustrated by **65** and **67**. 2-Halogenated pyridines are similar, structually, to the very reactive imino halides (e.g. **66**), which are the nitrogen analogues of acid chlorides obtained from phosphorus pentahalides and amides. 4-Halogenated pyridines may be considered as 'vinylogous' iminohalides, the nitrogen atom interacting with the

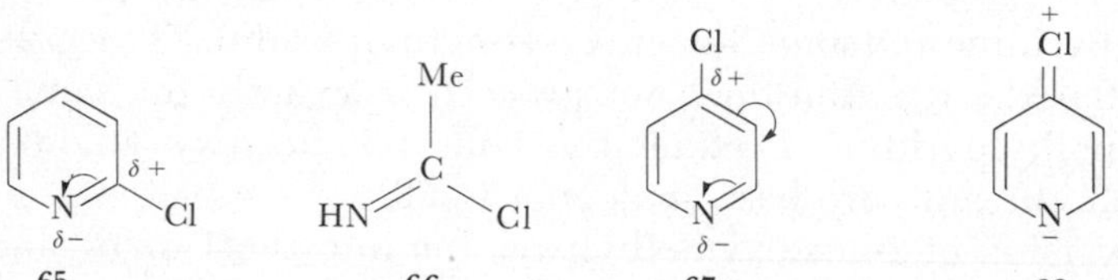

halogen through an additional double bond. In the case of 4-chloro-pyridine, dipole moment studies have shown that structure **68** is an important contributor to the resonance hybrid. Examples of (nucleo-

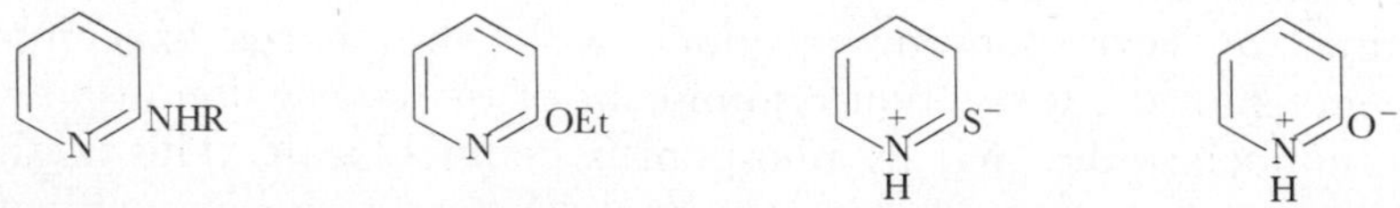

philic) attack by anions are the conversion of 2-bromo- or 2-chloro-pyridine into **69** with primary amines, into **70** with sodium ethoxide, into **71** with potassium hydrogen sulphide, and into 2-pyridone (**72**) with aqueous mineral acid. The 4-halogenated pyridines behave similarly.

4-Bromopyridine, but not 2-bromopyridine, which is more stable, reacts slowly with itself in the cold to give **73** and more complex products.

73

The methylation of 4-chloropyridine to the 1-methylpyridinium chloride increases the ease with which anions displace the chlorine atom from position 4, while conversion into the 1-oxide has the reverse effect. In the first case the positive charge on the nitrogen assists the attacking anion, while in the second the oxygen atom releases electrons to position 4 through a resonance interaction with the chlorine atom, and this discourages the negatively charged anion.

2-Bromopyridine does not form a Grignard reagent under ordinary conditions, but it will react with magnesium in the presence of reacting ethyl bromide. This is the 'entrainment' method of preparing Grignard reagents. 2-Pyridylmagnesium bromide has the normal reactions of a Grignard reagent. Halogen atoms at positions 2 and 4 of a pyridine ring are easily displaced by hydrogen on hydrogenation over palladium on strontium carbonate or Raney nickel in the presence of alkali. Chemical methods of reduction have also been used, but are not so convenient.

3-Bromopyridine is quite unlike its 2- and 4-isomers in chemical reactivity and is much more like bromobenzene in this respect. The bromine atom is not replaced by hydrogen under conditions which de-halogenate its isomers. It is displaced in the normal way by magnesium in ether giving a normal Grignard reagent and by butyllithium giving 3-pyridyllithium. Like bromobenzene, 3-bromopyridine gives 3-cyanopyridine with cuprous cyanide at 165–170°, but unlike bromo-benzene, which is inert under the conditions used, 3-bromopyridine re-acts with sodium methoxide in methanol (150°), and with ammonia and copper sulphate (150°). This suggests that the inductive effect of the

nitrogen atom is sufficient to activate the 3-position of the ring some-what towards nucleophilic reagents, and confirms observations made in this respect regarding 3-methylpyridine (p. 206). In agreement with this, the activation energy for the reaction of 3-bromopyridine with piperidine is less than that of the corresponding reaction with bromo-benzene.[54]

The reaction of 3-bromopyridine with acetophenone and sodamide in liquid ammonia (no reaction occurs in toluene) is of interest, as 4-substituted pyridines are formed.[55] Evidence is accumulating that 3,4- (e.g. **74**) and 2,3-pyridynes can be intermediates in reactions of this type.[56]

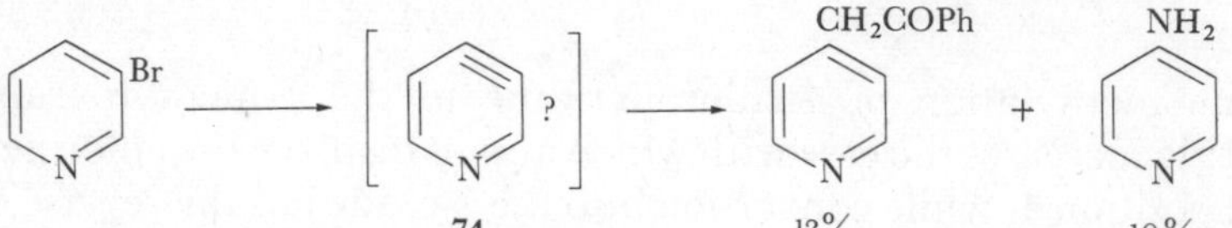

6. Nitropyridines

The direct nitration of pyridine is difficult and gives the 3-nitro derivative in poor yield. It is of little interest, as 3-aminopyridine, which can be obtained on reduction, is more easily prepared from nicotinamide (below).

2- and 4-Nitropyridines have been obtained by the hydrogen per-oxide–sulphuric acid oxidation of the corresponding amines, but 4-nitropyridine is now much more readily available from pyridine

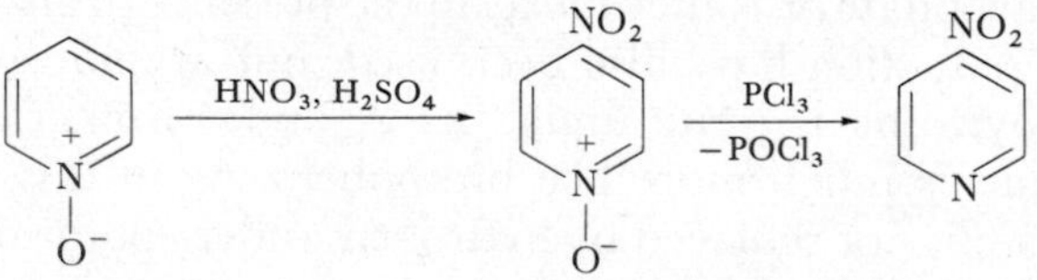

1-oxide. These nitropyridines have been little investigated. 4-Nitro-pyridine is less stable than 4-bromopyridine and rapidly polymerizes. 2-Nitropyridine 1-oxide cannot be prepared by the oxidation of

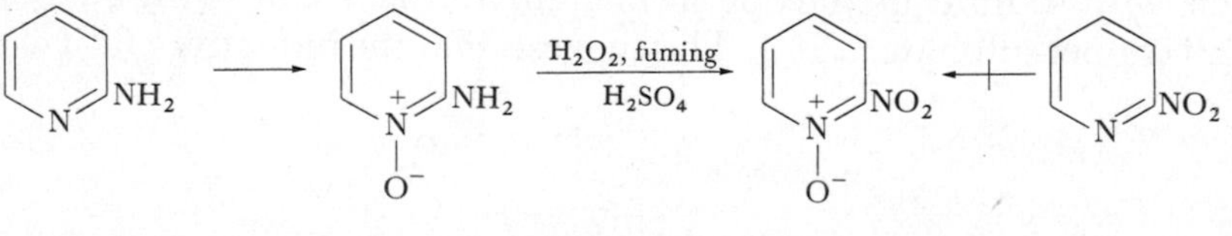

2-nitropyridine, but has been obtained[57] indirectly. Both 2- and 4-nitropyridine 1-oxides with acetyl chloride at 70° give the cor-responding chloropyridine 1-oxides, with the elimination of the nitro group, and 4-nitropyridine 1-oxide also reacts with sodium ethoxide or benzyloxide. This last displacement is similar in mechanism to the conversion of 1,2-dinitrobenzene to 2-nitrophenol by sodium hydroxide.

7. Aminopyridines

All the monoaminopyridines can be obtained from the appropriate halogenated pyridines and ammonia (pp. 212, 213), or from the corresponding acid amides via the Hofmann reaction. The most convenient methods of making 2-, 3-, and 4-aminopyridines, respectively, are from pyridine and sodamide in dimethylaniline (p. 198), from nicotinamide by Hofmann's reaction, and by reduction of 4-nitropyridine 1-oxide (p. 209).

3-Aminopyridine behaves as a typical aromatic amine, and will therefore receive little attention. It can be diazotized normally, and 3-pyridyldiazonium salts undergo the same reactions as benzenediazonium salts.

The structures of 2- and 4-aminopyridine have been subject to much discussion,[58] as tautomerism to the corresponding imino compounds is possible and the reactions of the compounds differ from those of 3-aminopyridine, where such tautomerism cannot take place. The structure of 2-aminopyridine (**75** ⇌ **76**) has been investigated[59] by a comparison of its ultraviolet absorption spectrum with those of the N-methyl compounds **77** and **78**. As it has been shown that the replacement of a hydrogen atom by a methyl group in such circumstances usually causes comparatively little change in the spectrum, compounds **77** and **78** serve as 'spectral models' for the tautomers **75** and **76**, respectively. Because the absorption spectrum of 2-aminopyridine is

quite dissimilar to that of **78** but virtually identical with that of **77**, it appears that 2-aminopyridine is best represented as the amino tautomer. Similar results have been obtained in the 4-aminopyridine series, and it has been estimated that the amount of imine tautomer (e.g. **76**) in these pyridines is less than 0·1% under the conditions of examination.

Another approach to the amine–imine problem can be made from a study of dissociation constants on the assumption that the replacement of a hydrogen atom attached to a nitrogen atom by a methyl group does not affect the basicity of an amine very much.[58] This assumption is thought to be sufficiently valid in the cases under consideration. The addition of a proton to the amine (**79**) or imine (**81**) tautomer gives the same mesomeric cation (**80**).

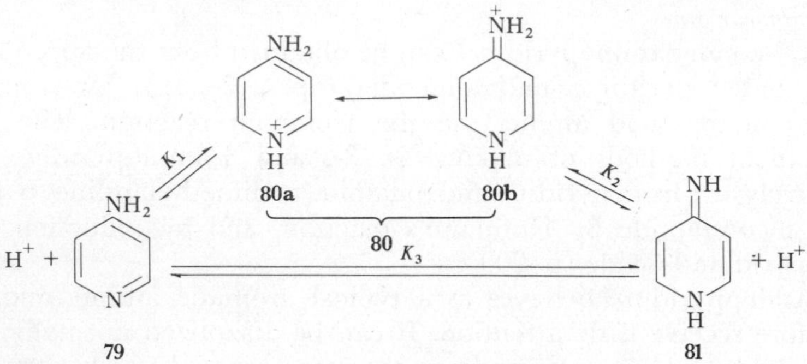

Three equilibria therefore exist, and approximations to the equilibrium constants K_1 and K_2 may be found experimentally by potentiometric

$$K_1 = \frac{[79][H^+]}{[80]} \qquad\qquad K_2 = \frac{[81][H^+]}{[80]}$$

$$K_3 = \frac{[\text{amino tautomer}]}{[\text{imino tautomer}]} = \frac{K_1}{K_2} = 2 \times 10^3$$

titrations of the appropriate methyl derivatives of **79** and **81**. These would be **82** and **83** respectively. In this particular instance titrations

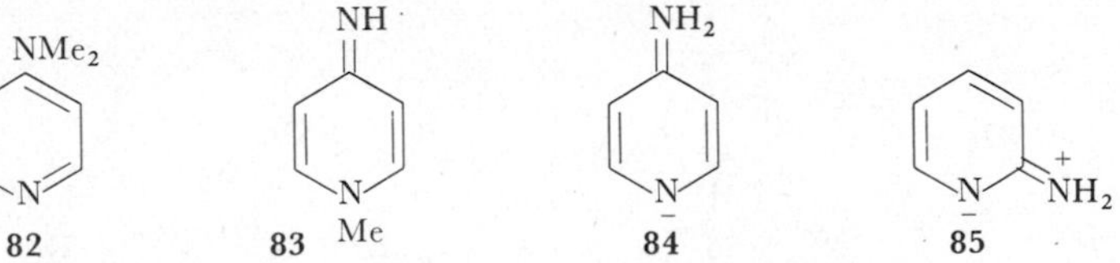

of **83** and 4-aminopyridine itself were carried out. As the results show that the amino structure is very much more stable than the imino form, the substitution of the dissociation constant of 4-aminopyridine for that of 4-dimethylaminopyridine (**82**) does not introduce much error. Very similar results were obtained in the 2-aminopyridine series, thus confirming the deductions made from absorption spectrum measurements. The dipole moment of 4-aminopyridine (4·36 D) is appreciably larger than that calculated by combining the dipole moments of aniline and pyridine. This shows that there is an additional resonance inter-action in this pyridine which is due to a contribution from **84** to the resonance hybrid. A similar charged contributor **85** can be written in the case of 2-aminopyridine but not for 3-aminopyridine.

The addition of a proton to the ring nitrogen atom of 4-amino-pyridine (**79**), but not the amino nitrogen atom, gives an ion (**80a**) for which an additional resonance structure (**80b**), above those usually associated with the pyridine ring, can be written. As this monocation has more resonance energy ('additional ionic resonance') than 4-aminopyridine itself, it will have a big tendency to form, and 4-amino-

pyridine is therefore a strong base. 2-Aminopyridine is similar, and these two compounds may be compared with amidines (e.g. **86**) which are also strongly basic and form monocations (e.g. **87**) possessing much resonance energy. 3-Aminopyridine is a much weaker base than its isomers, as the addition of a proton cannot give a molecular species with additional resonance possibilities. It is almost impossible to add a second proton to the monocation (**80**) of 4-aminopyridine because if this occurred the 'additional ionic resonance' would necessarily be lost.

Attempted diazotization of 2- and 4-aminopyridines in aqueous acid gives the corresponding pyridone; no trace of diazonium salt can be detected by attempted coupling with alkaline 2-naphthol. However, 2-aminopyridine with boiling sodium ethoxide and amyl nitrite gives the sodium diazotate (**88**), which couples with 2-naphthol in the normal manner. It therefore appears that the failure to obtain a diazonium salt under ordinary conditions is due to its reactivity and not to its inherent instability. This reactivity is almost certainly due to the pyridine ring of the diazonium cation (**89**) being protonated in the mineral acid solution. The positive charge on the ring will greatly facilitate the attack of nucleophilic reagents, including water and hydroxyl ions, at position 2, with the elimination of nitrogen. The situation is similar to the attempted diazotization of 2,4,6-trinitroaniline under ordinary conditions, when the product is 2,4,6-trinitrophenol. 2-Bromopyridine can be obtained in excellent yield from 2-aminopyridine hydrobromide perbromide in 48% hydrobromic acid and sodium nitrite. Here the bromide anion successfully competes with the water molecule for the pyridinium–diazonium dication (**89**). 4-Chloropyridine has been obtained similarly from 4-aminopyridine and sodium nitrite in concentrated hydrochloric acid.

2-Aminopyridine on irradiation in dilute hydrochloric acid gives a dimer[60] which is structually analogous to that from 2-pyridone (p. 221).

4-Aminopyridine 1-oxide is easily prepared from pyridine 1-oxide by nitration and subsequent reduction with ammonium hydrogen sulphide or hydrogen over palladium. It can tautomerize but, as in the case of 4-aminopyridine, ultraviolet absorption studies have shown that the

amino form preponderates. This 1-oxide is of particular interest, as it can be diazotized in the usual way, and the diazonium salt undergoes the common reactions of aromatic diazonium compounds. As 1-oxides are easily reduced to the corresponding pyridines, this is a convenient route to 4-substituted derivatives. 4-Aminopyridine 1-oxide gives 4-aminopyridine with sodium hydrosulphite or with hydrogen and palladium in the presence of hydrochloric acid.

2-Aminopyridine 1-oxide is obtained directly from 2-aminopyridine with peracetic acid. It also exists largely in the amino form, and can also be diazotized and coupled with alkaline 2-naphthol. The greater stability of these diazonium salts of the 1-oxides, in comparison with those derived from pyridine itself, is probably due both to an electron release from the oxygen atom, which discourages attack by water molecules and anions on the ring, and to a resonance stabilization of the cation.

8. *Hydroxypyridines*

3-Hydroxypyridine (**90**) is best obtained by fusing pyridine-3-sulphonic acid with potassium hydroxide, but has been prepared by decomposing pyridine-3-diazonium salts with water. 3-Hydroxy-

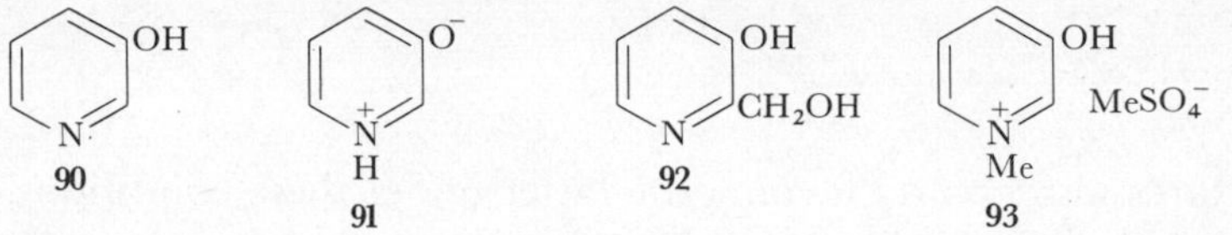

pyridine does tautomerize partially to a betaine (**91**), but it cannot tautomerize to an amide-like structure as do its 2- and 4-hydroxy isomers. 3-Hydroxypyridine has many typical phenolic properties. It gives a ferric chloride colour, it gives **92** with formaldehyde, and it nitrates and sulphonates at position 2. Both diazomethane and methyl sulphate with alkali attack the ring nitrogen in preference to the hydroxyl group, and in the second instance **93** is the product. However, with diazomethane in *t*-butyl alcohol at −15° it gives 3-methoxy-pyridine (70% yield).[61]

2-Pyridone, which is sometimes written as the tautomeric 2-hydroxy-pyridine, is obtained most readily from 2-aminopyridine and nitrous acid or from pyridine 1-oxide and acetic anhydride. It can also be pre-

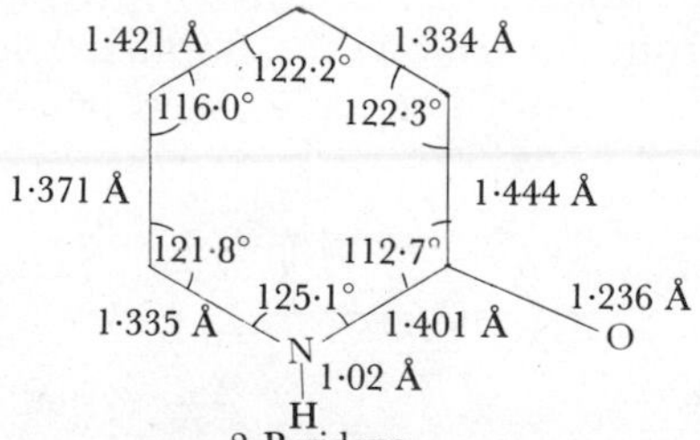

2-Pyridone

pared from pyridine and potassium hydroxide at about 300°, or from 2-chloropyridine with hot dilute mineral acid. It is a colourless solid, m.p. 107°, soluble in alcohol and water, and its structure in the crystal has been determined by x-ray methods.[62] The results show clearly that the keto tautomer is present and that the lattice is hydrogen bonded. In methanol the ultraviolet absorption spectrum of the compound is very similar to that of 1-methyl-2-pyridone (**94**), but it differs markedly from that of 2-ethoxypyridine (**97**). The infrared absorption spectra both of 1-methyl-2-pyridone and of the unmethylated compound show a similar absorption band in the carbonyl region, which is completely absent in 2-methoxypyridine.[63] It therefore appears that the equilibrium between the 2-hydroxypyridine (**96**) and 2-pyridone (**95**)

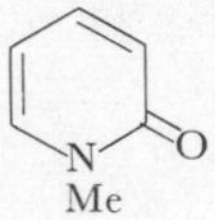

| 94 | 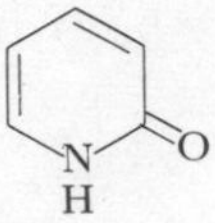 95 | 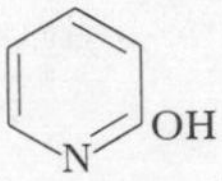 96 | 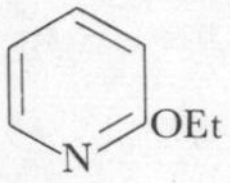 97 |

structures also greatly favours the latter under these conditions. As 2-pyridone is very weakly basic, has no normal carbonyl properties, and has a strongly aromatic type of ultraviolet absorption spectrum, it cannot be represented accurately by structure **95**. It is better written as **98** to emphasize its aromatic character and considered as a resonance hybrid to which contribute both the uncharged structure **95** and charged

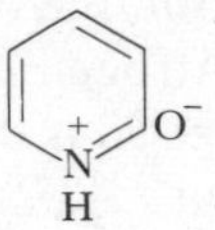

| 98 | 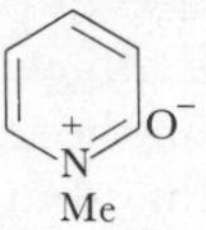 99 |

structures such as **98**, where the ring is benzenoid and has its usual various Kekulé forms. 1-Methyl-2-pyridone (**94** and **99**) is similar.

2-Pyridone forms salts with sodium ethoxide and with strong acids, such as hydrogen chloride in ether or concentrated sulphuric acid. These salts are derived from the resonance-stabilized ions **100** and **101**[64] respectively. 2-Pyridone can behave as such or as 2-hydroxypyridine

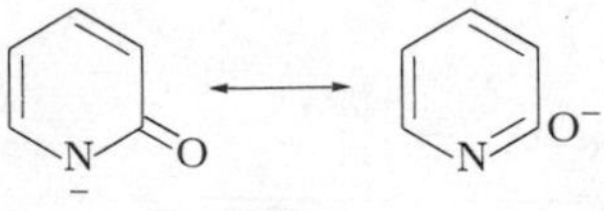

| 100 | 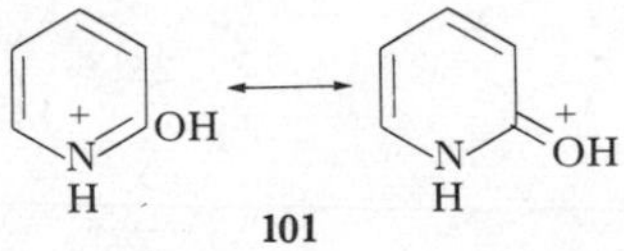 101 |

towards chemical reagents. With methyl iodide it gives 1-methyl-2-pyridone, while with diazomethane 2-methoxypyridine is formed. This last compound can also be obtained by the alternative sequence

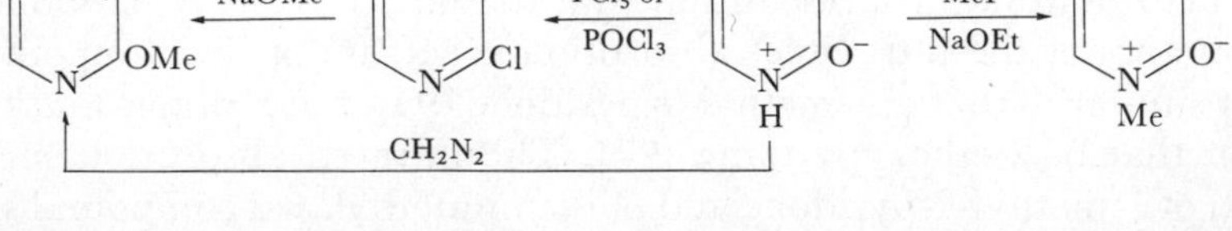

shown above, and is hydrolysed by aqueous mineral acid to methanol and 2-pyridone. This reaction is similar to the hydrolysis of imino ethers (e.g. **102**) to amides by water. 2-Allyloxypyridine undergoes a

$$\text{MeCN} \xrightarrow{\text{MeOH, HCl}} \underset{\underset{\text{OMe}}{\overset{\overset{+}{\text{NH}_2}\ \ \text{Cl}^-}{\big|}}}{\text{MeC}} \xrightarrow{\text{H}_2\text{O}} \text{MeCONH}_2 + \text{MeOH} + \text{HCl}$$

102

normal Claisen rearrangement giving a mixture of equal quantities of 1- and 3-allyl-2-pyridone.[65] 2-Pyridone is easily halogenated to first the 5- and then the 3,5-disubstituted derivative, and nitration also takes place preferentially at position 5.

Both 2-pyridone (**98**) and its 1-methyl derivative (**99**) are dimerized[66] by ultraviolet light, possibly via the formation of an intermediate 1,4-diradical, to **103**.

103, R = H or Me

4-Pyridone is readily obtained by the route indicated; 4-chloro-pyridine is presumably first formed and reacts with pyridine to give the salt (**104**). The structure of 4-pyridone, according to ultraviolet

absorption measurements, is exactly analogous to that of 2-pyridone, and the compound is best represented as a resonance hybrid involving the pyridone tautomer (**105–105a**) almost exclusively. A large contribution by the charged structure (**105a**) is indicated by the high dipole moment of 6·0 D. The reactions of 4-pyridone are exactly parallel to those of 2-pyridone and under the appropriate conditions, for example with methyl iodide or diazomethane, it will give *N*- or *O*-methyl derivatives respectively, and it protonates on the oxygen atom.[64] On bromination or nitration it gives 3- and 3,5-substitution products, and its sodium salt, like sodium phenate (Kolbe's reaction), combines with carbon dioxide at 230° to give the sodium salt (**106**); subsequent reaction gives **107**.[67]

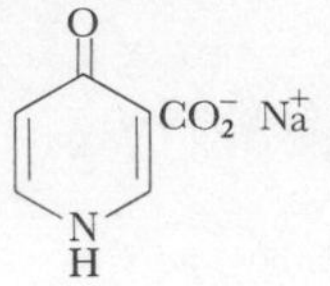

106 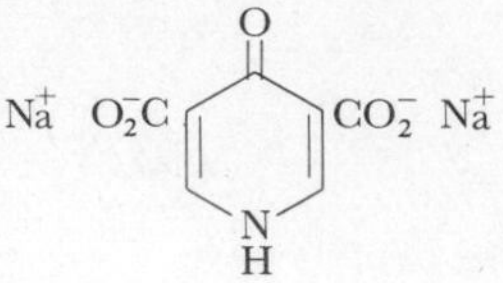   107

'2,4-Dihydroxypyridine' (**108**) is of interest, as three tautomeric structures are possible. From an absorption spectra study[68] it has been shown that **109–110** is predominant in 50% aqueous ethanol. This is expected, as the charge separation in the ionic resonance form (**110**) of

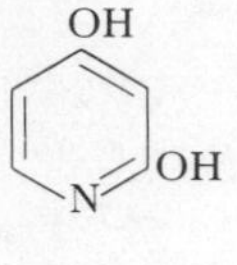

108 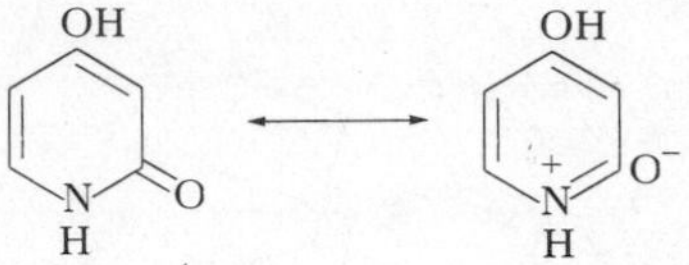   109   110 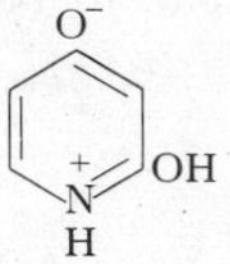   111

this structure is less than that in the 4-pyridone tautomer (**111**).

The 1-oxides of 2- and 4-pyridones have been obtained by the catalytic debenzylation of the benzyloxypyridines. On the whole, physical evidence suggests that in the strongly hydrogen-bonded 2-hydroxypyridine 1-oxide the pyridone tautomer (**112**) is the more stable, while in the case of the 4-hydroxy isomer there is little difference in stability between the two possible formulations.[69]

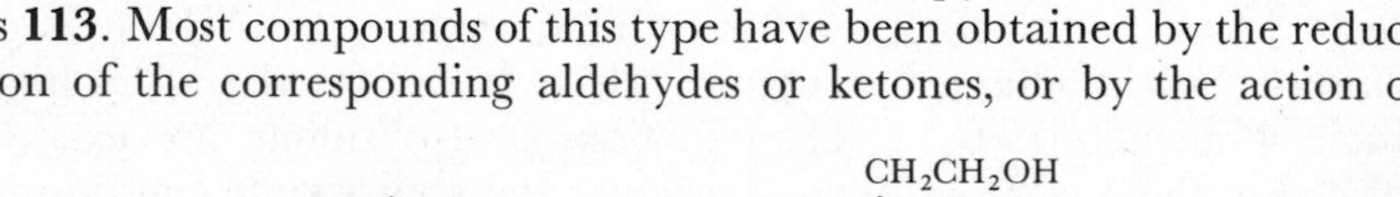

112

9. Pyridine alcohols, aldehydes, and carboxylic acids

Comparatively little work has been done on pyridinemethanols such as **113**. Most compounds of this type have been obtained by the reduction of the corresponding aldehydes or ketones, or by the action of

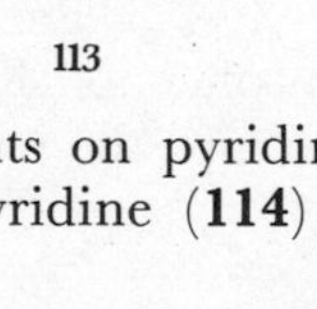

113 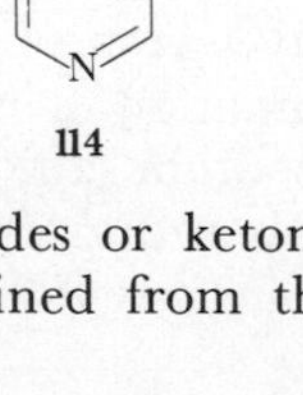   114

Grignard reagents on pyridine aldehydes or ketones. 2- and 4-(2-Hydroxyethyl)pyridine (**114**) are obtained from the corresponding

methylpyridines with formaldehyde, and they dehydrate readily
to the vinylpyridines, which have been discussed earlier (p. 205).

Pyridine aldehydes have been investigated comparatively little.[70]
The direct oxidation of the methylpyridines under laboratory conditions usually gives poor yields, but a vapour-phase aerial oxidation has
been used technically. Both the 2- and 3-carbaldehydes can be obtained

115

in fair yield by the Grignard method, and the 3-carbaldehyde (b.p.
202°) is perhaps most easily prepared (60–70% yield) by the oxidation
of the hydrazide (115) with sodium metaperiodate and ammonia.[71]
Pyridine-2-carbaldehyde (b.p. 181°) is readily available from 2-
methylpyridine 1-oxide by a convenient laboratory procedure involving hydrolysis of the diacetate (p. 211), and this method has been
used in other instances.

The pyridine aldehydes are all water-soluble colourless liquids, which
on oxidation with hydrogen peroxide give the corresponding acids.
They have many of the usual reactions of aromatic aldehydes. Pyridine-
2-carbaldehyde with aqueous potassium cyanide undergoes a normal
condensation with the precipitation of 2-pyridoin (116), which actually
exists as the tautomer (117) in neutral or weakly acid solution.[72]

116   117   118   119

Pyridine-3-carbaldehyde gives no precipitate under the same conditions, and the reaction products are not known, while pyridine-4-
carbaldehyde gives a mixture of the acid (118) and the alcohol (119).
These are the products expected of a Cannizzaro reaction which is
perhaps initiated by reaction with potassium hydroxide formed by the
hydrolysis of the potassium cyanide.

Pyridinecarboxylic acids are obtainable from many pyridine syntheses, and can be prepared by general methods, including the oxidation
of alkylpyridines with alkaline potassium permanganate. Many of the
acids were first obtained by the oxidation of natural products at early
dates, and have been given trivial names which are still widely used.

Picolinic acid,
m.p. 137°

120

Nicotinic acid,
m.p. 229°

Isonicotinic acid,
m.p. 299°

The oxidation of the alkaloid nicotine gives nicotinic acid. This acid is of particular importance, as it is a vitamin for man, and it is obtained commercially by the oxidation of quinoline. The first product, quinolinic (pyridine-2,3-dicarboxylic) acid, can be isolated and subsequently selectively decarboxylated, or both reactions can be carried out together. A similar oxidation of isoquinoline gives pyridine-3,4-dicarboxylic acid, which on decarboxylation gives pyridine-3-carboxylic (nicotinic) acid along with some pyridine-4-carboxylic (isonicotinic) acid. Assuming the structures of quinoline and isoquinoline, these relationships prove the structures of the pyridinemonocarboxylic acids involved, and the remaining one must be picolinic acid. In the decarboxylation of pyridine acids carboxyl groups at position 2 are always

Quinoline

Se, H_2SO_4, 300°

lost preferentially and then usually carboxyl groups at position 4. The mechanism of decarboxylation is discussed on p. 260.

Pyridinecarboxylic acids in general have properties normal to the pyridine ring and aromatic carboxyl groups. They are betaines (e.g. **120**), at least to some extent, and it is interesting that picolinic acid melts (137°) much lower than its isomers. This is because interaction between the charged centres of the zwitterion (**120**) has more intra-molecular character than is possible with its isomers. Pyridine-2-carboxylic acids give a yellow-brown colour with ferrous salts, Skraup's test.[73] The constitution of the coloured complex from picolinic acid is not known with certainty, but may be **121**. Pyridine-3- and -4-carboxylic acids do not give a colour under these conditions.

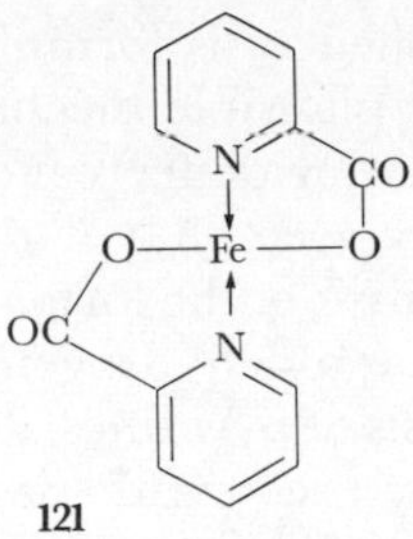

121

E. Synthetic methods

There are many ways in which the pyridine ring can be synthesized, but only syntheses of particular theoretical or practical interest will be considered here. The first, due to Hantzsch, was published in 1881.

(1) Pyridine has been synthesized from glutaconic aldehyde (**122**) and from pentamethylenediamine (p. 190). These syntheses confirm the ring structure but have little practical interest.

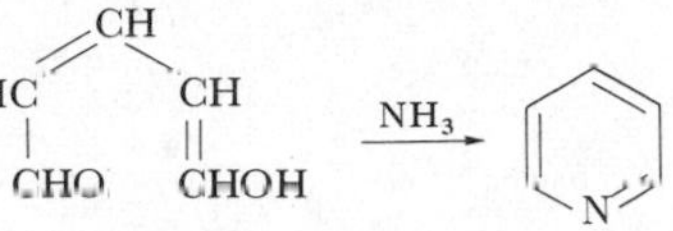

122

(2) Many aldehydes and ketones can react with ammonia to give pyridines under the correct conditions. Owing to the availability of the reactants, this type of synthesis has attracted much interest, but mixtures are often formed, even if yields are good. 5-Ethyl-2-methyl-pyridine (**123**) can be obtained from ammonia and acetaldehyde. In the laboratory the reaction is best carried out by heating paraldehyde, ammonia, and ammonium acetate to 230° for an hour in a steel autoclave, when 50–53% yields can be obtained along with some 2-methyl-pyridine. Yields of up to 70% of the pyridine (**123**) have been reported

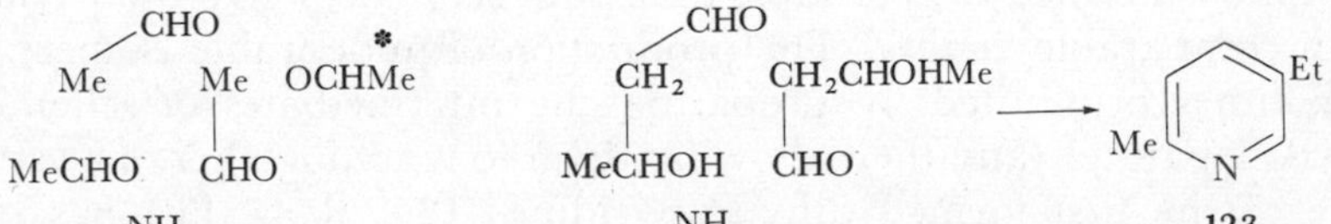

123

occasionally. The mechanism of the reaction is not clear, although it almost certainly proceeds via aldol condensations. These may involve acetaldehyde or the corresponding imine, acetaldimine, which will be present at least to some extent in the mixture. For simplicity, only one of the possible reaction sequences is formulated, and it must be emphasized that other equally plausible mechanistic routes are possible, and that direct experimental evidence concerning any mechanism is entirely lacking. It is easily seen that if the acetaldehyde molecule marked with an asterisk is missing, the formation of 2-methylpyridine is accounted for, providing that a dehydrogenation can take place.

(3) The Hantzsch synthesis of pyridines, if variations are included, is the most flexible and widely used synthesis of pyridine derivatives. It consists of essentially in treating a β-keto ester with an aldehyde in the presence of ammonia. A 1,4-dihydropyridine (124) is first formed, and this is oxidized *in situ*, often with nitric acid, to the pyridine (125).

$$
\begin{array}{ccc}
\text{R} & & \\
\text{CHO} & & \\
\text{EtO}_2\text{CCH}_2 \quad \text{CH}_2\text{CO}_2\text{Et} & \xrightarrow{\text{A}} & \text{EtO}_2\text{CCH} \quad \text{CCO}_2\text{Et} \\
\text{MeCO} \quad \text{OCMe} & & \text{MeC} \quad \text{COMe} \\
\text{NH}_3 & & \text{NH}_2
\end{array}
$$

(Scheme: first structure labelled with R/CHO, EtO₂CCH₂, MeCO, CH₂CO₂Et, OCMe, NH₃ → via A → R HC=, EtO₂CCH, MeC, CCO₂Et, COMe, NH₂)

B ↓   A ↗

$$
\begin{array}{ccccc}
\text{R} & & & & \\
\text{CH} & & & & \\
\text{EtO}_2\text{CCH} \quad \text{CHCO}_2\text{Et} & \xrightarrow{\text{B}} & \text{EtO}_2\text{C} \quad \text{CO}_2\text{Et} & \xrightarrow{\text{HNO}_3} & \text{EtO}_2\text{C} \quad \text{CO}_2\text{Et} \\
\text{MeCO} \quad \text{OCMe} & & \text{Me} \quad \text{Me} & & \text{Me} \quad \text{Me} \\
\text{NH}_3 & & \text{N} & & \text{N} \\
& & \text{H} & & \\
& & \textbf{124} & & \textbf{125}
\end{array}
$$

Examples are the condensations of acetaldehyde and of benzaldehyde with ethyl acetoacetate. Two routes by which the reactions could proceed are outlined, and as excellent yields of pyridines are often obtained when the suggested intermediates of either scheme are used, it may be concluded that equilibrium between the intermediates of both schemes is rapidly attained or, perhaps, that both sequences give the pyridine with comparable facility. The production of undesirable isomers can sometimes be limited by preparing the intermediates of scheme A (or B) separately and then allowing them to react together. The structure of the first formed dihydropyridine (124, R = Ph) has been established[74] by ozonolysis to phenylacetic acid. A careful examination[75] of the reaction between crotonaldehyde and β-aminocrotonic ester in the presence of pyridine has shown the formation of three products. On distillation *in vacuo* the dihydropyridine (126) gives some 127, doubtless through disproportionation; a similar disproportionation of **126** to **127** and **128** takes place on shaking with a palladium-on-charcoal hydrogenation catalyst. Occasionally in the Hantzsch synthesis the substituent, which should appear at position 4 of the final pyridine, is lost. This is particularly the case when it is big and an electron-releasing group.[76]

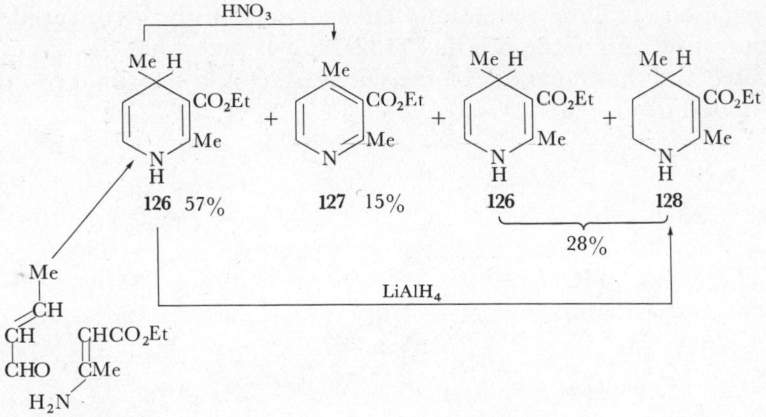

Reaction of the 1,5-diketone (**129**) of route B (above) with hydroxylamine, instead of ammonia, gives the pyridine directly.

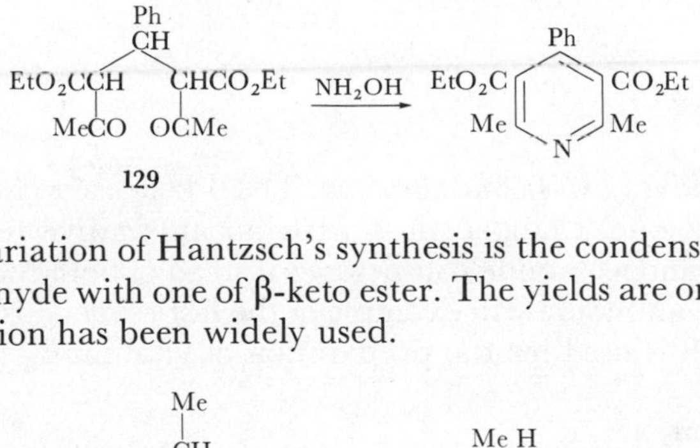

Another variation of Hantzsch's synthesis is the condensation of two moles of aldehyde with one of β-keto ester. The yields are only 20–30%, but the reaction has been widely used.

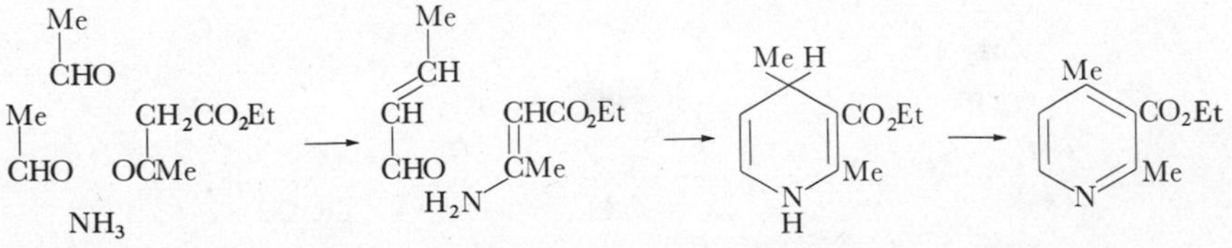

The structure of **130**, prepared by Hantzsch's synthesis, has been proved by its nuclear magnetic resonance spectrum,[77] which is not consistent with a 1,2-dihydro formulation (**131**). The compound reacts with maleic anhydride to give a product (**132**) which absorbs two moles of

I*

hydrogen on catalytic reduction. This, coupled with the infrared absorption spectrum of the product (132), shows that it has the structure indicated and that it cannot be the Diels–Alder adduct which could be anticipated from structure 131.

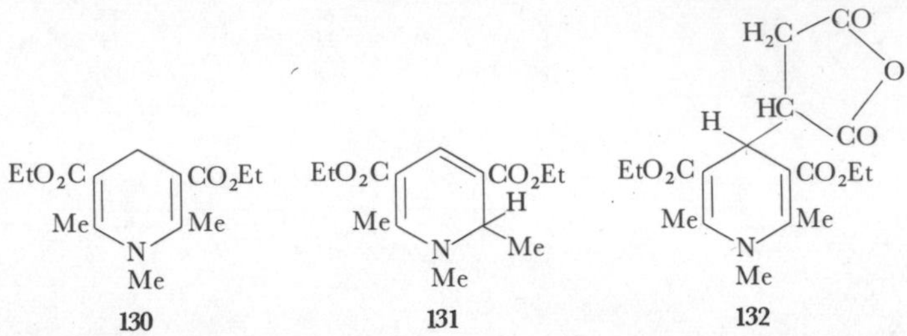

130   131   132

Guareschi and Thorpe have used β-keto esters instead of the two acetaldehyde molecules in the above variation, and in this case it is necessary to use cyanacetic ester or amide as the second component. As the oxidation state of the reactants is higher than that employed in the original Hantzsch synthesis, a pyridine is formed directly. There are

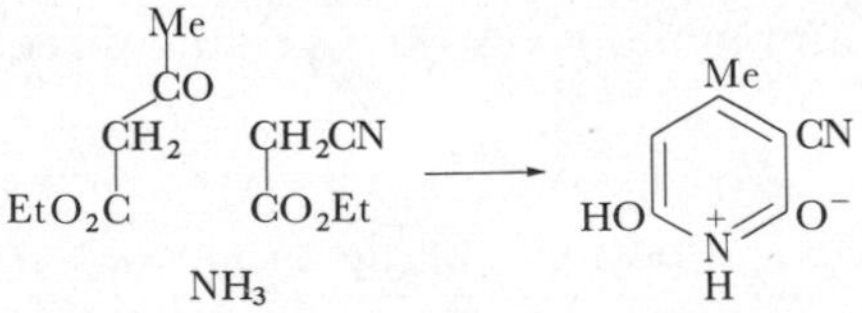

many variations of this condensation. The β-keto ester can be replaced by a 1,3-diketone, cyanoacetic acid is an alternative to cyanoacetic ester, and cyanoacetamide can be used instead of both the cyanoacetic ester and the ammonia. An example of the last reaction is the synthesis of 133, which is used for the preparation of vitamin B_6 (p. 233).

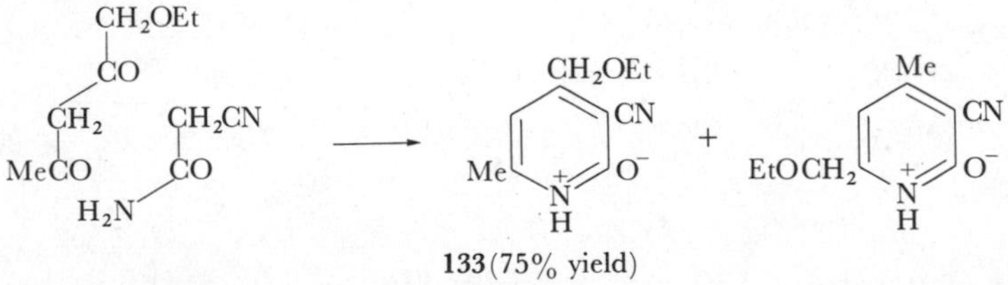

133 (75% yield)

Another variation[78] of the synthesis which leads directly to a pyridine starts from an acetylene.

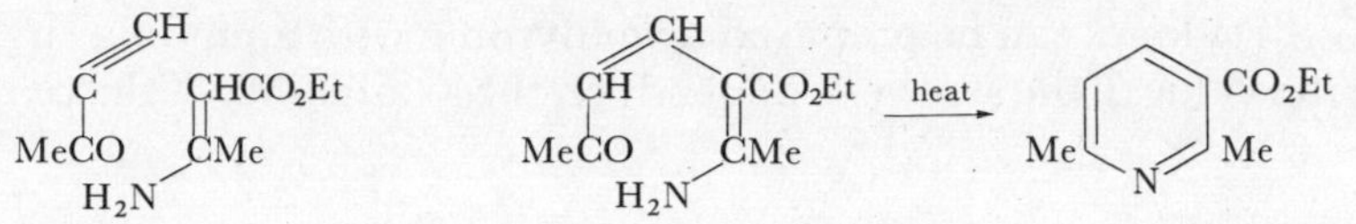

Two adaptable and useful syntheses of pyridines from furans have been developed recently. Many 2-furyl ketones (**134**) on heating with ammonia and ammonium chloride give 3-hydroxypyridines.[79] Another route,[80] starting from 2-acetylfuran, gives the pyridone 1-oxide (**135**).

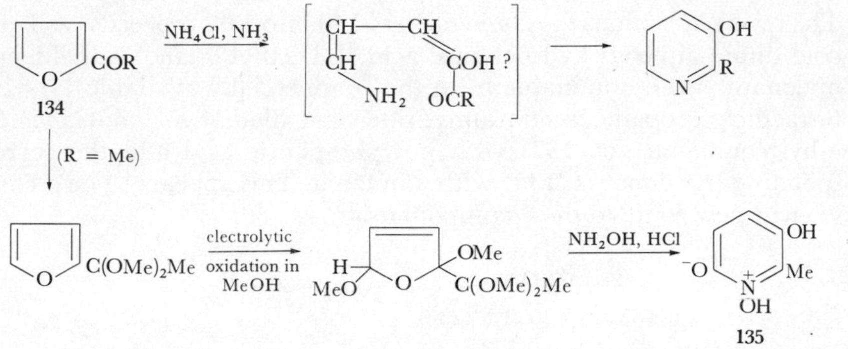

A third synthesis[81] starts from **136**, which can be prepared by the reductive acetylation (hydrogen, Raney nickel, and acetic anhydride) of 2-acetylfuran oxime. Pyridoxine (vitamin B_6) has been prepared by an

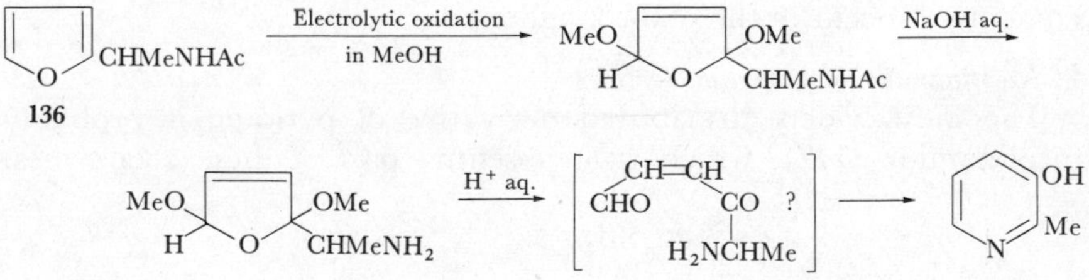

adaptation of this method.[81]

(5) The Diels–Alder reaction has been used very recently[82] to build up the pyridine ring, and the combination of butadiene and cyanogen at 400° provides a synthesis of 2-cyanopyridine.[83]

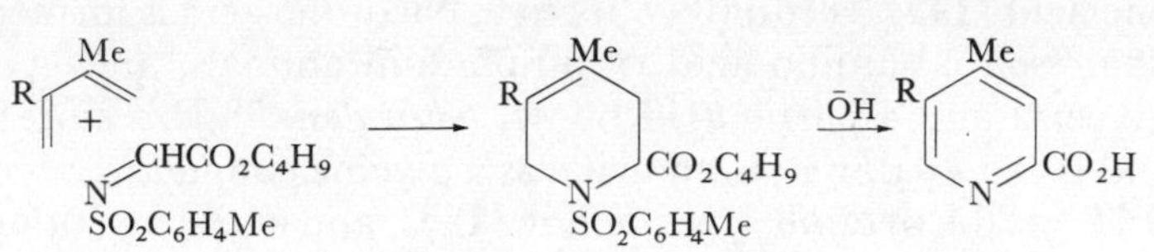

(6) Pyridones can be prepared from pyrones with ammonia (p. 240), and the value of the synthesis depends on the availability of the pyrones.

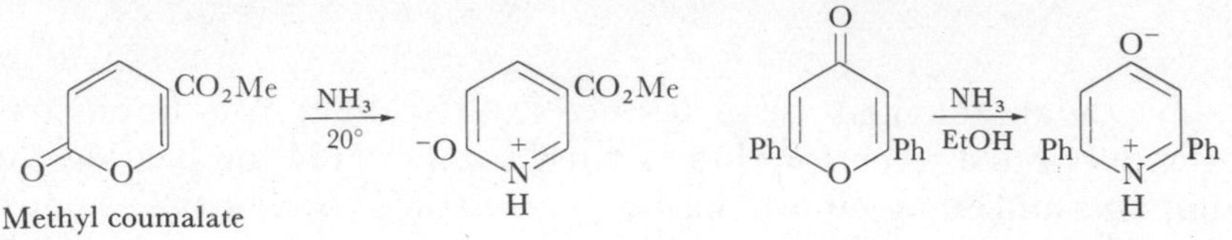

Methyl coumalate

137   138   139   140

The reverse reaction, the conversion of **140** into **139**, proceeds easily in cold dilute aqueous hydrochloric acid.[84] Diethyl 3-ethoxyallylidene-malonate (**141**), obtainable from the commercially available 1,1,3,3-tetraethoxypropane, acetic anhydride, and diethyl malonate, yields ethyl coumalate (cf. **137**) with polyphosphoric acid and the corresponding pyridone (cf. **138**) with ammonia. This appears to be a convenient new route to these compounds.[85]

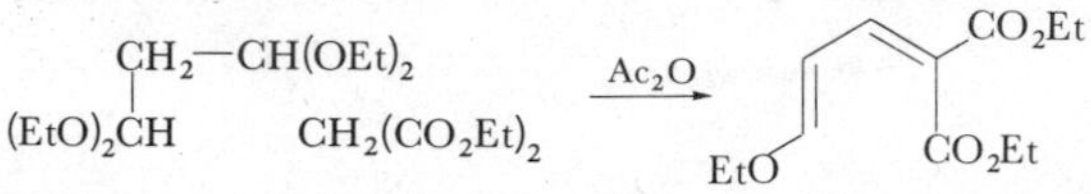

141

F. Natural occurrence and compounds of special interest

Pyridine itself does not occur free in nature, although piperidine is present as a salt in black pepper. Numerous derivatives of both these compounds occur in the plant kingdom.

1. *Nicotinamide adenine dinucleotides*

The most widely distributed derivative of pyridine is probably nicotinamide (**142**), which is an essential part of these coenzymes.

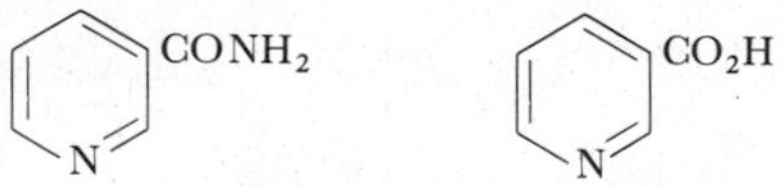

142   143

Nicotinamide was identified in 1937 as the substance necessary for the prevention of the deficiency disease, pellagra, in man. The free acid, nicotinic acid (**143**), is equally effective. Nicotinic acid is formed *in vivo* from the essential amino acid tryptophan in animals, and is built up from glycerol and aspartic acid by *M. tuberculosis*.[86] It is stored in the liver and is excreted in human urine as a glycine conjugate, nicotinuric acid (**144**), as the betaine, trigonelline (**145**), and as the pyridone (**146**).

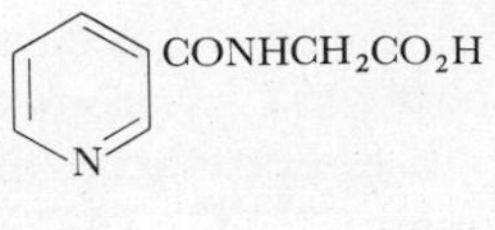

144 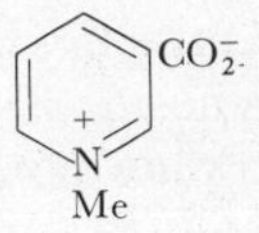   145 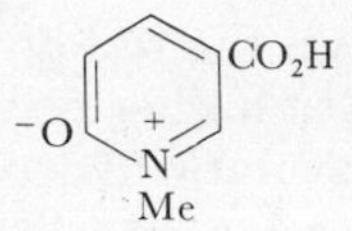   146

Nicotinamide adenine dinucleotide (NAD, **147**) and its phosphate (NADP, **148**), also known as di- (DPN) and tri-phosphopyridine nucleotide (TPN), respectively, are very widely distributed. They are involved in oxidation–reduction processes in living organisms. It is very probable that during the reduction a proton and two electrons are

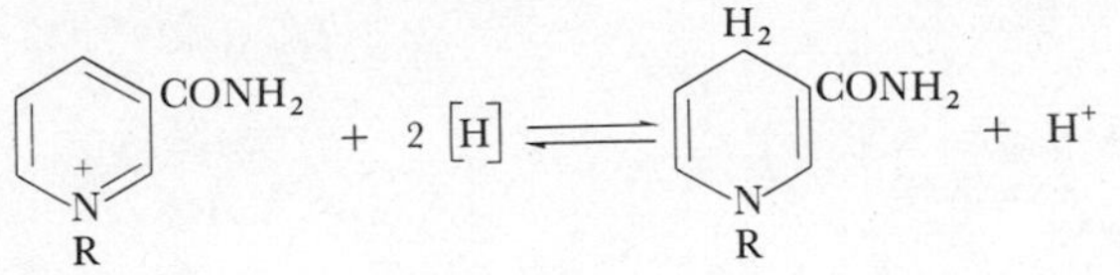

added to the pyridine ring to give, effectively, a planar 1,4-dihydropyridine.[87]

The structure of NAD (**147**) was first deduced by degradative

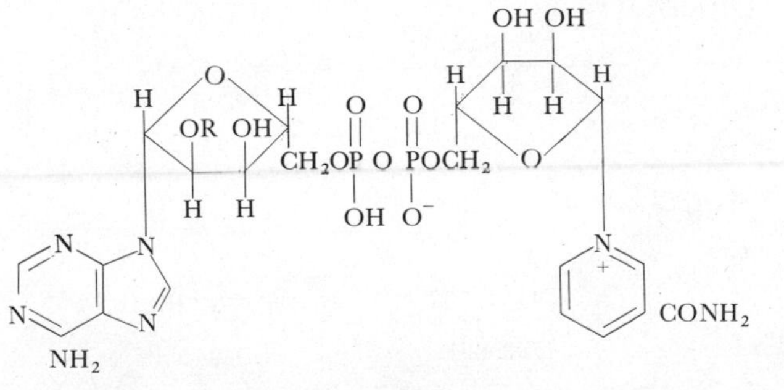

147, R = H. Nicotinamide adenine nucleotide (NAD)
148, R = PO$_3$H$_2$. Nicotinamide adenine nucleotide phosphate (NADP)

studies[88] and later confirmed by synthesis.[89] Acid hydrolysis of the nucleotide (**147**) gives adenine (**149**), ribose-5-phosphate (**150**), and nicotinamide (**151**). Dilute cold alkali splits off the nicotinamide and

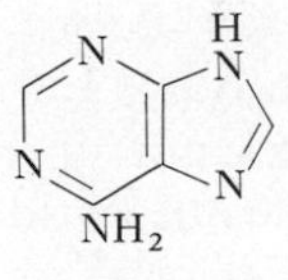

149 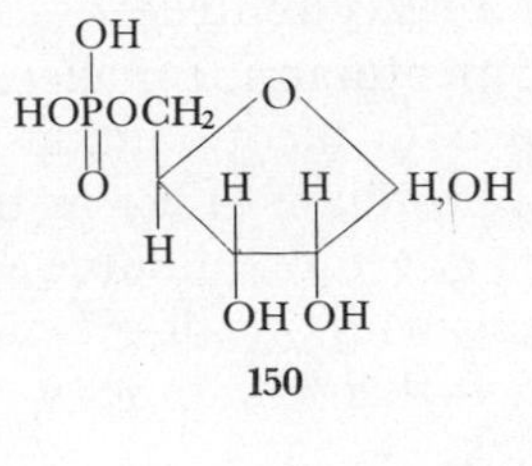   150 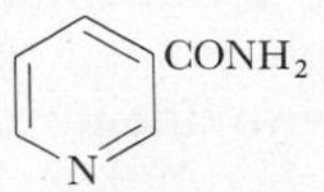   151

leaves the rest of the molecule intact, while if this hydrolysis is carried out at higher temperatures adenosine-5′-phosphate (157) is produced. Enzymatic hydrolysis with phospho-mono- and -di-esterases gave nicotinamide-riboside (155), adenosine, and phosphate. NAD (147) was also shown to be monoacidic and so its structure was on a firm basis before being confirmed by synthesis.

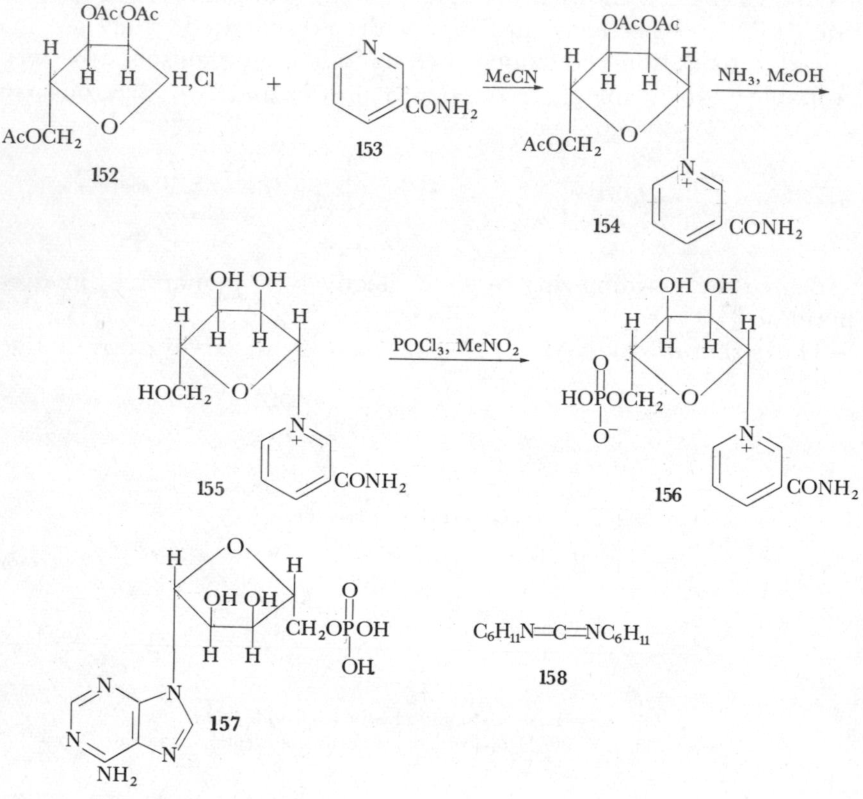

Acetylchlororibofuranose (152), prepared from ribose by acetylation and subsequent treatment with ethereal hydrogen chloride, reacts with nicotinamide (153) in acetonitrile as solvent giving 154. On hydrolysis with ammonia, nicotinamide nucleoside (155) is formed and is phosphorylated as shown to nicotinamide nucleotide (156). This reacts with adenosine-5′-phosphate (157) in the presence of dicyclohexylcarbodiimide (158) to give nicotinamide adenine nucleotide (147). The diimide probably reacts with one or other of the phosphates (159) to give an ester (160), which then combines with the other phosphate.

$$
\underset{\substack{| \\ \text{OH} \\ \mathbf{159}}}{\overset{\substack{\text{O} \\ \parallel}}{\text{ROPOH}}} \xrightarrow{\mathbf{158}} \underset{\substack{| \\ \text{O} \\ | \\ \text{HOPOR} \\ \parallel \\ \text{O} \\ \mathbf{160}}}{C_6H_{11}N{=}C{-}NHC_6H_{11}} \xrightarrow{R'OP(OH)_2} \underset{\substack{\parallel \quad | \\ \text{O} \quad \text{OH} \\ \mathbf{161}}}{\overset{\substack{\text{OH O} \\ | \quad \parallel}}{\text{ROP O POR}'}}
$$

$$+$$

$$C_6H_{11}NHCONHC_6H_{11}$$

$$\mathbf{162}$$

The pyrophosphate (**161**) and the urea (**162**) are the products. Dicyclohexylcarbodiimide is also used as a dehydration reagent in the synthesis of penicillin (p. 48).

2. *Pyridoxine*

Pyridoxine, or vitamin B_6, is the factor required to prevent the development of a dermatitis in rats, and through the use of this property for assay it was isolated in several laboratories in 1938. Chemical studies soon disclosed the structure (**163**) of the vitamin. It was amphoteric, gave a positive ferric chloride colour test, and showed the presence of three active hydrogens by reaction with methylmagnesium iodide (Zerewitinoff's method).

The absorption spectrum of pyridoxine closely resembled that of 3-hydroxypyridine, and with diazomethane the ether (**164**) was obtained. The acid (**165**), obtained on oxidation of the ether, gave a phthalein with resorcinol. This indicated a 1,2-arrangement of the carboxyl groups. The acid gave no colour with ferrous sulphate, which showed that no carboxyl group was at position 2 of the pyridine ring (p. 224). These data leave only two possible structures for pyridoxine, and the formation of **166** through decarboxylation of the acid confirms one (**163**) and excludes the other, which has the methyl group at position 6.

The commercial synthesis of Harris and Folkers is outlined on the next page; other syntheses have been carried out subsequently.

Pyridoxine is converted into pyridoxal-5-phosphate (**167**) *in vivo*, and this phosphate is required in a great variety of enzymic reactions involving amino acids. Snell[90] has succeeded in reproducing a number of these reactions by incubating pyridoxal and a metal (copper, cobalt, or

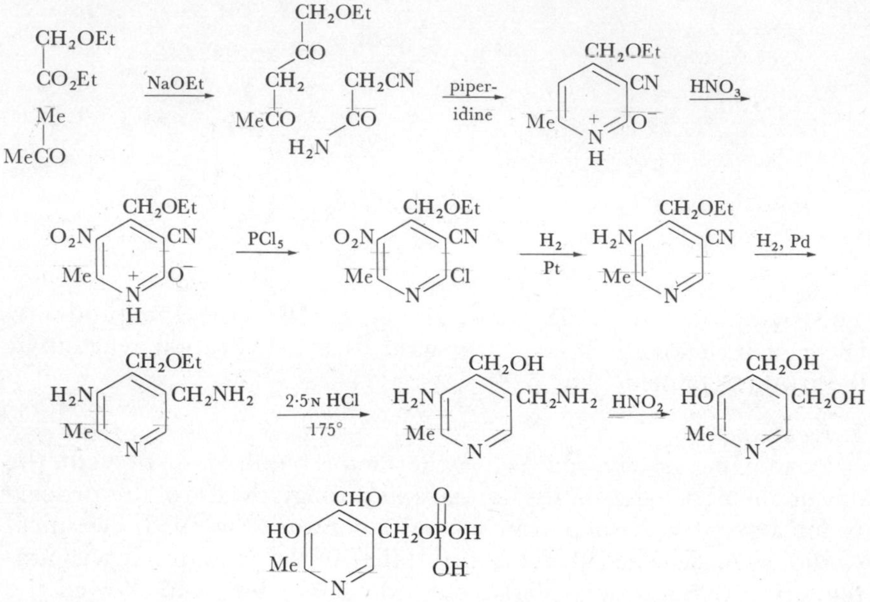

167

iron) salt with the amino acid, and has suggested a general mechanism. This requires the formation of the complex **168** from the metal ion, pyridoxal, and the amino acid. The succeeding reactions all depend on the ability of the electron-attracting groups in the molecule (**168**) to withdraw electrons from the region of the α-carbon atom of the amino acid moiety. Ionization of a hydrogen atom by the breaking of bond (a) to give **169** followed by recombination to **168** and hydrolysis gives the original amino acid, racemized. Structure **169**, which requires the loss of the resonance energy of the pyridine ring, is perhaps unlikely for the ionized intermediate involved in the racemization. This intermediate is certainly better considered as a resonance hybrid to which **169** and **170** contribute. Hydrolysis of this intermediate at (d) gives pyridoxamine (**171**) and a keto acid. This mechanism for the reversible conversion of an amino acid to the corresponding keto acid explains how the amino group of one molecule of amino acid can be interchanged with the amino group of another molecule of the same, or a different, amino acid *in vivo*. This interchange is called 'transamination'.

There are other ways in which a complex of type **169**–**170** can break up if the substituent (R) permits. One example is the complex **172**

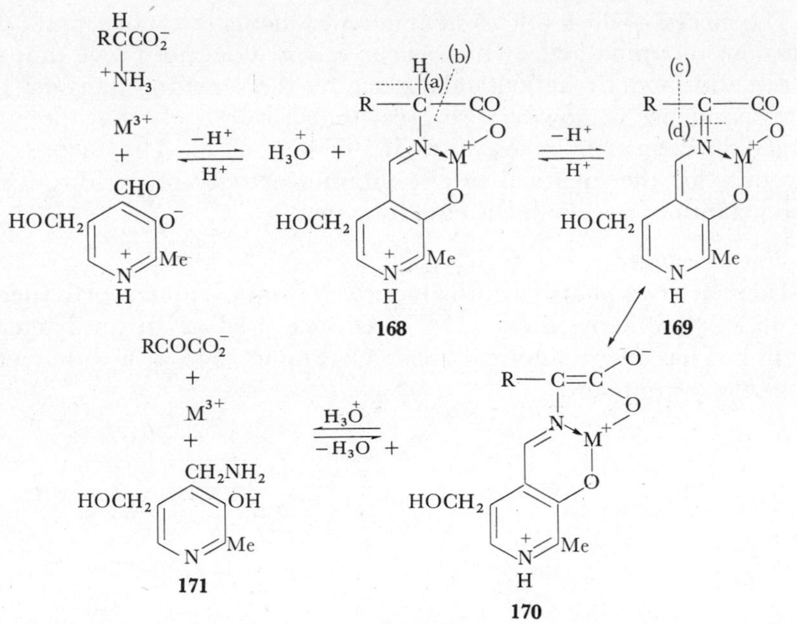

168   **169**

171   **170**

derived from serine. The bond (c) can break giving **169–170** (R = H), a proton and formaldehyde. Subsequently **169–170** (R = H) hydrolyses

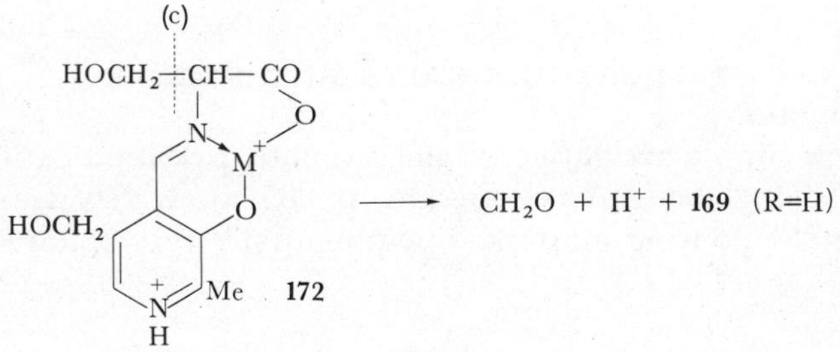

$$ \longrightarrow CH_2O + H^+ + \mathbf{169} \ (R{=}H) $$

172

to glycine and pyridoxal. The overall reaction therefore is as shown below.

$$ HOCH_2CH(NH_2)CO_2H \rightarrow CH_2O + H_2NCH_2CO_2H $$

Another decomposition, leading to pyridoxal, carbon dioxide, and the amine corresponding to the amino acid could occur by scission of bond (b) of **168**; enzymic decarboxylations of α-amino acids usually require pyridoxal.

The success of the model system in reproducing the above, and other reactions of amino acids which occur *in vivo*, does not prove that the *in vivo* and model reactions take place by the same mechanism. The correspondence is, however, so great that it is unlikely that there are major differences in mechanism in the two cases. The theory also accounts for the identical *in vivo* vitamin activity of pyridoxal and pyridoxamine; pyridoxine is equally potent.

3. *Pharmaceuticals*

There are two pharmaceuticals derived from pyridine worth special mention. 'Sulphapyridine' (**174**) was once used as an antibacterial agent but has severe side-reactions. 'Coramine' (**173**) is a widely used respiratory stimulant.

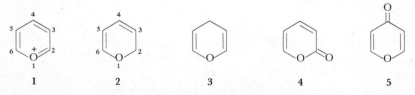

2   PYRYLIUM SALTS AND PYRANS

A. Introduction

Very few simple derivatives of the aromatic pyrylium cation (**1**) are known, although benzopyrylium salts (p. 285) are widely distributed as flower petal colouring matters. The potentially very reactive 4-pyran

(**3**) has been obtained recently and the pyrones (**4** and **5**) are well known. 2,3-Dihydro-4-pyran (**6**) has received some attention now it is easily available, and tetrahydropyran (**7**) is used as a solvent and as a synthetic intermediate. The sulphur analogues of these compounds have received little attention until very recently.

6   7

B. Pyrylium salts

The sodium salt of glutaconic aldehyde (p. 194) with perchloric acid at $-20°$ gives a red oxonium salt, which on standing at $0°$ cyclizes to the colourless pyrylium perchlorate (**8**). This perchlorate has received little attention, but with ammonia it yields pyridine. 2,4,6-Triphenyl-

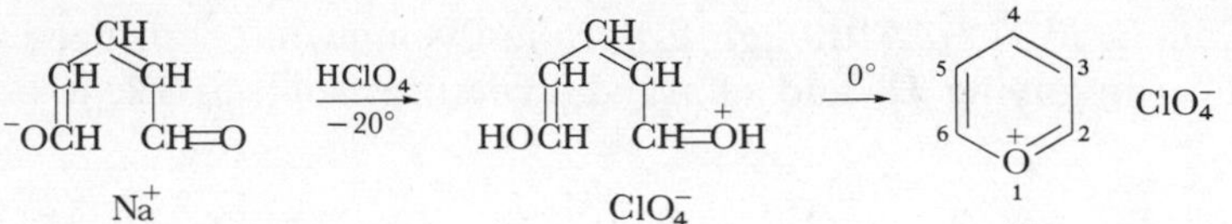

pyrylium ferrichloride (**9**) can be prepared quite easily, and a number of related compounds have been obtained by essentially the same method. It is extremely stable in acid solution and nitrates with

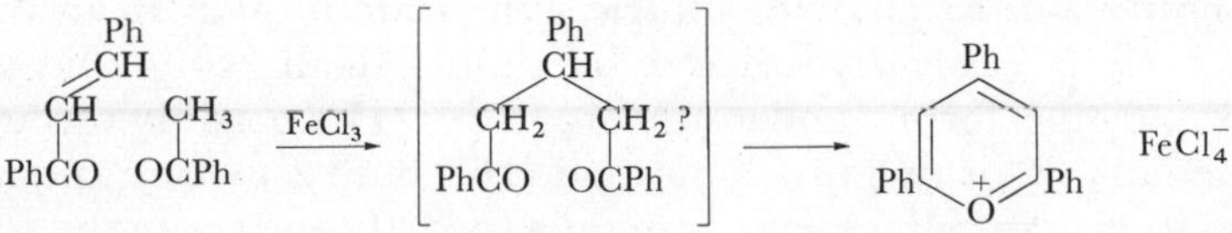

difficulty in the phenyl groups. With ammonia it yields 2,4,6-triphenyl-pyridine while with alkali the ring is opened, yielding **11**, possibly through the intermediary of a pseudo-base (**10**). 2,4,6-Triphenyl-

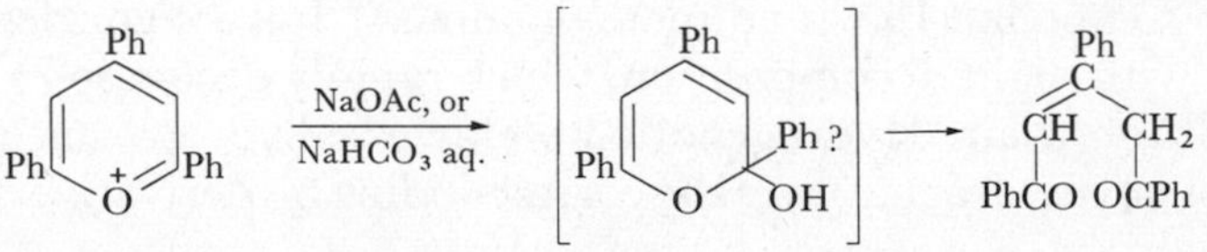

pyrylium borofluoride with triphenylphosphine methylene loses its oxygen atom giving 1,3,5-triphenylbenzene.[91] The methyl group of 2-methyl-4,6-diphenylpyrylium chloride is active and combines with phenyldiazonium salts and nitroso compounds.[92]

C. 2-Pyrones

2-Pyrone, or α-pyrone (**13**), can be prepared from malic acid in two stages. The sulphuric acid decarbonylates malic acid as a typical α-hydroxy acid, and the resulting formylacetic acid self-condenses to

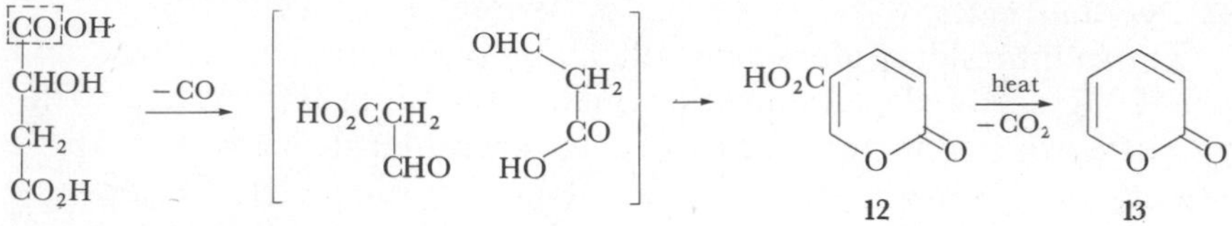

coumalic acid (**12**). Although 2-pyrone is somewhat stabilized by resonance, involving **13** and charged structures such as **14**, it behaves

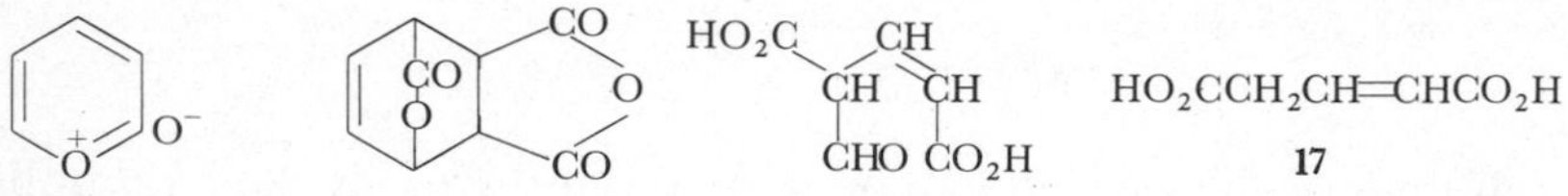

primarily as an aliphatic compound. Like other dienes, it polymerizes on standing and reacts with maleic anhydride to give **15** in the first instance. It is easily hydrolysed by dilute alkali; coumalic acid is similar and gives formic and glutaconic acids (**17**), possibly through the intermediary of formylglutaconic acid (**16**). Both 2-pyrone and methyl coumalate give pyridines with ammonia (p. 230), and coumalic acid can be converted into furans (p. 118).

D. 4H-Pyrans and 4-Pyrones

4H-Pyran (**20**), the structure of which has been established[93] from its nuclear magnetic resonance spectrum, has been obtained from the pyrolysis of the acetate (**18**) and by the dehydrohalogenation of the dichloro compound **19** with dimethylaniline.[94] It is a colourless liquid, b.p. 84° with slight decomposition, which rapidly decomposes at room temperature in air. Hydrogenation yields tetrahydropyran, and 2,4-dinitrophenylhydrazine gives the corresponding bis derivative of glutardialdehyde.

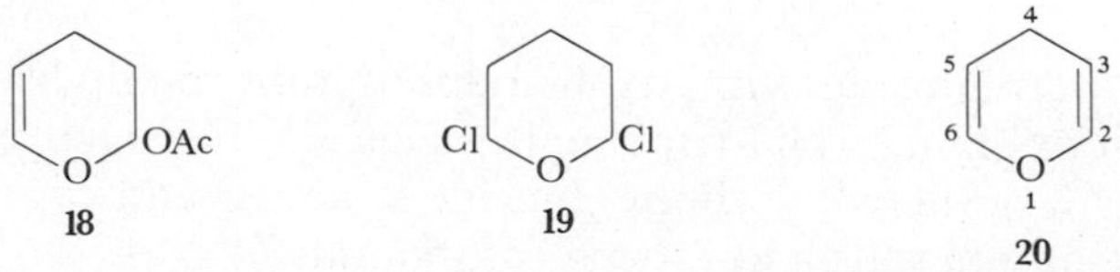

The cyclization of α,α'-dioxopimelic acid (21) by sulphuric acid gives 1,4-pyran-2,6-dicarboxylic acid (22), but no successful decarboxylation to 4H-pyran itself has yet been reported. A similar cyclization of

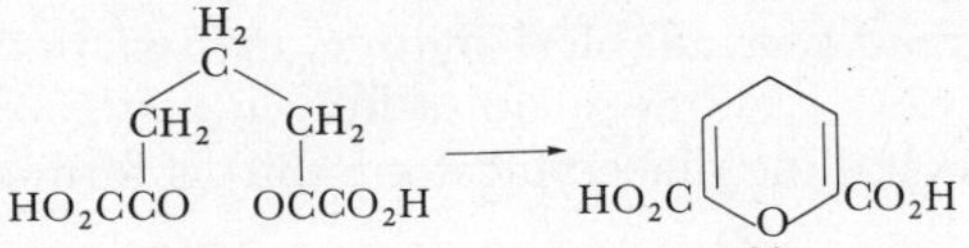

the diketone (23) gives the triphenyl-1,4-pyran.

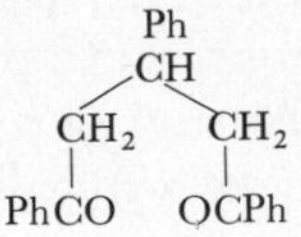

4-(or γ-)Pyrone (26) can be obtained from ethyl acetonedioxalate (24). Treatment with hydrochloric acid gives chelidonic acid (25), which on decarboxylation over copper gives the pyrone.

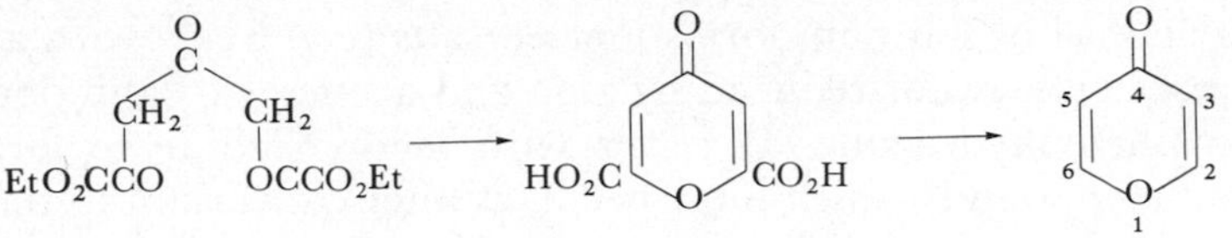

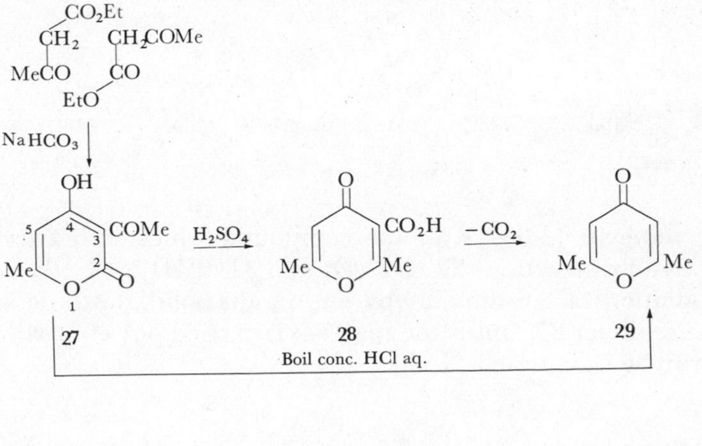

Dehydroacetic acid (27) is perhaps the most fully investigated simple pyrone. The acidic properties are due to the ionization of the hydrogen atom at position 4 under the influence of the carbonyl groups. It is one of the products obtained by pyrolysis of ethyl acetoacetate, but is best prepared from the ester by self-condensation in the presence of sodium bicarbonate. It undergoes an interesting rearrangement with sulphuric acid to 2,6-dimethyl-4-pyrone-3-carboxylic acid (28). The ring clearly opens and closes in the alternative fashion. The structure of the acid (28) has been proved by its conversion with ammonia into 2,6-dimethyl-4-pyridone-3-carboxylic acid, which was synthesized by an independent route. Decarboxylation of the carboxylic acid gives 2,6-dimethyl-4-pyrone (29).

In contrast to the less readily available 4-pyrone, the reactions of its 2,6-dimethyl derivative (29) have been quite fully investigated. On treatment with alkali, crystalline diacetylacetone (30) is formed, and

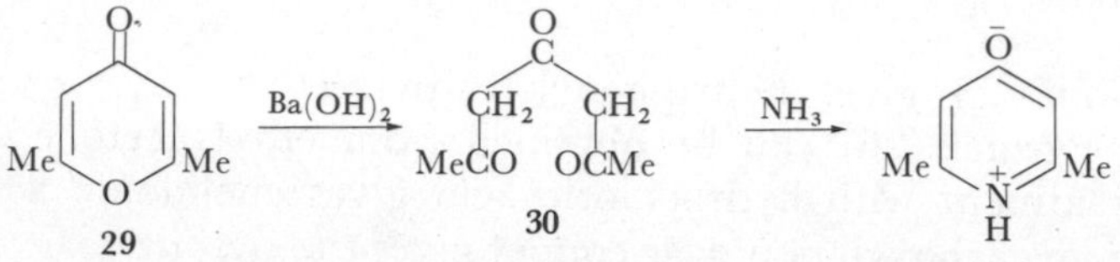

this gives the corresponding pyridone with ammonia. The 4-pyrone (29) is neutral in solution, forms ionized salts (e.g. 31)[95] with a wide variety of acids, is not reduced by zinc and acetic acid, and does not form a phenylhydrazone. It reacts with methyl iodide to form an addition compound, which must be 32, as after conversion to the perchlorate and heating with ammonium carbonate 4-methoxy-2,6-dimethylpyridine is formed.

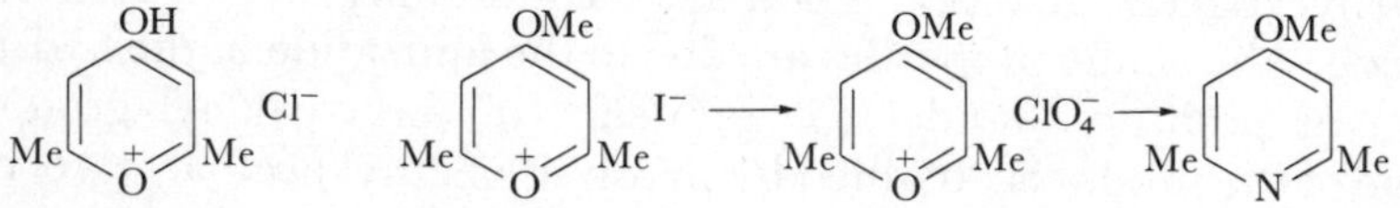

The pyrone cannot therefore be correctly represented as 29, but it must be considered as a resonance hybrid to which 29 and charged structures such as 33–36 contribute. This is in agreement with the observed

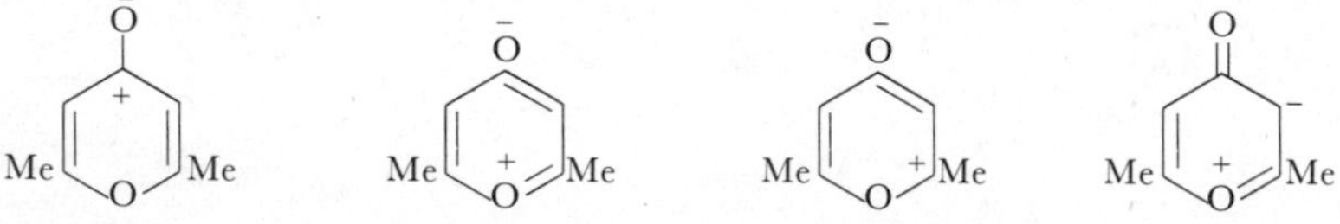

dipole moment (4·05 D) of the compound which is between those calculated for structures 29 (1·75 D) and 34 (22 D).

Irradiation of 2,6-dimethylpyrone in the solid state, or solution, yields the dimer 37, but if the reaction is carried out at great dilution the furan 38 is obtained.[96]

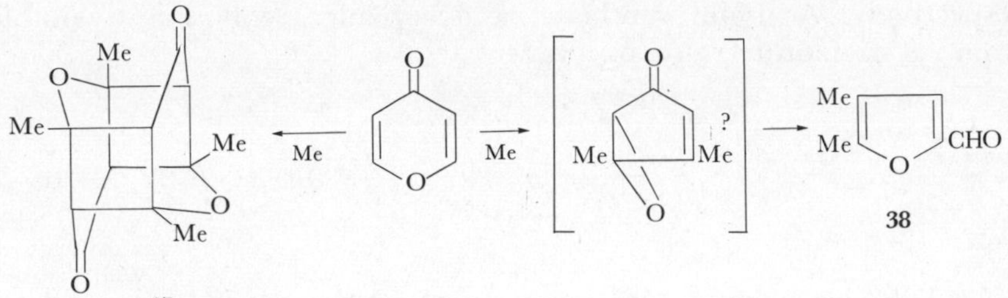

E. Reduced pyrans

2,3-Dihydro-4-pyran (**39**) is easily obtained from tetrahydrofurfuryl alcohol (p. 104) and derivatives have been obtained from Diels–Alder reactions between butadienes and aldehydes or ketones.[97] This dihydropyran (**39**) is of particular interest owing to the reactivity of its double bond. It reacts vigorously with water forming **40** and **41**, and

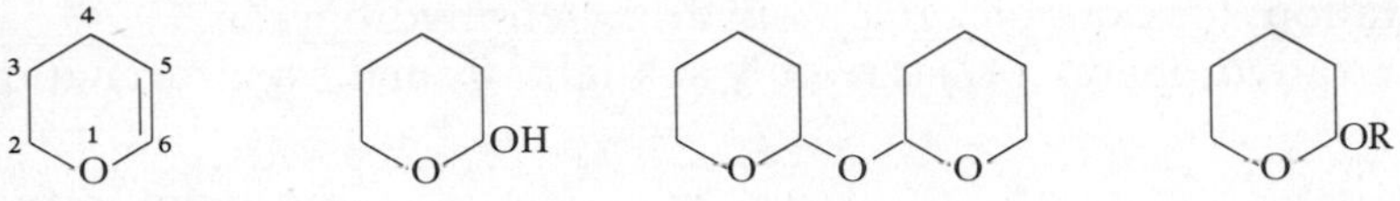

with other hydroxylic compounds such as alcohols, phenols, and acids to give ethers or esters (**42**). As these last compounds (**42**) are stable to alkali, but are easily split to 2-hydroxytetrahydropyran (**40**) and the parent hydroxylic compound by dilute acids, a very useful method is available for the protection of alcoholic groups in the presence of alkalis. 2-Hydroxytetrahydropyran is the semiacetal of the tautomeric 5-hydroxypentanal (**43**). The equilibrium is in favour of the cyclic form.

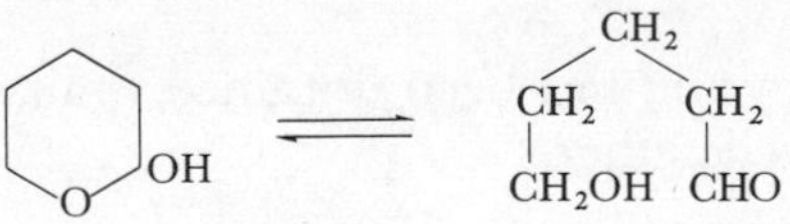

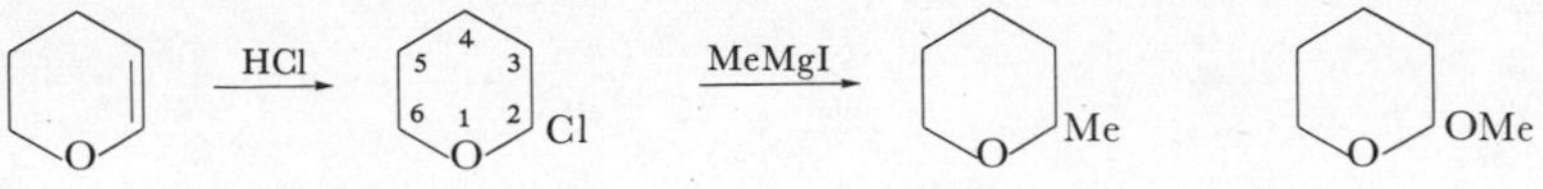

Halogens and hydrogen halides add to 2,3-dihydro-4-pyran. In the products the halogen at position 3 is relatively inert, but that at position 2 is reactive as in typical α-chloro ethers. It can be displaced by methylmagnesium iodide and sodium methoxide giving **44** and **45**, respectively. A useful synthesis of acetylenic alcohols is available from 2,3-dichlorotetrahydropyrans.

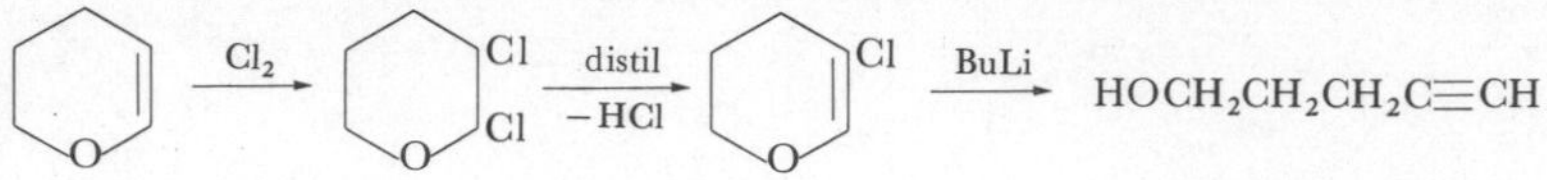

2,3-Dihydro-6-pyran (**46**) has normal ethylenic properties and on

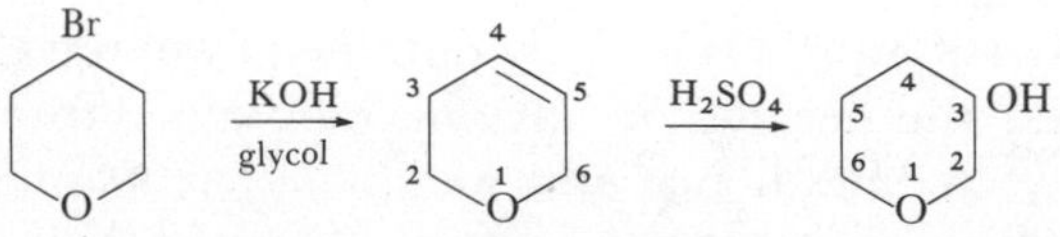

hydration, for example, gives 3-hydroxytetrahydropyran.

Tetrahydropyran (**47**) is readily available from the hydrogenation of

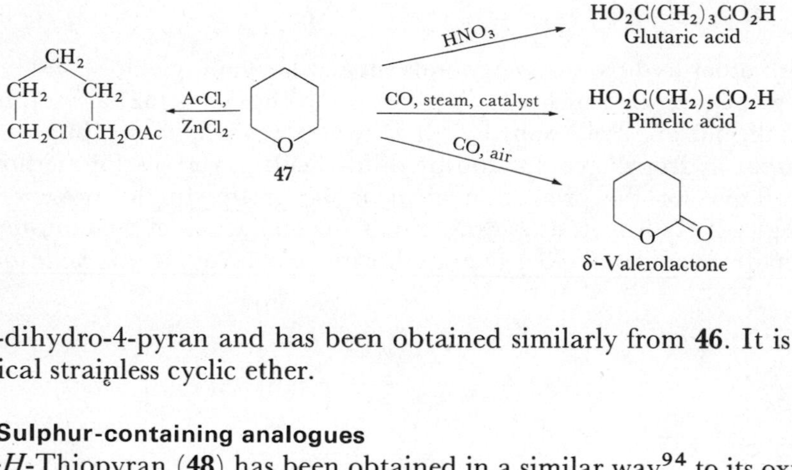

2,3-dihydro-4-pyran and has been obtained similarly from **46**. It is a typical strainless cyclic ether.

F. Sulphur-containing analogues

4*H*-Thiopyran (**48**) has been obtained in a similar way[94] to its oxygen analogue (p. 238) and has b.p. 30° at 12 mm. It is readily oxidized[98] by chlorine to thiapyrylium (**49**) chloride, and an alternative way[99]

of making this class of compound is outlined. 2,4,6-Triphenylthia-pyrylium perchlorate (50) with phenyllithium (alkyl Grignards are similar) gives the deep purple 1,2,4,6-tetraphenylthia(IV)benzene (51).[100] This last compound is very reactive and does not possess the aromatic character which its formula might suggest. On standing it isomerizes to the colourless 4H-thiapyran (52), and it reacts with oxygen forming a peroxide.

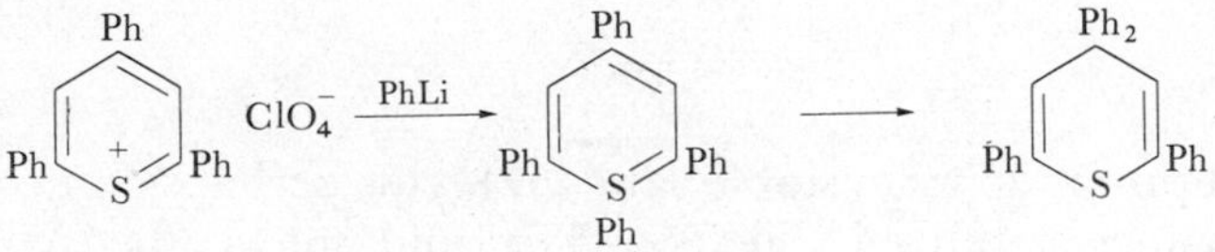

1-Methyl-3,5-diphenylthia(IV)benzene 1-oxide (53) has been obtained as indicated below. It has m.p. 148° and can be sublimed at near this temperature at 0·05 mm pressure. The compound is therefore very much more stable than thia(IV)benzenes such as 51. Acetic acid catalyses the exchange of the hydrogen atoms at positions 2, 4, and 6, and sodium methoxide those of the methyl group, for deuterium when deuterium oxide is present.[101]

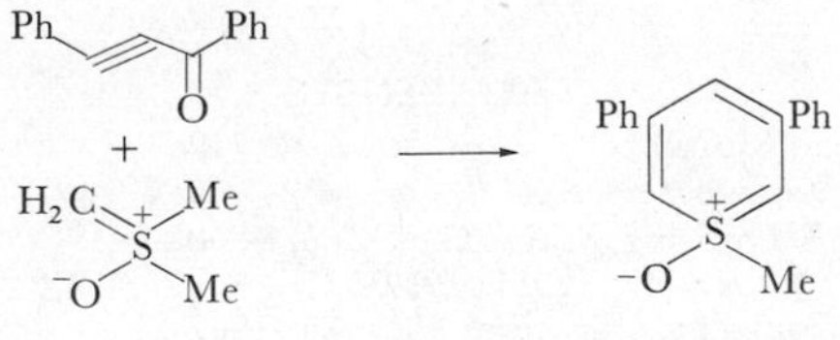

G. Phosphabenzene

The phosphorus analogue of pyridine (54) has not been reported, and by analogy with the phosphole series (p. 145) might be expected to show greater aromaticity than that possessed by 1,1-diphenylphosphabenzene (56) which has been obtained[102] as a yellow powder by route shown below. In solution it is easily oxidized, and with acids it accepts a proton to form stable salts (**57**). It is perhaps best considered as a resonance stabilized ylid (**55a–55b**) and not as a benzene derivative at all.

GENERAL ·BIBLIOGRAPHY

Pyridines

Klingsberg, *Pyridine and its Derivatives*, Parts 1–4, Interscience, New York, 1960–1964.

Sidgwick's Organic Chemistry of Nitrogen, revised by Taylor and Baker, Oxford University Press, London, 1937.

Mosher, in *Heterocyclic Compounds*, Vol. I, ed. Elderfield, Wiley, New York, 1950.

Wibaut, in *Progress in Organic Chemistry*, Vol. II, ed. Cook.

Pyrylium Salts, Pyrones, and Pyrans

Dean, *Naturally Occurring Oxygen Ring Compounds*, Butterworths, London, 1963.

Balaban, *Advan. Heterocyclic Chem.*, **5**, in press.

Fried, in *Heterocyclic Compounds*, Vol. I, ed. Elderfield, Wiley, New York, 1950.

Jones and Taylor, *Quart. Rev.*, **4**, 195 (1950).

REFERENCES

1. Bedford, Beeder, and Mortimer, *J. Chem. Soc.*, 2039 (1963).
2. Bak, Hansen, and Rastrup-Andersen, *J. Chem. Phys.*, **22**, 2013 (1954).
3. Miller, Lykos, and Schmeising, *J. Am. Chem. Soc.*, **84**, 4623 (1962).
4. Dewar and Maitis, *J. Chem. Soc.*, 2521 (1957).
5. von Dobenek and Goltzsche, *Chem. Ber.*, **95**, 1484 (1962).
6. Kosower, *J. Am. Chem. Soc.*, **77**, 3883 (1955).
6a. Lyle and Gauthier, *Tetrahedron Letters*, 4615 (1965).
7. Glusker, Thompson, and Mulliken, *J. Chem. Phys.*, **21**, 1407 (1953).
8. Walker, *J. Org. Chem.*, **27**, 2966 (1962).
9. Cook and Lyons, *J. Am. Chem. Soc.*, **87**, 3283 (1965).
10. Taylor, *J. Chem. Soc.*, 3332 (1965).
11. Acheson, *Advan. Heterocyclic Chem.*, **1**, 125 (1963).
12. Currell and Zechmeister, *J. Am. Chem. Soc.*, **80**, 205 (1958).
13. Katritzky and Ridgewell, *J. Chem. Soc.*, 3753 (1963).
14. Taylor, *J. Chem. Soc.*, 4881 (1962).
15. Jones and Jones, *Tetrahedron Letters*, 2117 (1964).
16. Pearson, Hargrove, Chow, and Southers, *J. Org. Chem.*, **26**, 789 (1961).

17. Garcia, Greco, and Hansberger, *J. Am. Chem. Soc.*, **82**, 4430 (1960).
18. den Hertog, von der Does, and Landheer, *Rec. Trav. Chim.*, **81**, 864 (1962).
19. Wibaut, *Experientia*, **5**, 337 (1949).
20. Hey *et al.*, *J. Chem. Soc.*, 3963 (1955); 3787 (1960).
20a. Brown, *J. Chem. Soc.*, 272 (1956).
21. Setton, *Compt. Rend.*, **244**, 1205 (1957).
22. Badger and Sasse, *Advan. Heterocyclic Chem.*, **2**, 179 (1963).
23. Bachman and Schisla, *J. Org. Chem.*, **22**, 858 (1957).
24. Schenker and Druer, *Helv. Chim. Acta*, **42**, 1960, 1971 (1959).
25. Andersen and Lyle, *Tetrahedron Letters*, 153 (1964).
26. Kosower and Poziomek, *J. Am. Chem. Soc.*, **86**, 5515 (1964).
27. Lukes and Pliml, *Collection Czech. Chem. Commun.*, **21**, 638 (1956).
28. Zinner, *Arch. Pharm.*, **289**, 714 (1956).
29. Hageman, *Org. Reactions*, **7**, 198 (1963).
30. Jerchel, Bauer, and Hippchen, *Chem. Ber.*, **88**, 156 (1955).
31. Miller, *Diss. Abstr.*, **17**, 2159 (1957).
32. Brown and Murphey, *J. Am. Chem. Soc.*, **73**, 3308 (1951).
33. Lochte and Cheavens, *J. Am. Chem. Soc.*, **79**, 1667 (1957).
34. Schmidle and Mansfield, *J. Am. Chem. Soc.*, **78**, 1702 (1956).
35. Ochiai, *J. Org. Chem.*, **18**, 534 (1953).
36. Moodie, Schofield, and Williamson, *Chem. Ind. (London)*, 1577 (1964).
37. Katritzky, Ridgewell, and White, *Chem. Ind. (London)*, 1576 (1964).
38. van Ammers and den Hertog, *Rec. Trav. Chim.*, **78**, 586 (1959).
39. Katritzky, *Quart. Rev.*, **10**, 395 (1956).
40. van der Plas, den Hertog, van Ammers, and Haase, *Tetrahedron Letters*, 32 (1961).
41. van Ammers, den Hertog, and Haase, *Tetrahedron*, **18**, 227 (1962).
42. van Ammers and den Hertog, *Rec. Trav. Chim.*, **81**, 124 (1962).
43. Dyall and Pausacker, *J. Chem. Soc.*, 18 (1961).
44. Kato and Yamanaka, *J. Org. Chem.*, **30**, 910 (1965).
45. Feely, Lehn, and Boekelheide, *J. Org. Chem.*, **22**, 1135 (1957).
46. Boekelheide and Feely, *J. Am. Chem. Soc.*, **80**, 2217 (1958).
47. Feely, Evanega, and Beavers, *Org. Syn.*, **42**, 30 (1962).
48. Muth and Darlak, *J. Org. Chem.*, **30**, 1909 (1965).
49. de Villiers and den Hertog, *Rec. Trav. Chim.*, **76**, 647 (1957), and earlier papers.
50. Ford and Swan, *Australian J. Chem*, **18**, 867 (1965).
51. Traynelis and Pacini, *J. Am. Chem. Soc.*, **86**, 4917 (1964).
52. Oae, Kitao, and Kitaoka, *J. Am. Chem. Soc.*, **84**, 3359 (1962).
53. Oae, Kitao, and Kitaoka, *J. Am. Chem. Soc.*, **84**, 3362 (1962).
54. Brower, Samuels, Way, and Amstutz, *J. Org. Chem.*, **18**, 1648 (1953).
55. Levine and Leake, *Science*, **121**, 780 (1955).
56. Martens and den Hertog, *Rec. Trav. Chim.*, **83**, 621 (1964).
57. Brown, *J. Am. Chem. Soc.*, **79**, 3565 (1957).
58. Angyal and Angyal, *J. Chem. Soc.*, 1461 (1952).
59. Anderson and Seeger, *J. Am. Chem. Soc.*, **71**, 340 (1949).
60. Taylor and Kan, *J. Am. Chem. Soc.*, **85**, 776 (1963).
61. Prins, *Rec. Trav. Chim.*, **76**, 58 (1957).
62. Penfold, *Acta Cryst.*, **6**, 591, 707 (1953).
63. Hoegerle and Erlenmeyer, *Helv. Chim. Acta*, **39**, 1203 (1956).
64. Katritzky and Reavill, *J. Chem. Soc.*, 753 (1963); Bell, Shoffner, and Bauer, *Chem. Ind. (London)*, 1435 (1963).
65. Dinan and Tieckelmann, *J. Org. Chem.*, **29**, 892 (1964).
66. Ayer, Hayatsu, de Mayo, Reid, and Stothers, *Tetrahedron Letters*, 648 (1961).
67. Bojarska-Dahling and Natka-Namirski, *Roczniki Chem.*, **29**, 1007 (1955).
68. den Hertog and Buurman, *Rec. Trav. Chim.*, **75**, 257 (1956).
69. Gardner and Katritzky, *J. Chem. Soc.*, 4375 (1957).
70. Mathes and Sauermilch, *Chem. Ztg.*, **80**, 475 (1956).

71. Wingfield, Harlan, and Hanmer, *J. Am. Chem. Soc.*, **74**, 5796 (1952).
72. For refs. see *Ann. Reports Chem. Soc.*, **50**, 239 (1953).
73. Acheson and Taylor, *J. Chem. Soc.*, 4141 (1959).
74. Kuss and Karrer, *Helv. Chim. Acta*, **40**, 740 (1957).
75. Tsuda, Satch, Ikekawa, and Mishima, *J. Org. Chem.*, **21**, 800 (1956).
76. Leov and Snader, *J. Org. Chem.*, **30**, 1914 (1965).
77. Sims, *Proc. Chem. Soc.*, 282 (1958) Traber and Karrer, *Helv. Chim. Acta*, **41**, 2066 (1958).
78. Bohlmann and Rahtz, *Chem. Ber.*, **90**, 2265 (1957).
79. Leditschke, *Chem. Ber.*, **86**, 123 (1953).
80. Nielsen, Elming, and Clauson-Kaas, *Acta Chem. Scand.*, **9**, 30 (1955).
81. Elming and Clauson-Kaas, *Acta Chem. Scand.*, **9**, 23 (1955).
82. Albrecht and Kresze, *Chem. Ber.*, **98**, 1431 (1965).
83. Janz and Monahan, *J. Org. Chem.*, **29**, 569 (1964).
84. Neelakantan, *J. Org. Chem.*, **23**, 741 (1958).
85. Windholz, Peterson, and Kent, *J. Org. Chem.*, **28**, 1443 (1963).
86. Cross, Schütte, Hübner, and Mothes, *Tetrahedron Letters*, 541 (1963).
87. Meyer, Mahler, and Baker, *Biochem. Biophys. Acta*, **64**, 353 (1962).
88. Schlenk, in *The Enzymes*, ed. Sumner and Myrback, Vol. II, Part I, Academic Press, New York, 1951, p. 250.
89. Hughes, Kenner, and Todd, *J. Chem. Soc.*, 3733 (1957).
90. Metzler, Ikawa, and Snell, *J. Am. Chem. Soc.*, **76**, 648 (1954); Junk and Sevec, *J. Org. Chem.*, **29**, 944 (1964).
91. Märkl, *Angew. Chem.*, **74**, 696 (1962).
92. Khromov-Borisov and Gavrilova, *Zh. Obshch. Khim.*, **32**, 3211 (1962), and earlier papers.
93. Masamure and Castellucci, *J. Am. Chem. Soc.*, **84**, 2452 (1962).
94. Strating, Keijer, Nolenaar, and Brandsma, *Angew. Chem.*, **74**, 465 (1962).
95. Cook, *Can. J. Chem.*, **41**, 505 (1963).
96. Yates and Jorgenson, *J. Am. Chem. Soc.*, **85**, 2956 (1963), and earlier papers.
97. Kubler, *J. Org. Chem.*, **27**, 1435 (1962); Achmatowicz and Zamojski, *Roczniki Chem.*, **35**, 1251 (1961).
98. Molanaar and Strating, *Tetrahedron Letters*, 2941 (1965).
99. Degani, Fochi, and Vincenzi, *Tetrahedron Letters*, 1167 (1963).
100. Price, Hori, Parasaran, and Polk, *J. Am. Chem. Soc.*, **85**, 2278 (1963) and earlier papers.
101. Hartman, *J. Am. Chem. Soc.*, **87**, 4972 (1965).
102. Märkl, *Angew Chem.*, **75**, 669 (1963); **77**, 1109 (1965).

CHAPTER VI

HETEROCYCLIC ANALOGUES OF NAPHTHALENE
WITH ONE HETEROATOM

The most investigated compounds of this group contain a nitrogen atom, and theoretically can be derived from naphthalene by the substitution of a carbon, or carbon and hydrogen atoms, by a nitrogen atom. The same results can be obtained by fusing a benzene ring on to that of pyridine, and three structures result. Derivatives of all three ring systems, of quinoline (**1**), of isoquinoline (**2**), and of the quino-

1, Quinoline

2, Isoquinoline

3, Quinolizinium

lizinium (or pyridocolinium) cation (**3**) occur naturally in the form of alkaloids, although those derived from the last-named system are comparatively rare. Quinoline and isoquinoline have received much attention from research workers for many years, but interest in simple quinolizinium salts is comparatively recent. These three types of compound are essentially aromatic in character, and to varying degrees combine the properties of pyridine and naphthalene. In this chapter emphasis will be placed on properties which differ from those which might be anticipated by analogy to behaviour in the pyridine series.

The oxygen analogues of naphthalene which will be considered here are those derived from the benzopyrylium cation (**4**) and the benzopyrans (**5** and **6**), in which the oxygen atom is adjacent to the carbocyclic ring. Derivatives of these systems occur widely in plants, and the anthocyanins, substituted benzopyrylium salts, are responsible for most red and blue flower colours. Very few sulphur analogues

247

4, Benzopyrylium   **5,** 2*H*-Benzopyran   **6,** 4*H*-Benzopyran

of these oxygen-containing compounds are known, and at present they are not of general interest.

1. QUINOLINE

A. Introduction

In 1834 Runge isolated crude quinoline from coal tar, and in 1842 the same compound was obtained by heating the alkaloid cinchonine with alkali. Another forty years elapsed before the identity of the materials from these two sources was established.

The positions of the quinoline ring are usually numbered (**1**), but occasionally letters (**1a**) are employed, as in the pyridine series. A great many quinolines are known, and most have been obtained by direct

1   **1a**

synthesis involving the building of the nitrogen-containing ring or by the transformation of existing substituents. The direct introduction of substituents into the nucleus, and particularly into the carbocyclic ring, is easier than in the pyridine series.

B. Physical properties and structure

Quinoline is a colourless liquid, which turns yellow on standing (cf. pyridine, p. 195) and which possesses a characteristic odour resembling that of pyridine. It has f.p. $-15 \cdot 6°$, b.p. $237°$, and d_4^{15} $1 \cdot 097$. It is miscible with most organic solvents, dissolves in water to about $0 \cdot 7\%$ at room temperature, and is a useful high-boiling solvent for many types of organic compounds.

The structure now accepted for quinoline was first proposed by Körner, and was supported at an early stage by the oxidation to

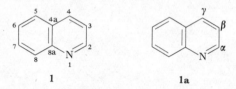

1   **2**

quinolinic acid (2) and by several syntheses, of which Friedlander's is shown.

The resonance energy of quinoline (47·3 kcal/mole), calculated by Klages' method[1] from heat of combustion data, is substantially less than that of naphthalene (61·0 kcal/mole); this method of calculation also gives an unexpectedly low value for the resonance energy of pyridine. The interatomic distances in quinoline have not yet been determined, but are probably between those of naphthalene[2] and pyridine.

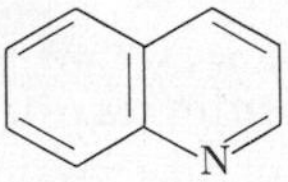

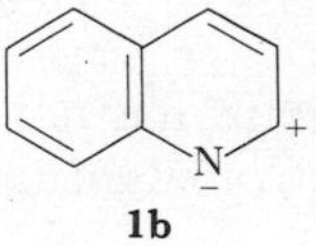

Quinoline is best considered as a resonance hybrid which corresponds to that of naphthalene in regard to the uncharged contributing structures (1, 1d, and 1e). As in the case of naphthalene, where bond-length determinations[2] have confirmed the supposition that some 'bond fixation' occurs, chemical evidence (p. 258) suggests that structure 1 with the symmetrical double-bond arrangement in the rings is probably

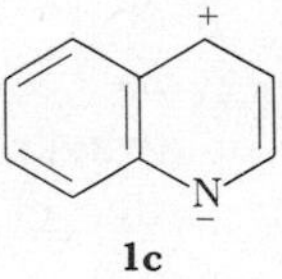

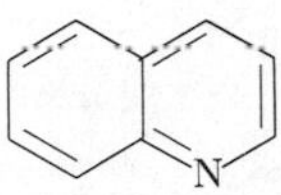

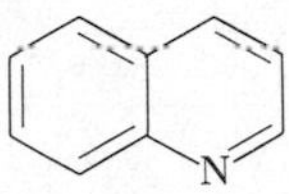

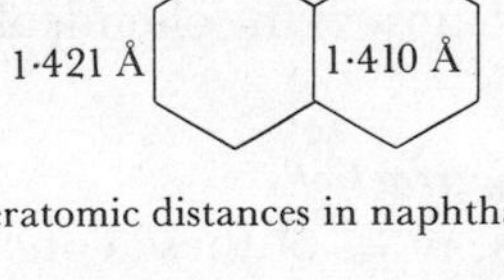

Interatomic distances in naphthalene

the most important. The dipole moment (2·10 D) and the facile nucleophilic substitutions which take place at positions 2 and 4 (p. 257) of quinoline indicate that charged structures such as 1b, 1c and similar structures with different bond arrangements in the carbocyclic ring, must also contribute significantly to the resonance hybrid. All this is in agreement with the general, but not detailed, similarity of the ultraviolet absorption spectra of quinoline and naphthalene.

Ozone attacks quinoline preferentially at the 5,6- and 7,8-positions in conformity with the idea that some 'bond fixation' occurs. The initial product is a diozonide, and further reaction is slow; decomposition of the diozonide gives pyridine-2,3-dicarbaldehyde and glyoxal;[3] confirmatory results have been obtained with 6,7- and 5,8-dimethylquinolines. The π-electron densities have been calculated for quinoline by the molecular-orbital method.[4] The results are only broadly in agreement with the positions occupied by entering substituents (pp. 355, 356), but of course the polarizability of different positions of the

molecule by attacking reagents has not been considered and need not follow the order of π-electron densities (cf. purine, pp. 355, 356).

π-Electron densities

The localization energies, for instance, for electrophilic attack on the quinolinium cation are lowest at positions 5 and 8 (p. 254).

C. Chemical properties

The chemical properties of quinoline are, in general, those which might be anticipated from an amalgamation of those of pyridine and naphthalene. The effect of the nitrogen atom is largely confined to its own ring, which possesses most of the chemical properties of the pyridine system.

1. *Addition and ring-opening reactions*

With a few exceptions, most of these concern the heterocyclic ring. Quinoline is a slightly weaker base ($pK_a = 4.94$) than pyridine (pK_a 5.23), and forms many salts which are sparingly soluble in water. It readily forms a 1-oxide (p. 256), and quaternary salts with reagents such as methyl iodide, methyl sulphate, and benzoyl chloride. 1-Alkylquinolinium salts, such as **3**, with alkali give the corresponding hydroxides (**4**). These are certainly in equilibrium with the corresponding pseudo bases (e.g. **5**), but the position of equilibrium in water is not known with any certainty. Analogy with naphthalene and benzene, where conversion into the 'corresponding' dihydro derivatives (styrene and buta-1,3-diene) involves the loss of 21 and 33 kcal/mole of resonance energy, respectively, suggests that the position of equilibrium is further towards the pseudo hydroxide than in the pyridine series. The pseudo hydroxide could also tautomerize to an open-chain form (**6**). The oxidation of **4** with alkaline potassium ferricyanide gives 1-methyl-2-quinolone (**7**, compare 1-methyl-2-pyridone, p. 193).

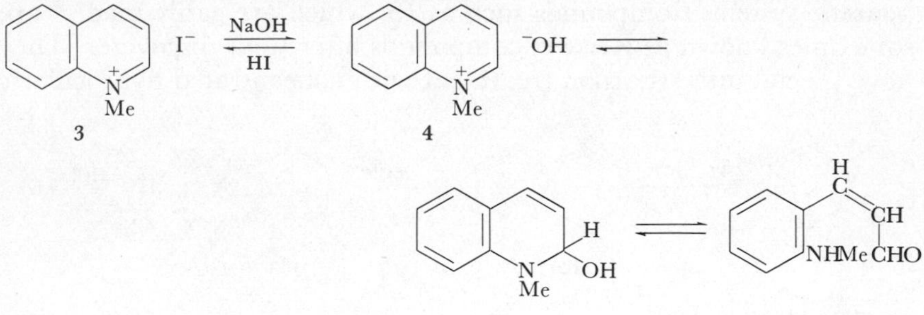

Crystallization of the hydroxide (**5**) from ethanol gives the corresponding ethoxide, which can have either an ionic (**8**) or covalent (**9**) structure.

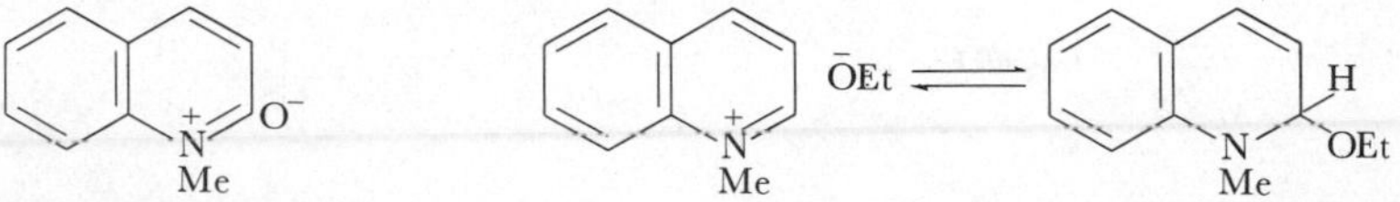

Treatment of 1-methylquinolinium iodide (**3**) with potassium cyanide gives a compound (**10**) corresponding to the pseudo base (**5**), but where the cyanide group has unexpectedly entered position 4. This is proved by successive oxidation and thermal decomposition, when 4-cyanoquinoline is formed. The whole sequence is a useful synthetic

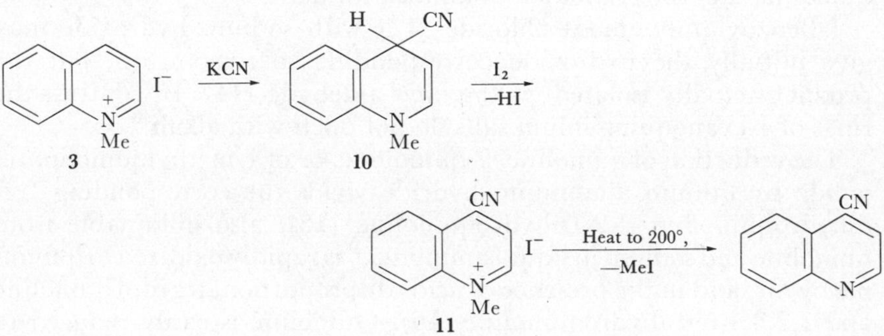

K

procedure, and it is noteworthy that the decomposition of 1-alkyl-quinolinium halides (e.g. **3** and **11**) is quite general and may be carried out *in vacuo* or in a high-boiling solvent such as ethyl benzoate.

1-Benzoylquinolinium chloride (**12**) behaves differently with potassium cyanide and, perhaps more understandably, gives **13**, where the double bond of the 'pyridine' ring is still conjugated with the benzene system. Compounds such as **13**, which are easily made,[5] are sometimes known as Reissert compounds after their discoverer. They have special interest, as on treatment with concentrated hydrochloric

acid they break up as shown to give quinoline-2-carboxylic acids. The mechanism proposed[6] is consistent with the facts that 2-cyanoquinoline is not an intermediate, that the reaction proceeds similarly with isoquinoline and phenanthridine but not with acridine (p. 280), where no cyclic intermediate is possible, and with the isolation of some quinoline-2-carboxyamide as a minor product.

1-Benzoylquinolinium chloride (**12**) with sodium hydroxide may give initially the hydroxide corresponding to structure **5**, but the product actually isolated[7] is the *trans* aldehyde (**14**). In contrast the rings of 1-cyanoquinolinium salts do not open with alkali.[8]

The reduction of quinoline, 2-quinolone, or of 1-methylquinolinium iodide by lithium aluminium hydride yields the corresponding 1,2-dihydroquinoline. 1,2-Dihydroquinoline (**15**), also obtainable from quinoline and sodium in liquid ammonia,[9] is rapidly oxidized to quinoline by air, and in the presence of acids disproportionates into quinoline and 1,2,3,4-tetrahydroquinoline (**16**). Quinoline is easily reduced to this tetrahydroquinoline by tin and hydrochloric acid, or by hydrogenation. This preferential reduction of the 'pyridine' ring can be altered by substitution. 1,2,3,4-Tetrahydroquinoline is a stronger base

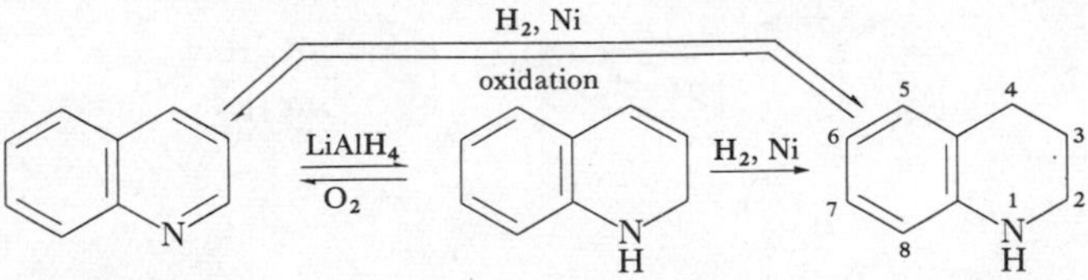

15   16

than quinoline, it has most of the properties of a secondary aromatic amine, and it is dehydrogenated to quinoline by many oxidants, including even iodine. It gives a quaternary salt with excess methyl iodide. The corresponding hydroxide (**18**), contrary to earlier ideas, does[10] undergo the Hofman degradation to 2-allyldimethylaniline (**17**) which must be distilled out *in vacuo*. As at ordinary pressures the degradation leads to methanol and 1-methyl-1,2,3,4-tetrahydroquinoline (cf. **16**) it appears that the formation of **17** from the quaternary hydroxide (**18**) is reversible. Reduction of the hydroxide with sodium amalgam (Emde's method, see also p. 272) opens the heterocyclic ring in the alternative mode giving **19**, and is a useful complementary procedure. 1-Benzoyl-1,2,3,4-tetrahydroquinoline under-

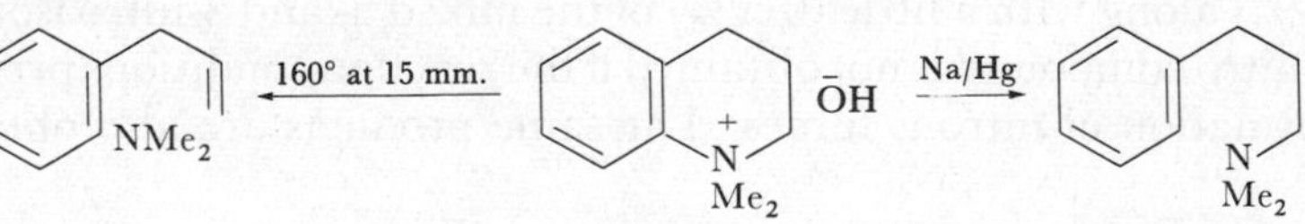

17   18   19

goes the normal von Braun ring opening (p. 203). Powerful hydrogenation of quinoline in acetic acid over platinum gives a mixture of *cis*- and *trans*-decahydroquinoline.

Oxidation of quinoline itself opens the carbocyclic ring (p. 224), but in other cases, such as 2-phenylquinoline (**20**) and pseudo hydroxides (**21**), the nitrogen-containing ring can be split.

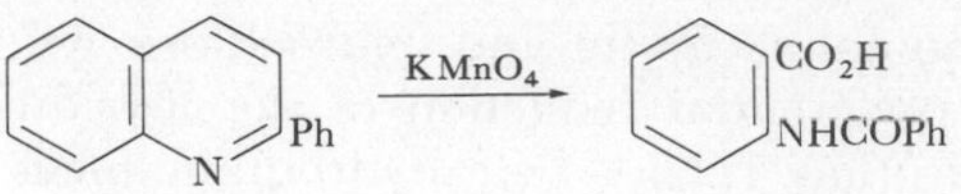

20

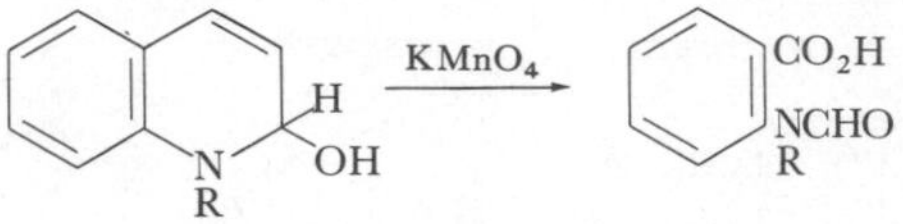

21

2. Substitution reactions

In concentrated sulphuric acid, quinoline is converted almost entirely into the cation. Bromination,[11] and both chlorination and iodination[12] with silver sulphate, in this solvent yield a mixture of the 5- and 8-halogenated quinolines. Sulphonation at 220° gives largely the 8-sulphonic acid, which will rearrange to the 6-sulphonic acid at 300°, and fuming sulphuric acid gives a mixture of the 5-, 7-, and 8-sulphonic acids. Nitration in sulphuric acid at 0° is rapid and also gives[13] a mixture of 5- (52·3%) and 8-nitroquinolines (47·7%); no other isomers were detected by methods which would easily have estimated quantities of the order of 1%. The reaction kinetics[14] show that the quinolinium cation is the species actually nitrated, and that the proton is present in the transition state. These results are in agreement with molecular-orbital calculations[15] which show that the localization energies for electrophilic attack on the quinolinium cation are lowest at positions 5 and 8, and do not follow (cf. purine) from the electron-density map on p. 250.

Nitration in acetic anhydride,[13] however, gives 3-nitroquinoline (up to 6·8%) along with a little (0·5%) of the mixed 5- and 8-nitro isomers; the 3-nitro compound is not obtained if the reaction conditions preclude the formation of nitrous fumes. The same products are also obtained

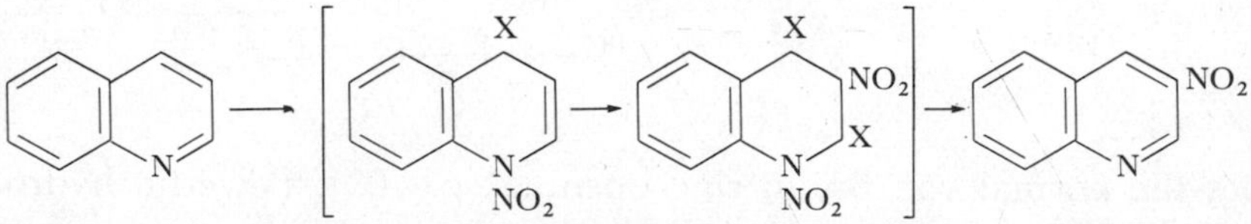

22, X = NO_2 or AcO

on nitration with dinitrogen tetroxide. The positions chosen by the entering groups do not suggest a free-radical attack. A possible course of reaction is through an initial addition, giving compound (22) followed by electrophilic attack on position 3 and subsequent eliminations. This appears to be the reaction scheme which gives the highest electron density at the 3-position of the intermediate (e.g. **22**) which must be substituted.[16] Hyponitrous acid $(H_2N_2O_2)$ and quinoline give a low yield of the 5-, 6-, 7-, and 8-nitro compounds.

Bromine combines with quinoline to give, in the first place, a π-donor complex (**23**),[17] which in hot carbon tetrachloride in the dark gives 43% of 3-bromoquinoline.[18] 3-Bromoquinoline (25% yield) can also be obtained by a vapour-phase bromination over

23

pumice at 300°, by bromination in the presence of sulphur, or sulphur chloride, or by heating quinoline in hydrochloric acid with bromine. The mechanism is probably similar to that of nitration at position 3. Vapour-phase bromination at 500° gives 2-bromoquinoline (60%), presumably via a free-radical attack.

Phenyl radicals, obtained through the decomposition of benzoyl peroxide, attack quinoline, giving a mixture of all the phenylquinolines.[19] 8-Phenyl- (30% yield) and 4-phenyl-quinoline (20%) are the major products, although substitution mostly at position 2 might have been expected by analogy with the free-radical bromination.

Nucleophilic reagents, such as sodamide (p. 258), potassium hydroxide at 250–260° (p. 259), Grignard reagents, dialkylmagnesiums,[20] and aryl- or alkyl-lithiums[21] attack quinoline at position 2 preferentially, and otherwise on occasion at position 4, as is the case in the pyridine series.

D. Derivatives of quinoline

Substituted quinolines can be divided into two classes, depending on whether the substituent under consideration is attached to the carbocyclic (**24**, ring A) or heterocyclic (**24**, ring B) ring. In general, substituents of these rings have properties corresponding to those of the analogous naphthalene or pyridine respectively.

2-Methyl- (quinaldine, **25**) and 4-methyl-quinoline (lepidine, **27**) occur to a small extent in coal tar and have methyl groups which are very reactive in an analogous way to those of 2- and 4-methylpyridine

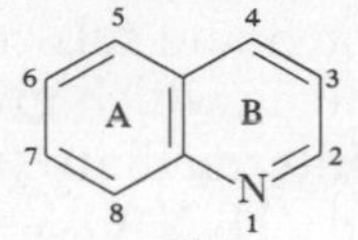

24

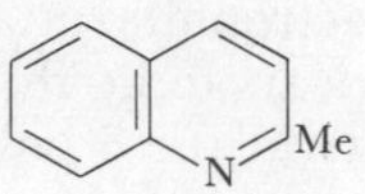

25

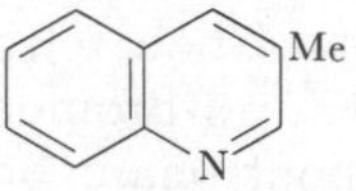

26

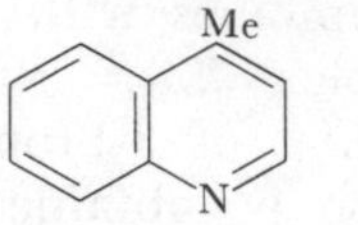

27

(p. 204). The methyl group of 3-methylquinoline (**26**) is similar to that of 3-methylpyridine (p. 205), and is comparatively unreactive.

Quinoline 1-oxide is interesting, as the products obtained on nitration depend on the temperature.[22] Between 0° and 10° in sulphuric acid

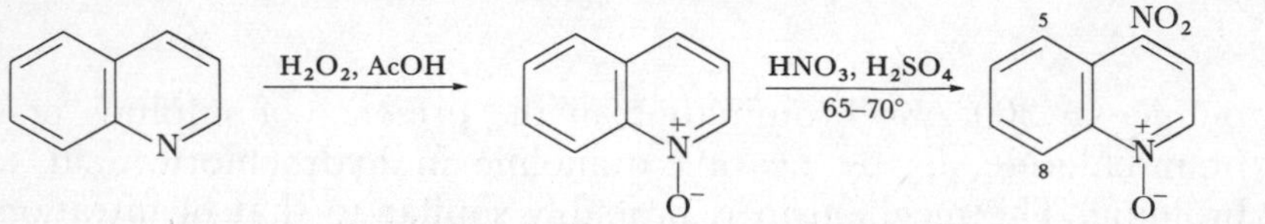

solution a mixture of 5- and 8-nitroquinoline 1-oxides is obtained, while at 65–70° 4-nitroquinoline 1-oxide is the main product and corresponds to results in the pyridine series (p. 208). Quinoline 1-oxide with benzoyl chloride and potassium cyanide gives benzoic acid and 2-cyanoquinoline quantitatively. The reaction probably proceeds through the formation of 1-benzoyloxyquinolinium chloride.[6] Very different results are obtained if the 1-oxide is replaced by quinoline itself (p. 252).

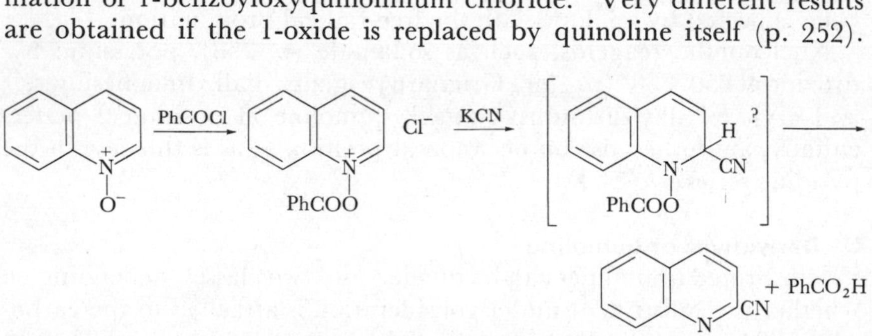

Quinoline 1-oxide undergoes a photochemical rearrangement[23] to 2-quinolone (**29**), and quinaldine 1-oxide is particularly interesting as it gives three products under similar conditions.[24] This suggests that cyclization to the oxaziridine (**28**) occurs initially, and that this then decomposes.

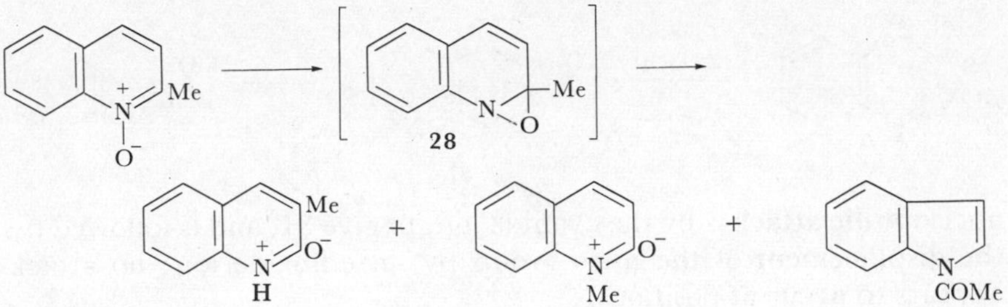

2- and 4-Chloro- or bromo-quinolines can be obtained from the quinolones (e.g. **29**) by treatment with phosphorus halides, and have very reactive halogen atoms for the same reasons as with the corresponding pyridines (p. 211); 3-bromoquinolines are unreactive. The rate of formation of bromide ion in the reaction of 5-, 6-, 7-, and 8-bromoquinoline with piperidine has been studied kinetically.[25] Although the activation energies for the four reactions are all very similar, the rates of reaction increased steadily for the compounds in the order given. Hence structures **30** and **30a**, which can be written for quinoline and which would facilitate nucleophilic attack at positions 5 and 7, do not contribute greatly to the resonance hybrid. It can,

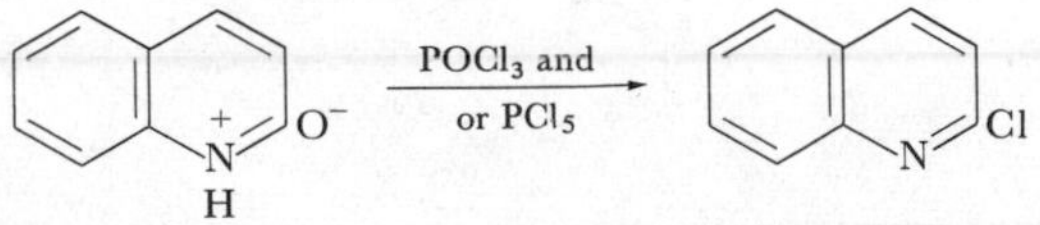

however, be concluded that **30a** makes a larger contribution than **30**, as 7-bromoquinoline reacts faster than 5-bromoquinoline in the above reaction and because 7-aminoquinoline is a stronger base than 5-aminoquinoline (see p. 258).

Nitroquinolines can be obtained by direct nitration (p. 254) or by syntheses outlined later. 6-Nitroquinoline nitrates at position 8, and nucleophilic attack takes place at position 5, which corresponds to the 'active' α-position of naphthalene. In the example shown the initial nucleophilic attack is by the cyanide ion, to give **31**, and is followed by the displacement of the nitro group by an ethoxide ion; no attack appears to occur at position 7.

5-, 6-, 7-, and 8-Aminoquinoline can be obtained by the reduction of the corresponding nitro compounds, or by one of the synthetic methods; 2- and 4-aminoquinoline are obtained by methods analogous to those of the pyridine series (p. 215), while 3-aminoquinoline is prepared from 3-bromoquinoline and ammonia in the presence of copper (cf. 3-bromopyridine, p. 213). The chemical properties of the aminoquinolines, with the exception of the 2- and 4-derivatives, which structurally and chemically resemble 2- and 4-aminopyridine, are comparable with those of aniline. 6- and 7-Aminoquinoline couple with aromatic diazonium compounds at the 5- and 8-positions respectively in con-

TABLE 1. The first dissociation constants (pK_a) of the aminoquinolines in water at 20°

Substituent	pK_a	Substituent	pK_a
Unsubstituted	4·94	5-Amino-	5·51
2-Amino-	7·34	6-Amino-	5·62
3-Amino-	4·95	7-Amino-	6·65
4-Amino-	8·46	8-Amino-	3·93

formity with the 'bond fixation' expected of a naphthalene. 2- and 4-Aminoquinolines are relatively strong bases on account of 'additional ionic resonance', which is discussed in connexion with the corresponding pyridines (p. 217). The fact that 7-aminoquinoline also shows enhanced basicity indicates that some 'additional ionic resonance' involving both rings is possible (cf. p. 257), and the low basicity of 8-aminoquinoline is probably due to interaction of the amino group with the nitrogen atom in the adjacent ring (Table 1).

Carbostyril or 2-quinolone (**32**), a colourless material of m.p. 199°, is very similar to 2-pyridone in chemical properties (p. 219), and likewise does not tautomerize appreciably to 2-hydroxyquinoline (33); the lactam structure is supported by ultraviolet and infrared absorption spectrum measurements. The oxidation of carbostyril by potassium

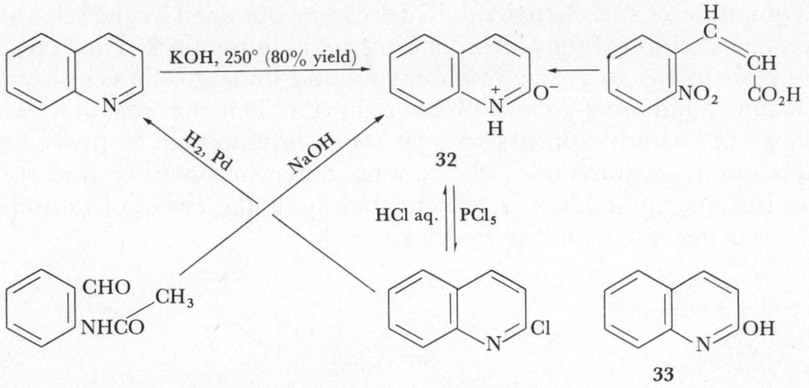

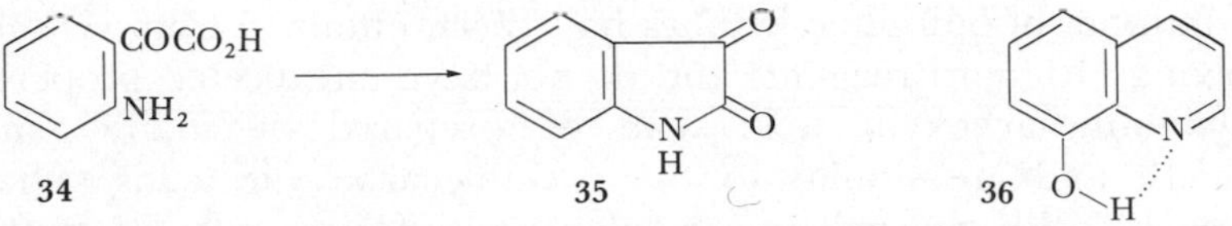

permanganate gives isatin (35), through the intermediary of isatinic acid (34).

4-Quinolone[26] is similar in constitution and properties to 4-pyridone (p. 221), while in contrast, all the other hydroxyquinolines, obtainable by general methods, are phenolic in nature. The most important of these is 8-hydroxyquinoline (36) or oxine,[27] which can be obtained in excellent yields either from quinoline-8-sulphonic acid by fusion with alkali or from 2-amino- or 2-nitro-phenol by the Skraup synthesis (p. 261) under special conditions. The volatility of oxine in stream and its low melting point (75–76°) suggest that it is hydrogen bonded as indicated. Its importance lies in the fact that with many metals it forms very sparingly soluble chelated complexes of suitable characteristics for gravimetric determinations. Volumetric determinations are also possible, as the complexes, after filtration and washing until free of unreacted oxine, are decomposed to oxine by dilute hydrochloric acid. The liberated oxine is treated with standard aqueous bromine, it reacts, giving the 5,7-dibromo derivative, and the excess bromine is estimated volumetrically.

Quinoline-2- and -4-carbaldehydes can be obtained by the selenium dioxide oxidation of the corresponding methylquinolines. They possess many properties of aromatic aldehydes and undergo the Cannizzaro reaction. Quinoline-2-carbaldehyde in the benzoin reaction with potassium cyanide appears to give some 2-quinaldoin,[28] proved by oxidation to 2-quinaldil (**38**), among other products of uncertain constitution. Quinaldoin is present mainly as the ene–diol tautomer (**37**) as is the case with 2-pyridoin (p. 223).

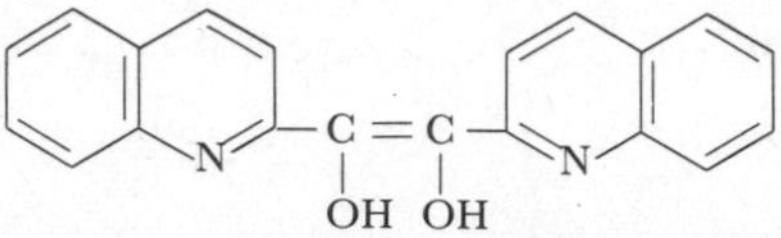

37

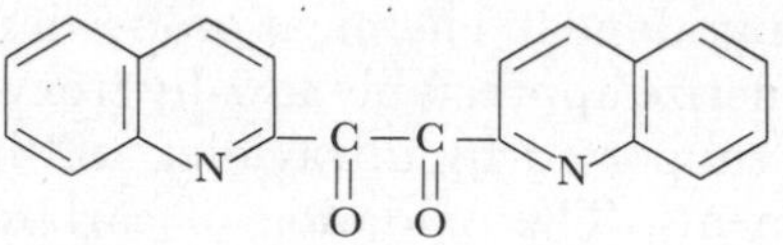

38

A number of quinoline ketones have been obtained from syntheses involving Grignard reagents and do not have unexpected properties.

Quinolinecarboxylic acids can be prepared by many general methods, and are similar to the pyridinecarboxylic acids. The 2-carboxylic acids give yellow-red colours with ferrous salts (cf. p. 224), the 8-carboxylic acids give red colours or precipitates, while the other acids give no visible reaction. The colours are due to the formation of chelated complexes.

Quinolinecarboxylic acids can be decarboxylated quite readily[29] and in the case of polycarboxylic acids this occurs preferentially at positions 2 and 4. The thermal decomposition of quinoline-2-carboxylic (quinaldinic) acid is thought to involve the zwitterion (**39**), and not the acid itself, and to proceed through the formation of the anion **40**. The presence of this reactive intermediate, which can be compared with the

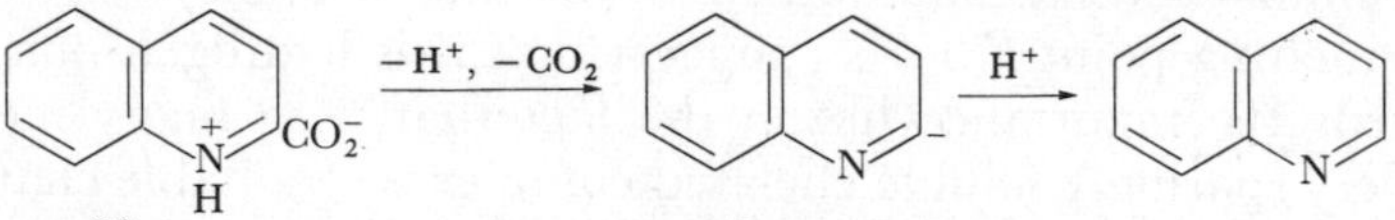

39　　40

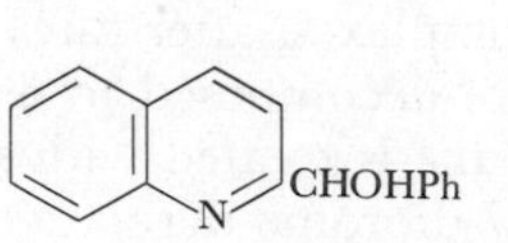

41

cyanide ion in some ways, has been shown by performing the decarboxylation in the presence of benzaldehyde, when some **41** is formed. Similar results have been obtained in the presence of other anion-trapping agents and with pyridine-2-carboxylic and isoquinoline-1-carboxylic acids.

E. Synthetic methods

(1) The most widely used synthesis of quinoline is that of Skraup,[30] and it can be applied to the synthesis of many derivatives, providing that the substituents present are unchanged by the reaction conditions. Quinoline itself (**44**) is prepared by heating aniline, glycerol, concentrated sulphuric acid, and an oxidizing agent, which may be nitrobenzene, stannic chloride, ferric salts, oxygen, or arsenic pentoxide. The initial stages of the reaction may be very vigorous, and can be moderated by the presence of some ferrous sulphate; yields are often further improved by the addition of boric acid. The glycerol is first converted into acrolein, which with aniline gives the aldehyde (**42**); cyclization to a tetrahydroquinoline (**43**) is now followed by dehydration and oxidation.[31] Many attempts to prepare quinoline directly from acrolein have been made, but high yields, comparable to those of

Skraup's procedure, were obtained only when acrolein vapour was passed into a mixture of aniline, sulphuric acid, and an oxidizing agent. Under ordinary conditions it appears that the acrolein is polymerized before it can combine with the aniline.

The general mechanism of the synthesis follows from the formation of 2- and 4-methylquinolines, when the glycerol, or acrolein, is replaced by crotonaldehyde or methyl vinyl ketone respectively. If the carbonyl group combined first with the aniline to give a Schiff's base, and this then cyclized on to the benzene ring, the positions of the methyl groups would be reversed. Intermediates of type **42** have been isolated, as

have the two geometric forms of the intermediate corresponding to
43 from 4-toluidine and crotonaldehyde.[31]

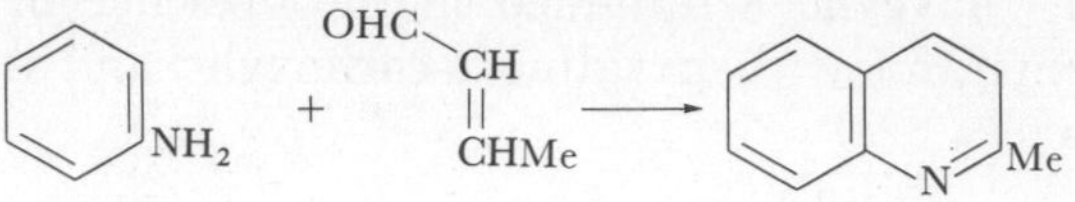

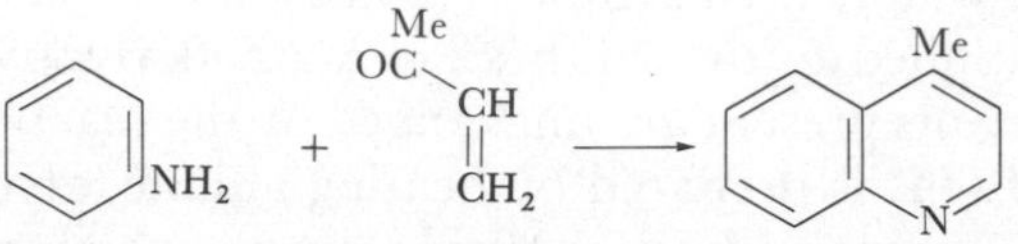

In the case of 3-substituted anilines cyclization can occur in two
ways. Where the 3-substituent is a strongly activating one, such as a
methyl, hydroxyl, or methoxyl group, only a 7-substituted quinoline is
obtained from the reaction. With 3-bromo, -chloro, or -dimethylamino

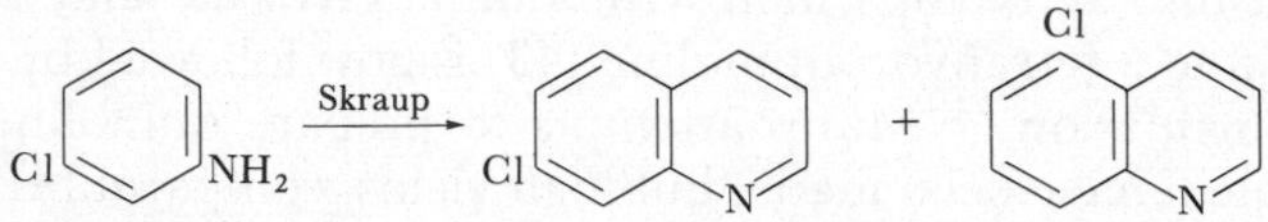

groups both isomers are isolable, with the 7-substituted quinoline as
the major product, but in the case of 3-nitro- and 3-carboxy-anilines
the ratio of 5- to 7-substituted quinoline produced is about 4:1.

When acid-sensitive groups are present the synthesis may fail under
ordinary conditions but be successful when very short times (e.g. 90
seconds)[32] are employed. Good yields of nitroquinolines, for example
6-methoxy-8-nitroquinoline (**59**, p. 266), can be obtained from the
nitroanilines if arsenic pentoxide is employed as an oxidizing agent.

(2) The Döbner–von Miller synthesis is closely related to that of
Skraup, and consists of heating a primary aromatic amine with an
aldehyde in the presence of hydrochloric acid. No oxidizing agent is

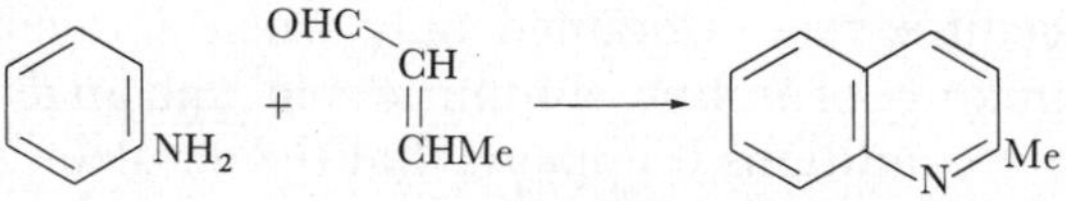

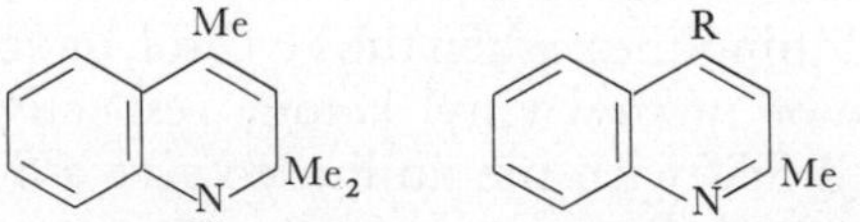

45   46

used, and it is probable that in the case of aniline and acetaldehyde self-condensation of the aldehyde to crotonaldehyde occurs, followed by reaction with the amine.

N-Ethyl- and n-butyl-aniline are by-products. This suggests that a part of the aniline combines with the acetaldehyde and crotonaldehyde to form Schiff's bases, and that these dehydrogenate the first-formed dihydroquinoline to the quinoline. Replacing the acetaldehyde by acetone gives a dihydroquinoline (**45**), the hydrochloride of which on heating with a trace of *t*-butyl hydroperoxide aromatizes to 2,4-dimethylquinoline in 47% yield;[33] other compounds are of course formed. Using a mixture of acetone and an aldehyde in the synthesis leads to quinolines of structure **46**.

47

Heating aniline, acetaldehyde, and pyruvic acid in acetic acid also yields a quinoline, possibly through the Schiff's base (**47**) as indicated. The yields obtained in this synthesis (also discovered by Döbner), which is applicable to substituted anilines and acetaldehydes, are often poor, but the method has been used for the characterization of aliphatic aldehydes.

(3) Friedlander's synthesis of quinoline from 2-aminobenzaldehyde (p. 248) is of little value because of the inaccessibility of this class of aldehyde, but Pfitzinger's later use of isatin has given a synthesis of

great value and diversity. Many substituted isatins and carbonyl compounds undergo the reaction, and the resulting quinoline-4-carboxylic acids are easily decarboxylated to the corresponding quinolines. Ambiguities in the synthesis can, however, arise if R and R' contain active methylene or carbonyl groups.

(4) Ethyl acetoacetate combines with aniline in two ways, and the products can be converted to different quinolines. Reaction in the cold, or at about 100°, gives the anil (**48**). This cyclizes (Conradt–Limpach

synthesis) to the quinolone (**49**) on dropping into a hot inert solvent, one of the best being a diphenyl–diphenyl ether mixture. On boiling ethyl acetoacetate with aniline the anilide (**50**) is formed and is cyclized by concentrated sulphuric (Knorr's synthesis) or polyphosphoric acid to the quinolone (**51**).

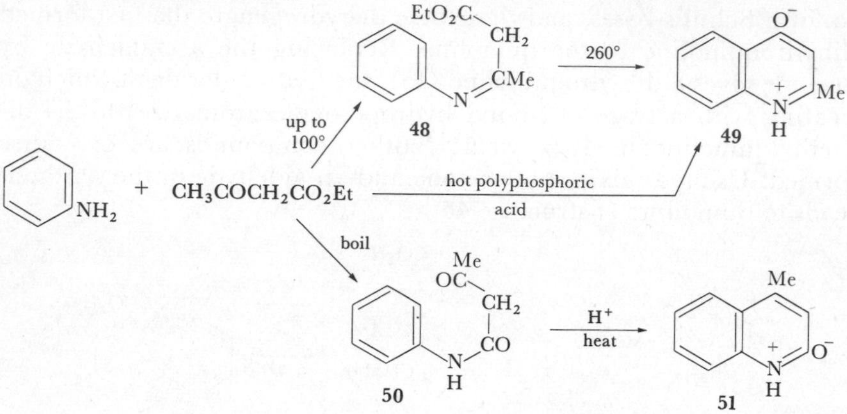

In a similar way anils from 1,3-dicarbonyl compounds, such as **52**[34] and **53**, obtained from aniline and nitromalondialdehyde and acetylacetone respectively, can be cyclized to the corresponding quinolines.

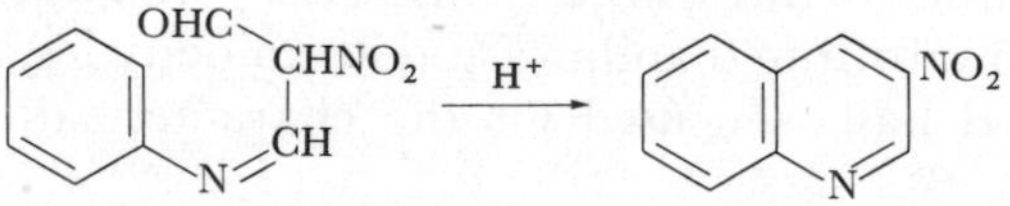

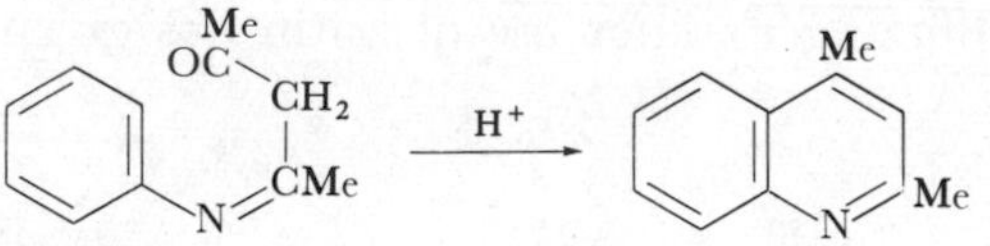

(5) A large number of quinolines have also been obtained by the cyclization of the appropriate aniline, often obtained from the corresponding nitro compound. 2-Quinolone (**54**) was synthesized in 1852 by the method outlined, and **55**, obtained from 2-nitrobenzaldehyde

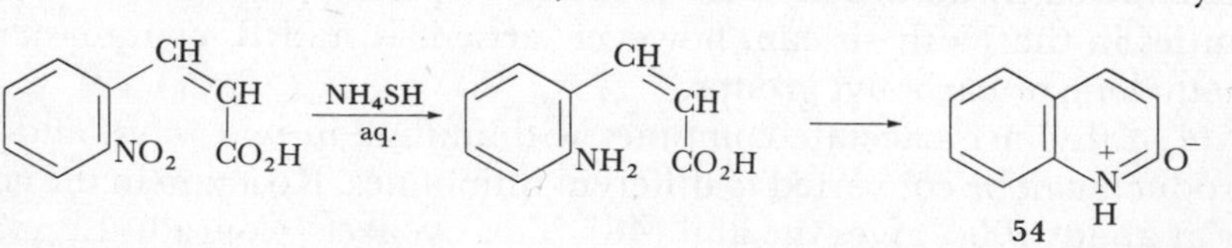

and acetone, cyclizes similarly in acidic reducing conditions. In the presence of hot alkali 2-nitrobenzaldehyde and acetone give indigo (**56**, see also p. 170). This reaction can be used as a test for 2-nitrobenzaldehydes.

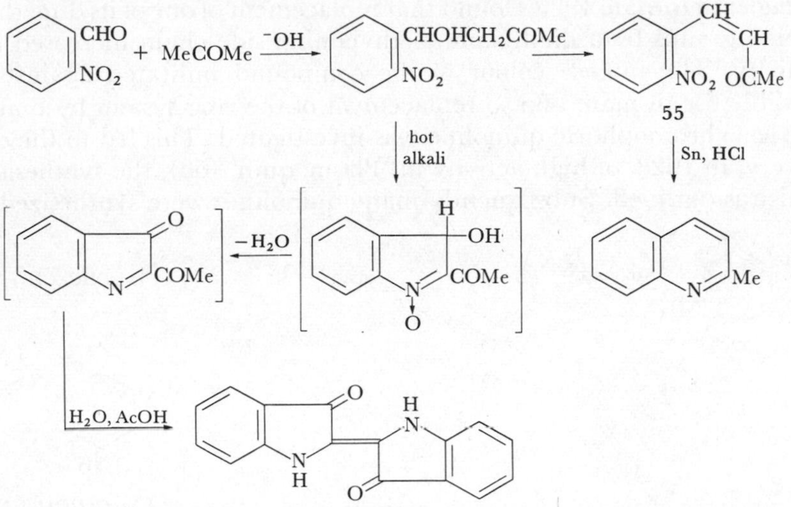

55

56

F. Natural occurrence and compounds of special interest

Quinoline itself does not occur in nature, although many alkaloids derived from the ring system are known and a concise account is available.[35] 8-Hydroxyquinoline, or oxine, is widely used as a chelating agent and has been discussed earlier (p. 259).

1. Chemotherapeutic quinolines

Cinchona bark has been used for several hundred years as a treatment for malaria. The active constituent is quinine (**57**), the structure of which (excluding stereochemistry) was proved by degradation in 1906.

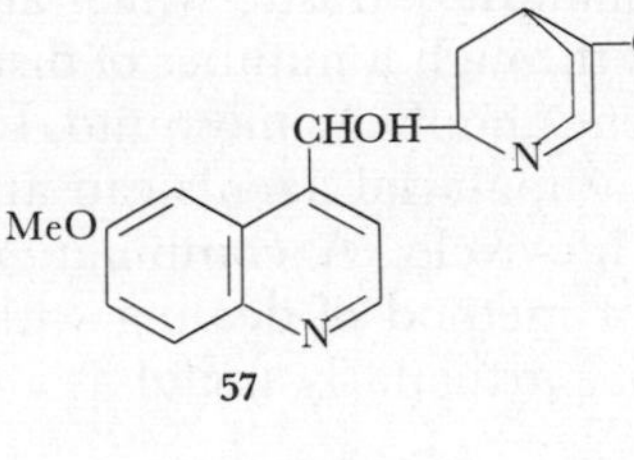

57 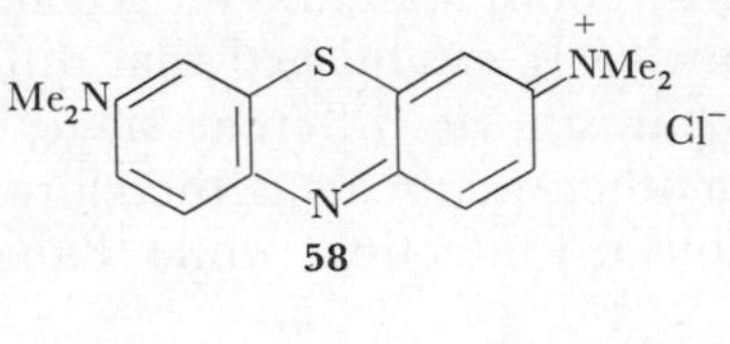   **58**

On the hypothesis that a structure–activity relationship might exist, many quinolines were synthesized in the hope of finding a better anti-malarial drug than quinine, but in the early stages little success was obtained. Following the observation of Ehrlich that methylene blue (58) had some antimalarial activity, Schulemann, Schönhofer, and Wingler in the late 1920's found that replacement of one of its dimethyl-amino groups by a diethylaminoethylamino side-chain increased the activity. The intense colour of the compound militated against its possible use in man, and so replacement of the ring system by that of the less chromophoric quinoline was investigated. This led to the dis-covery, in 1928, of high activity in 'Plasmoquin' (60), the synthesis of which is outlined. Subsequently many quinolines were synthesized as

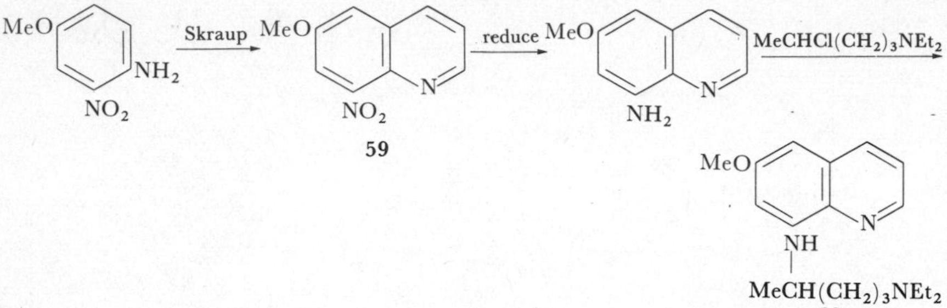

potential antimalarial agents, the best proving to be 'Plasmoquin', 'Pentaquine' (61), and 'Chloroquine' (62); other powerful anti-malarial agents are 'Atebrin' (p. 282) and 'Paludrine' (p. 369).

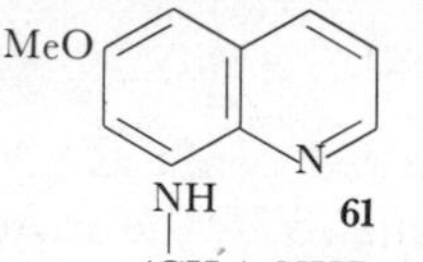

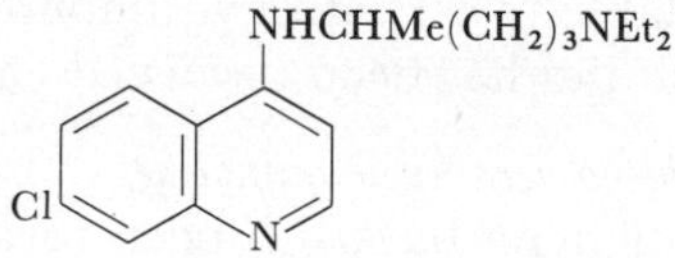

The life-cycle of the several types of malaria parasite which attack man is rather complicated and proceeds through a number of distinct stages in both man and the second host, the anopheles mosquito. It has been clearly established that different antimalarial agents can attack the parasite at different stages in its life-cycle. A combination of chemotherapeuticals is therefore the best method of dealing with an established infection, while 'Paludrine' is particularly useful as a prophylactic. An excellent discussion of the chemotherapy of malaria is available.[36].

'Nupercaine' (63) is a powerful, but rather toxic, local anaesthetic, and 'Vioform' (64) is a useful agent for the treatment of gastro-intestinal infections.

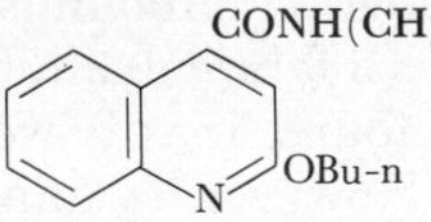

63 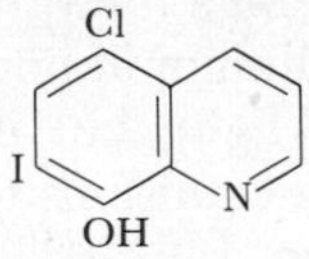   64

2. *Quinoline dyes*

Many commercially valuable dyestuffs are compounds with fused quinoline rings. A comprehensive account is available,[37] but of the simple quinolines only quinophthalone (65, quinoline yellow) has perhaps still a limited use in varnishes.

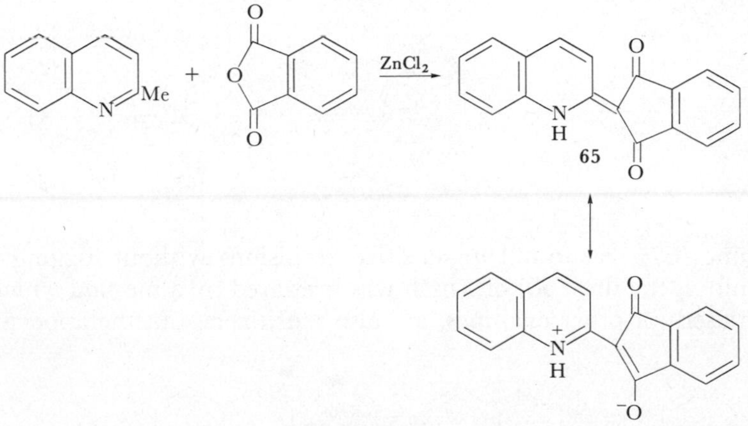

Some of the cyanine dyes, concisely reviewed by Hamer,[38] and more fully dealt with in a monograph,[39] are of immense importance in photography. The unprefixed term 'cyanine' is restricted to dyestuffs of this class possessing two quinoline nuclei connected through the 4,4'-positions; where the linkage is through other positions it should be specified; the prefixes iso, pseudo, xanthoapo, and erythroapo are sometimes used to indicate 2,4'-, 2,2'-, 2,3'-, and 4,3'-linkages respectively. Cyanines such as 66 and 67 are often named 'methincyanines', to indicate the presence of a methine group between the rings. On this system 71 and 72 are tri- and penta-methincyanines, respectively.

One, or both, of the quinoline rings can be replaced by other heterocyclic systems, the conjugated chain between them can be branched
or bear substituents, and very many of these compounds have been
made.

The blue dye, cyanine (66), was first obtained in 1856 by the action of
caustic alkali on a mixture of 1-ethyl-4-methylquinolinium iodide and
1-ethylquinolinium iodide. It is useless as a fabric dyestuff owing to its
instability to light, but in 1875 Vogel found that it would sensitize
photographic emulsions to green light. However, cyanine also fogged
the emulsions. In 1903 a great advance was made when the 2,4'-

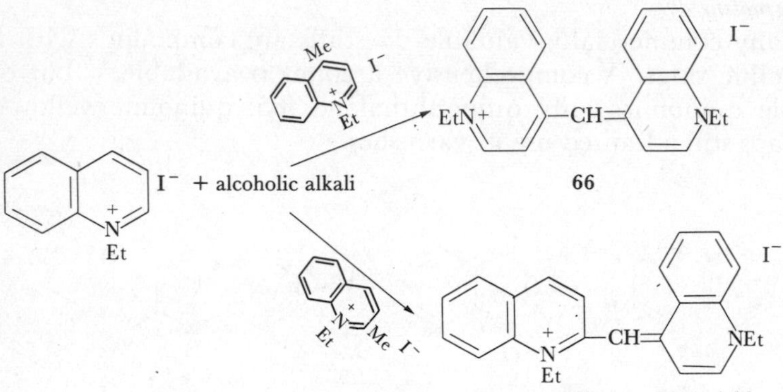

cyanine (67) was found to sensitize emulsions without fogging. 2,2'-
Cyanines, the first (68) of which was prepared by a method which has
been used for other cyanines, are also sensitizers, but the apocyanines

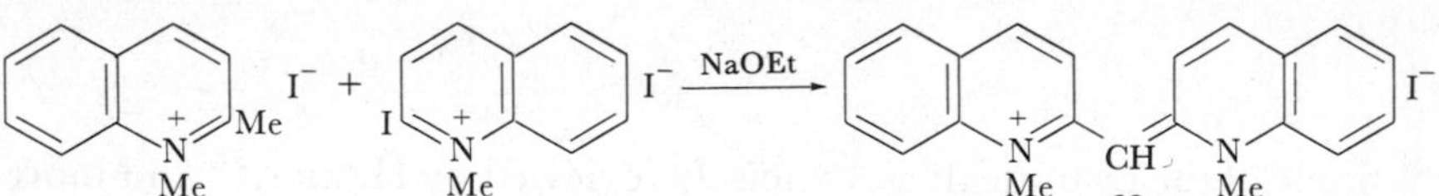

e.g. 69 and 70), which are yellow compounds possessing directly
linked quinoline rings, have no useful photographic properties.

Although in the formulae of the above cyanines the positive charge is
placed on one nitrogen atom, the other being tertiary, the compounds
are clearly resonance hybrids, of which the structures given are but one
canonical form. Increasing the conjugation between the rings, such as
in the trimethincyanine 'pinacyanol' (71) moves the position of

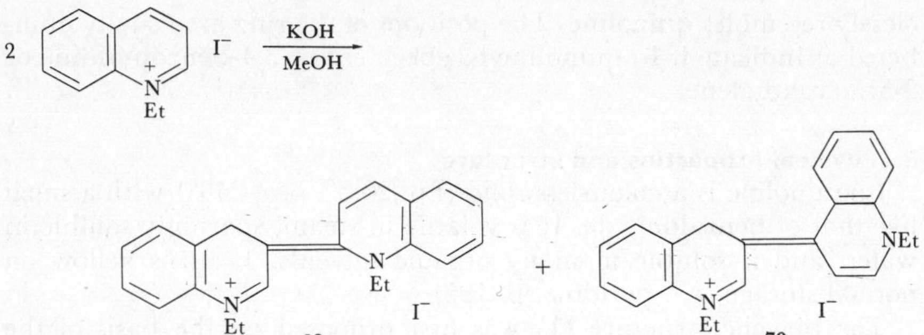

2 [structure] I⁻ $\xrightarrow{\text{KOH} \atop \text{MeOH}}$

[structures **69** and **70**]

maximum absorption of visible light towards the red and gave the first sensitizer to red light. Replacing the ethyl orthoformate of the

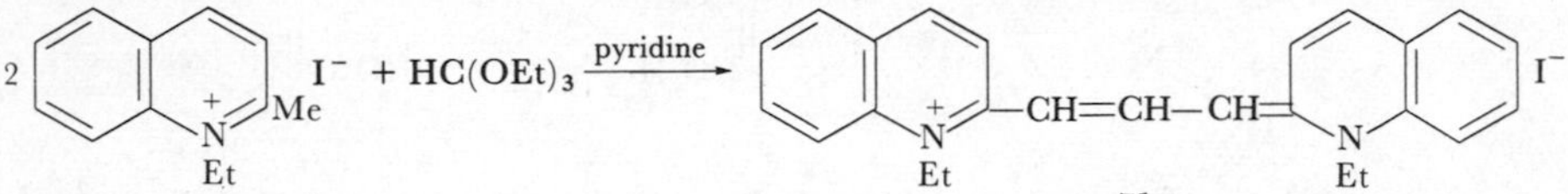

2 [structure] I⁻ + HC(OEt)₃ $\xrightarrow{\text{pyridine}}$ [structure] I⁻

71

above synthesis by β-anilinoacraldehyde gives the pentamethincyanine (**72**), while using glutaconic aldehyde (p. 194) dianilide in triethylamine at low temperatures the heptamethincyanine (**73**) is obtained. This last has been used to sensitize film in the 9000–10,000 Å region of the infrared.

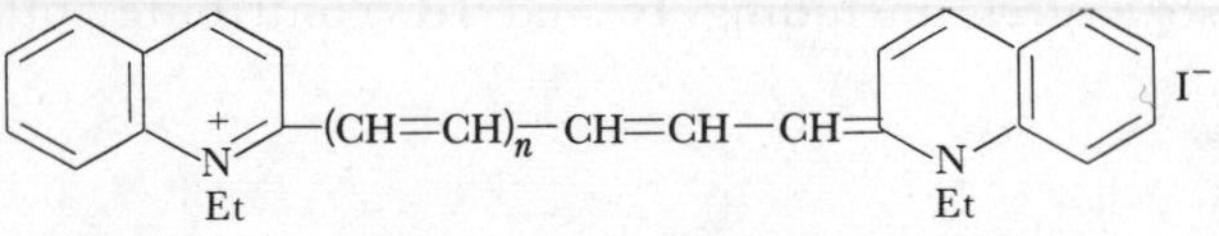

[structure] I⁻

72, n = 1   **73**, n = 2

2. ISOQUINOLINE

A. Introduction

Isoquinoline (**1**) was first isolated from the quinoline fraction of coal tar by fractional crystallization of its bisulphate in 1885; it has also been obtained from crude petroleum. It does not occur free in nature, but many alkaloids[35] (e.g. papaverine) contain either the aromatic, or the reduced, isoquinoline system. In physical and chemical properties it

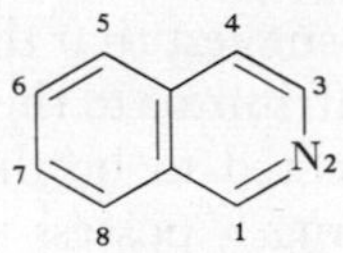

[structure]

Isoquinoline

closely resembles quinoline. The positions of the ring are usually numbered as indicated. Isoquinoline has been called 3,4-benzopyridine or
2-azanaphthalene.

B. Physical properties and structure

Isoquinoline is a colourless solid (f.p. 26·5°, b.p. 243°) with a smell
like that of benzaldehyde. It is volatile in steam, sparingly soluble in
water, and is soluble in many organic solvents. It turns yellow on
normal storage (c.f. pyridine, p. 195).

The bicyclic structure (**1**) was first proposed on the basis of the
oxidation to a mixture of phthalic and pyridine-3,4-dicarboxylic acids,
and was confirmed by synthesis. The bond lengths and resonance

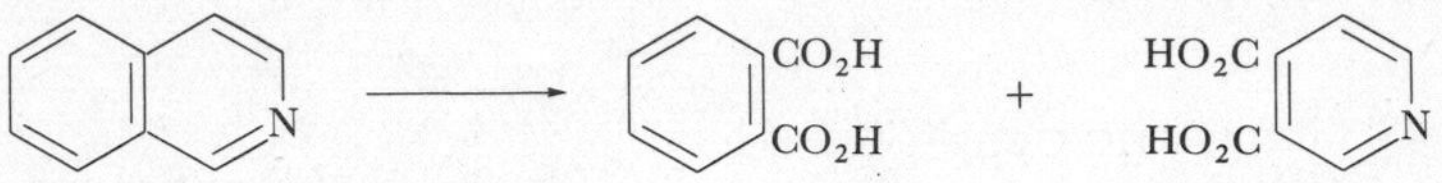

energy of the isoquinoline molecule have not been determined, but the
close similarity of its ultraviolet absorption spectrum to that of quinoline shows that it must have a very similar electronic structure. Its
dipole moment (2·60 D) is slightly higher than those of pyridine and
quinoline. These data suggest that isoquinoline is best considered as a
resonance hybrid to which uncharged structures (**1**, **1a**, and **1b**) and
charged structures, including **1c** and **1d**, contribute; other charged

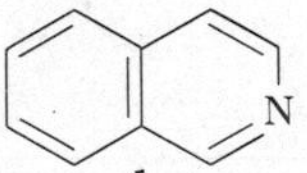

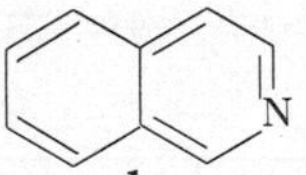

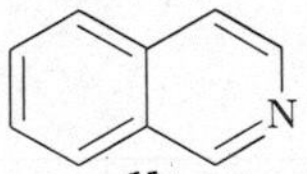

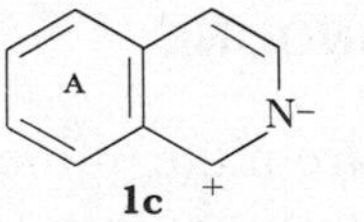

structures with the charges in different rings can also be written.
The chemical reactions of isoquinoline, as in the case of quinoline, are
in agreement with the postulate of some 'bond fixation' which occurs
in naphthalene (p. 249) and suggest that the symmetrical double-bond
structure (**1**) is the major contributor to the hybrid. Of the two charged
structures shown, **1c** is expected to be the more important, because
only in this structure does ring A possess a Kekulé form. This is confirmed by chemical evidence (pp. 274, 275) and with calculations[4] of the

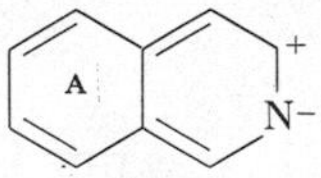

π-electron densities at various positions in the ring by the molecular-orbital method. In order to account for certain other reactions of iso-quinolines (pp. 274, 275), which are perhaps surprising, it is necessary to include smaller contributions to the resonance hybrid from structures,

π-Electron densities in isoquinoline

such as **1d**, in which the carbocyclic ring (A) must be written in the *ortho*-quinonoid form. While this does not at first sight fit in with the π-electron densities calculated by the molecular-orbital method, it must be noted that these densities do not necessarily bear a direct relation-ship to the energies of the transition states involved in the substitution reactions (p. 273; cf. purine, pp. 355, 356), and they refer only to the neutral molecule and not to the cation which is formed in acid solution.

C. Chemical properties

Isoquinoline resembles quinoline in many ways. The effect of the nitrogen atom is largely confined to its own ring. By analogy with pyridine both positions 1 and 3 would be expected to be 'positive' and susceptible to nucleophilic attack. While this is in fact the case, position 1 is far more reactive than position 3, for reasons discussed in the previous section. Reactions occurring at position 1, or to substituents at this positions, are usually analogous to those occurring at position 2 in the quinoline series.

Isoquinoline   Quinoline

1. *Addition and ring-opening reactions*

Isoquinoline (pK_a 5·14) is a stronger base than quinoline. It forms an *N*-oxide (p. 275) and reacts with alkylating agents at the nitrogen atom to give quaternary salts such as **2**. The corresponding hydroxide (**3**) is in equilibrium with the pseudo hydroxide (**4**, 1,2-dihydro-1-hydroxy-2-methylisoquinoline), and on oxidation gives the isoquinolone (**5**, cf. p. 251). Isoquinoline undergoes the Reissert reaction (p. 252), yielding isoquinoline-1-carboxylic acid. It also reacts with Grignard reagents and alkyllithiums to give 1-substituted-1,2-dihydroiso-quinolines, which are readily oxidized to the isoquinolines. Ozonolysis of isoquinoline gives phthalic acid and pyridine-3,4-dicarboxylic acid.[40]

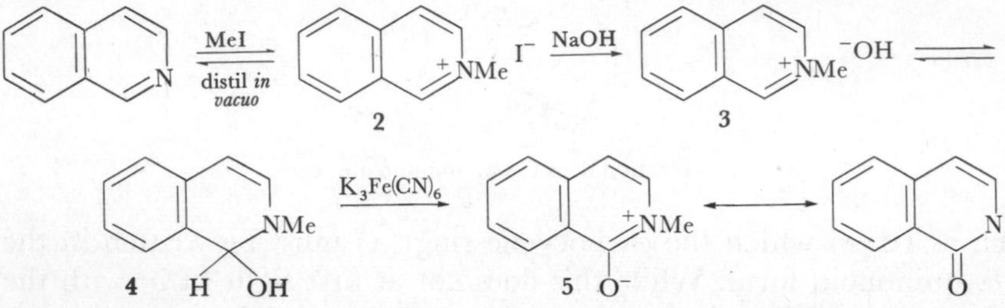

The reduction of isoquinoline by sodium in liquid ammonia[41] gives the reactive 1,2-dihydro derivative (6), which polymerizes to a trimer. Reduction with tin and hydrochloric acid, or further reaction with sodium in liquid ammonia, gives 1,2,3,4-tetrahydroisoquinoline (7), which has the properties of a secondary amine, while hydrogenation over platinum in the presence of acid fully reduces both rings to a mixture of cis- and trans-decahydroisoquinolines (8). All these compounds can be dehydrogenated to isoquinoline. Treatment of 7 with

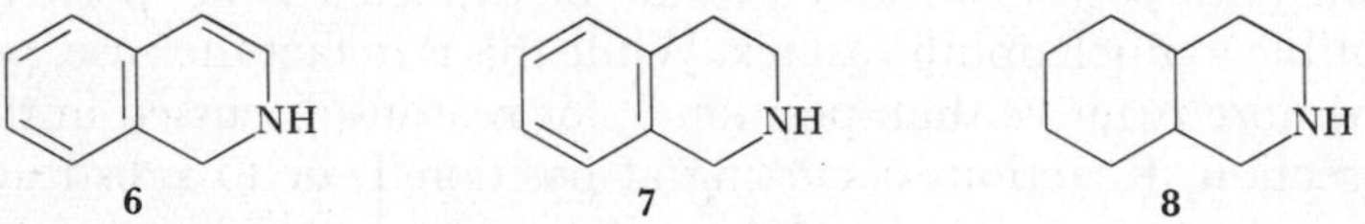

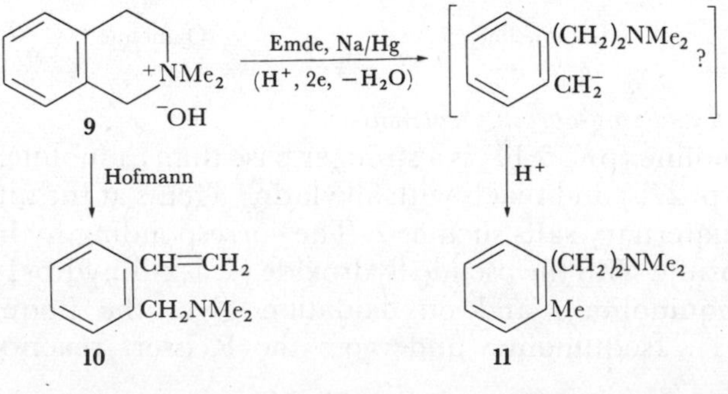

excess methyl iodide followed by alkali gives 1,2,3,4-tetrahydro-2,2-dimethylisoquinolinium hydroxide (9), which is interesting, as on degradation by Hofmann's method (p. 202) the ring breaks between positions 2 and 3, giving 10 while under Emde's conditions (p. 253) an alternative scission leads to 11. The first reaction probably proceeds by an *E*2 elimination of a proton from position 4, facilitated by the positive charge at position 2, while the second may involve the formation of a benzyl anion.

A number of isoquinolines can be converted into naphthalenes through successive ring opening and closure. For example, 1-benzyl-2-methylisoquinolinium iodide with alkali gives a pseudo hydroxide (**13**). This can lose water to yield the 'methylene base' (**12**), but on

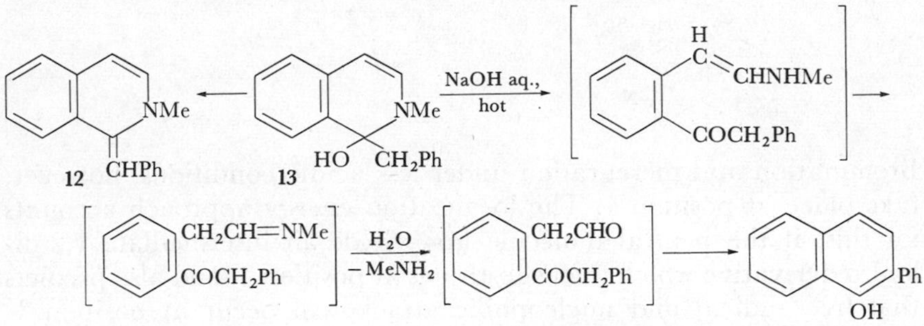

heating with aqueous sodium hydroxide methylamine is split out, giving 1-hydroxy-2-phenylnaphthalene. The addition product (**14**)

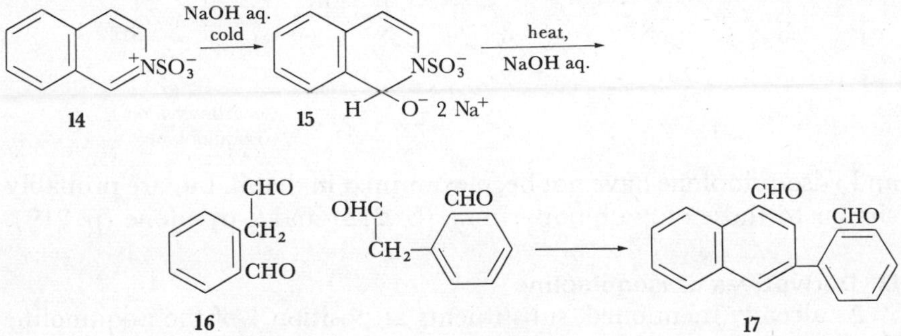

of isoquinoline and sulphur trioxide with cold alkali gives **15**, while hot alkali gives a dialdehyde (**16**), which self-condenses to **17**.[42]

2. *Substitution reactions*

Localization energy calculations[43] for the isoquinolinium cation suggest that electrophilic attack will occur preferentially at position 5, then at position 8. The species actually nitrated in over 71·3% sulphuric acid has been shown experimentally[44] to be the isoquinolinium cation and 5-nitroisoquinoline is formed mainly.[45] Sulphonation, and bromination in sulphuric acid[46], also occur at position 5 and bromination in the presence of aluminium chloride, which must coordinate with the nitrogen atom, gives successively 5-bromo-, 5,8-dibromo-, and 5,7-8-tribromo-isoquinoline.[47]

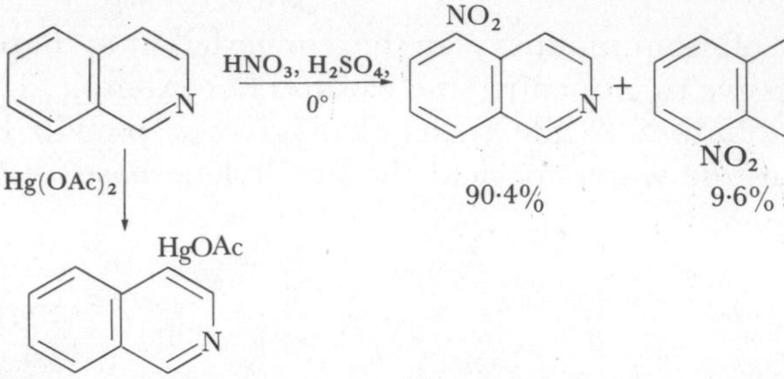

Bromination and mercuration under less acidic conditions, however, take place at position 4. The localization energy approach accounts for this, if the neutral molecule first yields an intermediate 1,2-di-hydro derivative which then substitutes at position 4, and also predicts that free radical and nucleophilic attack will occur at position 1. Bromine at 450° actually causes some 1-bromination and examples of nucleophilic attack are shown. The structures of 1-aminoisoquinoline

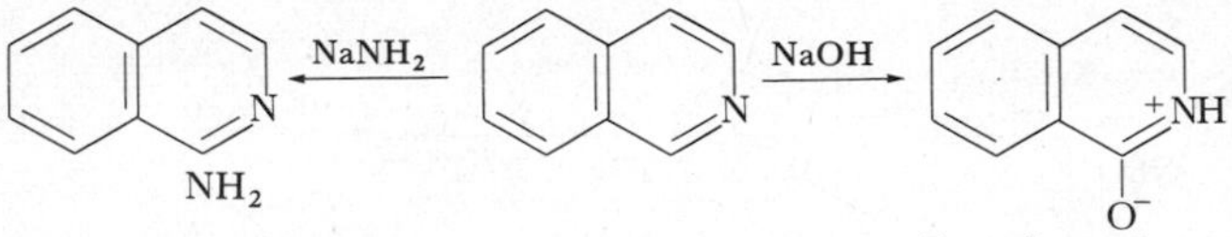

Isocarbostyril or isoquinolone

and 1-isoquinolone have not been examined in detail, but are probably similar to those of 2-aminopyridine (p. 215) and 2-pyridone (p. 219).

D. Derivatives of isoquinoline

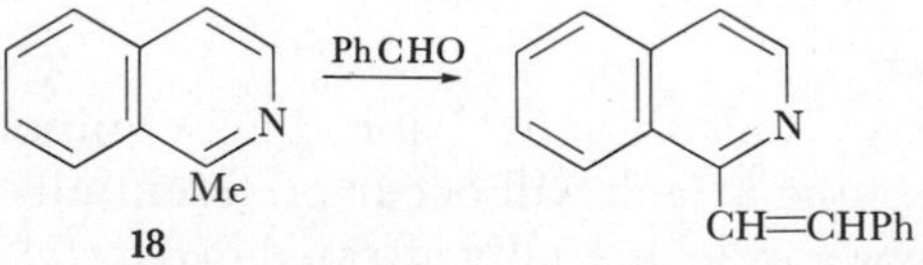

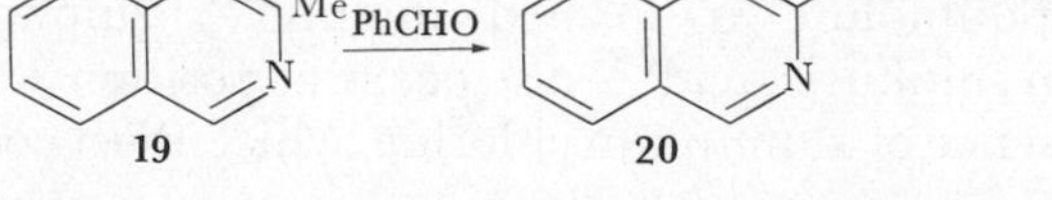

As already mentioned, substituents at position 1 of the isoquinoline ring have reactivities similar to those of corresponding 2-substituted quinolines or pyridines, while those at position 3 are much less reactive, and in the past have even been wrongly thought to possess none of the reactivity of their 1-substituted isomers. An example of this is 3-methylisoquinoline (**19**), which, like 1-methylisoquinoline (**18**) but under more vigorous conditions,[48] will condense with benzaldehyde in the presence of zinc chloride to give **20**. 1,3-Dichloroisoquinoline (**21**) on treatment with sodium methoxide gives **22**, thus showing the greater

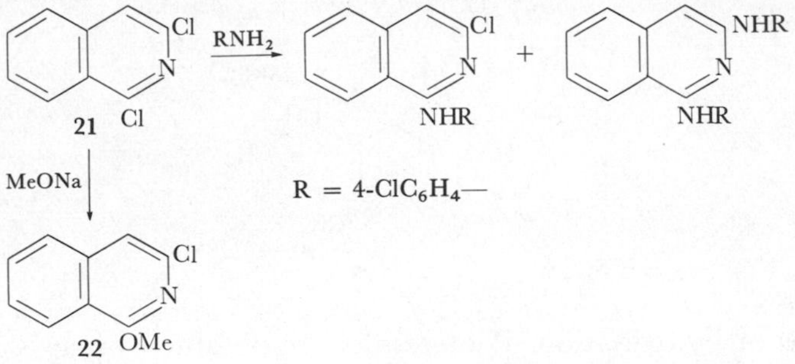

R = 4-ClC$_6$H$_4$—

reactivity of the chlorine atom at position 1. However, as the chlorine atoms at positions 1 and 3 are replaced successively when the compound is boiled with 4-chloroaniline,[49] it is clear that the 3-chlorine atom must be more reactive (cf. 3-bromopyridine, p. 213) than that of chlorobenzene.

Isoquinoline 2-oxide (**23**) on treatment with acetic anhydride gives[50] isoquinolone (**24**) and some 4-hydroxyisoquinoline (**25**). No 3-hydroxyisoquinoline is formed.

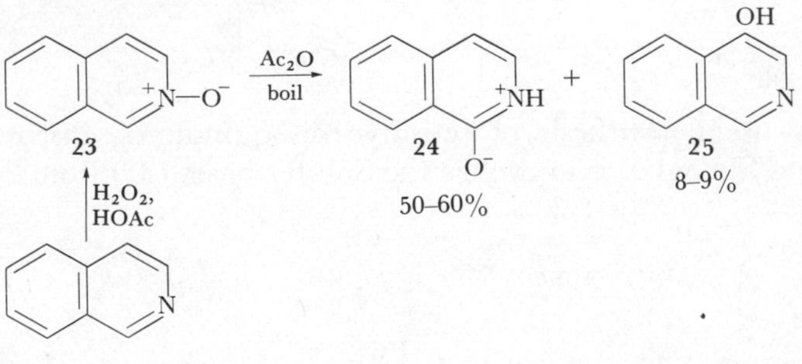

E. Synthetic methods

Most syntheses of isoquinolines start from 2-phenylethylamines and involve cyclization through an additional carbon atom provided by a carbonyl group of another compound. The syntheses described here have all been widely used and are reviewed in *Organic Reactions*.[51]

(1) The Bischler–Napieralski synthesis involves heating an acyl derivative (**27**) of a 2-phenylethylamine (**26**) with phosphorus oxychloride

or pentachloride in an inert solvent, or with phosphorus pentoxide in pyridine.[52] A dihydroisoquinoline (28) is formed, and may be converted into the isoquinoline by dehydrogenation with palladium on

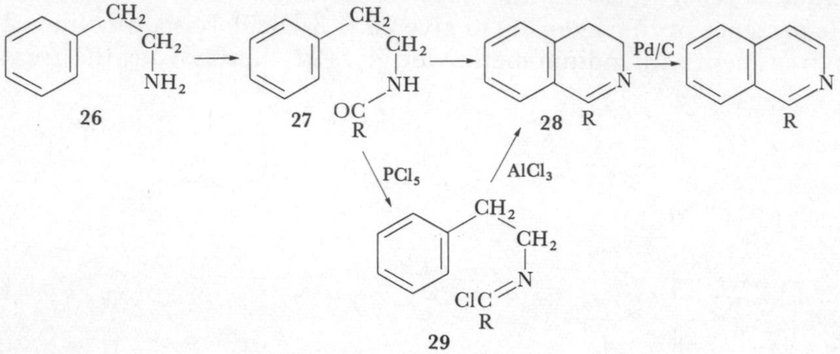

charcoal or by oxidation. Poor results are obtained when R = H. A variation of the synthesis is to convert the acyl derivatives into the iminohalides (29) and cyclize with aluminium chloride.[53]

Pictet and Gams applied the cyclization to hydroxy compounds such as 30. The isoquinolines are obtained directly, and this is a big advantage if an oxidation or dehydrogenation is undesirable.

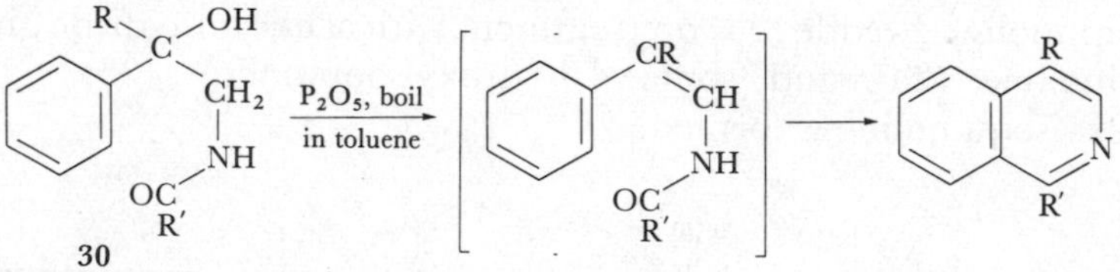

(2) A useful synthesis of tetrahydroisoquinolines, discovered by Pictet and Spengler, is to cyclize the Schiff's bases (31) from 2-phenyl-

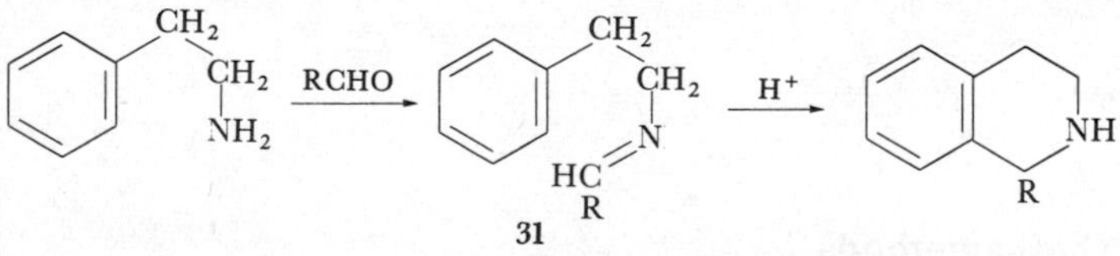

ethylamines with dilute hydrochloric acid. The tetrahydroisoquinolines can, of course, be dehydrogenated to isoquinolines.

(3) Another type of synthesis, that of Pomeranz and Fritsch, starts from aromatic aldehydes. Conversion into Schiff's bases (e.g. 32) with aminoacetal followed by cyclization gives isoquinolines. Poor results

are usually obtained with aromatic ketones, but then the alternative route[54] shown is better.

3. QUINOLIZINE

Although a number of alkaloids are complex derivatives of quinolizine, sometimes called pyridocoline, the parent compound has attracted attention only in recent years. The quinolizinium cation (2), which is isoelectronic with naphthalene, has an ultraviolet absorption spectrum similar to those of quinoline and isoquinoline in confirmation of its aromatic nature. Salts have been made[55, 56] by the two methods outlined, the first synthesis giving a 48% overall yield. The localization energies[57] for electrophilic and nucleophilic attack on the cation are in agreement with the observation that bromine in acetic acid does not cause substitution[58] although more vigorous conditions might do so.

Localization energies $(-\beta)$

Electrophilic attack   Nucleophilic attack

All efforts to prepare H-quinolizine, which can be written in three tautomeric forms (4, 4a and 4b) have been unsuccessful although complex derivatives of both $4H$- and $9aH$-quinolizines are well known.[59] The attempt[55] to aromatize 1 opened the ring and gave 2-butadienylpyridine (3), and although nucleophilic attack of lithium hydride[60] and Grignard reagents[61] apparently takes place at position 4 of the quinolizinium ring (2), in agreement with the theoretical predictions, the products isolated were again 3, and its δ-substituted derivatives. However as a series of hexahydro- and octahydro-quinolizines were isolated[60] from reductions of 2 involving sodium borohydride in ethanol it appears likely that $4H$-quinolizine can have a short independent existence. The 1,2,3,4-tetramethoxycarbonyl derivative of 4 has been reported as a very labile red compound obtainable from pyridine

4   4a   4b   5

and dimethyl acetylenedicarboxylate. It rapidly isomerizes to 5, the structure of which has been thoroughly established.[62]

1-and 3-Hydroxyquinolizinium salts have been synthesized; they brominate readily at positions 2 and 4 respectively, and have reactions of typical phenols. [63] In contrast the 2-hydroxy isomer (6)[63] behaves as quite a strong acid and easily loses its proton to give 2-quinolizone, which is in fact a vinylogous amide and can be represented as a resonance hybrid (**7**–**8**). 4-Quinolizone[64] (**9**) appears to be a weaker base than 2-quinolizone, and is not reduced by lithium aluminium hydride. It is perhaps best represented by the charged formulation (**10**). Nitration and bromination occur first at position 3, afterwards at position 1.[65]

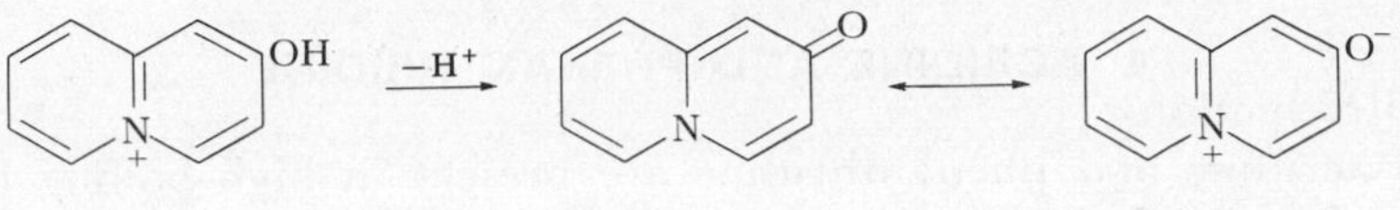

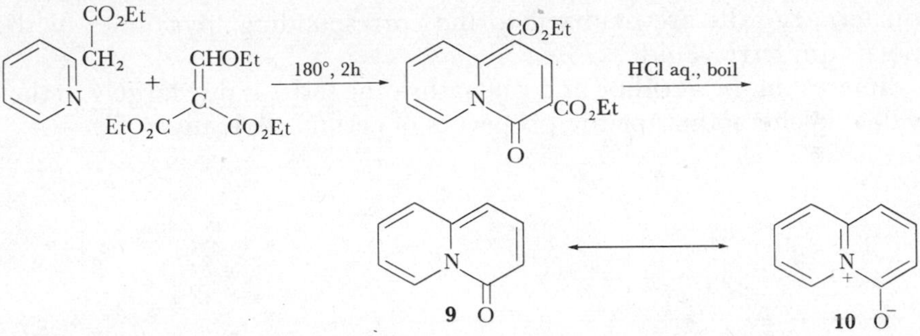

Quinolizidine (**12**) is an aliphatic tertiary base which undergoes the Hofmann degradation (p. 203). It has been obtained[64] from **1** by complete hydrogenation to the saturated amino alcohol, oxidation to the ketone (**11**), and reduction as indicated, and from[66] the bromo compound **13**. Direct methylation gives a quaternary salt with a *trans* ring junction (**16**), while the *cis* isomer (**15**) is obtained from the cyclization of **14**.[67]

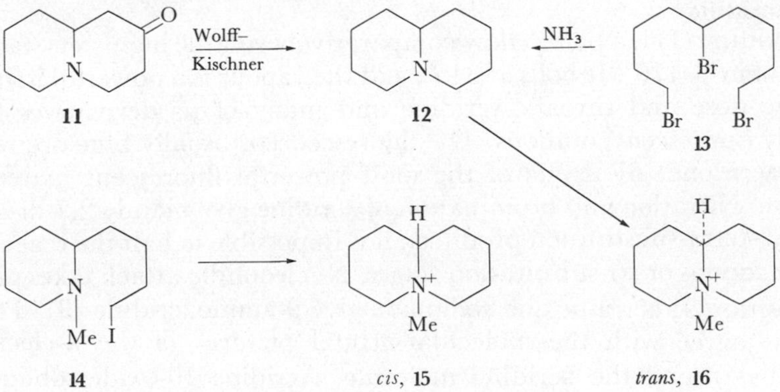

4. ACRIDINE AND PHENANTHRIDINE

A. Introduction

Both acridine and phenanthridine are present in high-boiling fractions of coal tar, but are most readily obtained by synthesis. They can be regarded respectively as aza derivatives of anthracene and phenanthrene, or as 2,3- and 3,4-benzoquinoline. The parent compounds have many properties which can be anticipated from those of pyridine or quinoline and which will not be considered in detail. Examples are the reactivity of halogen atoms and methyl groups at positions 9 in acridine and 6 in phenanthridine, and the formation of highly crystalline salts with acids and of quaternary salts with alkyl halides. The quaternary salts are oxidized to the corresponding 'pyridones' with potassium ferricyanide.

Interest in the acridine and phenathridine series is due largely to the valuable chemotherapeutic properties of certain derivatives.

Acridine

Phenanthridine

Alternative numbering systems
used occasionally

B. Acridine

Acridine (1) is a pale yellow comparatively volatile highly crystalline solid of m.p. 110°. It boils at 345°, and the vapour is a powerful irritant to the nose and throat. Acridine and many of its derivatives give highly fluorescent solutions. The fluorescence is usually blue or green, and acridone (6) is one of the most powerful fluorescent materials known. Nitration and bromination of acridine give mainly 2,7-di- and 2,4,5,7-tetra-substitution products; it is impossible to halt the reactions at the mono- or tri-substitution stages. Nucleophilic attack takes place at position 9; acridine and sodamide give 9-aminoacridine (9). These results agree with the molecular-orbital picture[4] of the π-electron densities round the acridine molecule. Acridine 10-oxide, obtained from acridine with perbenzoic acid, both nitrates and brominates[68] at position 9 (cf. pyridine 1-oxide, p. 207).

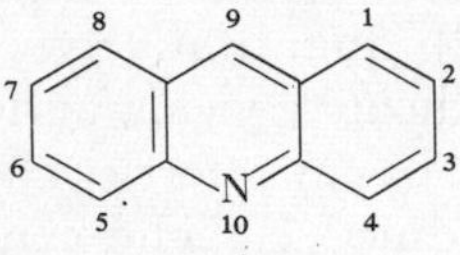

1

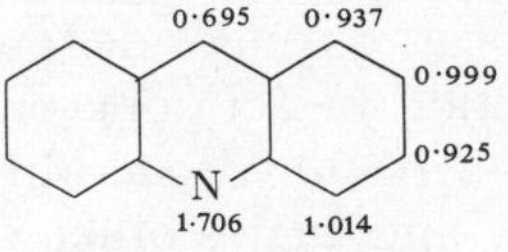

π-Electron densities

The most general synthesis of acridines starts with a diphenylamine-2-carboxylic acid and usually gives good results. Diphenylamine-2-carboxylic acids (e.g. **2**) are obtainable from anilines and 2-chlorobenzoic acids in the presence of a base and metallic copper (Ullmann's reaction); the exact function of the copper is unknown. The nucleophilic displacement of the chlorine atom is facilitated by the *ortho* (electron-attracting) carboxyl group. The complementary reaction, that of anthranilic acid and bromobenzene, does give some diphenylamine-2-carboxylic acid, but in poorer yield, as the bromine atom is not activated and the amino group is deactivated. Another valuable synthesis of diphenylamine-2-carboxylic acids involves the Chapman rearrangement, and often succeeds when that of Ullmann fails. In the case of diphenylamine-2-carboxylic acid the sodium derivative of methyl salicylate is treated with *N*-phenylbenzimido

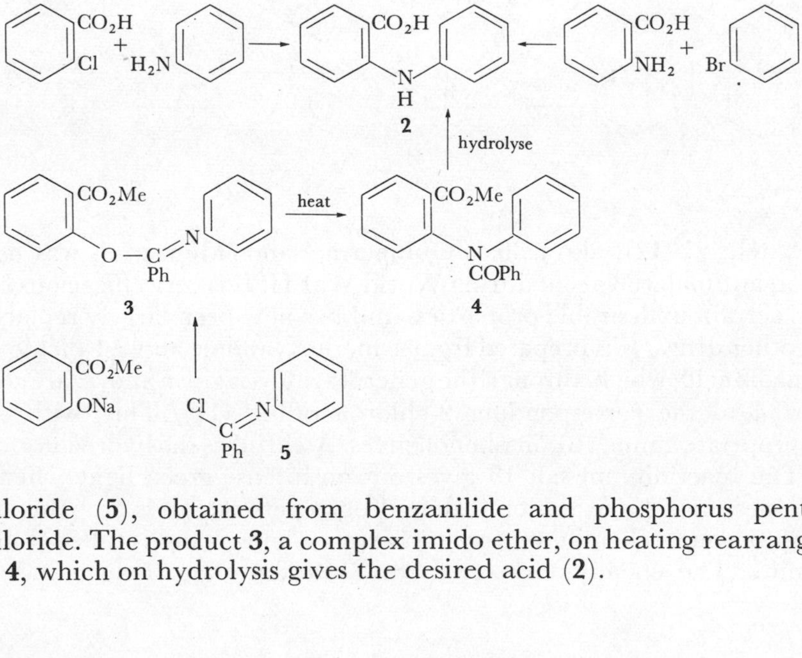

chloride (**5**), obtained from benzanilide and phosphorus pentachloride. The product **3**, a complex imido ether, on heating rearranges to **4**, which on hydrolysis gives the desired acid (**2**).

Cyclization of diphenylamine-2-carboxylic acid (2) to acridone (6), the structure of which is similar to that of 4-pyridone (p. 221), occurs with sulphuric acid under carefully controlled conditions, while phosphorus oxychloride gives 9-chloroacridine (7) quantitatively. Reduction of acridone or 9-chloroacridine as indicated yields acridan (8, 9,10-dihydroacridine), which is oxidized by air, ferric chloride, and many other oxidizing agents to acridine (1). The central ring of acridine, like that of anthracene, is readily reduced. The product, acridan (8), greatly resembles diphenylamine in chemical properties.

The halogen atom of 9-chloroacridine (7) is reactive and is displaced by ammonia in the presence of acid catalysts giving 9-aminoacridine (9). This is a strong base (cf. 4-aminoquinoline, p. 258), and the hydrochloride is a valuable antibacterial agent used mainly for minor injuries and burns.

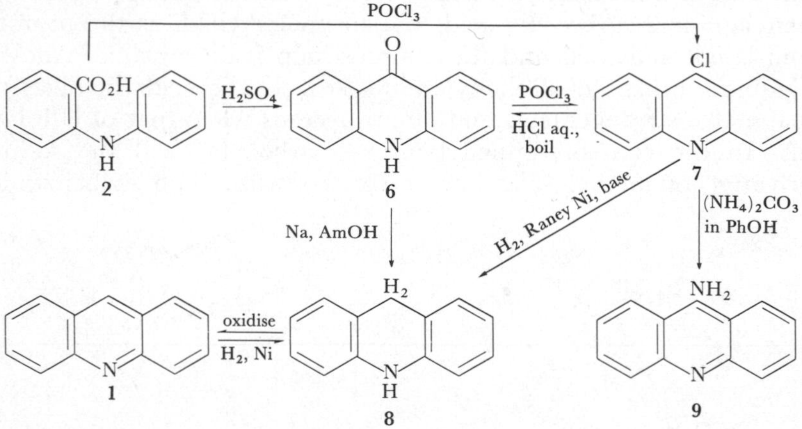

'Atebrin' (12), also called 'Quinacrine' and 'Mepacrin', was used as an antimalarial agent during World War II. It is very efficacious but has certain undesirable properties, and has now been largely replaced by other drugs. It is prepared from 4-methoxyaniline and 2,4-dichlorobenzoic acid, which, through the general synthesis given above, are converted to the corresponding 9-chloroacridine (11). This, with the appropriate amine (10) in phenol, gives 'Atebrin' as the hydrochloride.

The biacridinium salt 13 gives out an intense green light (chemiluminescence) on oxidation with hydrogen peroxide. It is probably the most powerful chemiluminescent substance known and is called 'Lucigenin'. The chemiluminescence can last for many hours, and its

$$CH_3COCH_2CO_2Et \xrightarrow[\text{Et}_2\text{NCH}_2\text{CH}_2\text{Cl}]{\text{NaOEt}} \underset{\underset{CO_2Et}{|}}{CH_3COCHCH_2CH_2NEt_2} \xrightarrow{\text{'ketonic hydrolysis'}}$$

$$CH_3CO(CH_2)_3NEt_2 \xrightarrow{\text{H}_2, \text{ Ni, in NH}_3 \text{ (liquid)}} \underset{\underset{NH_2 \ \mathbf{10}}{|}}{MeCH(CH_2)_3NEt_2}$$

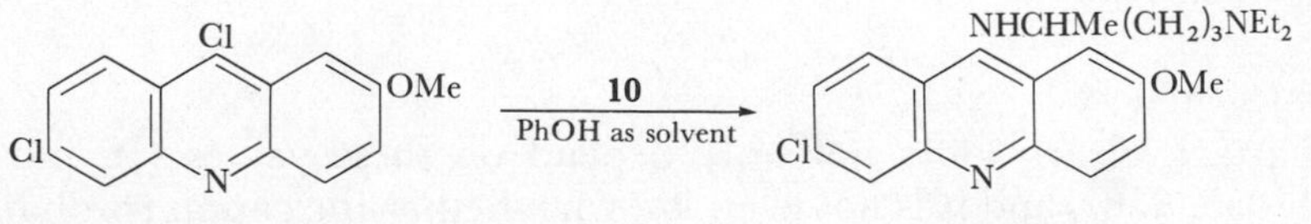

brightness is increased at the expense of duration by osmium tetroxide. The end product is 10-methylacridone.

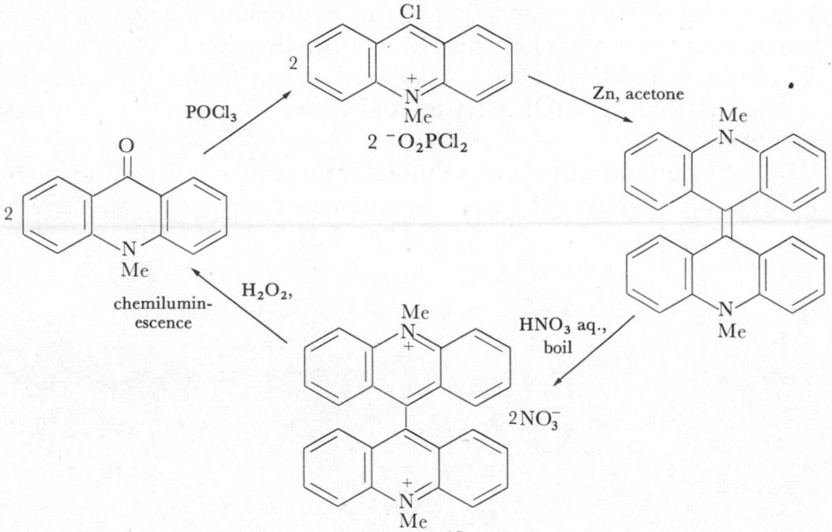

C. Phenanthridine

Phenanthridine (**14**) is a colourless crystalline compound, of m.p. 108°, with a weak blue fluorescence in dilute ethanol.

The substitution reactions of phenanthridine have not been thoroughly investigated. Nitration in sulphuric acid using one mole of nitric acid gives a mixture of 1- and 10-nitrophenanthridine with smaller proportions of the 2-, 3-, 4-, and 8-isomers. The π-electron densities have been calculated[69] for the neutral molecule. The position

L

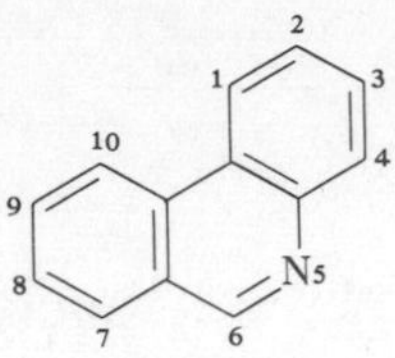

14

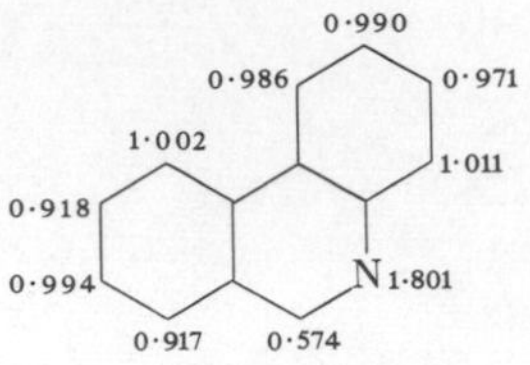

π-Electron densities

of attack clearly does not only depend on these values (cf. purine, pp. 355, 356), and it is not even known whether the cation (probably) or the neutral molecule is the reacting species in the nitration. Phenanthridine with potassium amide in liquid ammonia does, however, give 6-aminophenanthridine in conformity with the molecular-orbital picture. Phenanthridine undergoes the Reissert reaction (p. 252), and is easily reduced (tin and hydrochloric acid) or hydrogenated over Raney nickel to give 5,6-dihydrophenanthridine. This last has the properties of an *N*-alkylaniline and unlike 9,10-dihydroacridine (acridan, p. 282) is basic, and forms *N*-acetyl and *N*-nitroso derivatives.

The best method of preparing phenanthridine consists of cyclizing 2-formamidodiphenyl (15) with phosphorus oxychloride and stannic

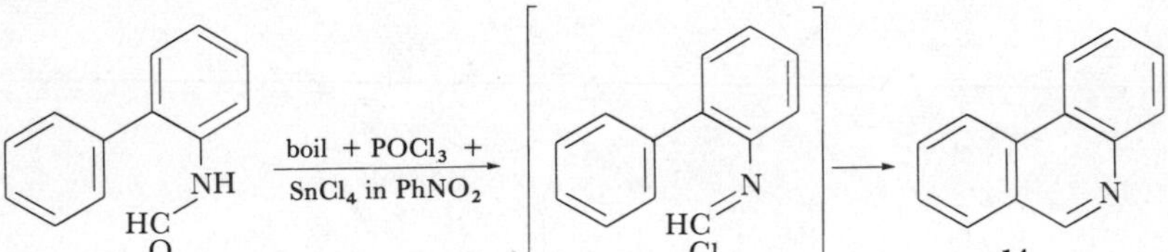

chloride in nitrobenzene; the iminochloride (16) is an intermediate. Many other 2-acylaminodiphenyls have been cyclized similarly.

Phenanthridone (17) is readily prepared and its structure and properties are similar to those of acridone (p. 282) and the pyridones (p. 219). It is attacked by electrophilic reagents at positions 2 and 4 and with phosphorus oxychloride it gives 6-chlorophenanthridine (18) which possesses an active chlorine atom.

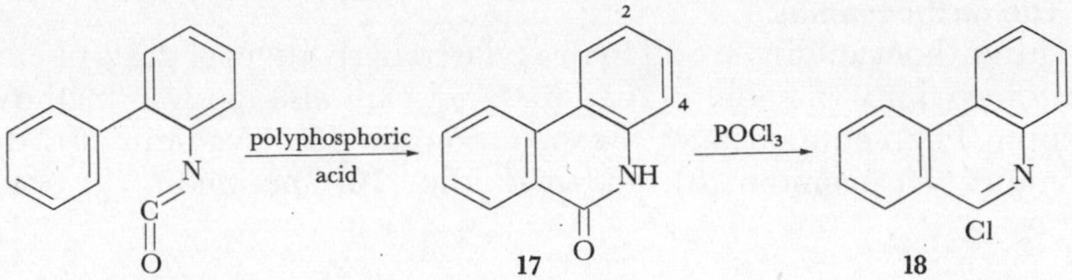

Certain phenanthridinium salts are remarkably active against try-panosome infections, and following the initial discovery of activity by

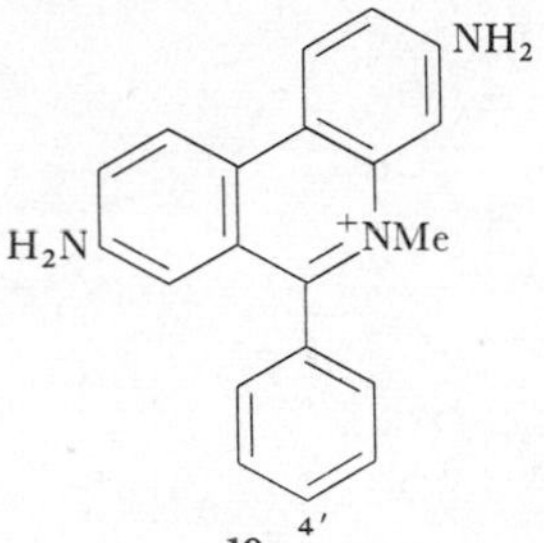

Browning in 1938, several hundred have been prepared and tested. Of these 'Dimidium bromide' (19) is currently used for treating *Try-panosoma congolense* in African cattle; its 4′-amino derivative is more active and is known as 'Trimidium bromide'.

5. BENZOPYRYLIUM SALTS AND BENZOPYRANS
A. Introduction
Many compounds belonging to these classes are found in the plant kingdom. Most red and blue flower petals contain anthocyanins, de-rivatives of the benzopyrylium cation (1), as the coloured material, and the yellow benzo-2- (2) and -4-pyrones (3) are also widely distributed.

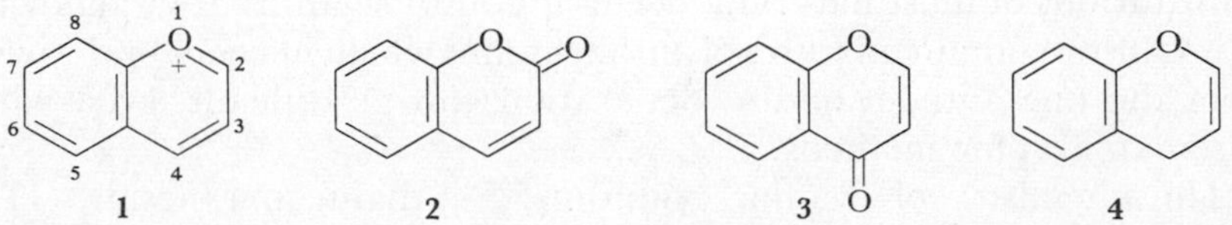

Sulphur analogues of 1 have been obtained synthetically[70] (cf. p. 242). Reduction products of these compounds, which can be treated as de-rivatives of benzopyran (4), are also common plant constituents.

B. The anthocyanins

The anthocyanidins are all hydroxylated derivatives of the 2-phenyl-benzopyrylium (flavylium) cation, and can also possess methoxyl groups. The common ones are pelargonidin (**5**), cyanidin (**6**), delphinidin (**7**), peonidin (**8**), and malvidin (**10**); petunidin (**9**) occurs rarely.

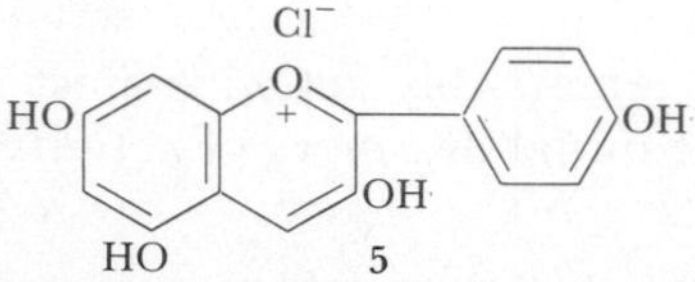

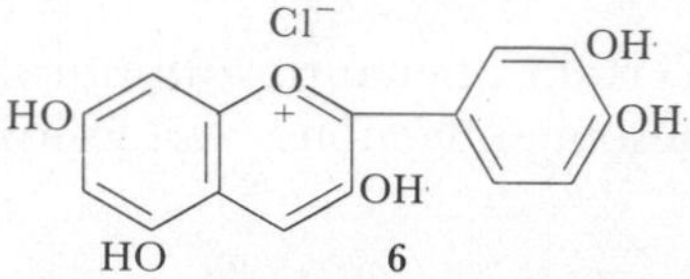

Anthocyanidins do not occur as such in plants but are present in the form of glycosides called anthocyanins. Those derived from cyanidin are most frequently encountered. Glycosidation occurs preferentially at the 3-hydroxyl, and the usual sugars involved are glucose, galactose, and rhamnose. A sugar group can also be attached to the 5-hydroxyl group, as in the case of cyanin (**11**), and recent work has shown that other hydroxyl groups can also be glycosidated.[71] Another complication is that the anthocyanin may be partially esterified with malonic, 4-hydroxybenzoic, or 2- or 4-hydroxycinnamic acids;[72] the exact constitutions of most naturally occurring anthocyanins are unknown. Plants often contain mixtures of anthocyanins which may not be derived from the one anthocyanidin. Separation can be difficult, even with chromatographic methods.

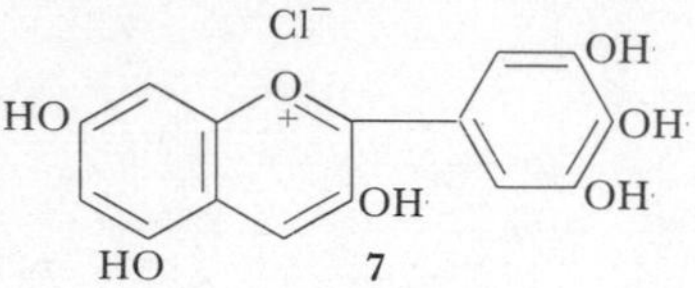

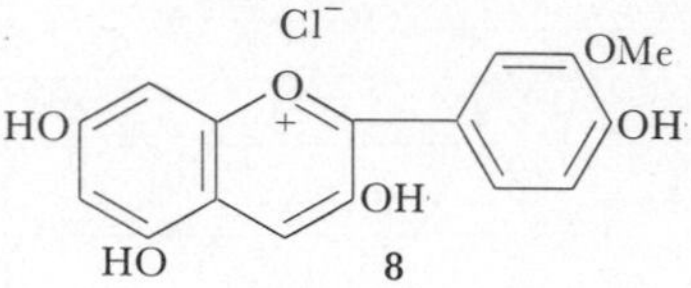

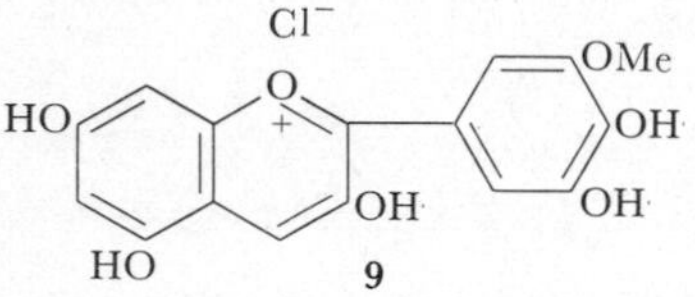

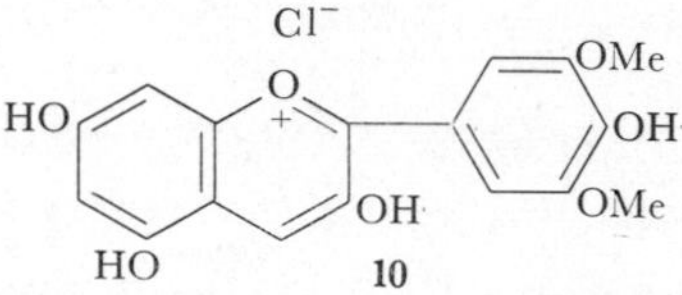

The chemistry of cyanin, cyanidin-3,5-β-diglucopyranoside (**11**), which can be isolated from *Centaurea cyanus* (cornflower) or *Rosa gallica* (rose), very closely resembles that of the other anthocyanins, and will be treated in some detail as an example. Cyanin can be extracted from the petals by cold 1% aqueous hydrochloric acid, or by acidified ethanol, and after much purification is obtainable as a very dark red, almost black, crystalline solid. Hydrolysis with boiling hydrochloric acid splits off the glucose, giving cyanidin (**6**), which can be extracted from the solution with amyl alcohol. The sugar remains in the aqueous layer. Nowadays chromatographic and colour reaction comparisons[73] of both the sugar and anthocyanidin with authentic samples would be used for their identification.

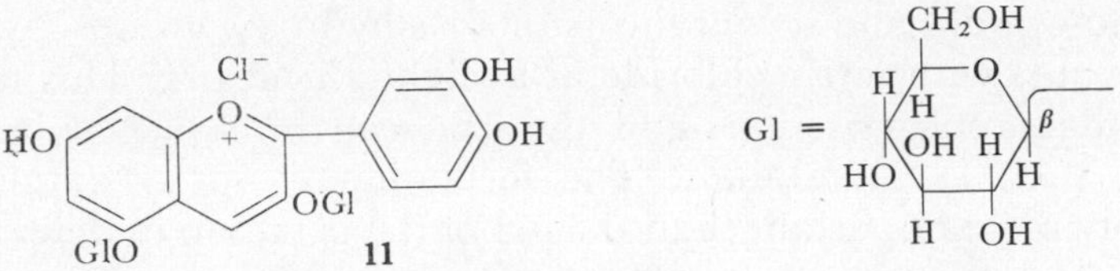

Cyanidin (chloride) is a pyrylium salt (cf. p. 236), which gives a deep red solution in dilute aqueous acid (pH 3). The cation (**12**) is best considered as a resonance hybrid to which other charged structures, such as **13**, contribute. On treating the solution with sodium acetate the colour changes to violet (pH 8), which slowly fades. This can be attributed to the formation of a violet quinonoid colour base (**15**), which adds water yielding the less conjugated (colourless) carbinol (**16**). Cyanidin with sodium hydroxide (pH 11) gives a deep blue solution, due to the formation of a resonant anion (possibly **14–14a**); acidification regenerates cyanidin.

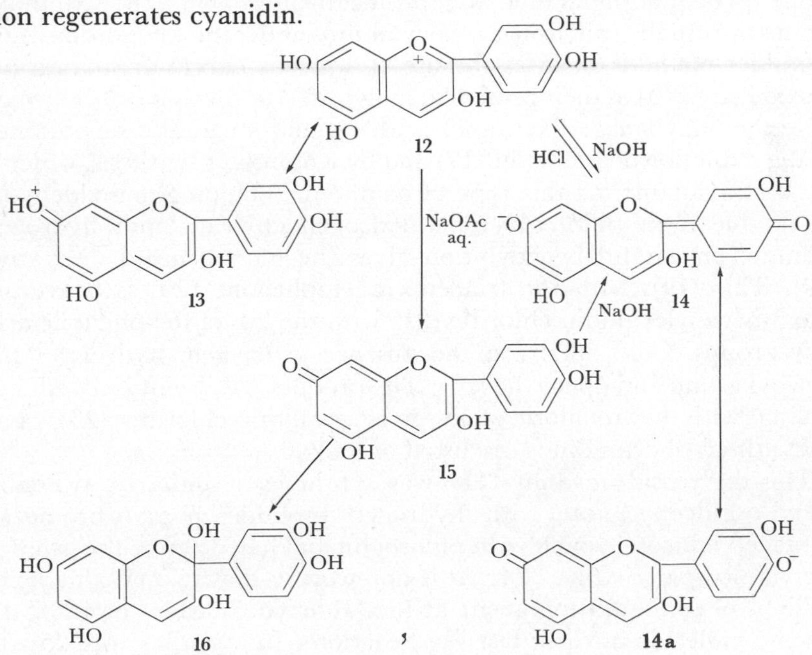

Antho-cyanins and -cyanidins with *ortho* hydroxyl groups give deep blue colours with ferric chloride at a slightly acid pH. This test is a useful diagnostic criterion, and the iron can be replaced by other metals, such as aluminium. The formation of such complexes is probably more important than the pH of the petal sap in determining flower-petal colours; other factors, such as the presence of copigments in the flower, are also important.

The structure of cyanidin (**12**) chloride is established by degradation, by its relationship to quercetin (**17**), and by synthesis. Fusion with

alkali gives phloroglucinol and protocatechuic acid (**18**). Methoxy groups are usually split from anthocyanidins under these conditions, and so milder methods, such as the use of aqueous baryta or sodium hydroxide, are used in their presence; malvidin (**10**) then gives 4-hydroxy-3,5-dimethoxybenzoic (syringic) acid. Cyanidin can also be obtained by the reduction of quercetin (**17**) and by Robinson's synthesis, which is the best available for this type of compound. Phloroglucinaldehyde, obtainable from phloroglucinol, hydrogen chloride, and hydrogen cyanide, on careful benzoylation gives the monobenzoyl derivative (**19**). This (**19**), with the triacetoxyacetophenone (**20**) is converted into 5-benzoylcyanidin chloride (**21**) with the loss of the phenolic acetoxy groups. Cold alkali, in the absence of oxygen, hydrolyses the benzoyl group and opens the ring. The product (**22**) is not isolated, but boiling with hydrochloric acid gives cyanidin chloride (**23**). The biosynthesis of cyanidin is discussed on p. 296.

The diglycoside cyanin (**11**) was synthesized similarly. β-Pentaacetyl-D-glucopyranose with hydrogen bromide gives α-bromo-*O*-tetraacetylglucose, which with phloroglucinaldehyde gives the β-tetraacetylglucose derivative (**24**). It is noteworthy that two (Walden) inversions of configuration occur at the 'aldehyde' carbon atom of the glucose molecule in these last two reactions. In a similar way **25** was

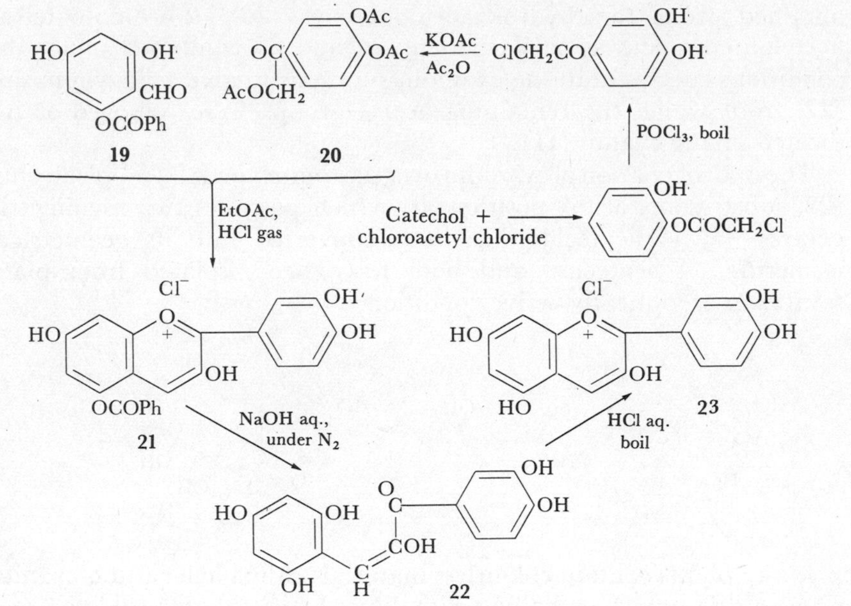
KOAc
Ac2O
ClCH2CO
POCl3, boil
EtOAc,
HCl gas
Catechol +
chloroacetyl chloride
OCOCH2Cl
NaOH aq.,
under N2
HCl aq.
boil
19
20
21
22
23

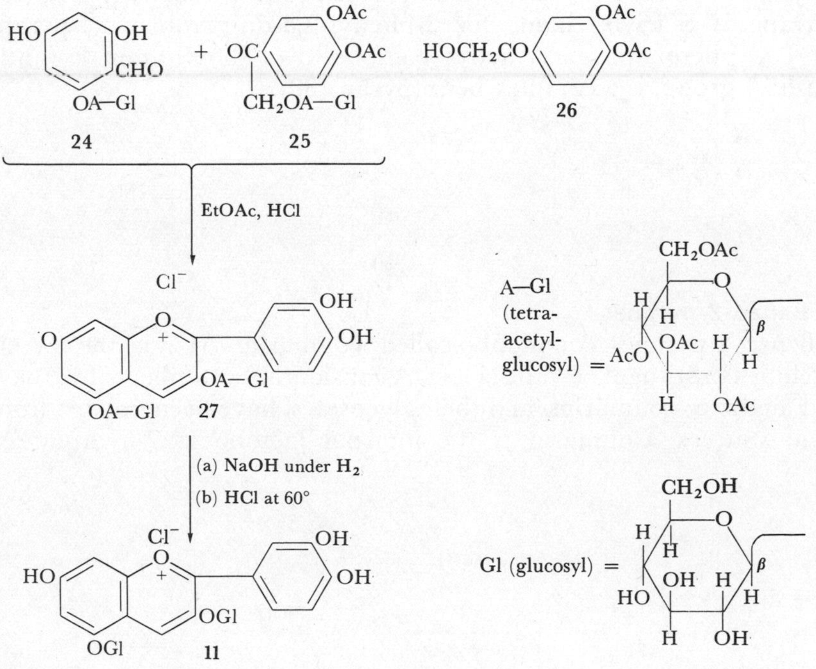
24
25
26
HOCH2CO
CH2OA—Gl
EtOAc, HCl
27
(a) NaOH under H2
(b) HCl at 60°
11
A—Gl
(tetra-
acetyl-
glucosyl) =
CH2OAc
Gl (glucosyl) =
CH2OH

obtained from the hydroxyacetophenone (**26**), α-bromo-*O*-tetra-acetylglucose, and silver carbonate. **24** and **25** combined under the conditions successful in the cyanidin synthesis to give a flavylium salt (**27**) from which the remaining acetyl groups were removed as indicated giving cyanin (**11**).

The hydrogenation of cyanidin over platinum yields ($\pm$)-epicatechin (**28**, substituents at 2,3-position *cis*) which possesses two asymmetric centres. ($\pm$)-Epicatechin has been converted into its geometrical isomeride ($\pm$)-catechin and both have been isolated from plant sources in an optically active condition.

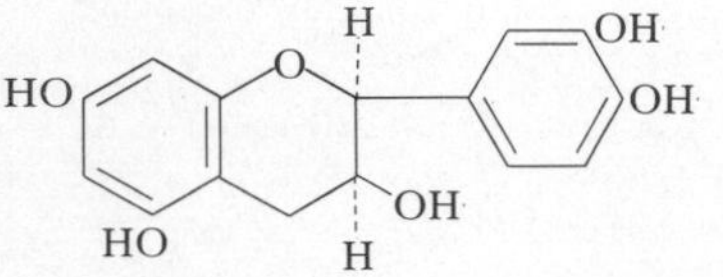

28 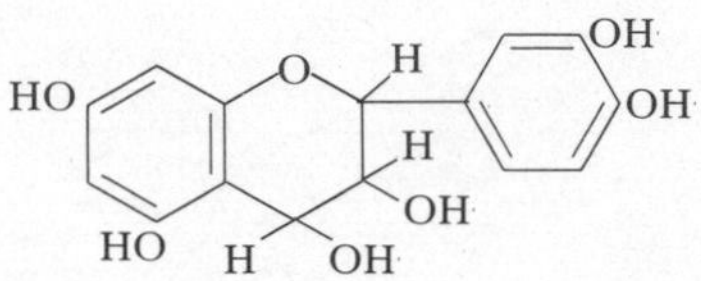   29

Many plants contain colourless materials called leucoantho-cyanins or-cyanidins, which on boiling with dilute hydrochloric acid lose water and are converted into anthocyanidins. It appears that they are flavane-3,4-diols, and leucocyanidin can therefore be written as **29**. Flavane is a trivial name for 2-phenyl-2,3-dihydrobenzo-4-pyran. D-γ-Tocopherol, the most active compound of the vitamin E (anti-sterility) group, is a complex benzopyran (**30**).[74]

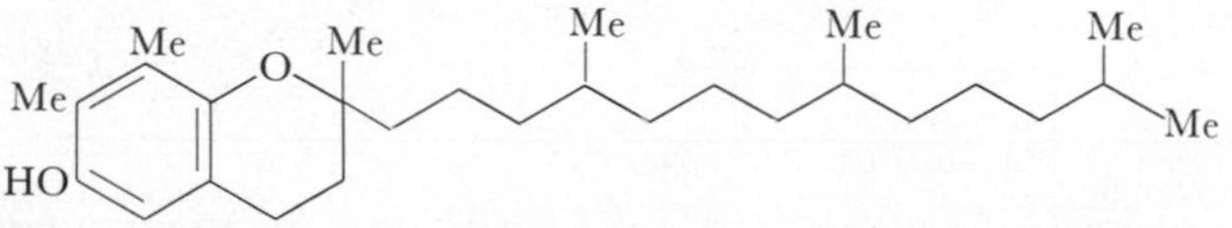

30

C. Benzo-2-pyrones

Benzo-2-pyrone, commonly called coumarin (**31**), is the sweet-smelling constituent of white clover. A considerable number of hydroxy- and methoxy-coumarins, and their glycosides, have been isolated from plant sources. Coumarin is the internal lactone of 2-hydroxy-*cis*-

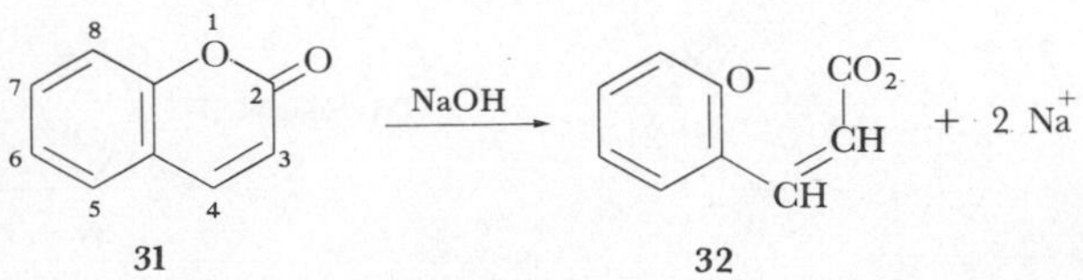

31   32

cinnamic acid, and the ring is opened with alkalis, giving salts of coumarinic acid (**32**). Bromine adds easily to the 3,4-double bond of coumarin, giving a dibromide which readily loses hydrogen bromide and can be readily converted into benzofuran (p. 179). Electrophilic attack on coumarin, as exemplified by nitration or diazo coupling, takes place at position 6.

Coumarin can be synthesized from salicylaldehyde, by a Perkin reaction. The other product is O-acetylcoumaric acid (**33**), which has the

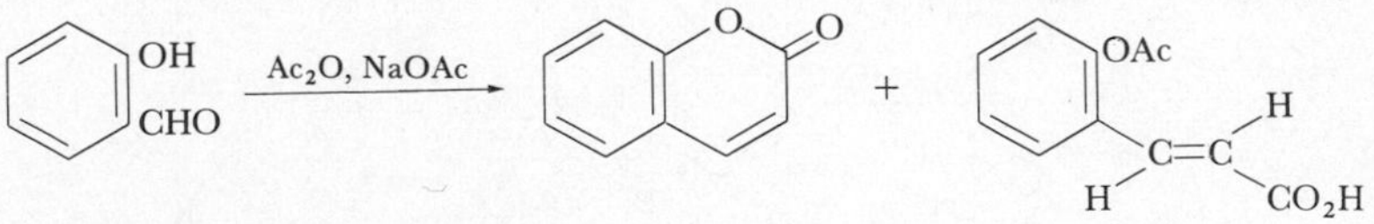

trans configuration. Another synthesis, due to von Pechmann,[75] is perhaps the most widely used for coumarins. Chromones can, however, also be obtained (p. 293). It consists of heating a phenol with a β-keto ester in concentrated sulphuric acid. A coumarinic ester (e.g. **34**) can

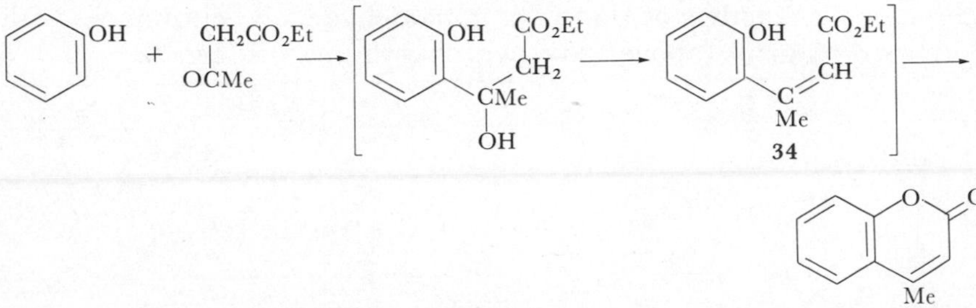

be an intermediate in the synthesis. Best results are obtained when the phenol possesses activating groups. Coumarin itself can be made in poor yield from phenol, and malic acid in sulphuric acid, a combination which gives β-formylacetic acid (p. 238).

'Dicoumarol' (**35**) is present in sweet clover. It is a blood anticoagulant and leads to the haemorrhagic sweet clover disease which kills cattle. 'Warfarin' (**36**) is a useful and powerful rodenticide which kills through its haemorrhagic properties.

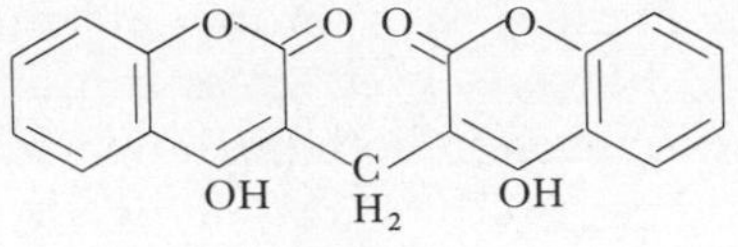

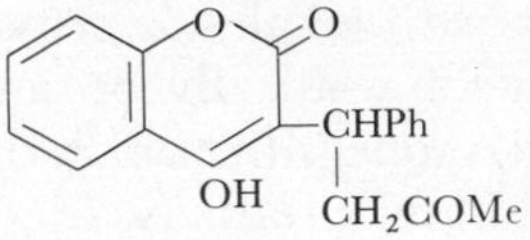

D. Benzo-4-pyrones

Benzo-4-pyrone, or chromone (**37**), has not yet been isolated from natural sources, although a few hydroxy derivatives occur in certain plants. In contrast, many 2-phenylbenzo-4-pyrones, usually called flavones (old name anthoxanthidins), and their glycosides (anthoxanthins) and a considerable number of isoflavones (3-phenylbenzo-4-pyrones) have been identified in plant extracts.

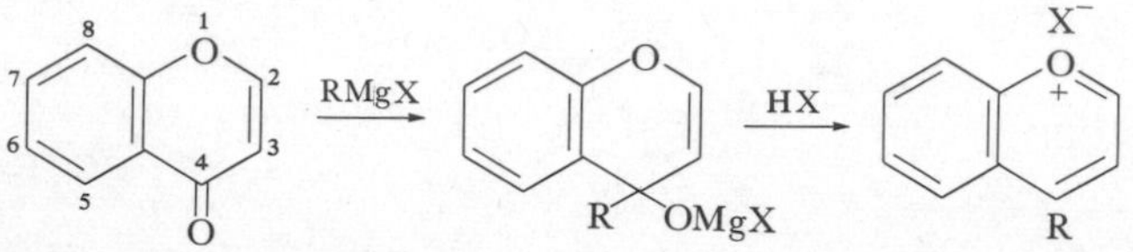

Chromone is best considered as a resonance hybrid analagous to that which represents 2,6-dimethyl-4-pyrone (p. 240). It behaves as an unreactive α,β-unsaturated ketone and gives an oxime, but not a phenylhydrazone, under ordinary conditions. The methyl group of 2-methylchromone is reactive, as that of crotonaldehyde, and chromones with Grignard reagents (above) give benzopyrylium salts (e.g. **38**).

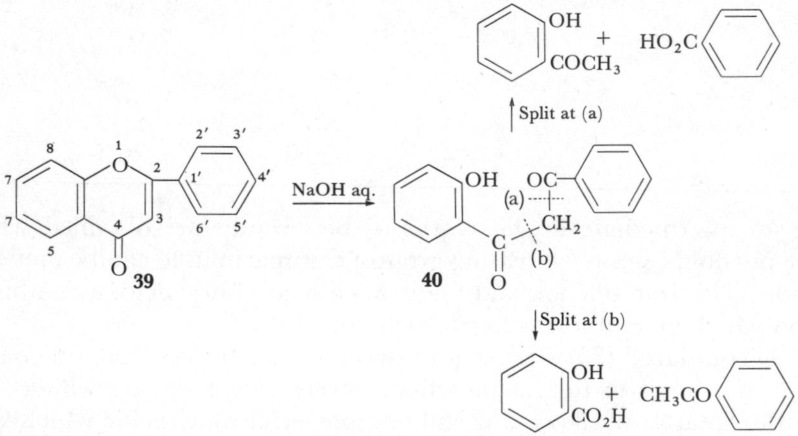

Flavone (**39**) has similar general properties to chromone. Degradation with alkali has proved a valuable method of structure determination for naturally occurring flavones. Flavone itself gives initially a β-diketone (**40**), which then undergoes scission in both possible ways to yield four products. Identification of these products usually leads to a unique structure for the parent flavone.

Chromones and flavones can be synthesized by a number of methods, three of which are shown.

(1) 2-Methoxyacetophenone (**41**) undergoes Claisen reactions with many esters, and the products (**42**) can be cyclized. Chromone itself (**43**, R = H) is made in this way from ethyl formate, and the method has been used for the preparation of many flavones, including luteolin (**46**).

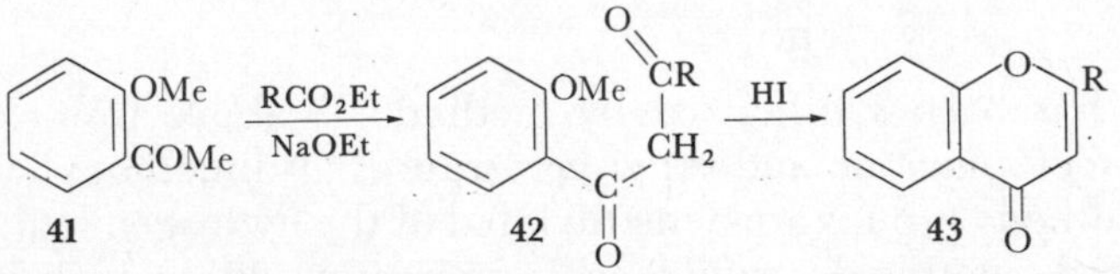

(2) 2-Hydroxyacetophenone with benzaldehyde and a basic catalyst gives the unsaturated ketone **44**. Cyclization with acid gives flavanone, or 2-phenylchromanone (**45**). Bromination, presumably at position 3, followed by dehydrobromination, or oxidation by selenium dioxide or phosphorus pentachloride, gives flavone (**39**).

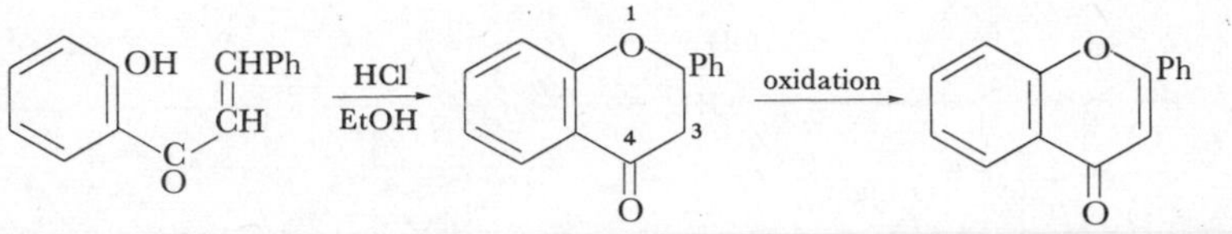

(3) Some chromones can be obtained from β-keto esters, phenols, and phosphorus pentoxide;[75] when sulphuric acid is used as a condensing agent coumarins are usually formed (p. 291).

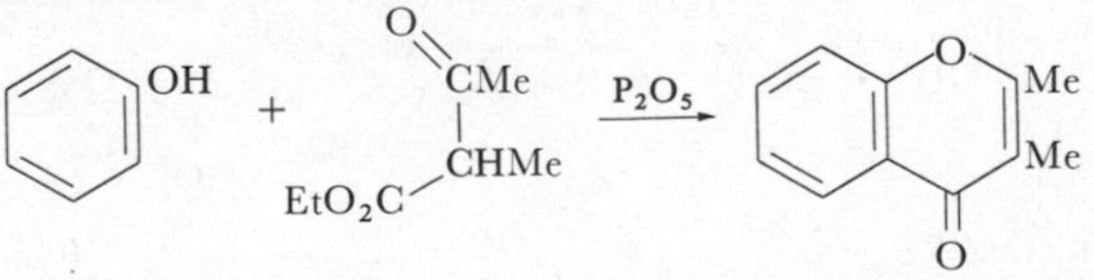

Most naturally occurring flavones are hydroxylated at positions 5 and 7. An example is luteolin (**46**), a yellow compound which was at one time extracted from *Reseda luteola* (wild wood) and used as a dyestuff. Its structure was deduced from the products of alkali fusion. These were 3,4-dihydroxyacetophenone, 3,4-dihydroxybenzoic (protocatechuic) acid, and phloroglucinol, the last presumably being derived from phloroglucinolcarboxylic acid and 2,4,6-trihydroxyacetophenone, which would be formed first (cf. alkali degradation of flavone, above).

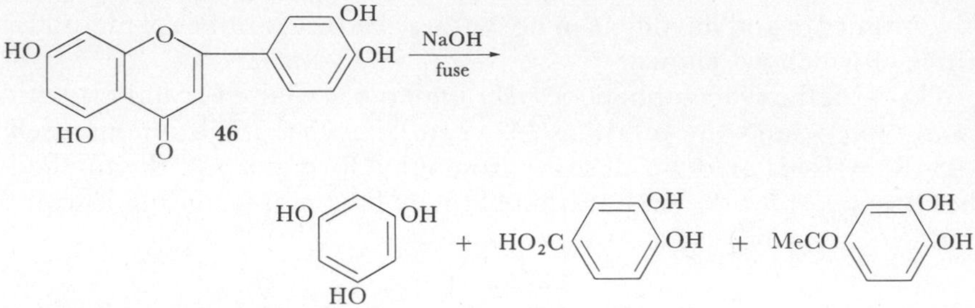

Luteolin has been synthesized by method (1) above from 2,4,6-tri-methoxyacetophenone and ethyl veratrate (3,4-dimethoxybenzoate). All the methoxy groups are demethylated at the hydrogen iodide stage.

A related pentahydroxyflavone is quercetin (**49**), which is one of

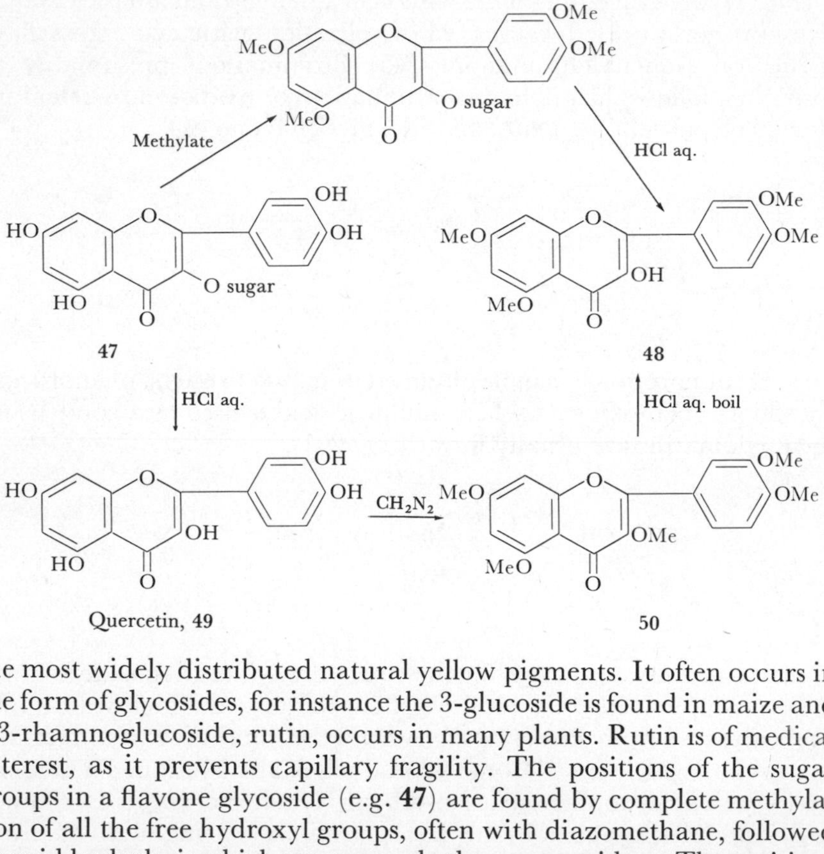

the most widely distributed natural yellow pigments. It often occurs in the form of glycosides, for instance the 3-glucoside is found in maize and a 3-rhamnoglucoside, rutin, occurs in many plants. Rutin is of medical interest, as it prevents capillary fragility. The positions of the sugar groups in a flavone glycoside (e.g. **47**) are found by complete methylation of all the free hydroxyl groups, often with diazomethane, followed by acid hydrolysis which removes only the sugar residues. The positions of the free hydroxy groups in the resulting aglycone (**48**) are then determined by degradation or comparison with synthetic materials and correspond to the position(s) of glycosidation. The 3-*O*-methyl group of quercetin pentamethyl ether (**50**) is quite readily hydrolysed. The only recognizable fragments from the alkali fusion of quercetin are phloroglucinol and protocatechuic acid. Quercetin has been synthesized from 3,4-dimethoxybenzaldehyde (veratraldehyde) and 2,4,6-trimethoxyacetophenone, which were first converted into the

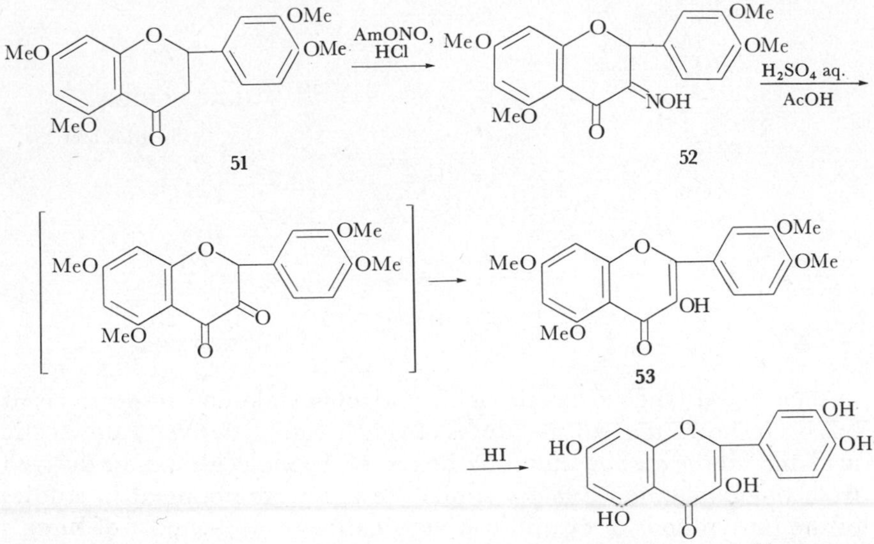

flavanone (**51**) by method (2) on p. 293. Amyl nitrite and hydrochloric acid attack the activated methylene group of this flavanone (**51**) in the usual way, forming an oxime (**52**). Hydrolysis gives a diketone which tautomerizes to **53** and on demethylation yields quercetin (**54**).

The positions of the hydroxyl groups of quercetin and cyanidin are identical. Cyanidin has not been converted into quercetin, although the reverse transformation can be effected by powerful reagents (p. 288). Because of these, and other reasons, Robinson suggested many years ago that these compounds were formed by parallel but not identical routes in plants, that ring A was derived from phloroglucinol and joined directly on to a C_6–C_3 fragment which completed the molecule. In support of this Birch showed that added radioactive phloroglucinol and phenylalanine (converted *en route* to 3,4-dihydroxycinnamic acid) were incorporated into quercetin synthesized by *Chlamydomonas eagamentos*. He also suggested that the phloroglucinol part (ring A) could be built up from three acetic acid molecules, and this has been confirmed[76] for quercetin synthesized by *Fagopyrum tataricum* (buckwheat). By growing wheat cuttings in the presence of methyl-labelled

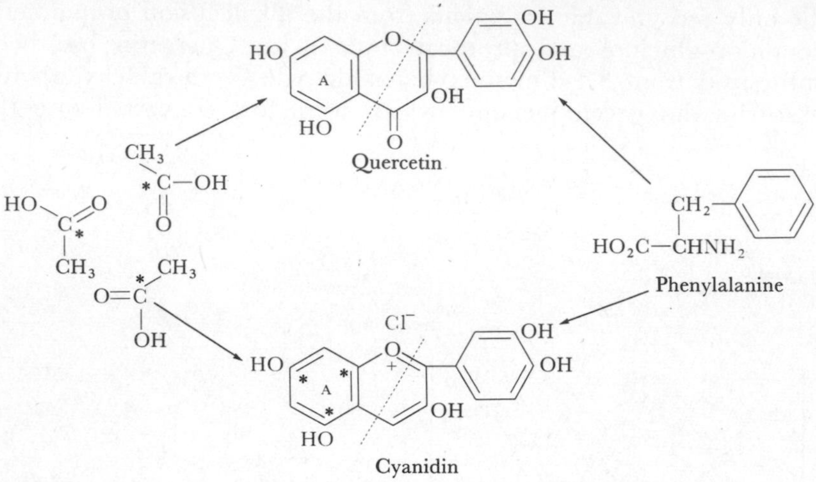

Quercetin

Phenylalanine

Cyanidin

and carboxyl-labelled acetic acid, and phenylalanine respectively it has been shown that all the atoms of ring A can be derived from acetic acid and all the carbon atoms of the rest of the molecule can be derived from phenylalanine. Exactly similar results were obtained in studies of the biosynthesis of cyanidin by red cabbage. In support of Birch's theory it was also shown that the carbon atoms bearing the hydroxyl groups of the phloroglucinol obtained on degradation of the cyanidin were those of the carboxyl groups of labelled acetic acid used. Cyanidin and quercetin are therefore built up from the acetic acid and phenylalanine carbon atoms as shown, but the mechanism by which this is done is not yet fully understood.[77]

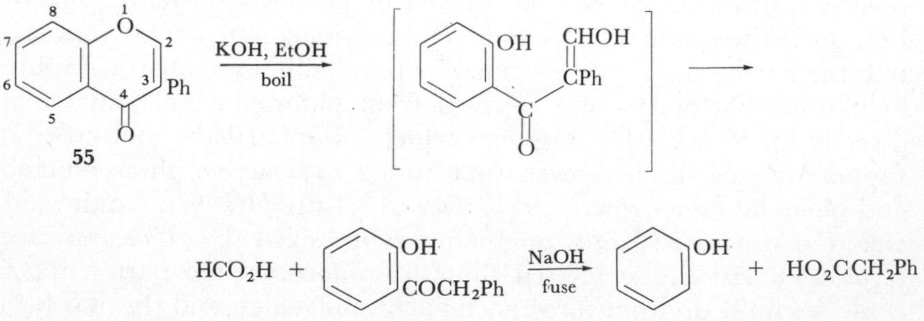

Only about a dozen derivatives of isoflavone (**55**, for a review see ref. 78) have been isolated from plant sources. They are formed *in vivo* from phenylalanine, like flavones, but a 1,2-shift of the phenyl group occurs at some stage. They often occur as glycosides, which are readily hydrolysed to the aglycones by dilute acid. The structures of these aglycones have usually been elucidated from those of the products of alkaline degradations; that of isoflavone itself is shown. Formic acid is obtained quantitatively in the first stage.

Isoflavones can be made by a 'reversal' of the alkaline degradation. Poor yields are generally obtained, especially if hydroxyl groups are present, as they generally are with naturally occurring isoflavones. An intermediate hydroxy compound (e.g. **56**) has been isolated in a few instances.

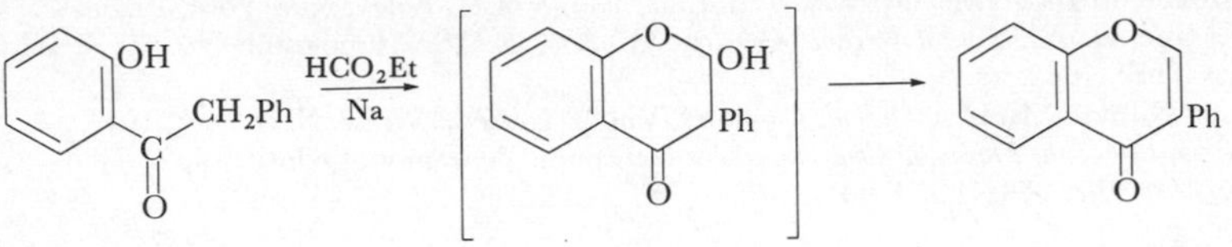

The synthesis of genistein (**58**, 5,7,4'-trihydroxyisoflavone) by a very much better method, using ethyl oxalyl chloride, is outlined. The first product (**57**) is readily hydrolysed by sodium carbonate and the resulting acid decarboxylated to give a 50% overall yield. Genistein is

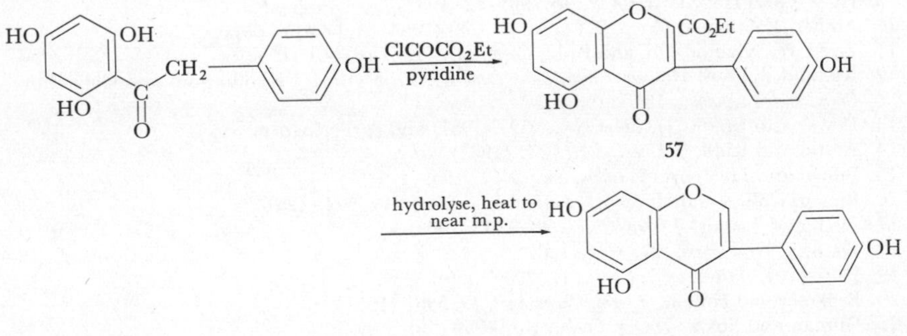

of particular interest in that it is an oestrogen about 10^{-5} times as active as oestrone. This was discovered during an investigation of an outbreak of sheep infertility in Australia. The sheep were eating an unusual amount of clover, which caused the trouble, and the active agent was genistein.

GENERAL BIBLIOGRAPHY

QUINOLINE AND ISOQUINOLINE

Sidgwick's Organic Chemistry of Nitrogen, Taylor and Baker, Oxford University Press, 1942.
Elderfield and Gensler, in *Heterocyclic Compounds*, ed. Elderfield, Vol. 4, Wiley, New York, 1952.
Campbell, in *Chemistry of Carbon Compounds*, ed. Rodd, Vol. IVA, Elsvier, New York, 1957.

QUINOLIZINE

Acheson, *Adv. Heterocyclic chem.*, **1**, 125 (1963).
Thyagarajan, *Adv. Heterocyclic chem.*, **5**, 291 (1965).

ACRIDINE

Acheson, *Acridines*, Interscience, New York, 1956.

PHENANTHRIDINE

Allen, *Six-Membered Heterocyclic Nitrogen Compounds with Three Condensed Rings*, Interscience, New York, 1958.

BENZO-PYRANS, -PYRONES, AND -PYRYLIUM SALTS

Wawzonek, in *Heterocyclic Compounds*, ed. Elderfield, Vol. 2, Wiley, New York, 1950.
Meyer and Cook, *Natural Organic Colouring Matters*, A.C.S. Monograph No. 89, Reinhold, New York, 1943.
Link, in Gilman, *Advanced Organic Chemistry*, Vol. 2, 2nd ed., Wiley, New York, 1942.
The Chemistry of the Flavonoid Compounds, ed. Geissman, Pergamon, Oxford, 1962.
Barry, *Chem. Rev.*, **64**, 229 (1964).

REFERENCES

1. Klages, *Chem. Ber.*, **82**, 358 (1949).
2. Cruickshank, *Acta Cryst.*, **10**, 504 (1957).
3. Wibaut *et al.*, *Rec. Trav. Chim.*, **74**, 241 (1955), and earlier papers.
4. Longuet-Higgins and Coulson, *Trans. Faraday Soc.*, **43**, 87 (1947).
5. Popp, Blount, and Soto, *Chem. Ind. (London)*, 1022 (1962).
6. McEwen and Cobb, *Chem. Rev.*, **55**, 511 (1955).
7. Elliott, *J. Org. Chem.*, **29**, 305 (1964).
8. Bramley and Johnson, *J. Chem. Soc.*, 1372 (1965) and earlier papers.
9. Hückel and Hagedorn, *Chem. Ber.*, **90**, 752 (1957).
10. Archer, Booth, and Crisp, *J. Chem. Soc.*, 249 (1964) and earlier papers.
11. La Mare, Kiamud-din, and Ridd, *Chem. Ind. (London)*, 361 (1958).
12. Kiamud-din and Haque, *Chem. Ind. (London)*, 1753 (1964); Kiamud-din and Choudhury, *Chem. Ind. (London)*, 1840 (1963).
13. Dewar and Maitlis, *J. Chem. Soc.*, 2521 (1957) and earlier papers.
14. Austin and Ridd, *J. Chem. Soc.*, 4204 (1963).
15. Brown and Harcourt, *J. Chem. Soc.*, 3451 (1959).
16. Brown, Coller, and Harcourt, *Australian J. Chem.*, **14**, 643 (1961).
17. Eisch and Jasekis, *J. Org. Chem.*, **28**, 2865 (1963).
18. Eisch, *J. Org. Chem.*, **27**, 1318 (1962).
19. Pausacker, *Australian J. Chem.*, **11**, 200 (1958).
20. Benkeser and Holton, *J. Am. Chem. Soc.*, **73**, 5861 (1951).
21. Gilman and Spatz, *J. Org. Chem.*, **16**, 1485 (1951).
22. Ochiai, *J. Org. Chem.*, **18**, 534 (1953).
23. Buchardt, *Acta Chem. Scand.*, **17**, 1461 (1963).
24. Ishikawa, Yamada, and Kaneko, *Chem. Pharm. Bull. (Japan)*, **13**, 747 (1965).
25. Brower, Samuels, Way, and Amstutz, *J. Org. Chem.*, **18**, 1648 (1953).
26. Reitsema, *Chem. Rev.*, **43**, 43 (1948).
27. Phillips, *Chem. Rev.*, **56**, 271 (1956).
28. Davies and Powell, *Nature*, **168**, 386 (1951).
29. Brown, *Quart. Rev. (London)*, **5**, 131 (1951).
30. Manske and Kulka, *Org. Reactions*, **7**, 59 (1953).

31. Badger, Crocker, Ennis, Gayler, Matthews, Paper, Samuel, and Spotswood, *Australian J. J. Chem.*, **16**, 814 (1963).
32. Elderfield *et al.*, *J. Am. Chem. Soc.*, **68**, 1584 (1946).
33. Zobian, Kelley, and Dunathan, *J. Org. Chem.*, **29**, 584 (1964).
34. Popp and Schuyler, *J. Chem. Soc.*, 522 (1964).
35. Bentley, *The Alkaloids*, Interscience, New York, 1957.
36. Ing, in *Organic Chemistry*, p. 449, ed. Gilman, Vol. III, Wiley, New York, 1953.
37. Venkataraman, *Synthetic Dyes*, Academic Press, New York, 1952.
38. Hamer, *Quart. Rev.*, **4**, 327 (1950).
39. Hamer, *The Cyanine Dyes and Related Compounds*, Interscience, New York, 1963.
40. Lindenstruth and VanderWerf, *J. Am. Chem. Soc.*, **71**, 3020 (1949).
41. Hückel and Graner, *Chem. Ber.*, **90**, 2017 (1957).
42. Potts, *J. Chem. Soc.*, 1269 (1956).
43. Brown and Harcourt, *Tetrahedron*, **8**, 23 (1960).
44. Moodie, Schofield, and Williamson, *Chem. Ind. (London)*, 1283 (1963).
45. Dewar and Maitlis, *J. Chem. Soc.*, 2521 (1957).
46. Kiamud-Din, in *Physical Methods in Heterocyclic Chemistry*, ed. Katritzky, Vol. 1, p. 124 (1963).
47. Gordon and Pearson, *J. Org. Chem.*, **29**, 329 (1964).
48. Erlenmeyer, Baumann, and Sorkin, *Helv. Chim. Acta*, **31**, 1978 (1948).
49. Haworth and Robinson, *J. Chem. Soc.*, 777 (1948).
50. Robison and Robison, *J. Org. Chem.*, **21**, 1337, (1956).
51. *Organic Reactions*, **6**, Chapters 2, 3, and 4.
52. Itoh and Sugasawa, *Tetrahedron*, **1**, 45 (1957).
53. Hey and Williams, *J. Chem. Soc.*, 1527 (1951).
54. Schlittler and Müller, *Helv. Chim. Acta*, **31**, 1119 (1948).
55. Boekelheide and Gall, *J. Am. Chem. Soc.*, **76**, 1832 (1954).
56. Glover and Jones, *J. Chem. Soc.*, 3021 (1958).
57. Acheson and Goodall, *J. Chem. Soc.*, 3225 (1964).
58. Richards and Stevens, *J. Chem. Soc.*, 3067 (1958).
59. Acheson, *Advan. Heterocyclic Chem.*, **1**, 125 (1963).
60. Miyadera and Kishida, *Tetrahedron Letters*, 905 (1965).
61. Miyadera, *Chem. Pharm. Bull. (Japan)*, **13**, 503 (1965).
62. Acheson and Taylor, *Proc. Chem. Soc.*, 186 (1959); *J. Chem. Soc.*, 1691 (1960).
63. Duke, Fozard, and Jones, *J. Org. Chem.*, **30**, 526 (1965) and earlier papers.
64. Boekelheide and Lodge, *J. Am. Chem. Soc.*, **73**, 3681 (1951).
65. Thyagarajan and Gopalakrishnan, *Tetrahedron*, **21**, 945 (1965).
66. Winterfield and Dünwald, *Naturwissenschaften*, **43**, 517 (1956).
67. Moynehan, Schofield, Jones, and Katritzky, *J. Chem. Soc.*, 2637 (1962).
68. Acheson, Adcock, Glover, and Sutton, *J. Chem. Soc.*, 3367 (1960).
69. Longuet-Higgins and Coulson, *J. Chem. Soc.*, 971 (1949).
70. Engelhard and Kolb, *Ann.*, **673**, 136 (1964); Degani, Fochi and Vincenzi, *Gazzetta chim. Ital.*, **94**, 451 (1964).
71. Forsyth and Simmonds, *Proc. Roy. Soc., B*, **142**, 549 (1954); Harborne and Sheratt, *Experientia*, **13**, 486 (1957).
72. Harborne, *Phytochemistry*, **3**, 151 (1964).
73. Bate-Smith, *Biochem. Soc. Symp.*, No. 3, 62 (1949).
74. Mayer, Schudel, Rüegg, and Isler, *Helv. Chim. Acta*, **46**, 963 (1963); Isler, Schudel, Mayer, Würsch, and Rüegg, *Vitamins Hormones*, **20**, 389 (1962).
75. Sethna and Phadke, *Org. Reactions*, **7**, 1 (1953).
76. Watkin, Underhill, and Neish, *Can. J. Biochem. Physiol.*, **35**, 219, 229 (1957).
77. Billek, (Ed.) *Biosynthesis of Aromatic Compounds*, Pergamon (1966).
78. Warburton, *Quart. Rev.*, **8**, 67 (1954).

CHAPTER VII

COMPOUNDS WITH TWO HETEROATOMS IN A
FIVE-MEMBERED RING

The great majority of the known compounds with two heteroatoms in a five-membered ring are aromatic and can be derived formally from pyrrole, furan, or thiophene by the replacement of one of the methine ($=CH$) groups by a nitrogen atom. They can be derived similarly from pyridine by replacing two methine groups ($-CH=CH-$) by an imino group (NH), or oxygen, or sulphur atoms, and the properties of the ring systems produced are, very roughly, an amalgamation of those of the parents. Partially reduced and fully reduced derivatives of the above ring systems are known. The dihydro (e.g. dihydroimida-

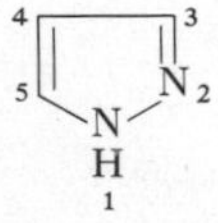

Pyrazole 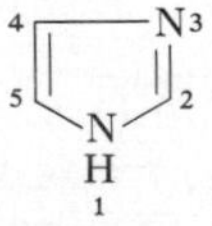   Imidazole 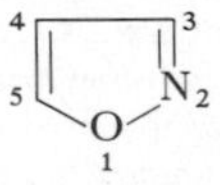   Isoxazole 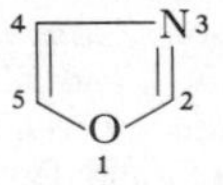   Oxazole

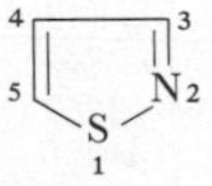

Isothiazole 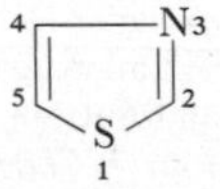   Thiazole

zole) and tetrahydro (e.g. tetrahydroimidazole) derivatives are named after the corresponding aromatic compound (e.g. imidazole) by replacing the -ole by -oline (e.g. imidazoline) and -olidine (e.g. imidazolidine) respectively. Three isomeric imidazolines can be formulated, differing in the position of the double bond (cf. pyrrolines, pp. 63, 68).

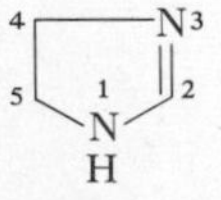

2-Imidazoline 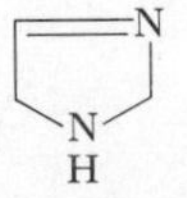   3-Imidazoline 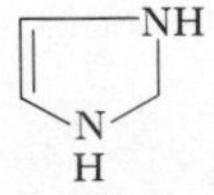   4-Imidazoline 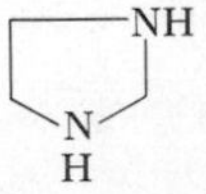   Imidazolidine

Where both heteroatoms are oxygen or sulphur it is not possible to have an uncharged aromatic ring, and compounds of these types have been studied less intensively than those where the ring contains nitrogen. The basic ring systems are named systematically, the posi-

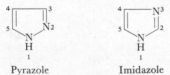

| 1,2-Dithiole | 1,3-Dithiole | 1,3-Oxthiole | 1,3-Dioxole | 1,3-Dioxolane |

tions of the heteroatoms are always given, and the endings -ole and -olane are used respectively for the unsaturated and saturated rings.

The numbering of rings which contain two heteroatoms follows the rules that the lowest numbers of the possible alternatives are used and that oxygen, sulphur, nitrogen (NH), and nitrogen ($=$N$-$) take this order of precedence (see p. 2). Certain difficulties can, however, arise in naming pyrazoles and imidazoles, and are discussed on the next page, in connexion with these compounds.

1. PYRAZOLE AND IMIDAZOLE

A. Introduction

As early as 1884 Knorr discovered the antipyretic (temperature-reducing) action of a pyrazole derivative in man. He named the compound antipyrine (p. 309). This stimulated interest in pyrazole chemistry, and although antipyrine is now little used, a number of pharmaceuticals and dyestuffs contain the ring system.

Pyrazole   Imidazole

Imidazole was first prepared in 1858 from glyoxal and ammonia, and called glyoxaline. This name is almost obsolete, and imidazole or iminazole is greatly preferred. In contrast to pyrazoles, which occur infrequently in nature, certain imidazoles are very important in living systems. Examples are the essential amino acid histidine (p. 311) and related compounds, vitamin B_{12} (p. 91), biotin (p. 138), 5-aminoimidazole-4-carboxyamide (p. 311), and the pilocarpine alkaloids. A number of imidazoles are useful chemotherapeutic agents.

B. Physical properties and structure

Pyrazole, m.p. 70°, and imidazole, m.p. 90°, are both highly crystalline solids which are soluble in water but almost insoluble in petroleum ether. They are both tautomeric, as either nitrogen atom of each ring can bear the hydrogen atom. An example is methylimidazole, for which structures **1** (4-methylimidazole) and **2** (5-methylimidazole) can be

written. As only one substance, which may be a single tautomer or an equilibrium mixture, is known, it would be incorrect to call it either 4- or 5-methylimidazole, as these names imply the definite structures given above. It is therefore called 4(5)-methylimidazole to avoid the difficulty. In a similar way the pyrazole **3**, and/or **4**, is named 3(5)-ethyl-5(3)-methylpyrazole. There is no evidence which suggests that 'pyrrolenine' tautomers (cf. pyrrole, pp. 65, 66) of pyrazole or imidazole exist in measurable concentrations.

TABLE 1. Boiling point and pK_a values of nitrogen heterocyclic compounds

Compound	Boiling point at 760 mm	Basic pK_a	Acidic pK_a
Pyridine	115°	5·6	—
Pyrrole	130–131°	−3·8	ca. 15
1-Methylpyrazole	127°	2·1	—
Pyrazole	187°	2·5	14
1-Methylimidazole	199°	7·4	—
Imidazole	256°	7·2	14·5

The boiling points in the Table 1 are easily accounted for on the basis of hydrogen bonding, which is absent in pyridine and present to a very small extent in pyrrole. 1-Methylpyrazole and 1-methylimidazole both boil much below the parent compounds, which shows the importance of the hydrogen atom at position 1. The large difference in boiling point between pyrazole and imidazole is remarkable. Both compounds associate in solution, but imidazole and some derivatives can give as little as 5% of the expected freezing-point depression in benzene. This shows that aggregates of the order of twenty molecules are formed. The results are best accounted for on the assumption that

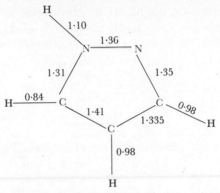

imidazole associates polymolecularly as in **5** while pyrazole forms largely a bimolecular complex **6**. Imidazole does not associate in water.

The dimensions of pyrazole, but not yet of imidazole, have been determined[1] by x-ray crystallography. From heats of combustion data, the resonance energies of pyrazole and imidazole have been calculated[2] as 29·3 and 14·2 kcal/mole, respectively. The chemical reactions of the

Mean lengths in Å

compounds are also consistent with the presence of a great deal of aromatic character. They suggest that the compounds are best considered as resonance hybrids to which charged structures such as **7**, and **8** and **8a**, contribute in the two cases. This is in agreement with electron density calculations[3] which suggest that electrophilic attack should occur at position 4 in pyrazole and in imidazole.

C. Chemical properties and synthetic methods

To the first approximation the chemical properties of pyrazole and imidazole are a combination of those of pyridine and pyrrole. Imidazole forms many stable crystalline salts and is a stronger base than pyridine (see Table 1). This agrees with the assumption that there is a little extra resonance energy associated with the cation because of the contribution of structures **9** and **9a** to the resonance hybrid, which represents

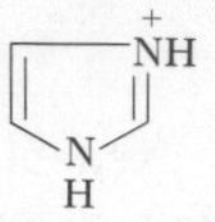

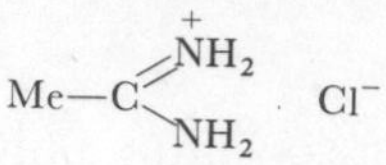

Acetamidine hydrochloride

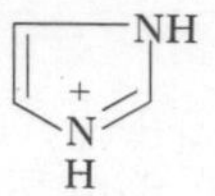

9   **9a**

the molecule (cf. resonance in the amidine cation, p. 217). Similar structures can be written for the cation derived from pyrazole, but in contrast this compound is a weaker base than pyridine. The acidic properties of pyrazole and imidazole are slightly more pronounced (Table 1) than those of pyrrole owing to the inductive effect of the 'pyridine' nitrogen atom. They react with potassium, and a few other metals, in the same way as pyrrole (p. 69). Imidazole forms a sparingly

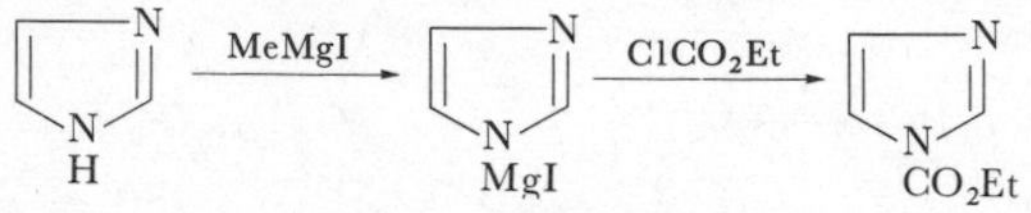

soluble silver salt with ammoniacal silver nitrate. These metal derivatives with alkyl or acyl halides give 1- (or *N*-) substituted pyrazoles or imidazoles.

When the imidazole or pyrazole is not substituted symmetrically, as in the case of 4(5)-methylimidazole, two different tautomeric structures are possible (**1** and **2**, p. 302), and in fact the compound behaves as a mixture in chemical reactions. It is worth noting that both tautomers give the same aromatic cation (**10**) and anion (**11**) by the respective addition or loss of a proton.

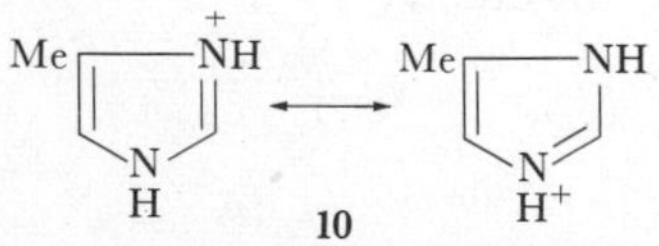

10 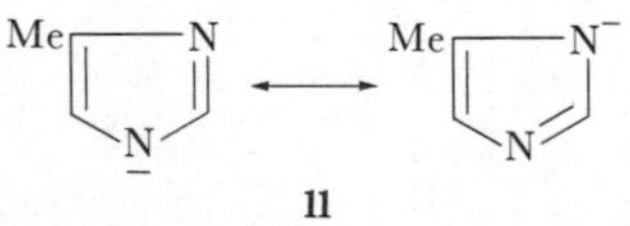   **11**

Pyrazole and imidazole are remarkably stable to acids and to oxidation. It is remarkable that pyrazole can be partially converted into imidazole on illumination with ultraviolet light; indazole similarly gives 30% of benzimidazole.[4] Imidazole is very resistant to reduction, but some pyrazoles can be reduced to pyrazolines and pyrazolidines.

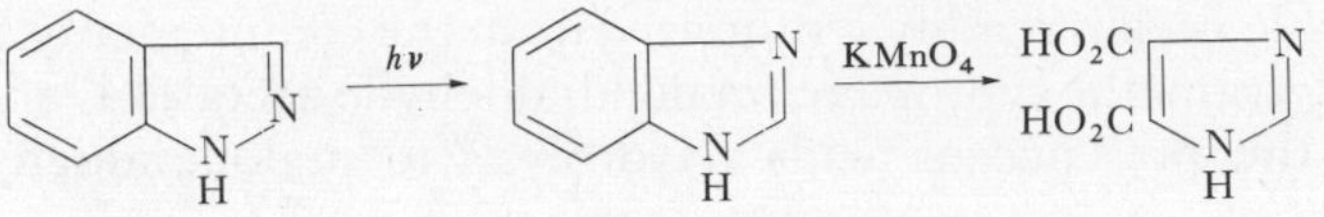

Indazole   Benzimidazole

The nitration of pyrazole in concentrated sulphuric acid, when the pyrazolium cation is actually attacked,[5] causes substitution at position 4 as does bromination and sulphonation. Pyrazole also undergoes base-catalysed iodination at position 4.[6] Although pyrazole does not couple with aromatic diazonium salts 3,5-dimethylpyrazole does react with nitrous acid, followed by sodium hydroxide, to give 3,5-dimethyl-4-diazopyrazole (12; cf. diazopyrrole p. 79) which couples with 2-naphthol to give a red dye (13).[7] 1,3,5-Trimethylpyrazole gives the 4-acetyl derivative in the Friedel–Crafts reaction with acetyl chloride and aluminium chloride,[8] and 1-phenylpyrazole with phenyl radicals, from benzoyl peroxide, gives 30% of 1,3-diphenylpyrazole along with much substitution in the original benzene ring.[9]

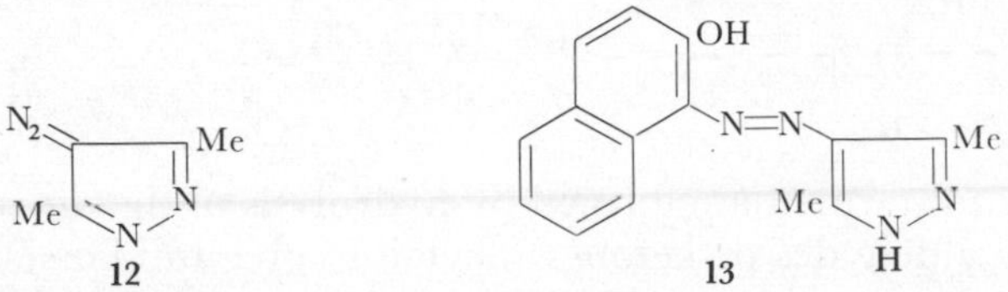

12   13

Imidazole (cf. structures 8 and 8a, p. 303) is more susceptible to electrophilic reagents. Nitration, of in fact the imidazolium cation in sulphuric acid solution,[5] occurs at position 4(5); iodination takes place initially[10] at the same position, but further reaction, as with bromination, leads to 2,4,5-trisubstitution. Diazo coupling takes place at position 2 in alkaline solution to give bright red azo dyes. The results of kinetic experiments[11] suggest that the imidazole anion (e.g. 11) is the reacting species in both iodination and diazo coupling. In view of the great stability of the imidazole ring, its opening under normal benzoylation conditions is remarkable; benzimidazole behaves similarly.

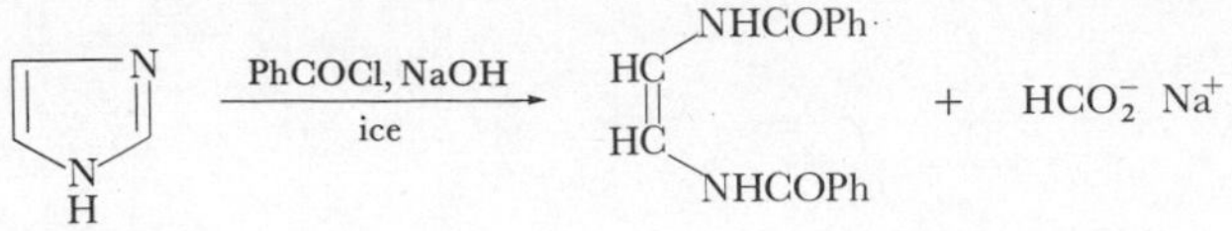

Pyrazole itself is readily synthesized from the commercially available 1,1,3,3-tetramethoxypropane (malondialdehyde acetal, **14**) and hydrazine in the presence of acids. Hydrolysis to malondialdehyde (**15**)

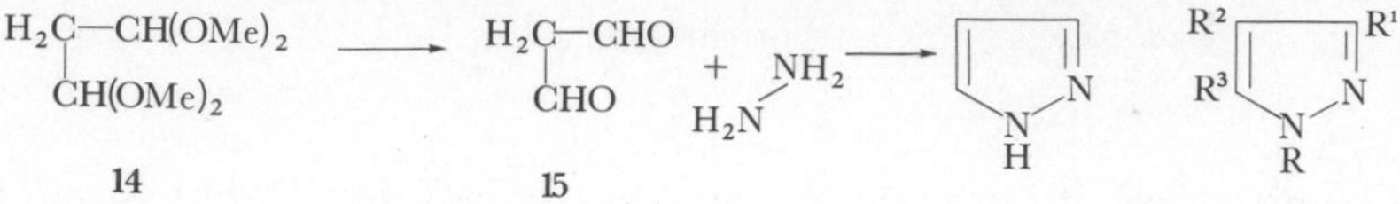

occurs and is followed by the formation of pyrazole. This type of synthesis is successful with almost any 1,3-dicarbonyl compound and monosubstituted hydrazine, and many pyrazoles of general structure **16** have been made in this way.

There is no synthetic procedure in the imidazole series so widely applicable as the pyrazole synthesis above. Imidazole itself is best obtained[12] from paraldehyde. Bromination in the presence of ethylene glycol gives a cyclic acetal of bromoacetaldehyde (**17**, 2-bromomethyl-1,3-dioxolane). This, on heating with formamide in the presence of ammonia, is converted to imidazole; bromoacetaldehyde is

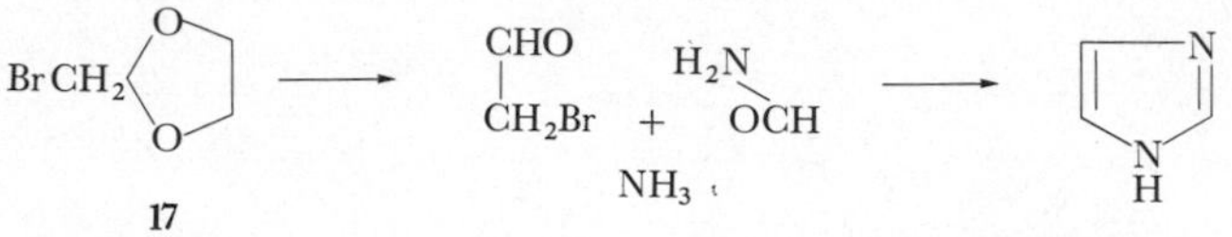

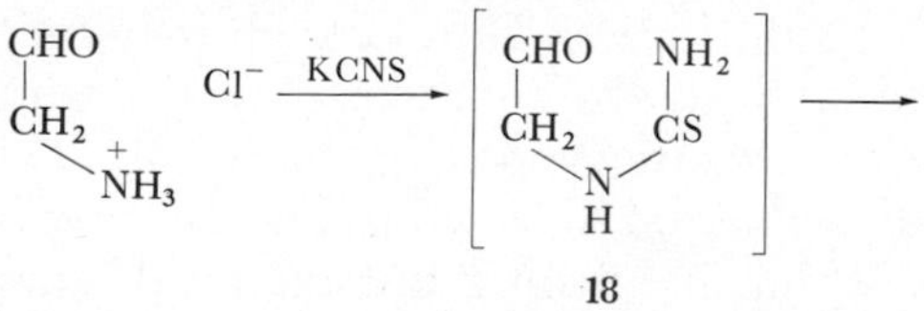

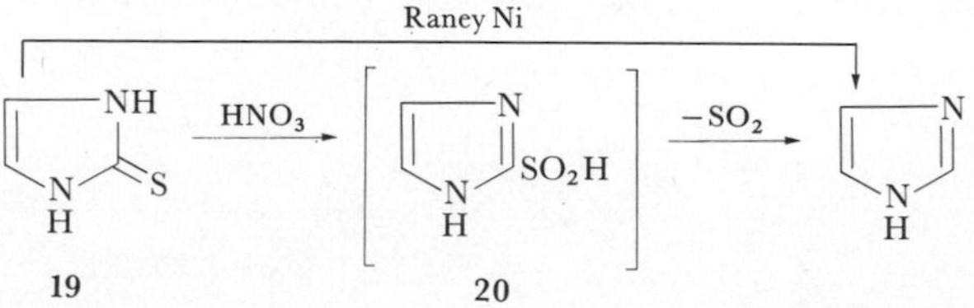

probably an intermediate formed by hydrolysis of the dioxolane (**17**). α-Hydroxy aldehydes or ketones (acyloins) give imidazoles similarly. There are many syntheses of limited scope available for imidazoles. The most general involves the condensation of an α-amino aldehyde or ketone hydrochloride with hot aqueous potassium thiocyanate. 4-Imidazoline-2-thione (**19**) is formed through the intermediary of an α-thioureido aldehyde (**18**). Desulphurization of the thione is easily effected with Raney nickel, or by oxidation with concentrated nitric acid. In this case a sulphinic acid (20) is formed and loses sulphur dioxide.

D. Derivatives of pyrazole and imidazole

Pyrazoline (21) has three possible tautomeric structures, but that shown is the most stable. It can be prepared as indicated and is a

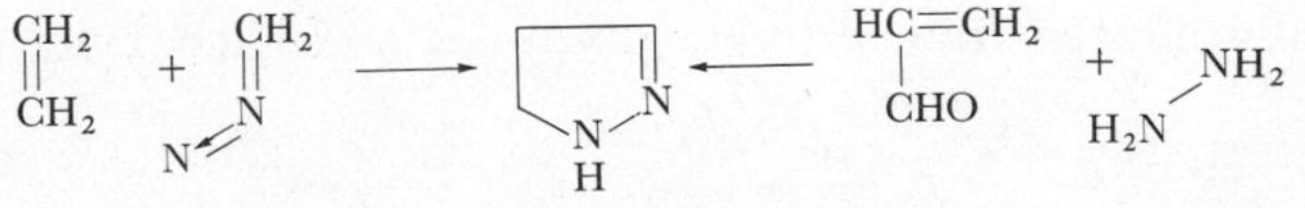

colourless liquid, b.p. 140°. In contrast to pyrazole, which is so stable to acids and bases, pyrazoline is decomposed by hot water. Olefines combine with diazomethanes to give in the first place 1-pyrazolines, and the original stereochemistry of the olefine is retained. For instance methyl tiglate (22) with diazomethane yields the *cis*-dimethyl-1-pyrazoline (23) in a reaction which is at least 98% stereospecific. The light-induced decomposition of 23 to the cyclopropane (24) is also stereospecific, but the corresponding thermal reaction is not.[13] 1-Pyrazolines can isomerize to the more stable 2-pyrazolines with a trace of acid.[14]

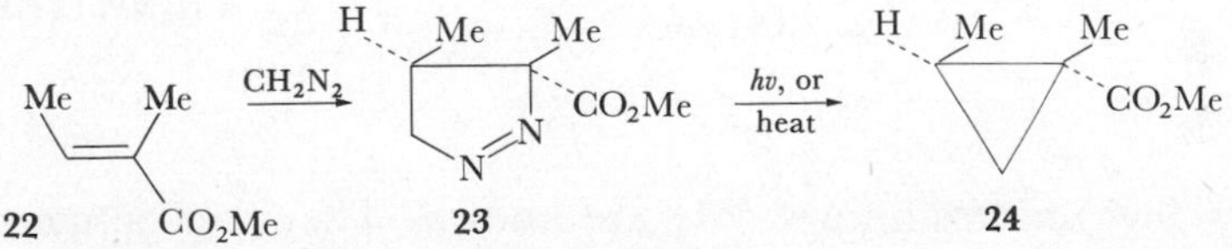

Pyrazolidine (25), b.p. 138°, is obtained, along with other products, from hydrazine and 1,3-dibromopropane. It behaves as a N,N'-dialkyl-

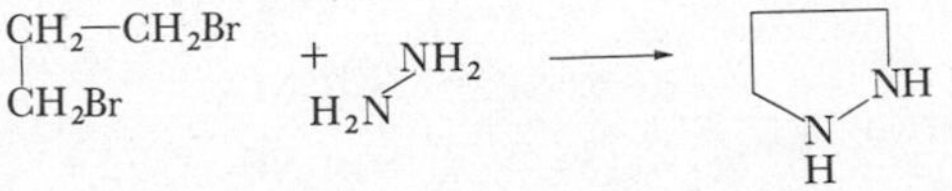

hydrazine in forming a N,N'-dibenzoyl derivative and in being readily oxidized to the corresponding pyrazoline (21).

Benzopyrazole is often called indazole (26) and is prepared from

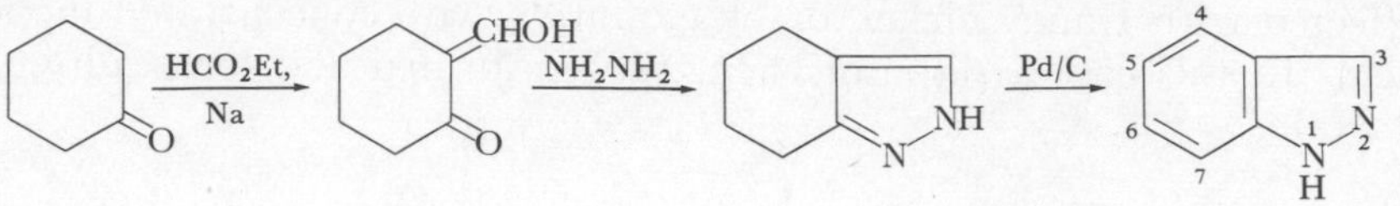

26

cyclohexanone.[15] Unlike benziminazole (p. 305), it is completely broken up on oxidation, and it has little current interest.

Imidazolines (**27**, for a review see ref. 16), and their derivatives are usually synthesized from ethylenediamines and carboxylic acids, or

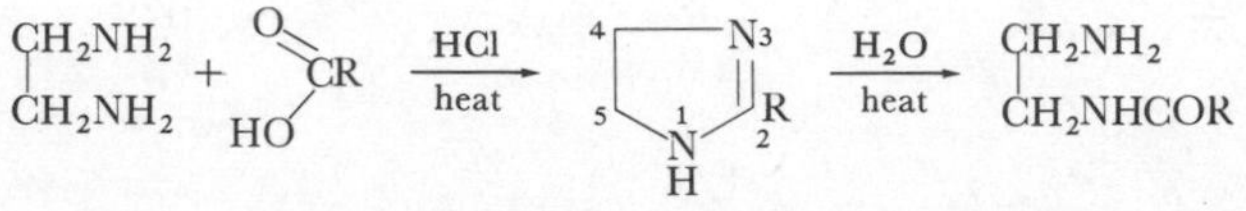

27

their derivatives. They are not obtainable by reduction or hydrogenation of imidazoles, nor can they be hydrogenated to imidazolidines. Partial hydrolysis takes place with hot water and is completed by alkali. Two imidazolines, 'Priscol' (**28**) and 'Privine' (**29**), are valuable vasodilating and vaso-constricting agents respectively, and 'Antistine' (**30**) is a useful antihistaminic drug.

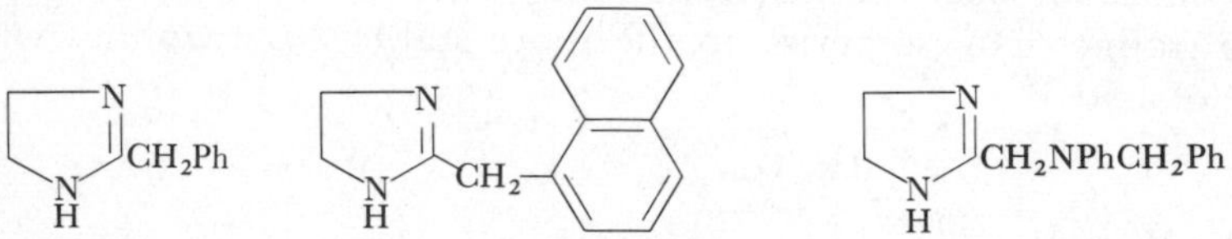

28   29   30

Very few imidazolidines (**31**) are known. They can be considered as cyclic aldehyde ammonias, and are hydrolysed very readily by dilute acids.

Imidazolid-2-one (**32**) is readily obtained as indicated, and is best considered as a substituted urea. Biotin (p. 138) is an important imidazolidone.

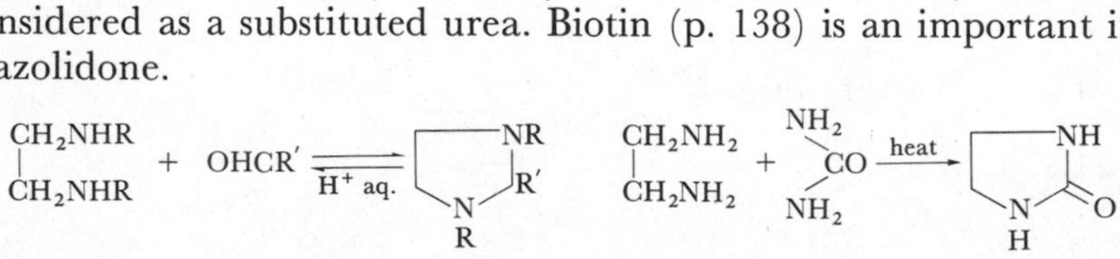

31   32

Hydantoin (**33**), or imidazolid-2,4-dione, occurs in beet sap and is readily prepared from aminoacetonitrile and cyanic acid; the immediate product of this reaction cyclizes with acids. Hydantoin can replace

CH$_2$O $\xrightarrow{\text{NH}_4\text{CN}}$ [CN / CH$_2$ / NH$_2$] $\xrightarrow{\text{HCNO}}$ [CN NH$_2$ / CH$_2$ CO / NH] $\xrightarrow{\text{H}^+}$ [structure 33]

acyl glycines in the synthesis of amino and keto acids (p. 317), and allantoin (p. 340), a derivative, is related to uric acid.

The benzimidazole (**34**) ring is of much greater interest than that of indazole, as it occurs in vitamin B$_{12}$ (p. 91) and in many biologically active compounds. Benzimidazoles are usually prepared from 1,2-diaminobenzenes by reaction with carboxylic acids or derivatives, such as nitriles or imido ethers, under acid conditions[17]. The benzimidazole

[structure: benzene ring with NH$_2$, NH$_2$] + [O=CR, HO] $\xrightarrow[\text{acid at 200°}]{\substack{\text{4 N HCl, boil} \\ \text{or polyphosphoric}}}$ [structure **34** R=H] [structure **35**]

system is highly aromatic. It is hard to oxidize (p. 305) or reduce and is stable to acids and bases (above; p. 304). Like imidazole, it forms salts and metal derivatives, and in sulphuric acid it nitrates at position 5(6). This is in agreement with π-electron density calculations[18] made on the assumption that the free base, and not the cation, is the species actually nitrated. Iodination of benzimidazole in alkaline solution gives 2-iodo-benzimidazole, which again is in agreement with π-electron density calculations[18] if the anion (**35**) is being attacked.

E. Compounds of special interest and natural occurrence

1. *Pyrazoles*

The first natural pyrazole, β-pyrazol-1-ylalanine, occurs in water-melon seeds.[19] The most important derivatives of pyrazole are in fact all pyrazolones. Antipyrine (**37**) is one of the earliest synthetic

[structure **36**] $\xrightarrow[\text{special conditions}]{\text{Me}_2\text{SO}_4, \text{NaOH}}$ [structure **37**]

[structure: CH$_2$—CMe / C=O / O OEt + NH$_2$ / HN–Ph]   [structure: CH$_2$–CMe / EtOC O + / O NHMe / HN–Ph]

drugs and is named after its antipyretic properties. It is still used to some extent. Butazolidine (38), another pyrazolone, is a powerful antiinflammatory drug used in rheumatic conditions, but it has

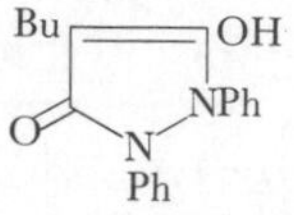

38

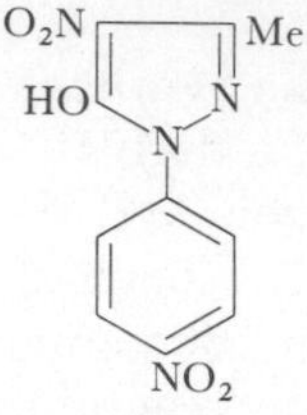

39

dangerous side reactions. Picrolonic acid (39) made by nitrating 36, usually forms highly crystalline salts suitable for the characterization of organic bases.

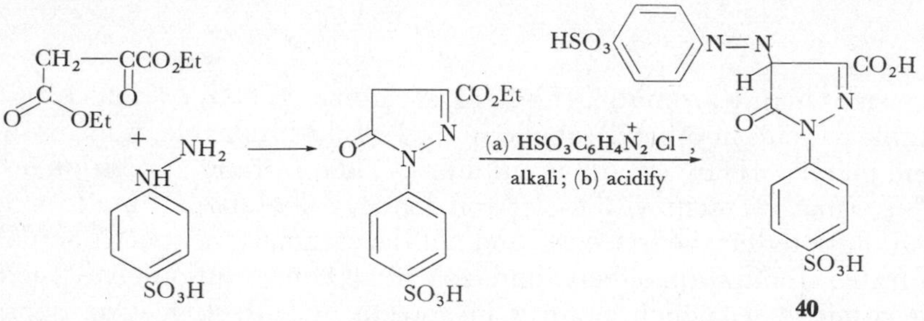

40

Tartrazine (40) is a yellow dye for wool, and other pyrazolone dyes have been gaining commercial importance in recent years. 3-Methyl-1-phenylpyrazol-5-one, an intermediate in the synthesis of antipyrine (37), can have several tautomeric formulations (e.g. 36 and 41), and gives a green-black dye (42) with 4-nitrosodimethylaniline or with 4-aminodimethylaniline and silver chloride in the presence of light. This type of process is of great importance in colour photography.[20]

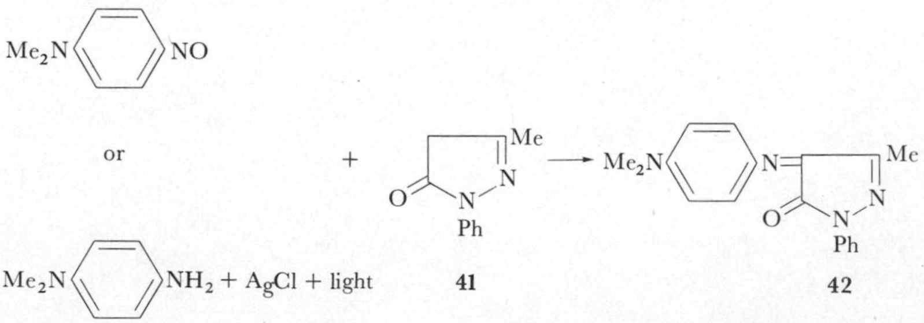

41   42

2. *Imidazoles*

Many imidazole derivatives have powerful pharmacological properties (p. 308). The imidazole ring occurs in a number of naturally occurring compounds discussed in chapter IX, and in the very widely distributed essential amino acid L-histidine (**43**) and its derivatives.

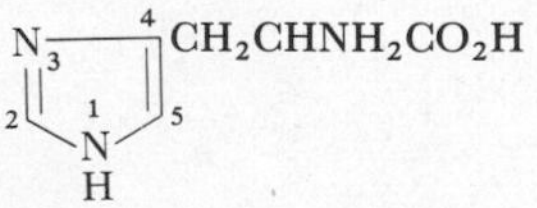

Carnosine (**45**) is a constituent of mammalian muscle. The structure of histidine was proved by successive reaction with silver nitrite and hydrogen iodide when the known imidazole-4(5)-propionic acid (**44**) was obtained. The best synthesis of histidine starts from imidazole which is first converted into imidazole-4(5)-carbaldehyde (**46**). This

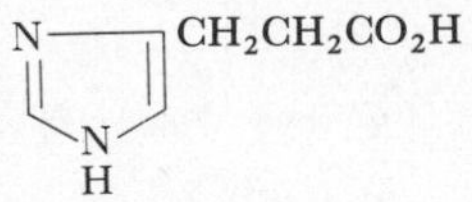

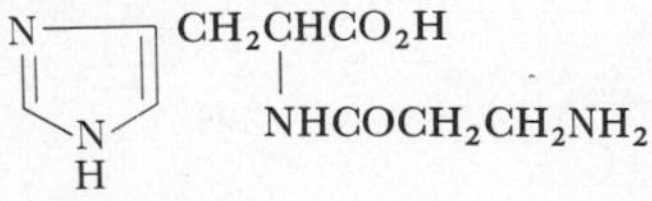

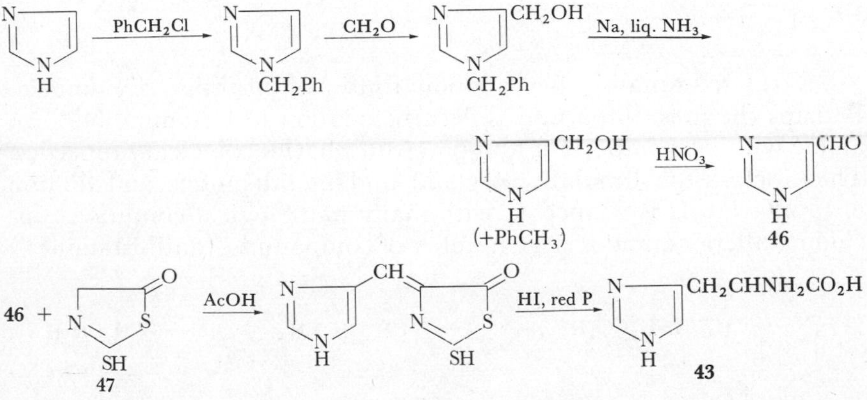

with 2-mercapto-5-thiazolone (**47**) in acetic acid followed by a reductive ring opening (cf. oxazolones, p. 317) gives histidine (**43**). Histidine is a basic amino acid, as both the primary amino group and the imidazole ring are basic and there is only one carboxyl group. Histidine will therefore form salts with organic acids, and the DL-histidine obtained by synthesis can be resolved through its salt with D-tartaric acid.

The biosynthesis of histidine appears to involve adenosine-5'-phosphate (p. 312), ribose-1-phosphate and glutamine.[21] 5-Amino-4-imidazolecarboxyamide (**48**) and histidinol phosphate are formed, and the latter gives histidine (**43**) after several transformations. The amide (**48**) can be converted again *in vivo* into adenosine-5'-phosphate.

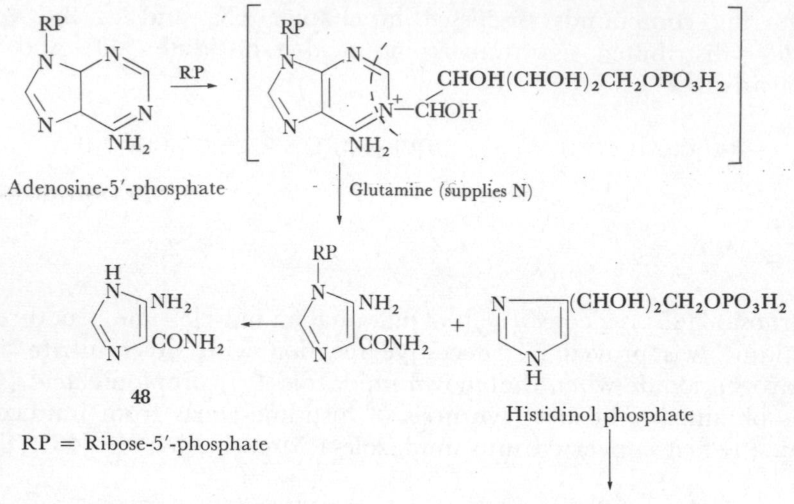

Adenosine-5'-phosphate   Glutamine (supplies N)

48

Histidinol phosphate

RP = Ribose-5'-phosphate

43

Several mammalian degradation routes of histidine are known. Perhaps the most important is decarboxylation to histamine (**49**), an amine with very important and powerful pharmacological properties. These include the stimulation of glands and smooth muscle, and dilation of capillaries. It is connected with many pathological conditions, including allergies, and a large number of compounds ('antihistamines')

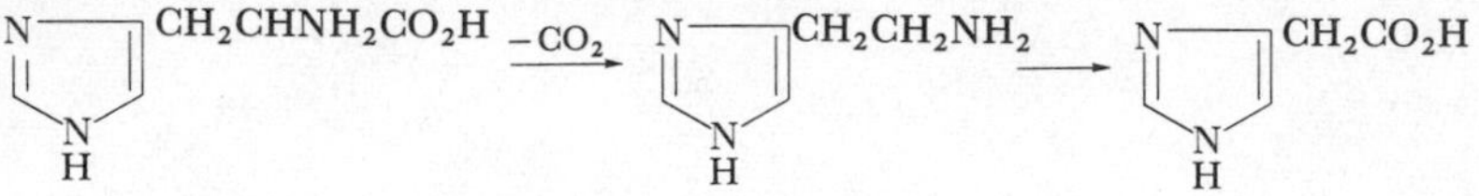

43 $-CO_2$ **49**   **50**

which antagonize the action of histamine in various biological systems have been found. Some of them have medicinal value. Histamine is further degraded *in vivo* to imidazole-4-acetic acid (**50**), and it is likely that the imidazole ring of this compound is opened in a similar way to that of histidine (opposite page).

Histidine is also broken down *in vivo* through urocanic acid (**51**) with ring scission leading to glutamic acid (**55**). Imidazolones, such as **52**, which has not been isolated, are known[22] to split up very easily.

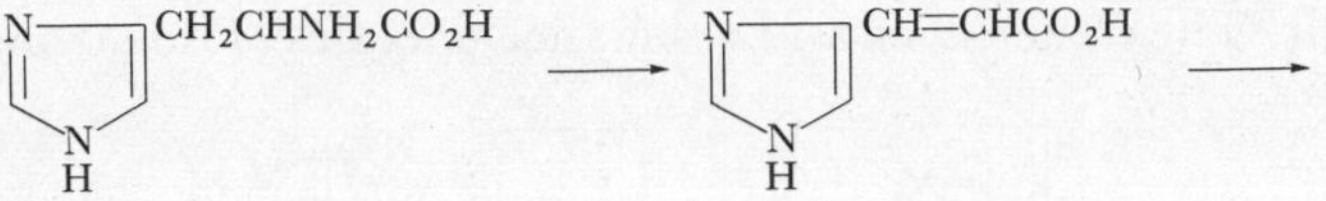

Formamidinoglutaric acid (**53**) is formed from histidine in the rat[23] and breaks up through formamidoglutaric acid (**54**) to glutamic acid (**55**).

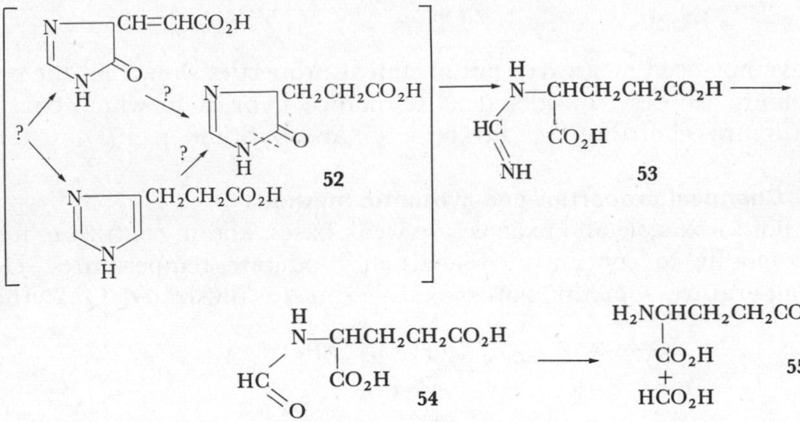

Ergothioneine (**56**) occurs in blood and animal tissues but its function is not yet known. The antibiotic azamycin is 2-nitroimidazole (**57**), which has been synthesized[24] from 2-aminoimidazole, buffered nitrous acid, and copper sulphate.

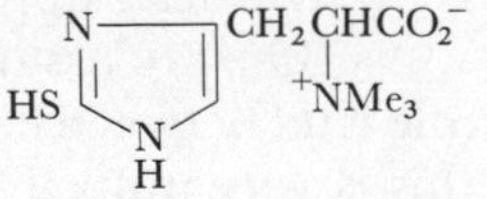

2. ISOXAZOLE AND OXAZOLE

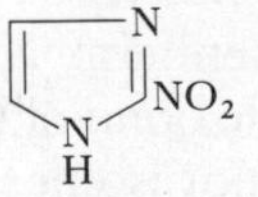

A. Introduction

Compounds containing these systems have so far not attracted much interest. Isoxazole was prepared in 1903, but oxazole was not synthesized until 1947.

B. Physical properties and structure

Isoxazole and oxazole are intermediate between furan and pyridine in boiling point. Simple oxazoles and isoxazoles usually resemble pyridine in odour. The dimensions and resonance energies of isoxazole

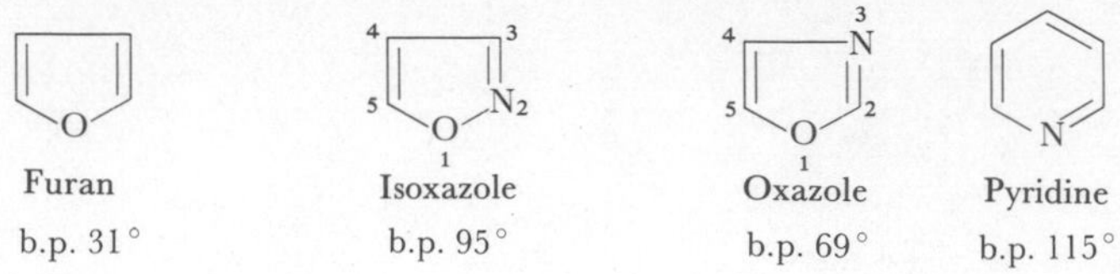

Furan
b.p. 31°

Isoxazole
b.p. 95°

Oxazole
b.p. 69°

Pyridine
b.p. 115°

have not been measured, but chemical properties show that the compounds are best considered as resonance hybrids to which charged
structures contribute (cf. furan, p. 95, and pyridine, p. 191).

C. Chemical properties and synthetic methods

Both isoxazole and oxazole are weak bases, and in contrast to furan
are stable to concentrated acids at moderate temperatures. High
temperatures sometimes open oxazole rings, as illustrated. Quaternary

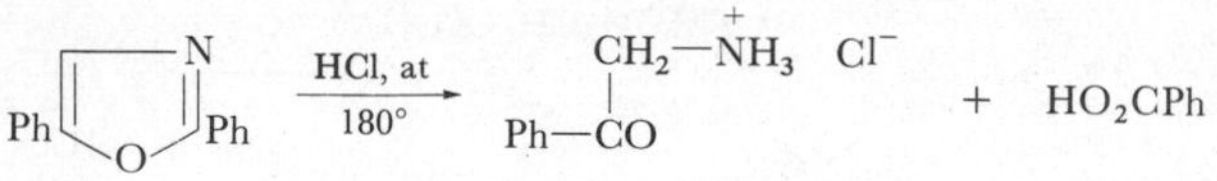

salts have been obtained from derivatives of both ring systems with
alkylating agents. Although oxazoles are stable to alkali, the isoxazole
ring is opened easily under these conditions; the direction and ease of
opening depends on the substituents present.

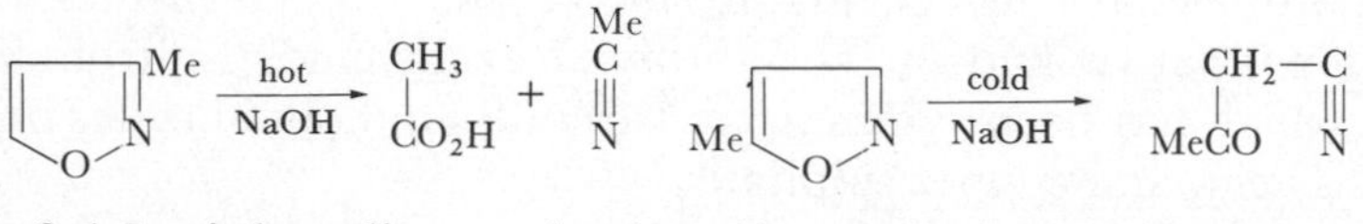

The 3,4,5-triphenylisoxazole ring (1, synthesis opposite page) was
opened by Meisenheimer by ozonolysis. On the assumption that the
remaining double bond of the isoxazole ring between carbon and nitrogen atoms does not isomerize, and this is very unlikely to occur under
the mild conditions used, the product has the structure shown. It is the
benzoyl derivative (2) of an oxime of known stereochemical configuration. Meisenheimer showed that this derivative corresponded to an
oxime (3) which on treatment with phosphorus pentachloride in ether
underwent the Beckmann rearrangement to give 4 and thereby proved
for the first time that the *trans* groups interchanged.

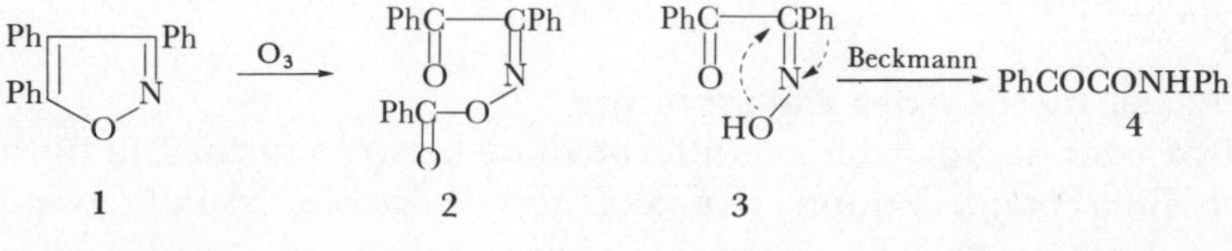

1   2   3

Phenyl-isoxazoles and -oxazoles are nitrated preferentially in the phenyl ring, thus showing that the deactivating effect of the ('pyridine') nitrogen atom overcomes the activating properties of the ('furan') oxygen atom. Electrophilic substitution can take place at position 4 of isoxazoles.

Isoxazole rings have so far always been built up from compounds (usually hydroxylamine) already possessing a nitrogen–oxygen bond. Isoxazole itself is obtainable from propargyl aldehyde and hydroxylamine; 1,3-dicarbonyl compounds also give isoxazoles with hydroxylamine in a very general synthesis.

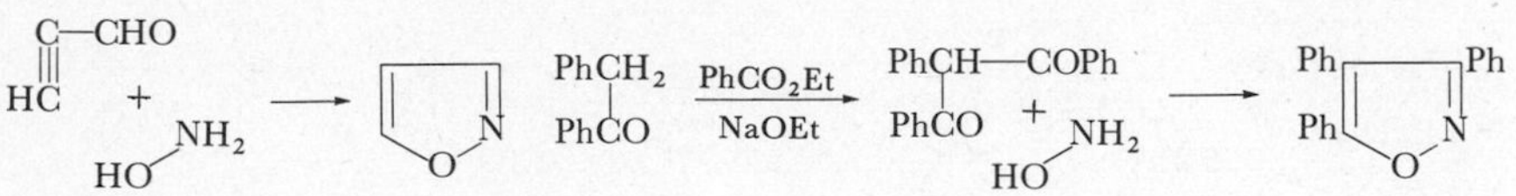

Oxazole was prepared by Cornforth by a method which can be used for substituted oxazoles.

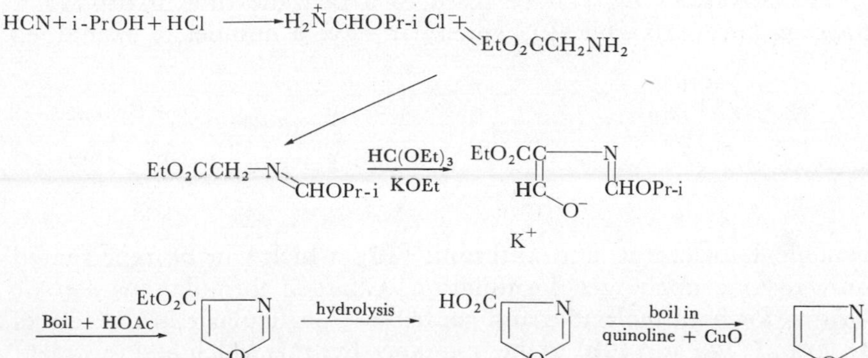

Another and much older synthesis is the cyclization of acylamido ketones, which are often obtained from oximes by reductive acylation.

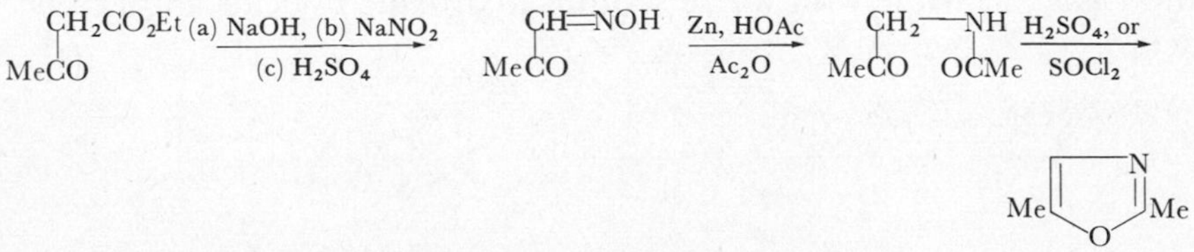

D. Derivatives and compounds of special interest

A number of 2-isoxazolines (e.g. 5) have been obtained by synthesis. They are insoluble in alkali in contrast to the isomeric unsaturated

M

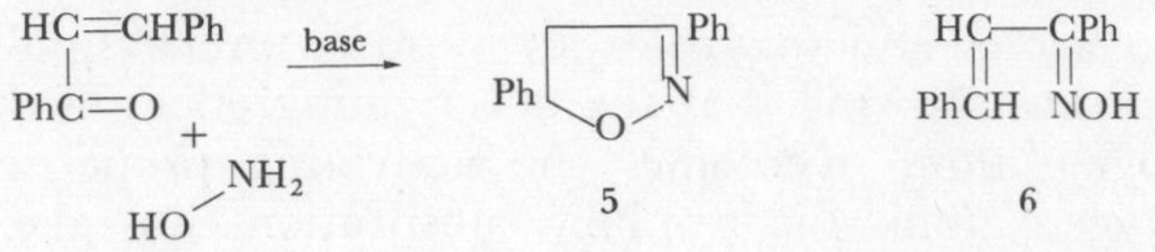

oximes (**6**), which are usually incapable of cyclization. This is perhaps because they have the wrong geometric configuration or that in isoxazoline formation the hydroxylamine first adds to the carbon–carbon double bond (Michael addition) and cyclization follows. Little is known about isoxazolidine (**7**), which can be considered as a *N,O*-dialkyl-hydroxylamine.

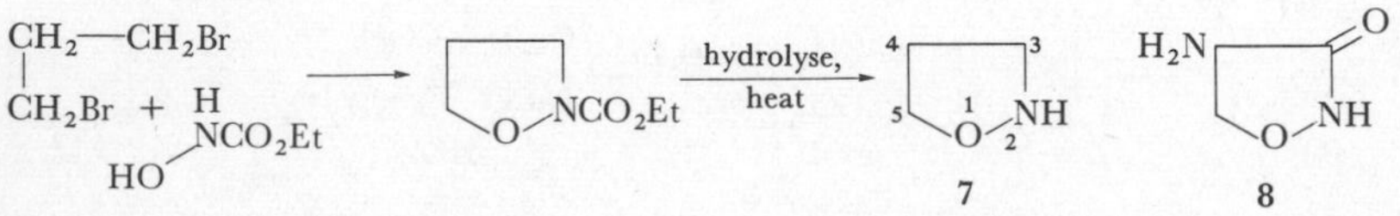

The antibiotic oxamycin, or cycloserine, is D-4-amino-3-isoxazolidone (**8**).

The isoxazole ring can be fused to a benzene ring in two ways, yielding benzoisoxazole (**9**), which can have a number of uncharged

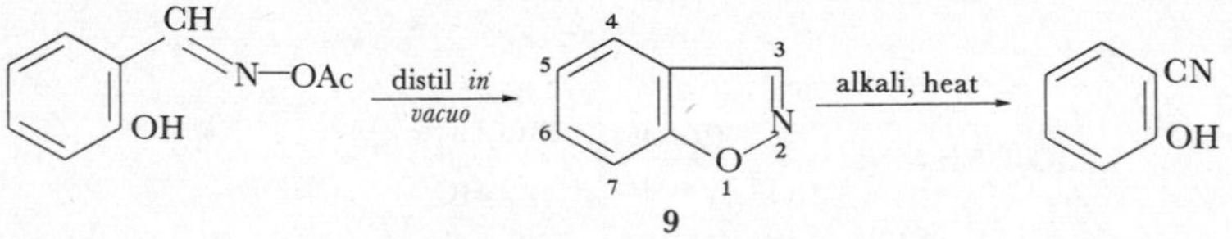

canonical structures, and anthranil (**10**), which can be represented only by one uncharged formulation. Charged formulations can be written for both molecules and contribute, particularly in the case of anthranil (**10a** and **10b**) to the resonance hydrids which best represent these compounds. Benzoisoxazole is a very feeble base and nitrates at position 5. Anthranil (**10**) is readily obtained from 2-nitrobenzaldehyde. Nitration [25] gives mainly the 5-nitro derivative with a little of the 7-isomer, while with warm sodium hydroxide it yields anthranilic acid.

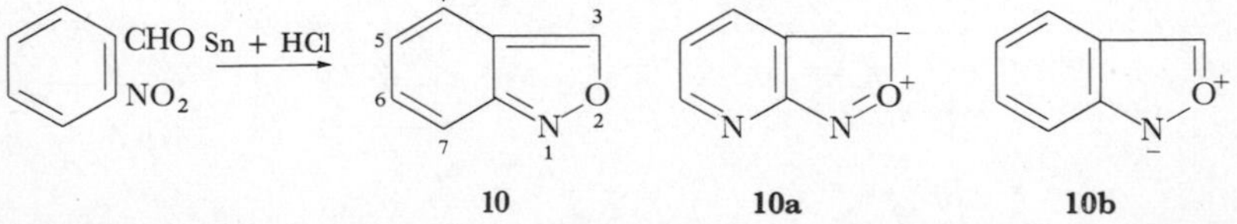

Three positions are possible for the double bond in the dihydro-oxazole, or oxazoline, ring, but only 2-oxazoline (**12**) and derivatives are known.[26] 2-Oxazoline, b.p. 98°, has most of the reactions of an imido ether (e.g. **14**). Examples are hydrolysis with boiling water to **13**, and the formation of an unstable hydrochloride which slowly rearranges to **11**.

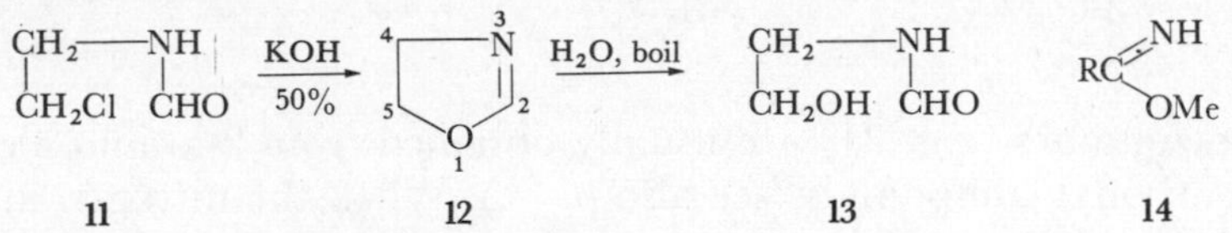

Certain derivatives of oxazoline, the oxazolones (azlactones[27]) are valuable intermediates in the Erlenmeyer synthesis of aromatic amino and keto acids. An example is the condensation of benzaldehyde with hippuric acid (benzoylglycine; acetylglycine can also be used) in the presence of acetic anhydride and sodium acetate. The reaction proceeds[28] through the formation of 2-phenyl-5-oxazolone (**15**), which can be considered as the anhydride of hippuric acid. This compound is very reactive and condenses at position 4 *in situ* with the aromatic aldehyde to give the benzylidene oxazolone (**16**). Aliphatic aldehydes

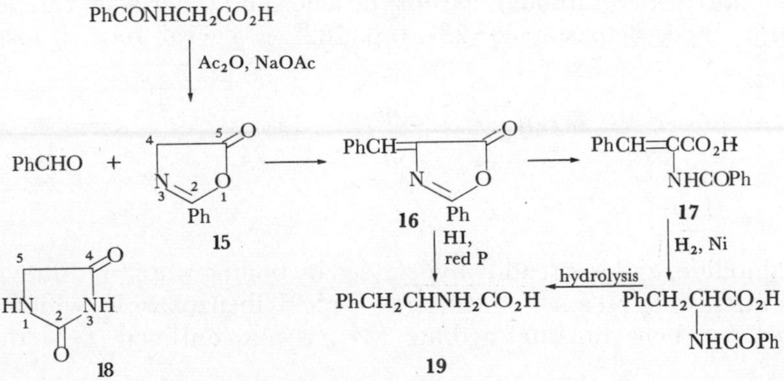

self-condense preferentially under the usual reaction conditions, but they usually react like aromatic aldehydes with 2-phenyl-5-oxazolone in the absence of acetic anhydride or other catalysts to give compounds analogous to **16**. The benzylidene oxazolone (**16**) can be converted into an α-amino acid (**19**) by reduction and hydrolysis. This can be done in several ways, including treatment with hot red phosphorus and iodine. Less drastic procedures are the opening of the ring with cold alkali or boiling water to **17**, followed by successive hydrogenation and hydrolysis. Hydrolysis of the acylamidocinnamic acid (**17**) by alkali, or better by acid, is a useful route to phenylpyruvic acid (**20**). The hippuric acid can be replaced by hydantoin (**18**), which reacts at position 5.

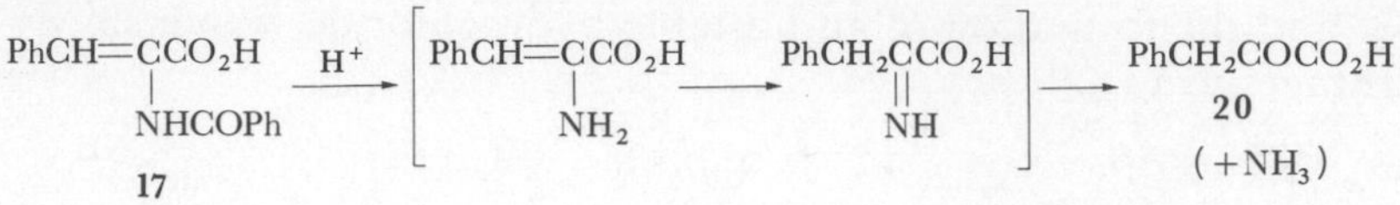

$$PhCH{=}CCO_2H \xrightarrow{H^+} \left[PhCH{=}CCO_2H \longrightarrow PhCH_2CCO_2H \right] \longrightarrow PhCH_2COCO_2H$$

$$\underset{\text{NHCOPh}}{|} \qquad \underset{\text{NH}_2}{|} \qquad \underset{\text{NH}}{\|}$$

17   20 (+NH₃)

Oxazolidines (e.g. **21**) are usually obtained from 2-amino alcohols and carbonyl compounds (see also p.   ). When the nitrogen atom is unsubstituted (e.g. **21**) the compounds are tautomeric with the corresponding Schiff's bases (e.g. **22**), and in this case infrared absorption spectrum studies have shown that the equilibrium mixture contains ca. 20% of **22**. Oxazolidines are readily hydrolysed by acid.

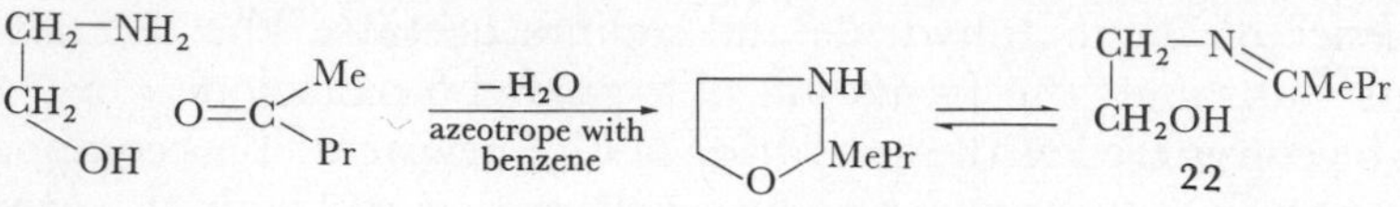

Benzoxazoles are usually prepared by heating 2-aminophenols with acid anhydrides, although carboxylic acids and other acid derivatives can be used. Benzoxazole (**23**), b.p. 182°, is a weak base, it forms a

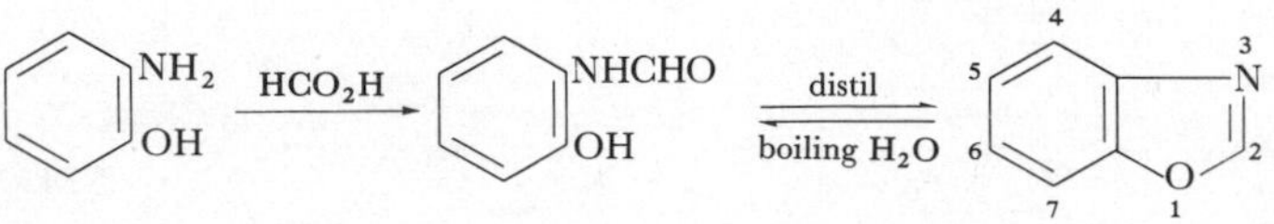

methiodide, and it is readily hydrolysed by boiling water or dilute acid. An interesting recent[29] synthesis of 2-phenylbenzoxazole, which may involve a benzyne intermediate (**24**), is also outlined. 6-Methoxy-

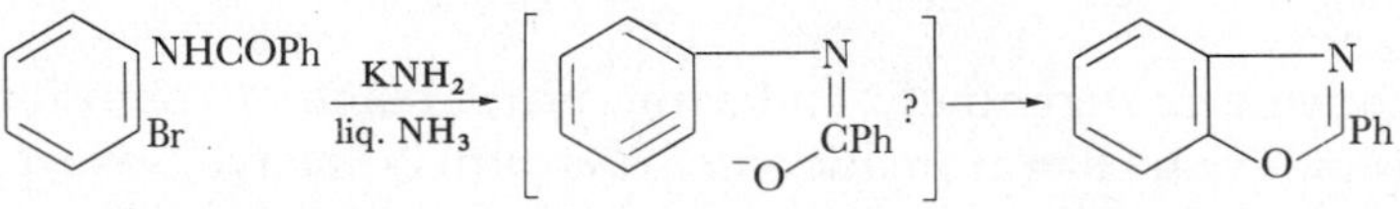

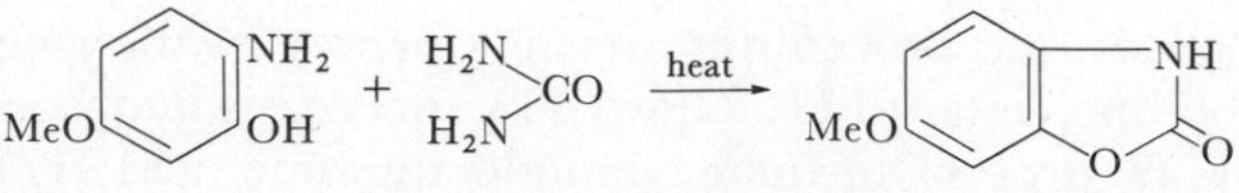

benzoxazolone (**25**) is of interest, as it occurs in corn and is the compound responsible for resistance to the corn borer.[30] Infrared studies[31] have shown that benzoxazol-2-ones (e.g. **25**) exist predominantely as the keto tautomers. An alkaloid (**26**)[32] and a mould metabolite (**27**)[33] are the first discovered naturally occurring oxazoles.

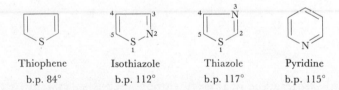

26   27

3. ISOTHIAZOLE AND THIAZOLE

A. Introduction

The penicillins (p. 46), vitamin B_1 (p. 323) and the antibacterial sulphathiazole (p. 326) are all derivatives of thiazole, and in consequence the chemistry of this ring system is well developed. Interest in isothiazole was singularly lacking before 1956.

B. Physical properties and structure

Both isothiazole and thiazole are weak bases and resemble pyridine in odour and boiling point. Their structures have not been investigated by physical methods, but the highly aromatic nature of both ring

Thiophene	Isothiazole	Thiazole	Pyridine
b.p. 84°	b.p. 112°	b.p. 117°	b.p. 115°

systems is shown in their chemistry. This, to a rough approximation only, is an amalgamation of that of pyridine and thiophene.

C. Isothiazoles

Isothiazole (**2**) can be obtained from propylene, sulphur dioxide, and ammonia at 200° over an aluminium catalyst,[34] from propynal (**1**),[35] and from the benzene derivative (**3**)[36] which constituted the first synthesis. It is a colourless liquid, which forms a crystalline chloroaurate and chloroplatinate.

Isothiazole with butyllithium at −70° gives the 5-lithium derivative, which has normal properties.[37] Nitration and halogenation occur at position 4,[38] and phenyl radicals, from benzoyl peroxide, attack all three positions.[39] 3-Methylisothiazole quaternizes slowly

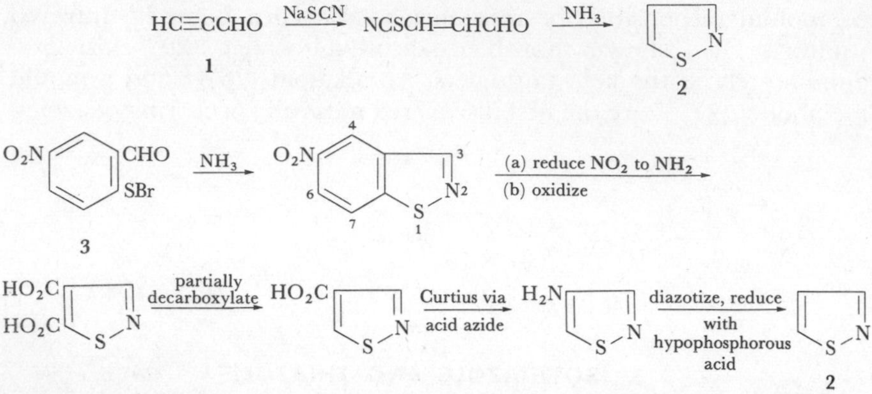

HC≡CCHO
NaSCN
NCSCH=CHCHO
NH3
N
S
1
2
O2N
CHO
SBr
NH3
O2N
4
3
6
N2
S
7
1
3
(a) reduce NO2 to NH2
(b) oxidize
HO2C
HO2C
N
S
partially decarboxylate
HO2C
N
S
Curtius via acid azide
H2N
N
S
diazotize, reduce with hypophosphorous acid
N
S
2

with methyl iodide,[40] but as it does not[41] condense with benzaldehyde nor react with selenium dioxide its 3-methyl group is inactive and unlike that of 2-methylpyridine. Isothiazole-3-carbaldehyde has the normal properties expected of an aromatic aldehyde.[41]

Isoselenazole (**4**), a colourless liquid b.p. 68° at 46 mm, has a pyridine-like smell and has been obtained from propinal (**1**) by successive reaction with selenocyanic acid and ammonia.[42]

4
3
5
N2
Se
1
O
NH
S
O2

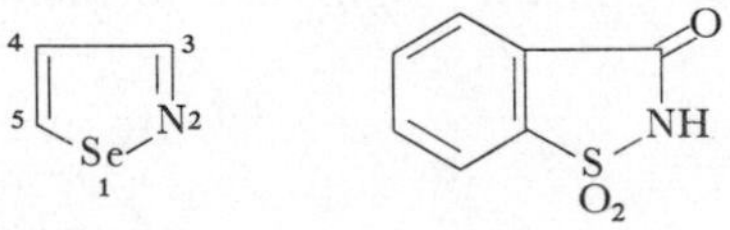

4 5

The only isothiazole of present importance is saccharin (**5**), which is prepared by the permanganate oxidation of 2-methylbenzene-sulphonamide. On account of its sweet taste it is used as a sucrose substitute.

D. Thiazole, chemical properties and synthetic methods

Thiazole (**6**) is a weaker base (pK_a 2·5) than pyridine (pK_a 5·2), but it forms a crystalline hydrochloride and an aurichloride. It also forms thiazolinium salts (e.g. **7**) with alkyl halides, and these (see thiamine p. 323), like 1-alkylpyridinium salts, are decomposed by alkali.

3
4
N
5
1
2
S
N
S
N
S
NMe
Cl⁻
S
N
Me
S

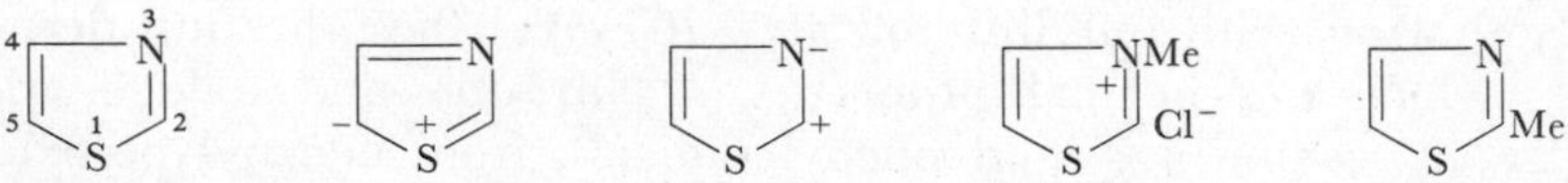

6 6a 6b 7 8

The major contributor to the resonance hybrid which represents thiazole is the uncharged canonical structure **6**, and chemical reactions show that charged structures such as **6a** (cf. thiophene, p. 121) and **6b** (cf. pyridine, p. 191) must have significance (Table 2). The fact that

TABLE 2. Calculated localization energies for thiazole in β units[43]

Position	Type of attack		
	Electrophilic	Nucleophilic	Radical
2	2·134	1·879	2·006
4	2·679	2·670	2·674
5	2·222	2·104	2·163

electrophilic substitution (sulphonation) occurs preferentially at position 5, otherwise at position 4, is not in agreement with the above localization energies, suggests that another species, the conjugate acid of thiazole, is probably being substituted. As the nitration of 2-, 3-, and 4-phenylthiazole effects substitution only at position 4 of the benzene rings it is clear that the thiazole ring is comparatively unreactive. The calculations are in excellent agreement with experiment for nucleophilic and radical attack. Thiazole with sodamide gives 2-aminothiazole, with butyllithium thiazole 2-lithium, or if the 2-position is alkylated the 5-lithium derivative.[44] Phenyl radicals, from benzoyl peroxide, give the 2-, 4-, and 5-phenylthiazoles in 55:15:30 ratio,[43] while bromine at high temperatures (radical?) forms 2-bromothiazole.

2-Methylthiazole (**8**), but not its 4- and 5-isomers, reacts with benzaldehyde and zinc chloride to give 2-styrylthiazole, and the halogen atom of 2-bromothiazole is reactive. Only substituents at the 2-position of thiazole, therefore, are comparable in reactivity to those at position 2 or 4 of pyridine (pp. 204 and 212).

In contrast to 2-aminopyridine (p. 217) a diazonium salt is obtained from 2- (and incidentally 5-) aminothiazole under conditions successful for aniline. This shows the pronounced effect of the sulphur atom in partially neutralizing the electron-demanding character of the carbon atom (position 2), which is most strongly under the influence of the ('pyridine') nitrogen atom.

Thiazoles are generally resistant to reduction, and to oxidation by nitric acid; potassium permanganate often opens the ring.

The most valuable thiazole synthesis[45] is that of Hantzsch and consists of heating an α-halogenated aldehyde, or ketone, with a thioamide.

$$\begin{array}{c}\text{CHO} \\ | \\ \text{CH}_2\text{Cl}\end{array} + \begin{array}{c}\text{H}_2\text{N} \\ \diagdown \\ \text{S} \diagup \text{CH}\end{array} \xrightarrow{\text{heat}} \quad \boxed{\begin{array}{c} 4 \quad N^3 \\ 5 \quad 1 \quad 2 \\ S \end{array}}$$

Unpurified thioamides, including thioformamide, which are often obtained from the amides and phosphorus pentasulphide, can be used successfully in the synthesis. The thioamide can even be thiourea, when a 2-aminothiazole is formed.

E. Derivatives of thiazole

Although three tautomeric structures can be written for dihydrothiazole, only 2-thiazoline (10), b.p. 139°, is known (cf. 2-oxazoline, p. 316). It has been obtained by the cyclization of the formyl derivative

$$\begin{array}{c}\text{CH}_2\text{—NH} \\ | \qquad\qquad \diagdown \text{CH} \\ \text{CH}_2 \qquad \text{O} \\ \diagdown\text{SH}\end{array} \quad \xrightarrow{\text{P}_2\text{O}_5} \quad \boxed{\begin{array}{c}3 \\ 4 \quad N \\ 5 \quad 1 \quad 2 \\ S\end{array}} \quad \xrightarrow{\text{H}^+ \text{ aq.}} \quad \begin{array}{c}\text{CH}_2\text{—NH}_2 \\ | \\ \text{CH}_2\text{—SH}\end{array} + \text{HCO}_2\text{H}$$

$$\qquad\qquad 9 \qquad\qquad\qquad\qquad 10$$

of 2-mercaptoethylamine (9) with phosphorus pentoxide. In general, thiazolines are hydrolysed by aqueous acids and behave as imido thioethers. Thiazolines can be reduced to thiazolidines by aluminium amalgam.

Thiazolidine itself (11), b.p. 165°, can be obtained from formaldehyde and 2-mercaptoethylamine, and it forms an N-acetyl derivative (12).

$$\begin{array}{c}\text{CH}_2\text{—NH}_2 \\ | \\ \text{CH}_2 \\ \diagdown\text{SH}\end{array} \quad + \quad \text{O=CH}_2 \quad \longrightarrow \quad \boxed{\begin{array}{c}3 \\ 4 \quad NH \\ 5 \quad 1 \quad 2 \\ S\end{array}} \qquad \boxed{\begin{array}{c} NCOMe \\ \\ S\end{array}}$$

$$\qquad\qquad\qquad\qquad\qquad\qquad\qquad\qquad 11 \qquad\qquad 12$$

The stability of thiazolidines depends greatly on the substituents present, but the synthetic reaction shown is easily reversible. This accounts for the decomposition of thiazolidines by mercuric chloride, or by mild oxidizing agents, when the mercaptide or disulphide corresponding to the original mercaptan is obtained respectively. Acylation increases the stability of the thiazolidine ring. Interest in thiazolidines stems largely from the presence of an acylated thiazolidine ring in the penicillins (p. 46).

Rhodanine, 4-oxothiazolidine-2-thione (13) is obtained from chloroacetic acid and ammonium dithiocarbamate. It reacts with aromatic

$$\begin{array}{c}CO_2H \\ | \\ CH_2Cl\end{array} + \begin{array}{c}NH_2 \\ | \\ CS \\ | \\ ^-S\end{array} \longrightarrow \quad \mathbf{13} \quad \xrightarrow{PhCHO} \quad \mathbf{14} \quad \longrightarrow PhCH_2CSCO_2H$$

$^+NH_4$

13   **14**

aldehydes at position 5, and on alkaline hydrolysis the products yield thiopyruvic acids (**14**). This can be compared with certain reactions of oxazolones (p. 317–318).

Benzothiazole (**15**), b.p. 234°, is prepared in a similar way to benzoxazole (p. 318). It is a weak base which forms salts with strong

$$\begin{array}{c}NH_2 \\ SH\end{array} + HCO_2H \longrightarrow \quad \mathbf{15} \qquad \mathbf{16}$$

15   **16**

acids and quaternary salts with alkyl halides. The methyl group at position 2 of 2,3-dimethylbenzothiazolinium iodide (**16**) is highly reactive, and this compound has been converted to cyanine-type dyes (p. 267) which are valuable photographic sensitizers. 2-Mercapto-benzothiazole (**17**) is an extremely good accelerator for rubber vulcanization.

$$\begin{array}{c}NO_2 \\ Cl\end{array} \xrightarrow[CS_2, \text{ heat}]{Na_2S_3} \left[\begin{array}{c}NO_2 \\ SH\end{array} \longrightarrow \begin{array}{c}NH_2 \\ SH\end{array} + \begin{array}{c}S \\ \parallel \\ C-S\end{array} \right] \longrightarrow \quad \mathbf{17}$$

17

F. Thiazoles of natural occurrence and special interest

Vitamin B_1 (**18**), often called thiamine and occasionally aneurin, is a thiazolium salt. Its pyrophosphate (**19**) is a coenzyme which has been isolated in crystalline form from yeast and rice polishings and which is involved in the decarboxylation of pyruvic acid to acetaldehyde. Thiamine can be converted into the pyrophosphate by heating with orthophosphoric acid and sodium pyrophosphate. Thiamine deficiency in man produces beriberi and polyneuritis.

$$\begin{array}{c}Me \\ N \\ NH_2 \\ CH_2N^+ \end{array} \begin{array}{c}Me \\ CH_2CH_2OR \\ S\end{array} \quad Cl^- \cdot HCl$$

$$\mathbf{18}, R = H \quad \mathbf{19}, \ R = \begin{array}{c}O \quad O \\ \parallel \quad \parallel \\ P-O-P-OH \\ | \quad | \\ OH \quad OH\end{array}$$

M*

The structure of the vitamin was deduced from the products of degradation and confirmed synthetically by R. R. Williams in 1935–36. Thiamine is quite stable at pH 3–6, but it decomposes quite rapidly in alkaline solution, with the opening of the thiazole ring. The final product (20) can be reduced back to thiamine by stannous chloride in hydrochloric acid.

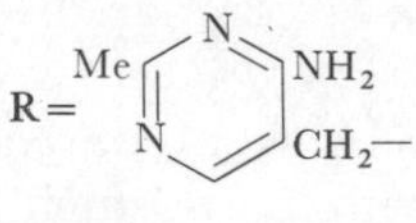

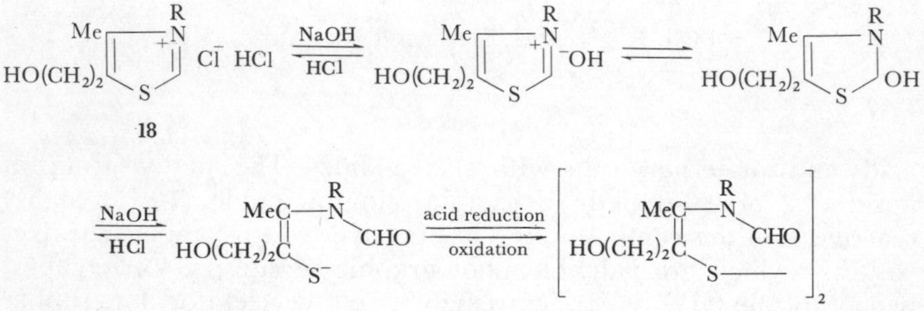

$$R= \quad \text{(pyrimidine structure with Me, N, NH}_2\text{, CH}_2\text{—)}$$

18

20

The key degradation which quickly led to the structure of the vitamin was effected by sodium sulphite. The products were a pyrimidine (21) and a thiazole (24), which on nitric acid oxidation gave the known 4-methylthiazole-5-carboxylic acid (25); this acid was also obtained by the direct nitric acid oxidation of thiamine. The pyrimidine (21)

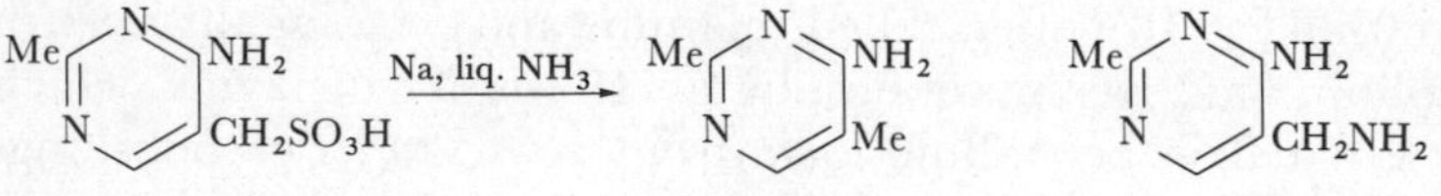

21   22   23

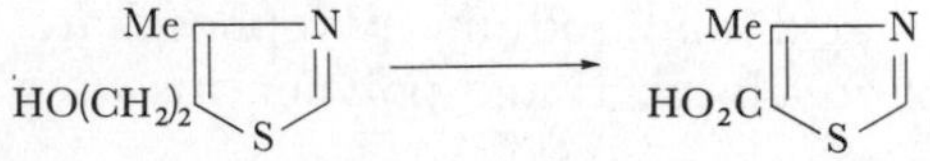

24   25

was converted into a known compound (22) on reduction, but the position of linkage between the two ring systems in the vitamin was not established. This point was clarified when thiamine and liquid ammonia were found to give the usual thiazole (24) and a new pyrimidine, (23), which was prepared from 26 and ammonia.

Thiamine has been synthesized by a number of routes, of which the most important is outlined below. It consists in preparing the pyrimidine **26** and the thiazole **27** by standard methods and condensing them together. The product is thiamine bromide hydrobromide (**28**), which is converted into the chloride hydrochloride (**18**) by silver chloride.

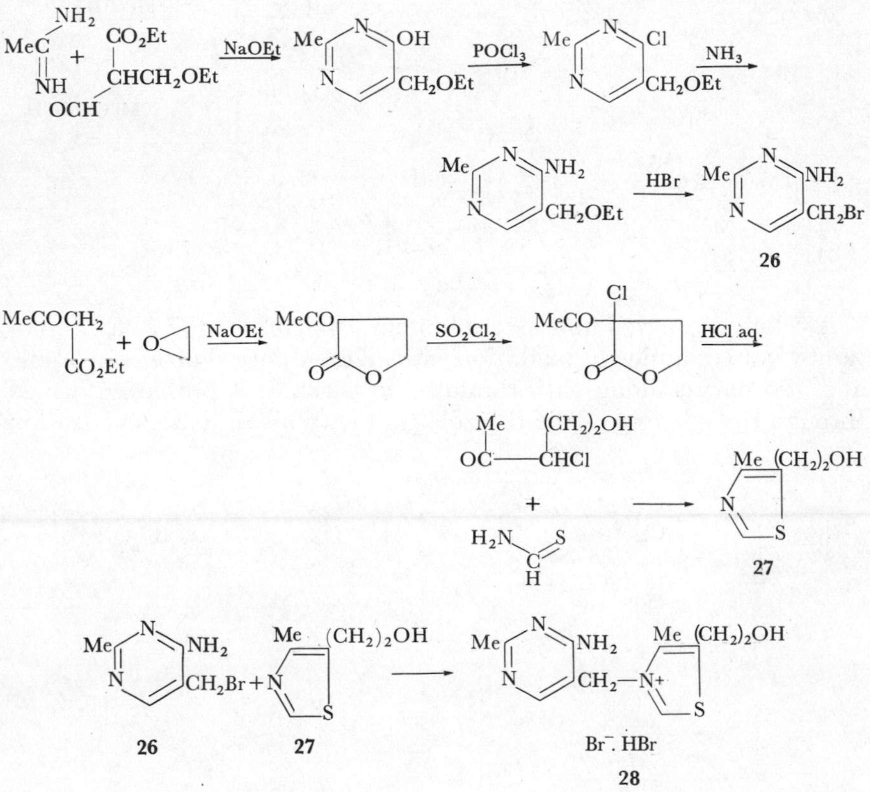

Thiamine pyrophosphate (**29**) is a coenzyme which is much involved in carbohydrate metabolism. It appears to lose the 2-hydrogen atom, to give a zwitterion (**30**) which then behaves as an anion (R^-) in its next reaction with pyruvic acid. The product (**31**), which has been isolated, decarboxylates to the thiazolium salt (**33**) which has also been isolated. This last compound can split up into acetaldehyde and thiamine pyrophosphate via **32** and **30**, but, reacting again via the ion (**32**), can also combine with acetaldehyde yielding acetoin (**34**) and reforming thiamine pyrophosphate.[46]

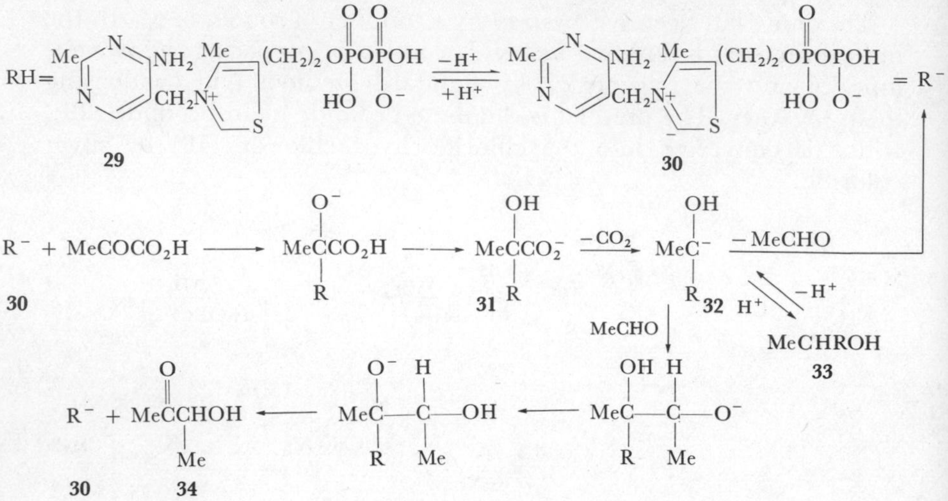

29   **30**

$$R^- + MeCOCO_2H \longrightarrow \underset{R}{MeCCO_2H} \dashrightarrow \underset{R}{MeCCO_2^-} \xrightarrow{-CO_2} \underset{R}{MeC^-} \xrightarrow{-MeCHO}$$

30   **31**   **32**

MeCHROH
33

$$R^- + \underset{Me}{MeCCHOH} \longleftarrow \underset{R \quad Me}{MeC-C-OH} \longleftarrow \underset{R \quad Me}{MeC-C-O^-}$$

30   **34**

A yellow strongly fluorescent pigment, thiochrome (**37**), can be obtained from thiamine by oxidation with alkaline potassium ferricyanide, and also occurs along with thiamine in yeast. It is probably formed through the opening of the thiazole ring with alkali to **35**, cyclization

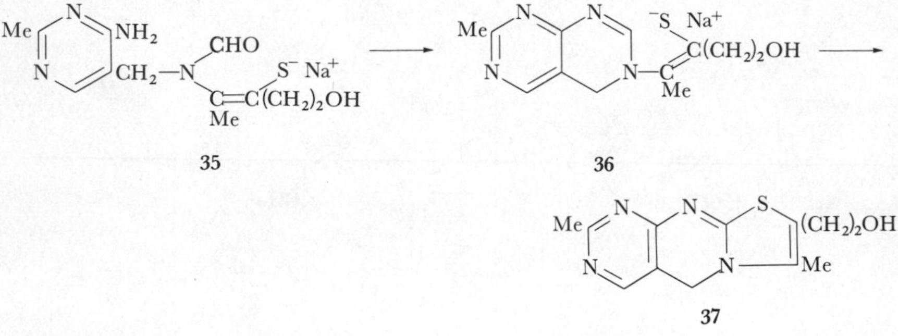

35   **36**

37

to **36**, followed by an oxidative cyclization, which probably involves a sulphur radical eventually giving thiochrome (**37**). Sulphathiazole (**38**) is a useful antibacterial agent.

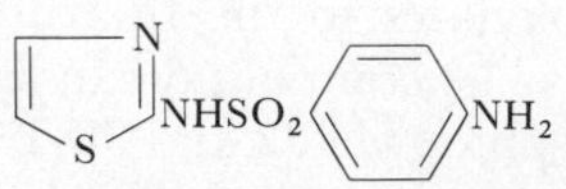

38

Luciferin, the chemiluminescent compound of the American firefly, is a Δ^2-thiazoline (**39**) and has been synthesized.[47]

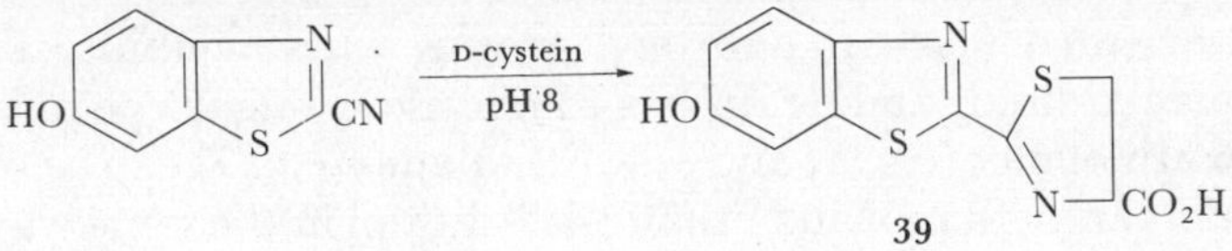

4. DIOXOLE, DIOXOLANE, AND THEIR SULPHUR ANALOGUES

1,3-Dioxole (**1**) is unknown, although derivatives such as **2**, in which the double bond is a part of an aromatic system, are fairly common.

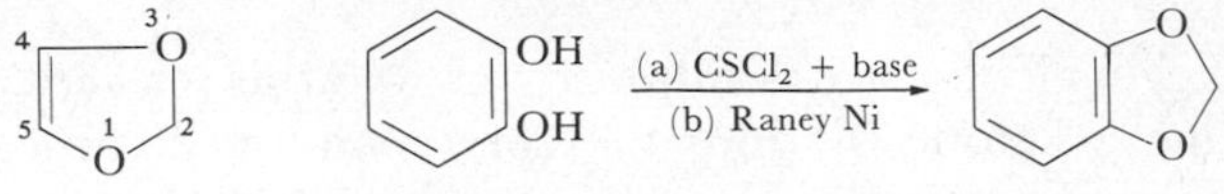

Methylenedioxybenzene (**2**) can be made from catechol as above, but poor results are obtained in the older one-stage conversions using sodium hydroxide and methylene iodide or sulphate.

1,3-Dioxolane (**3**) is obtained from ethylene glycol, or oxirane, and formaldehyde. In general, dioxolanes of this type are prepared from the aldehyde or ketone and ethylene glycol in the presence of an acid catalyst under such conditions that the water formed is removed. This is commonly done by azeotropic distillation with benzene or toluene.

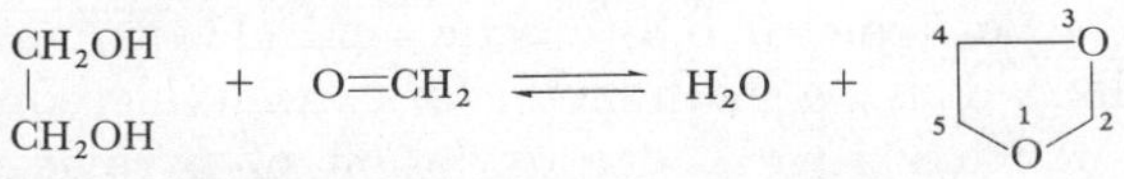

1,3-Dioxolanes are readily hydrolysed by dilute aqueous acid, but are stable to alkali. Dioxolane formation is therefore a very valuable and easy method of protecting carbonyl groups against alkali. Conversly, dioxolane formation, usually with acetone as the carbonyl component, is a very valuable procedure for protecting hydroxyl groups which are suitably oriented for ring formation. This application has many uses in sugar chemistry.

1,3-Dioxolan-2-one, or ethylene carbonate (**4**), is readily obtainable.

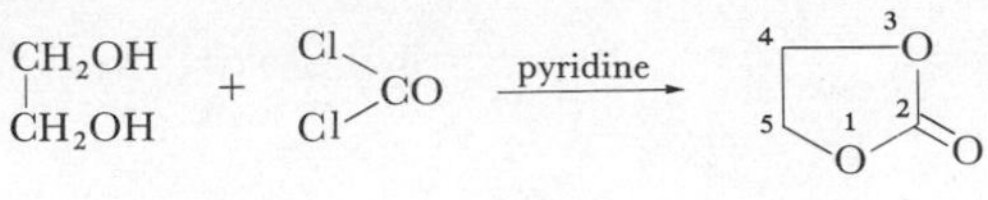

It is very much more stable to acids than 1,3-dioxolane, but is decomposed to ethylene glycol and carbon dioxide by alkali. The formation of such carbonates is therefore a complementary protection procedure for suitably oriented (1,2-*cis*) hydroxyl groups where stability to acidic reagents is required, and again has much use in sugar chemistry.

1,3-Oxathiolanes (e.g. **5**) and 1,3-dithiolanes (e.g. **7**) can be obtained from 2-mercaptoethanol and ethane-1,2-dithiol in the same way as 1,3-dioxolanes, and have similar properties. 1,3-Dithiolanes on boiling with

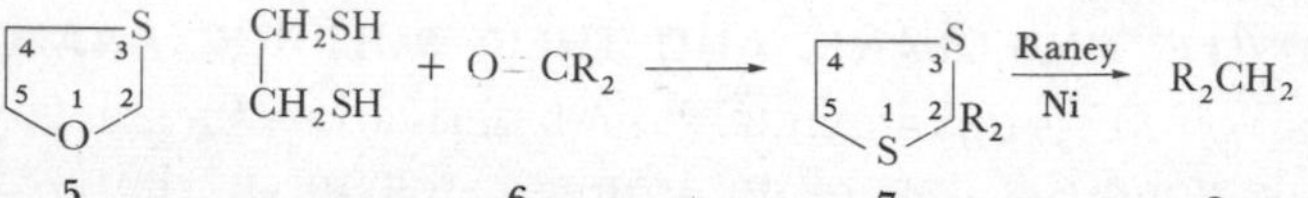

Raney nickel in alcohol are desulphurized, and this is a very useful way of converting a ketone (**6**) into the corresponding hydrocarbon (**8**). 1,3-Oxathiolanes on similar treatment give back the original ketone.

Although 1,2-dioxolane (**9**), which would be a cyclic dialkyl peroxide, is not known, 1,2-dithiolane (**10**) has been prepared. It is an un-

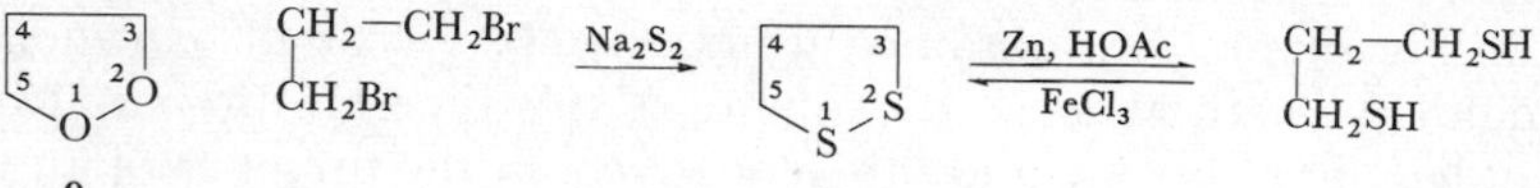

stable yellow oil with the properties of an aliphatic disulphide. A derivative, (+)-α-lipoic or 6,8-thioctic acid (**11**) is most interesting biochemically.[48] It is a growth factor for certain microorganisms, it is involved in the oxidative decarboxylation of pyruvic acid, and it may be involved in photosynthesis. Desulphurization with Raney nickel gives octanoic acid. The best synthesis[49] of racemic 6,8-thioctic acid is outlined.

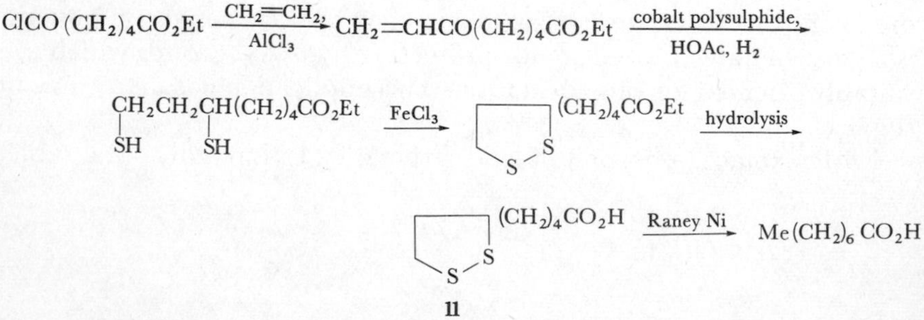

The aromatic 1,2- (12) and 1,3-dithiolium cations (13) have recently been prepared, and have been much investigated in the last few years.[50] An interesting type of resonance is shown[51] by one of these compounds (14–14a).

12   13   14   14a

GENERAL BIBLIOGRAPHY

Wiley, *Five- and Six-Membered Compounds with Nitrogen and Oxygen (Excluding Oxazoles)*, Interscience, New York, 1962.

Loudon, in *Chemistry of Carbon Compounds*, Vol. IVA, ed. Rodd, Elsevier, New York, 1957.

PYRAZOLE
   Wiley and Wiley, *Pyrazole and Its Derivatives*, Interscience, New York, 1964.
   Jacobs, in *Heterocyclic Compounds*, Vol. 5, ed. Elderfield, Wiley, New York, 1956.

IMIDAZOLE
   Hofmann, *Imidazole and its Derivatives*, Interscience, New York, 1953.
   Schipper and Day, in *Heterocyclic Compounds*, Vol. 5, ed. Elderfield, Wiley, New York, 1956.

ISOXAZOLE
   Kochefkov and Sokolov, *Advan. Heterocyclic Chem.*, 2, 365 (1963).
   Barnes, in *Heterocyclic Compounds*, Vol. 5, ed. Elderfield, Wiley, New York, 1956.

OXAZOLES
   Cornforth, in *Heterocyclic Compounds*, Vol. 5, ed. Elderfield, Wiley, New York, 1956.
   Filler, *Advan. Heterocyclic Chem.*, 4, 75 (1965).

THIAZOLES
   Sprague and Land, in *Heterocyclic Compounds*, Vol. 5, ed. Elderfield, Wiley, New York, 1956.

SELENAZOLES
   Bulka, *Advan. Heterocyclic Chem.*, 2, 344 (1965).

ISOTHIAZOLES
   Slack and Wooldridge, *Advan. Heterocyclic Chem.*, 4, 107 (1965).

1, 3-DIOXOLANES
   Elderfield and Short, in *Heterocyclic Compounds*, Vol. 5, ed. Elderfield, Wiley, New York, 1956.

REFERENCES

1. Ehrlich, *Acta Cryst.*, 13, 940 (1960).
2. Bedford, Edmondson, and Mortimer, *J. Chem. Soc.*, 2927 (1962).
3. Hamano and Hameka, *Tetrahedron*, 18, 985 (1962).
4. Tiefenthaler, Dörscheln, Göth, and Schmid, *Tetrahedron Letters*, 2999 (1964).
5. Austin, Blackborow, Ridd, and Smith, *J. Chem. Soc.*, 1051 (1965).
6. Vaughan *et al.*, *J. Am. Chem. Soc.*, 86, 2857 (1964).
7. Patel and Tedder, *J. Chem. Soc.*, 4589 (1963).
8. Grandberg, Vasina, Volkova, and Kost, *Zh. Obshch. Khim.*, 31, 1887 (1961).
9. Lynch and Khan, *Can. J. Chem.*, 41, 2086 (1963).
10. Grimison and Ridd, *Proc. Chem. Soc.*, 256 (1958).
11. Ridd *et al.*, *J. Chem. Soc.*, 3937 (1953); 1238 (1955).
12. Bredereck, Gompper, Bangert, and Herlinger, *Angew. Chem.*, 70, 269 (1958).
13. Van Auken and Reinhart, *J. Am. Chem. Soc.*, 84, 3736 (1962); Van Auken, *Diss. Abst.*, 22, 3413 (1962).

14. Overberger and Anselme, *J. Am. Chem. Soc.*, **84**, 869 (1962).
15. Ainsworth, *J. Am. Chem. Soc.*, **79**, 5242 (1957).
16. Ferm and Riebsomer, *Chem. Rev.*, **54**, 593 (1954).
17. Hein, Alheim, and Leavitt, *J. Am. Chem. Soc.*, **79**, 427 (1957).
18. Brown and Heffernan, *J. Chem. Soc.*, 4288 (1956).
19. Noe and Fowden, *Biochem. J.*, **77**, 543 (1960).
20. Mees, *The Theory of the Photographic Process*, 2nd ed., p. 592, Macmillan, New York, 1954.
21. Moyed and Magasanik, *J. Biol. Chem.*, **235**, 149 (1960).
22. Witkop and Kny, *Section 12–26, 4th Intern. Congr. Biochem.*, Vienna, 1958.
23. Kraml and Bouthillier, *Can. J. Biochem. Physiol.*, **34**, 783 (1956).
24. Beaman *et al.*, *J. Am. Chem. Soc.*, **87**, 389 (1965).
25. Wünsch, Linke, Boulton, and Rahman, *Chem. Commun.*, 408 (1965).
26. Perold, Steyn, and von Reiche, *J. Am. Chem. Soc.*, **79**, 462 (1957).
27. Baltazzi, *Quart. Rev.*, **9**, 150 (1955); Carter, *Org. Reactions*, **3**, 198 (1946).
28. Crawford and Little, *J. Chem. Soc.*, 729 (1959).
29. Hrutford and Bunnett, *J. Am. Chem. Soc.*, **80**, 2021 (1958).
30. Smissman, LaPidus, and Beck, *J. Am. Chem. Soc.*, **79**, 4697 (1957).
31. Gompper and Herlinger, *Chem. Ber.*, **89**, 2825 (1956).
32. Karimoto, Axelrod, Wolinsky, and Schall, *Phytochemistry*, **3**, 349 (1964).
33. Joshi, Taylor, Bhate, and Karmarkar, *Tetrahedron*, **19**, 1437 (1963).
34. Hübenett, Flock, and Hofmann, *Angew. Chem.*, **74**, 653 (1962).
35. Wille, Capeller, and Steiner, *Angew. Chem.*, **74**, 467 (1962).
36. Adams and Slack, *J. Chem. Soc.*, 3061 (1959).
37. Caton, Jones, Slack, and Wooldridge, *J. Chem. Soc.*, 446 (1964).
38. Buttimore, Jones, Slack, and Wooldridge, *J. Chem. Soc.*, 2032 (1963).
39. Hübenett, Flock, and Hansel, *Angew. Chem.*, **75**, 1189 (1963).
40. Chaplen, Slack, and Wooldridge, *J. Chem. Soc.*, 4577 (1965).
41. Jones, Slack, and Wooldridge, *J. Chem. Soc.*, 3114 (1964).
42. Wille, Ascherl, Kaupp, and Capeller, *Angew. Chem.*, **74**, 753 (1962).
43. Vitry-Raymond and Metzger, *Bull. Soc. Chim. France*, 1784 (1963).
44. Beraud and Metzger, *Bull. Soc. Chim. France*, 2072 (1962).
45. Wiley, England, and Behr, *Org. Reactions*, **6**, 367 (1951).
46. Steyn-Parvé and Monfoort in *Comprehensive Biochem.*, **12**, 3 (1963).
47. White, McCapra, and Field, *J. Am. Chem. Soc.*, **85**, 337 (1963).
48. Reed, *Advan. Enzymol.*, **18**, 319 (1957).
49. Bullock, Hand, and Stokstad, *J. Am. Chem. Soc.*, **79**, 1978 (1957).
50. Campaigne and Hamilton, *J. Org. Chem.*, **29**, 2877 (1964) and earlier papers; Klingsberg, *J. Am. Chem. Soc.*, **86**, 5290 (1964) and earlier papers; Leaver, McKinnon, and Robertson, *J. Chem. Soc.*, 32 (1965) and earlier papers; Lüttringhaus, Mohr, and Englehard, *Ann.*, **661**, 84 (1963) and earlier papers.
51. Klingsberg, *J. Am. Chem. Soc.*, **85**, 3244 (1963).

CHAPTER VIII

COMPOUNDS WITH TWO HETEROATOMS IN A SIX-MEMBERED RING

These compounds can be formally derived from benzene, and its reduction products, by suitable substitutions of carbon (and hydrogen) atoms by nitrogen, oxygen, and sulphur. The most thoroughly studied ring system of this class is that of pyrimidine, in which the two nitrogen atoms bear the same positional relationship to each other as in the amidines and in the imidazoles (p. 300). This is largely because it occurs

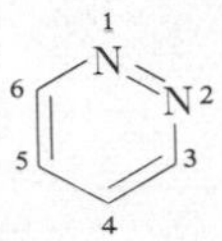

Pyridazine 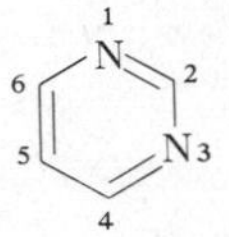   Pyrimidine 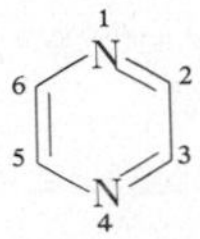   Pyrazine

in many compounds vital to living systems. A substantial number of synthetic pyrimidines, and other compounds with the ring systems described in this chapter, are valuable chemotherapeutic agents.

Six-membered rings containing one heterocyclic oxygen or sulphur atom cannot be aromatic unless they bear a positive charge (p. 188), and very few of these are known with a second heteroatom in the ring. More fully reduced rings with these atoms have been examined in greater detail, and a number will be considered. When oxygen and

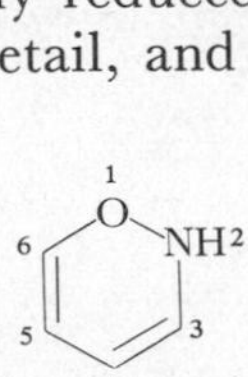

1,2-Oxazine 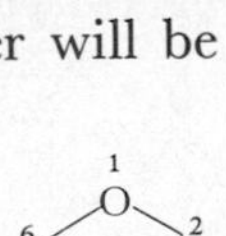   1,3-Oxazine 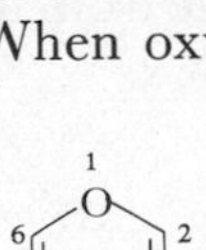   1,4-Oxazine

nitrogen atoms are present the name oxazine is used and the positions of the atoms are indicated by numbers. A similar nomenclature is used for the thiazines, which contain sulphur and nitrogen atoms. The term

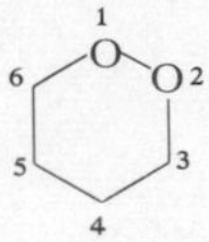

1,2-Dioxane 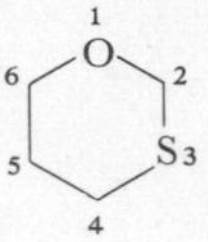　　　　1,3-Oxathiane 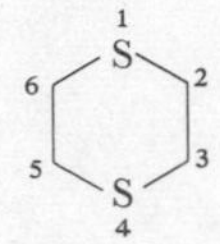　　　　1,4-Dithiane

dioxane is used for the saturated ring with two oxygen atoms, dioxene and dioxadiene refer respectively to the comparable rings with one and two double bonds, and a similar nomenclature applies to sulphur analogues.

1. PYRIDAZINE

Pyridazine (1) is a colourless liquid, b.p. 207°, miscible with both water and benzene but almost insoluble in cyclohexane. It has a dipole moment of ca. 4 D and a highly aromatic type of absorption spectrum. The compound is therefore best considered as a resonance hybrid to which the non-equivalent structures 1 and 1a are the major contributors. Its resonance energy is stated to be only 12·3 kcal/mole.[1] This value may be too low (cf. pyrazine, p. 345).

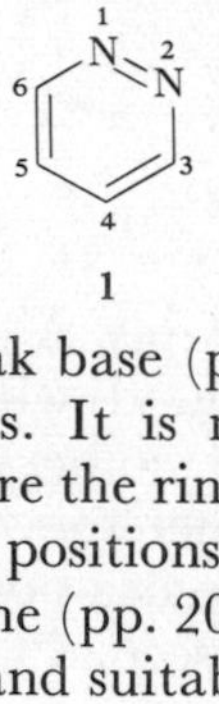

1 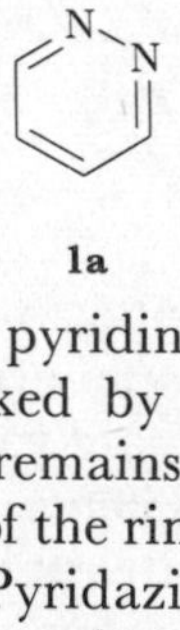　　　　　　　1a

Pyridazine is a weak base (pK_a 2·33; pyridine has pK_a 5·23) which forms crystalline salts. It is not attacked by electrophilic reagents under conditions where the ring system remains intact. Methyl groups and halogen atoms at positions 3 and 6 of the ring are active, like those at position 2 of pyridine (pp. 204, 212). Pyridazines are usually obtainable from hydrazine and suitable dicarbonyl compounds (e.g. 2, often obtainable from furans, pp. 99, 117). Pyridazine itself, however, is best

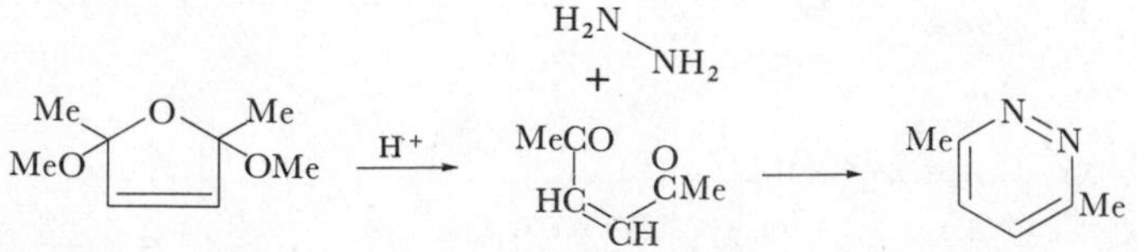

2

prepared from maleic anhydride and hydrazine. The first product is the tautomer 5, there being no detectable amounts of 3 and 4 present.[2] The halogen atoms of 3,6-dichloropyridazine (6), being reactive, are readily replaced by hydrogen.

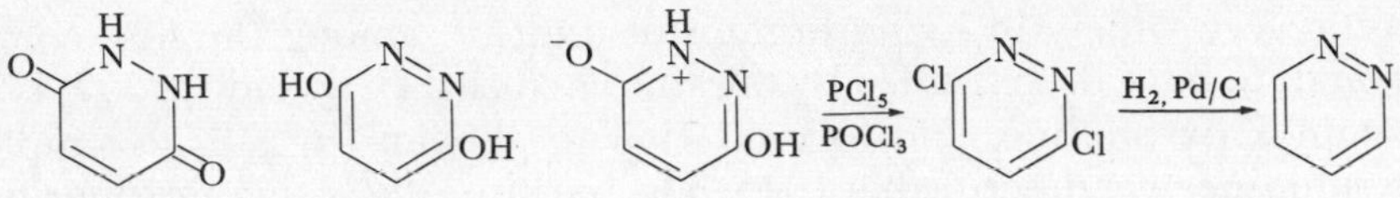

Maleic hydrazide, with *t*-butyl hypochlorite at -50 to $-77°$, is oxidized to the extremely reactive 2,3-diazaquinone (**7**). On warming it loses nitrogen yielding **8**, and with butadiene it gives **9**.[3]

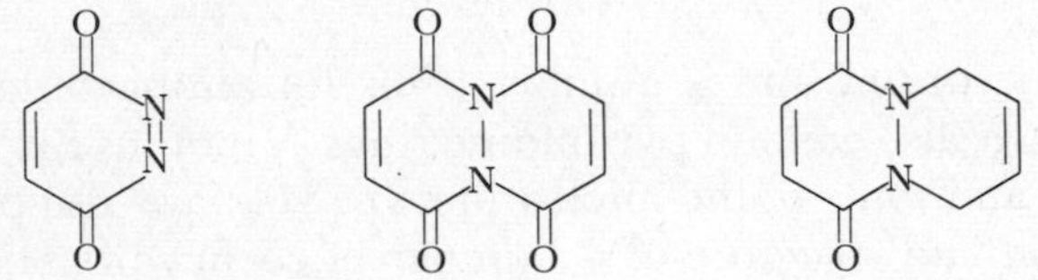

The pyridazine ring can be fused on to a benzene ring in two ways, giving cinnoline (**10**) or phthalazine (**11**). Phthalhydrazide (**12**), the

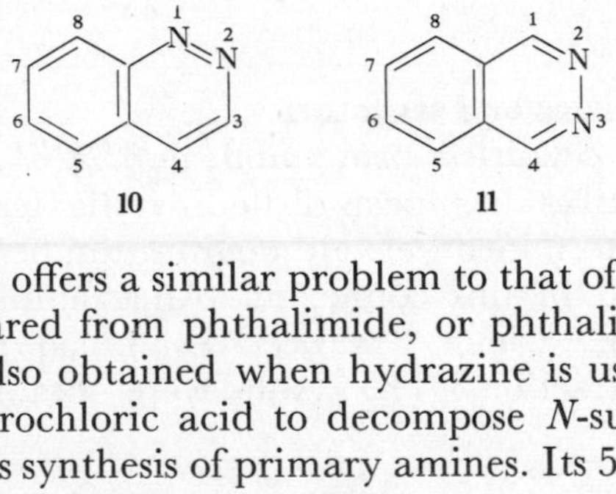

structure of which offers a similar problem to that of maleic hydrazide (**3**, **4**, **5**), is prepared from phthalimide, or phthalic anhydride, and hydrazine. It is also obtained when hydrazine is used instead of hot concentrated hydrochloric acid to decompose *N*-substituted phthalimides in Gabriel's synthesis of primary amines. Its 5-amino derivative

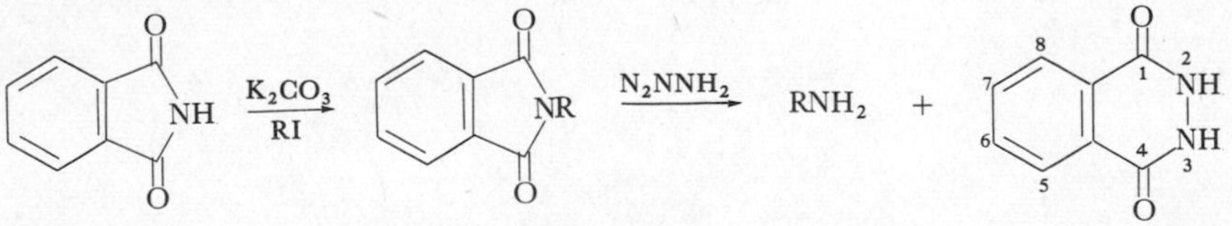

(luminol) is especially interesting, as with a number of oxidizing agents in the presence of alkali it emits a blue light (chemiluminescence).

2. PYRIMIDINE

A. Introduction

Pyrimidine derivatives, which strictly include the purines (p. 354), occur very widely in living organisms and are among the first compounds to have been studied by organic chemists. Uric acid (p. 357) is a complex pyrimidine, and its oxidation to alloxan (p. 339), a simple pyrimidine, was described in 1845. The barbiturates, valuable soporific

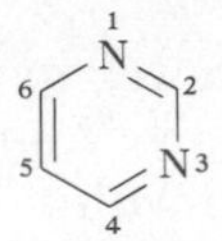

Pyrimidine

and hypnotic drugs, and a number of useful antibacterial and anti-malarial drugs also contain pyrimidine rings. Vitamins B_1 (p. 323) and B_2 (p. 366) and some of the nucleotides (p. 344) are also pyrimidines. The function and structure of a number of coenzymes possessing the pyrimidine ring have been established. Of these many contain the pyrimidines uracil and cytosine, and are known to be concerned principally with the biosynthesis of complex carbohydrates and lipids. At present great interest is being taken in the chemistry and biochemistry of pyrimidines.

B. Physical properties and structure

Pyrimidine is a colourless compound, m.p. 22·5°, b.p. 124°, which unlike its derivatives has been little investigated. Its dimensions have not been determined yet, although a number of its derivatives have been studied in this connexion. An example is 4-amino-2,6-dichloropyrimidine, which has been examined in the crystalline form by x-ray diffraction.[4] The results were obtained with sufficient

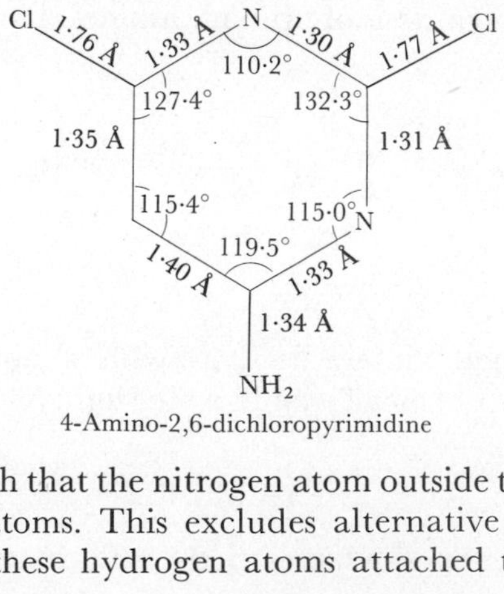

4-Amino-2,6-dichloropyrimidine

accuracy to establish that the nitrogen atom outside the ring is attached to two hydrogen atoms. This excludes alternative tautomeric structures with one of these hydrogen atoms attached to a ring nitrogen atom (cf. 2- and 4-aminopyridines, p. 215). Although the ring is not symmetrical, neither of the two carbon–carbon bond distances (1·40 and 1·35 Å) approaches that of the aliphatic carbon–carbon single bond distance (1·54 Å). One is very close to the carbon–carbon distance (1·40 Å) of benzene and the other is between this and the carbon–carbon distance (1·33 Å) of ethylene. The general similarity of the size and shape of the pyrimidine ring to that of benzene and pyridine (p. 190) is consistent with its highly aromatic chemical characteristics. The differences between the bond angles and distances of these ring systems

suggest that that of pyrimidine is the least aromatic. This is in agreement with the resonance energies calculated by molecular-orbital methods:[5] benzene 36, pyridine 31, and pyrimidine 26 kcal/mole. The resonance energy of pyrimidine, 8·0 kcal/mole, calculated from heat of combustion data,[6] is probably too low (cf. pyrazine, p. 345).

Pyrimidine is best considered as a resonance-hybrid to which the uncharged equivalent Kekulé structures 1 and 1a and the charged structures 1b–1g contribute. The self-consistent π-electron densities, calculated for the ground state of pyrimidine, are 0·776, 0·825, and 1·103 for positions 2, 4, and 5 respectively.[7]

C. Chemical properties of pyrimidine and its derivatives

Although an enormous amount of work has been done with pyrimidine derivatives, most of which have been obtained directly from the excellent syntheses available, the chemical reactions of pyrimidine itself (1) have been investigated only recently. This is partly because pyrimidine was not readily available, but it can now be obtained quite easily by the decarboxylation of pyrimidine-4,6-dicarboxylic acid[8] or by the catalytic dechlorination of 2,4-dichloropyrimidine (p. 338).[9]

Pyrimidines can be considered best as derivatives of pyridine, and to a lesser extent as cyclic amidines. Pyrimidine (pK_a 1·3) is a much weaker base than pyridine (pK_a 5·23) or imidazole (pK_a 7·2), or amidines in general. This is because, unlike imidazole and the amidines, the addition of a proton does not increase the possibilities for resonance and hence the resonance energy. It is a surprisingly weaker base than pyridazine (pK_a 2·33). Only one of the nitrogen atoms of pyrimidine is alkylated by alkylating agents, such as methyl sulphate,[8] but the much more powerful agent, triethyloxonium borofluoride, alkylates both nitrogen atoms to give a ring bearing two positive charges.[10] Pyrimidine forms only a mono-N-oxide[8] which unlike pyridine 1-oxide (p. 207) has not been nitrated successfully.[8]

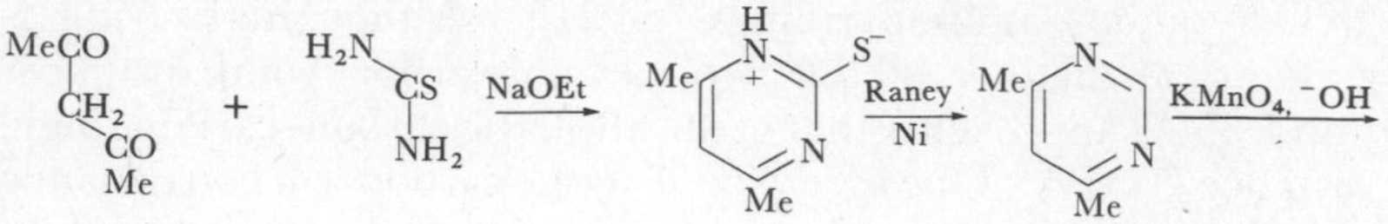

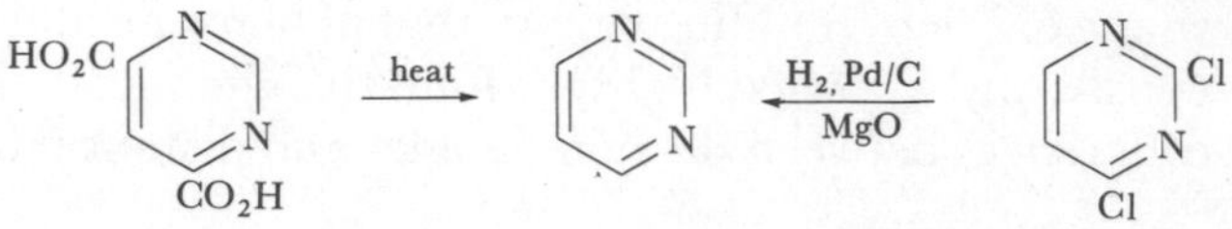

From a consideration of the charged structures which contribute to the resonance hybrids which represent pyrimidine (p. 335) and pyridine, and the π-electron densities, (p. 335), it is clear that position 5 of pyrimidine should correspond to position 3 of pyridine and be the most susceptible in the ring to electrophilic attack. Pyrimidine (like

Pyrimidine   Pyridine

pyridine, p. 197) hydrochloride is brominated at position 5, but no other electrophilic substitution of pyrimidine itself has been claimed. If activating groups, such as hydroxyl or amino, are present at other positions in the molecule, then electrophilic substitution (nitration, nitrosation, diazo coupling) usually occurs, but only at position 5. Groups present at position 5 generally have similar properties to those exhibited by the same substituents at position 3 of pyridine, or present in a benzene ring. An example is 5-hydroxypyrimidine (2), which has been obtained as outlined.[11] It has phenolic properties

CHO H_2N CS

MeOCH + NH_2 →   MeO ... S^- Raney Ni   MeO ... $\xrightarrow{P_2S_5}$ MeO ... Raney Ni

CO_2Me

MeO ... $\xrightarrow[\text{HOCH}_2\text{CH}_2\text{OH}]{\text{KOH in}}$ HO ...

2

and gives a red ferric chloride colour. 5-Aminopyrimidine, however, unlike 3-aminopyridine (p. 215), reacts with nitrous acid, but neither 5-hydroxypyrimidine nor a diazonium salt could be detected in the product, which remains unidentified. The synthesis of 5-hydroxy-pyrimidine shows two instances of the Raney nickel desulphurization of mercaptopyrimidines, and as mercaptopyrimidines are easily synthesized, this desulphurization procedure has had many applications.

In a similar way positions 2, 4, and 6 of pyrimidine formally corre-spond to those of 2 or 4 of pyridine and, in the few cases investigated, are attacked by nucleophilic reagents such as sodamide and phenyl-magnesium bromide.[11] Substituents at these positions also have com-parable reactivities and properties in the two series. For instance,

Me ... $\xrightarrow{NaNH_2}$ Me ... NH_2 +   Me ... NH_2

2,4,6-trimethylpyrimidine (cf. 2-methylpyridine, p. 204) reacts with benzaldehyde to give 2,4,6-tristyrylpyrimidine; the 2-methyl group

... $\xrightarrow{PhMgI}$ ... Ph $\xrightarrow{KMnO_4}$ ... Ph

appears to be the most reactive. Pyrimidine is attacked at the 2- and 4-positions by the 4-nitrophenyl radical.[12]

X-ray diffraction studies[13] have shown that the arrangement of the atoms in crystalline uracil (2,4-dihydroxypyrimidine, 4) is analogous to that in 2-pyridone (p. 219) and that likewise there is considerable hydrogen bonding between molecules. In general, often by ultraviolet absorption spectrum comparisons, it has been shown that hydroxy- and mercapto-pyrimidines adopt the tautomeric keto structure as long as the aromaticity of the ring can be maintained by a suitable electron distribution (e.g. as in **4**), while aminopyrimidines do not tautomerize appreciably to the imino forms. This is the same as in the pyridine series. Some reactions of uracil, which could easily

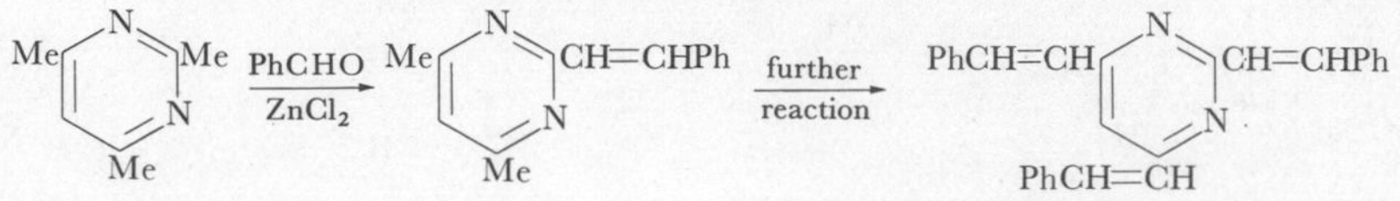

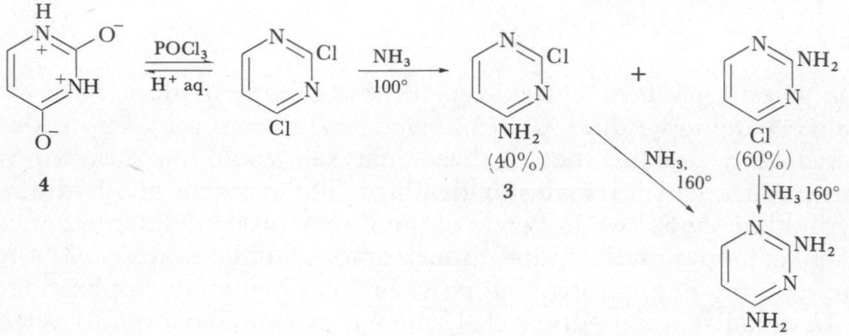

have been predicted from the pyridine analogy, are outlined above. Halogen atoms and methoxy and methylmercapto groups at positions 2, 4, or 6 of a pyrimidine can be replaced by amino groups on treatment with ammonia, or by hydroxyl groups on hydrolysis with dilute mineral acid. These are very valuable synthetic procedures, especially as such replacements can often be carried out stepwise in a poly-substituted pyrimidine. An example of this, which also illustrates another use of the mercapto group in pyrimidine chemistry, is the synthesis of cytosine (**7**, 4-amino-2-(1H)pyrimidone).[14] 4-Hydroxy-2-mercaptopyrimidine (**5**) prepared from thiourea and ethyl formyl-acetate (p. 118), and which is probably most accurately written in the zwitterionic form shown (cf. **4**, above), gives the S-ethyl, and not the N-ethyl, derivative (**6**) with ethyl iodide and sodium ethoxide.

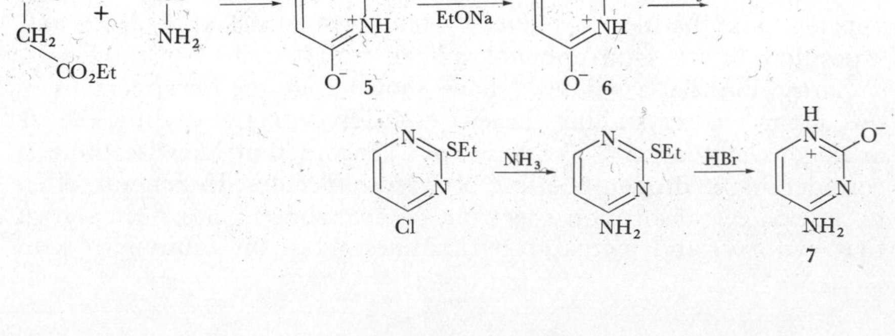

Cytosine is then obtainable as indicated; an alternative synthesis is hydrolysis of **3**.

4-Amino-2,6-dimethylpyrimidine (**8**) on irradiation in aqueous or anhydrous media gives 2-amino-3-cyanopent-2-en-4-imine (**10**) in quantitative yield. It is thought that the primary photoproduct is **9** which then breaks down.[15]

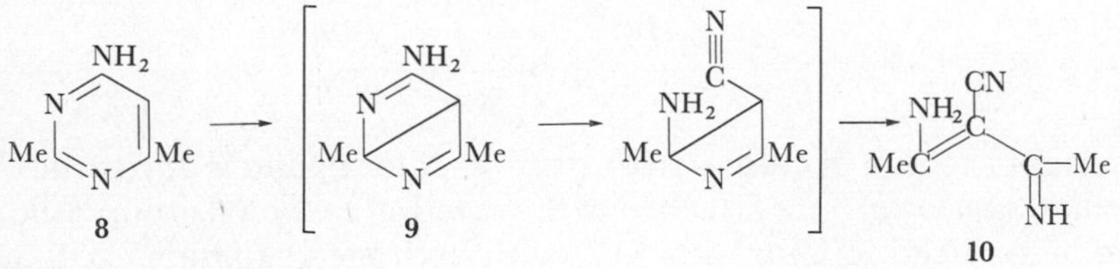

Barbituric acid (synthesis pp. 341–342) is a tautomeric substance which can be formulated in many ways. X-ray studies[16] of the solid have shown that it has structure **13**, although it is often represented as 2,4,6-trihydroxypyrimidine (**11**) or as **12**. It is a much stronger acid than

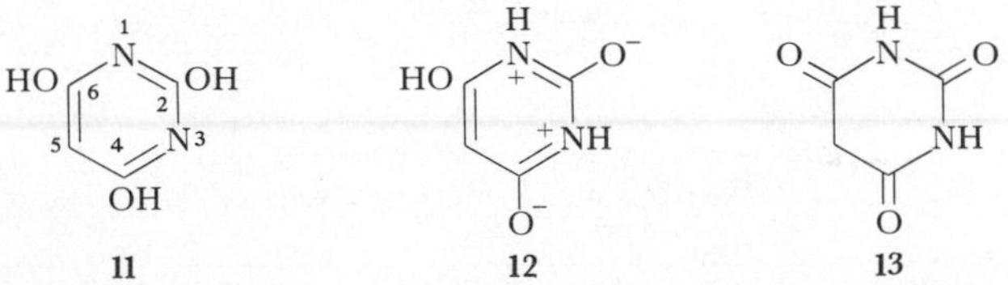

its 5,5-dialkyl derivatives and has a different ultraviolet absorption spectrum from them. Alkali[17] removes protons successively from positions 1, then 3, of **13**, giving anions, and alkylation under basic conditions does, however, give 5,5-dialkyl derivatives (synthesis, p. 341) before further reaction takes place at the nitrogen atoms. 5-Arylbarbituric acids cannot be prepared by a similar arylation, but are synthesized from phenylmalonic ester by the standard procedure (p. 294).

On nitrosation barbituric acid yields the tautomeric violuric acid (**14**), which forms purple salts. Violuric acid is also formed from alloxan (**15**), a degradation product of uric acid (p. 357), and hydroxylamine. Alloxan has the unusual property of causing a type of diabetes in experimental animals. It is normally obtained as the monohydrate (**16**), which is difficult to dehydrate. The formation of the hydrate is

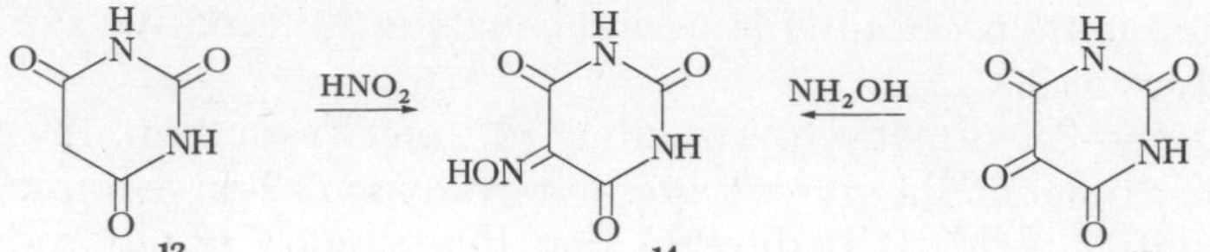

13   14   15

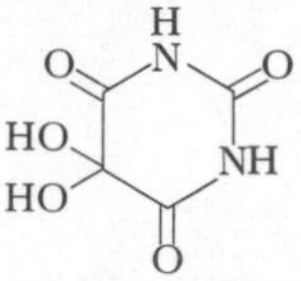

16

analogous to that of chloral hydrate from chloral, and is due to the electron-attracting groups attached to the reacting carbonyl group. Alloxan can be reduced to alloxantin (17) with hydrogen sulphide, to dialuric

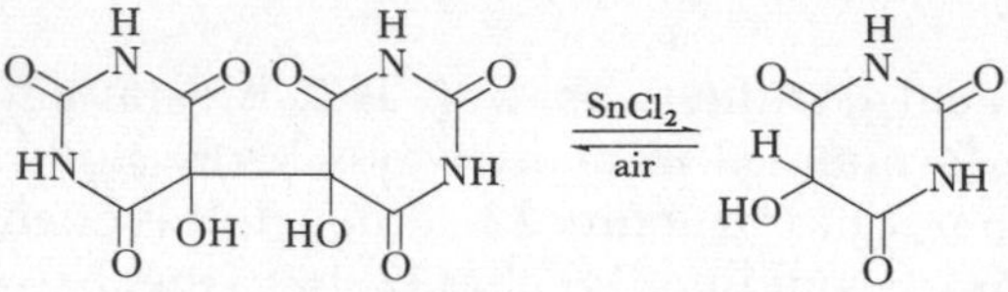

17   18

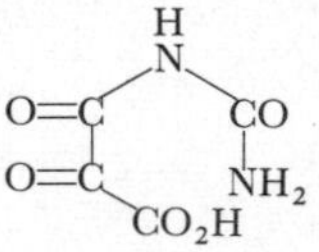

19 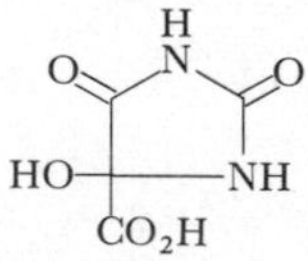   20

acid (18) with stannous chloride, and with sodium carbonate alloxan gives 20, possibly by hydrolysis to 19 and cyclization. Murexide (21), a purple substance formed from alloxantin, ammonium acetate,

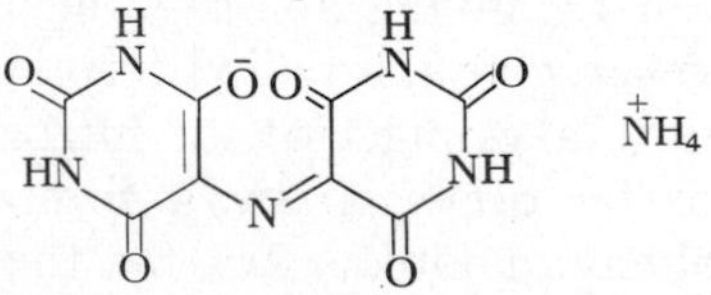

21

and glacial acetic acid, is the colouring matter produced in Wöhler and Liebig's test for uric acid (p. 357). The 'murexide test' consists in evaporating the suspected uric acid with concentrated nitric acid and subsequently adding ammonia. Murexide is used as an indicator in complexometric titrations.[18]

Hydrogenation of pyrimidine, and often of derivatives, under acid conditions gives 1,4,5,6-tetrahydropyrimidine (**22**), which has the

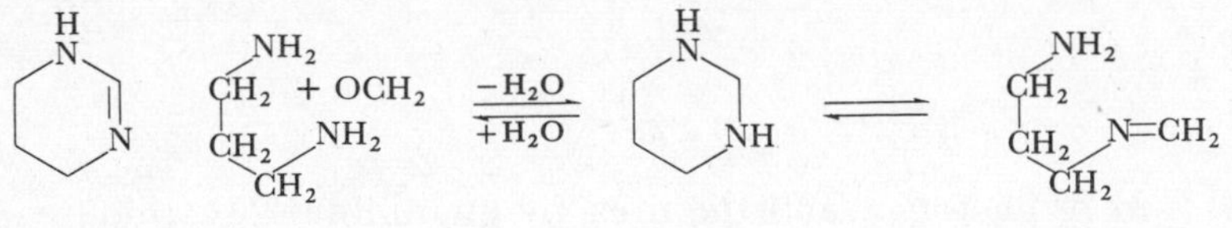

22   23   24

properties of an aliphatic amidine. It has also been prepared from propylene-1,3-diamine with formamidine, or ethyl formate followed by pyrolysis.[19] Hexahydropyrimidine (**23**) can be obtained from formaldehyde and 1,3-diaminopropane. It appears to exist in equilibrium with the tautomeric Schiff's base (**24**), and is very readily hydrolysed to the starting materials.

Benzopyrimidine (**25**) is usually called quinazoline, and a few alkaloids contain this ring system. Quinazoline is readily reduced to 3,4-dihydroquinazoline (**26**).

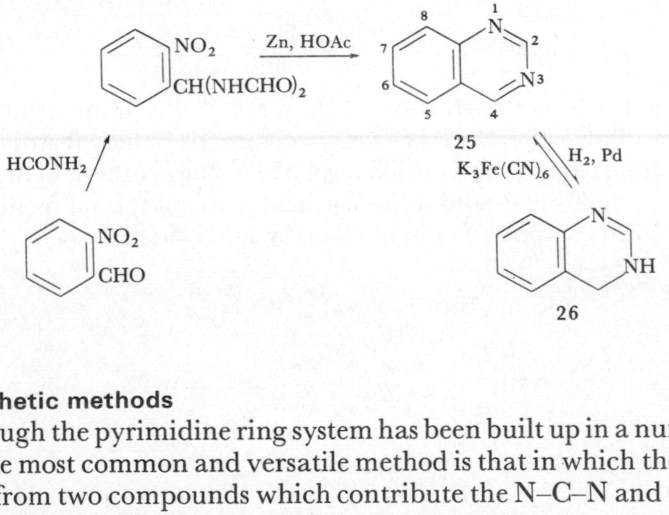

D. Synthetic methods

Although the pyrimidine ring system has been built up in a number of ways, the most common and versatile method is that in which the ring is formed from two compounds which contribute the N–C–N and C–C–C atoms respectively.

(1) The earliest synthesis of this type, published in 1879, is of barbituric acid (**13**) from urea, malonic acid, and phosphorus oxychloride. An improvement is to use ethyl malonate and sodium ethoxide, and this variation, which also works with mono- and di-substituted malonic esters, is used for the preparation of many of the barbituric acids used as hypnotics (p. 345). The malonic ester can be replaced by many β-keto

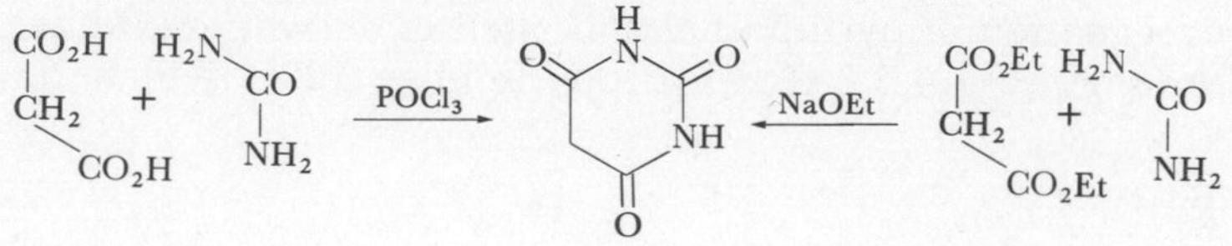

13

esters and β-diketones, and the urea by guanidine (**28**), thiourea, *S*-alkylthioureas, and by amidines (Traube's synthesis). Amidine hydrochlorides (**27**) are readily available from the corresponding nitriles, as indicated, but formamidine is more conveniently obtained by the

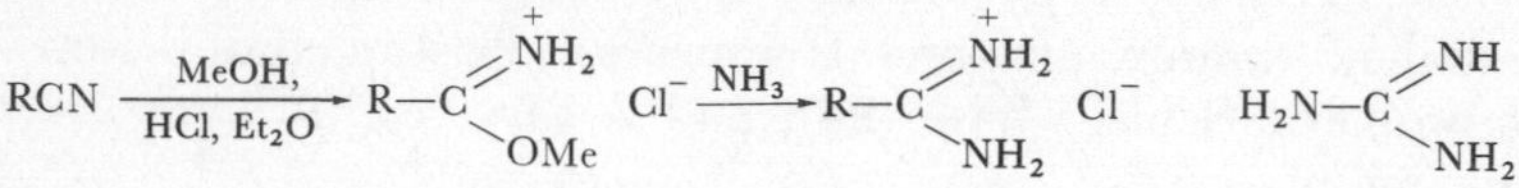

27   **28**

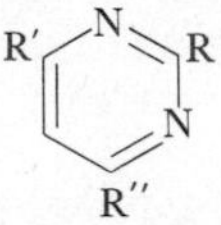

29

Raney nickel desulphurization of thiourea.[20] Pyrimidines of general structure **29** can therefore be obtained directly, and substituents can often be inserted later at position 5 (p. 336). The synthesis of uracil (**31**) from urea, malic acid, and sulphuric acid is worth special mention; the malic acid decomposes *in situ* to formylacetic acid (**30**, see p. 118).

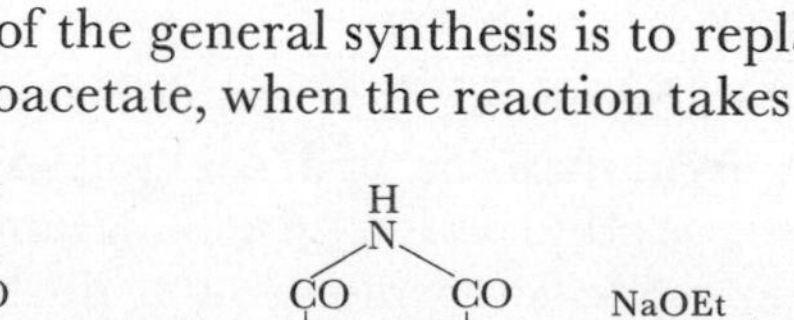

30   **31**

(2) A variation of the general synthesis is to replace the ethyl malonate by ethyl cyanoacetate, when the reaction takes place in two stages.

If a hydrogen atom is required at position 4 it is often preferable to use an ethoxymethylene compound, such as **32**, which can be obtained from ethyl cyanacetate and ethyl orthoformate in the presence of sodium ethoxide, instead of the corresponding β-formyl ester. The

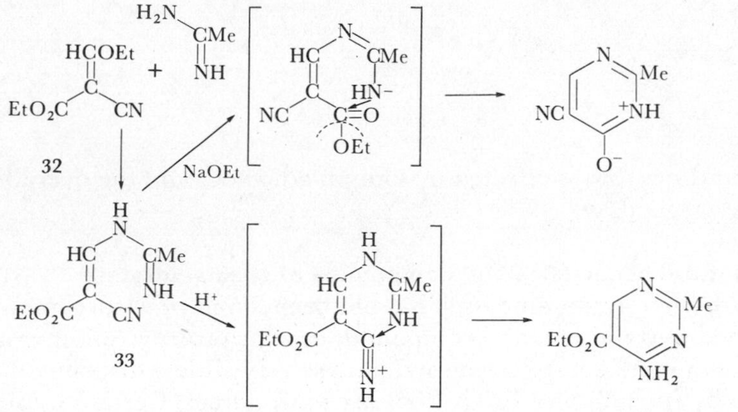

differing modes of cyclization of **33**, according to the conditions, are of interest.

(3) Another synthesis involves the condensation of amidines, or ureas, with unsaturated compounds such as ethyl crotonate under basic conditions. It is possible that a Michael addition to the double bond is

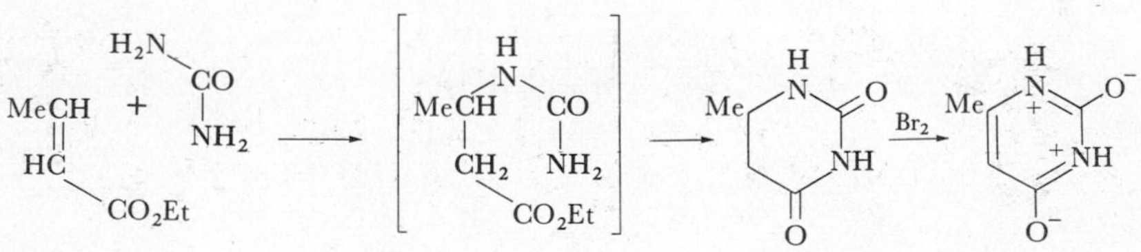

followed by cyclization. The resulting dihydropyrimidine is readily oxidized.

(4) A synthesis of another type, discovered[21] in 1953, appears to be quite general and is very convenient. Ethyl orthoformate reacts with ureas or thioureas to give the corresponding formamidines (**34**), and these, on refluxing in an inert solvent with compounds possessing an active methylene group, yield complex ethylenes (**35**); often both reactions can be carried out simultaneously by heating the three reactants together in an inert solvent. Cyclization of these ethylenes to the

$$2 \text{ NH}_2\text{CONH}_2 \xrightarrow{\text{HC(OEt)}_3} \text{H}_2\text{NCON}{=}\text{CH} \quad \underset{34}{\overset{\text{CO}}{\underset{\text{NH}_2}{\mid}}} \xrightarrow[-\text{NH}_2\text{CONH}_2]{\text{NCCH}_2\text{CO}_2\text{Et},}$$

$$\underset{35}{\overset{\text{CH} \quad \text{CO}}{\underset{\text{EtO}_2\text{CC} \quad \text{NH}_2}{\|}}} \xrightarrow{\text{NaOEt}} \underset{36}{\overset{\text{EtO}_2\text{C}}{\quad \text{NH}_2}}$$

pyrimidines (**36**) is effected by sodium ethoxide, and the overall yields are very good.

E. Natural occurrence and compounds of special interest

Although pyrimidine itself has not been found in nature, many substituted pyrimidines, and compounds in which the pyrimidine ring is a part of a more complex ring system, are very widely distributed. Vitamins B_1 (p. 323) and B_2 (p. 366) are pyrimidines. Certain pyrimidine (and purine) ribosides and deoxyribosides, called nucleosides, occur as phosphoric esters, the nucleotides, in most living cells. Some coenzymes are nucleotides and play a key role in metabolic processes. The nucleic acids[22] are macromolecules (cf. starch) which consists of many nucleotide molecules linked together through phosphate groups,

R = OH, Uridine or uracil riboside
R = NH$_2$, Cytidine or cytosine riboside

R = NH$_2$, R′ = H, Cytosine deoxyriboside
R = OH, R′ = Me, Thymidine
R = NH$_2$, R′ = Me, 5-Methylcytosine
         deoxyriboside

and which can vary considerably in their purine–pyrimidine ratios. They occur as such, or in association with proteins, in all living cells and are constituents of chromosomes and viruses. The common pyrimidine nucleosides, which are obtained on alkaline hydrolysis of ribonucleic and deoxyribonucleic acids, are formulated above. Their structures have been determined by degradation, and in some cases confirmed by synthesis. The methods used are quite similar to those employed in the case of the purine glycoside adenosine (p. 359), which is treated in detail as an example.

Derivatives of barbituric acid (p. 339) are perhaps the most widely used pyrimidines in medicine. 'Veronal' (**37**) and 'Luminal' (**38**) are valuable hypnotics, while 'Pentothal' (**39**) is used as a quick-acting anaesthetic. Other pyrimidines of current medicinal interest are the

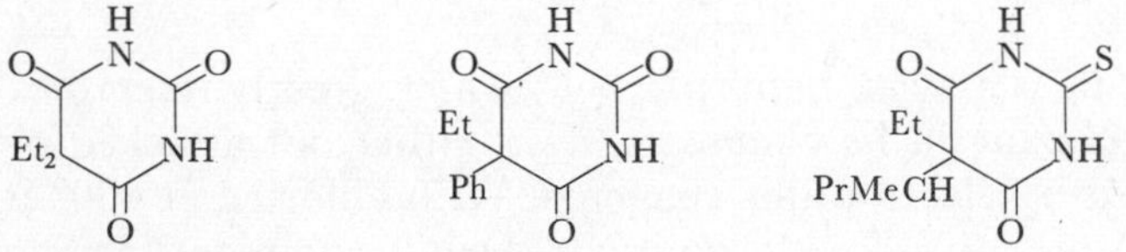

antibacterial agents sulphadiazine (**40**), sulphamerazine (**41**), and sulphamezathine (**42**). The antibiotic 'bacimethrin' is a comparatively simple pyrimidine (**43**) and has been synthesized.[23]

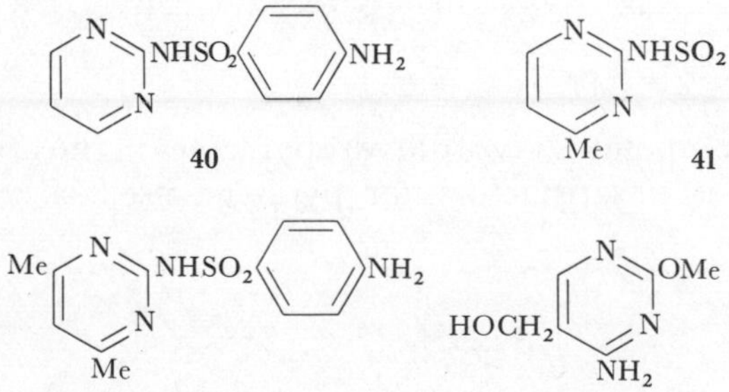

3. PYRAZINES

Pyrazine (**1**) is a colourless solid, m.p. 54°, b.p. 121°. Its dipole moment is zero, and the molecular dimensions for the 2,3,5,6-tetramethyl derivative, obtained from an x-ray study,[24] show that the ring is planar and that the carbon–carbon distance is longer than that of benzene (1.40 Å). The resonance energy of pyrazine is 24·3 ± 2·7 kcal/mole,[25] the earlier value of 8·0 kcal/mole, obtained by a different procedure,[6] being much too low.

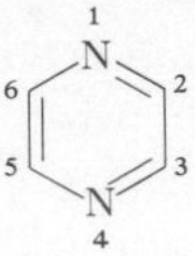

Pyrazine

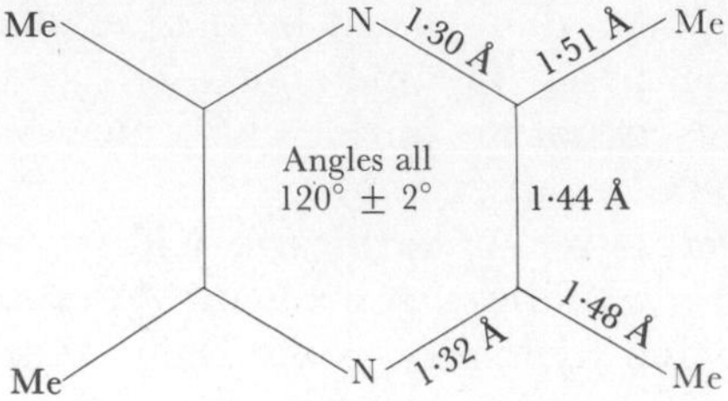

2,3,5,6-Tetramethylpyrazine

Pyrazine is a weak base (pK_a 0·6) which greatly resembles pyridine and pyridazine in its chemistry. It is either not attacked or it is decomposed by electrophilic reagents. With chlorine at 400° it (radical mechanism?) gives 2-chloropyrazine, with sodamide 2-aminopyrazine is formed, and both pyrazine mono- and di-N-oxides have been prepared.

The general method of pyrazine synthesis, the self-condensation of

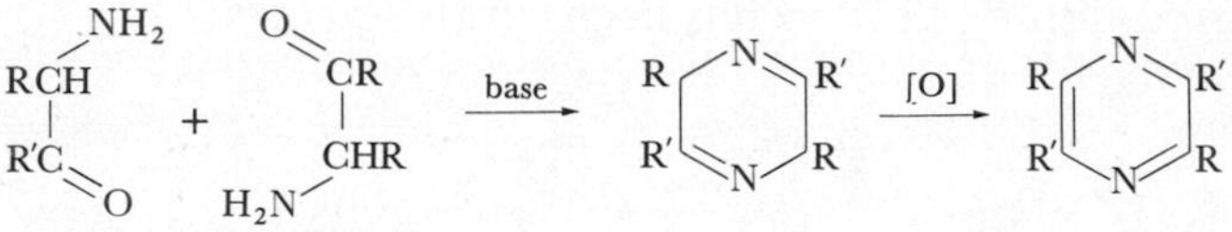

α-amino carbonyl compounds gives dihydropyrazines in the absence of air. This synthesis is unsatisfactory for pyrazine itself as α-amino-

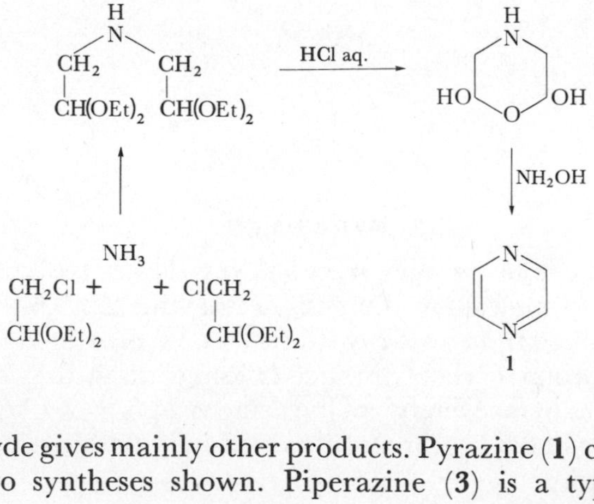

acetaldehyde gives mainly other products. Pyrazine (**1**) can be obtained by the two syntheses shown. Piperazine (**3**) is a typical aliphatic secondary diamine, and can be prepared in the laboratory from aniline by the general secondary aliphatic amine synthesis shown. It is widely used for treating certain parasitic infections of the pig.

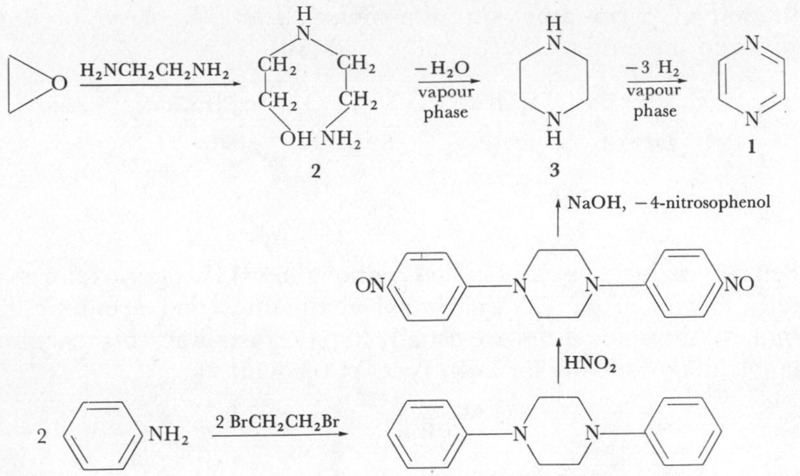

2,5-Dioxopiperazines, such as **4**, which is perhaps more accurately represented as **4a**, can be obtained by the thermal dehydration of α-amino acids. 2,5-Dioxopiperazine on careful partial hydrolysis yields

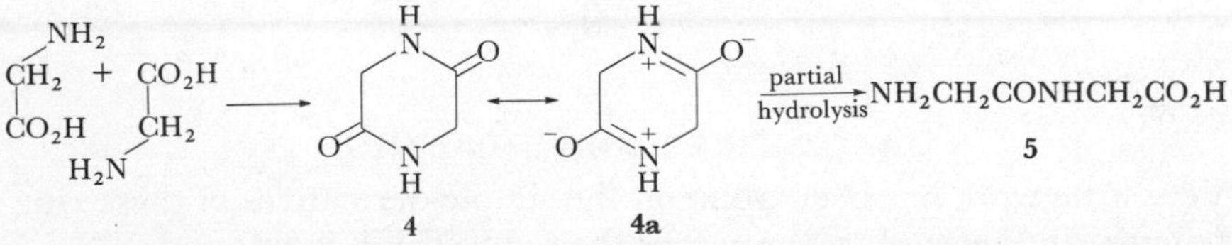

glycylglycine (**5**), and it will also give a silver salt (**6**). This with methyl iodide gives the *N*-dimethyl derivative (**7**), while treatment with benzyl chloride yields **8**. **8** is an imido ether and is very readily hydrolysed to benzyl alcohol and 2,5-dioxopiperazine by dilute aqueous acid.

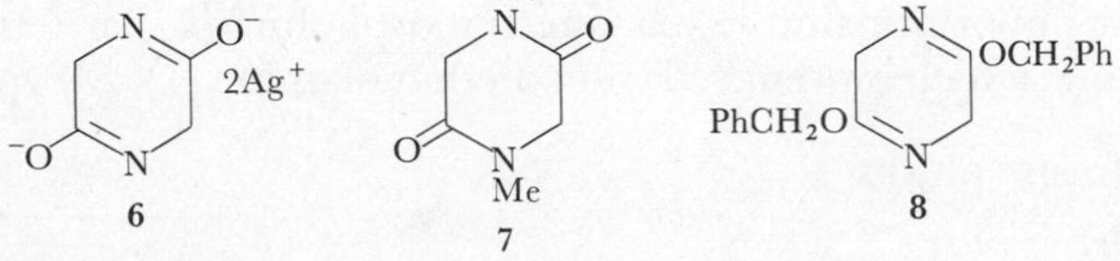

The pyrazine ring is present in a number of naturally occurring compounds. Most of these are pteridines (p. 364), where the ring is fused

N

with that of pyrimidine, but the mould *Aspergillus flavus* produces both **9** and the antibiotic aspergillic acid (**10**).

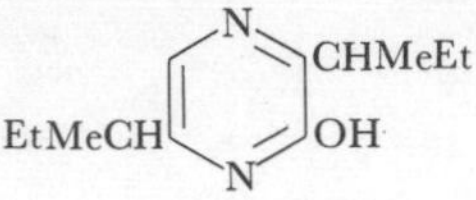

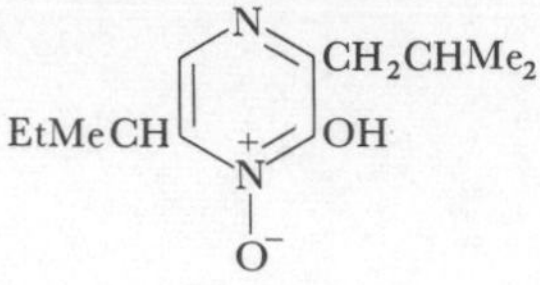

Benzopyrazine is usually called quinoxaline (**11**). Quinoxalines are readily formed from 1,2-dicarbonyl compounds and aromatic 1,2-diamines. As quinoxalines are usually highly crystalline, this reaction is valuable diagnostically for both types of reactant.

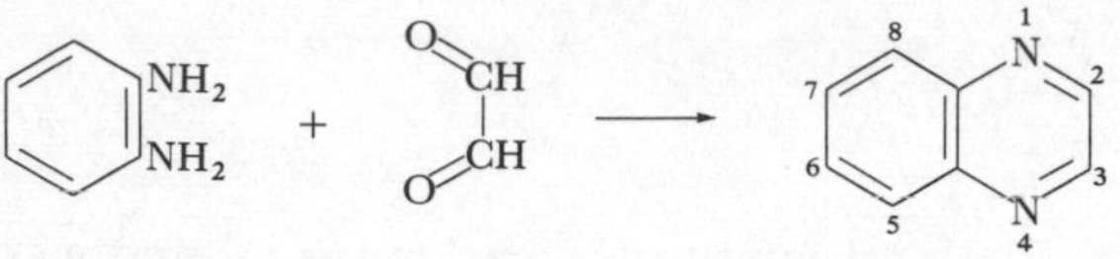

Dibenzopyrazine is called phenazine (**12**).

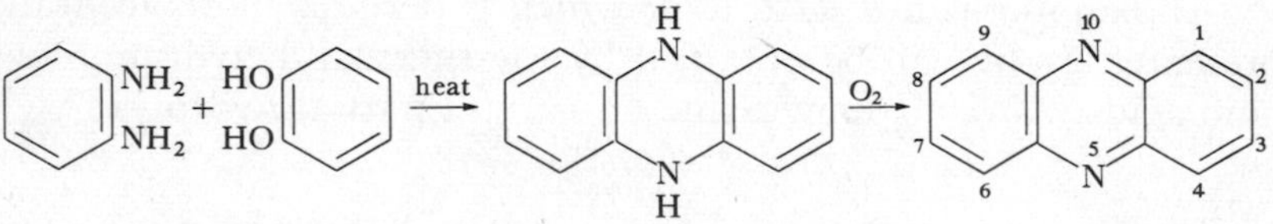

4. OXAZINES AND THIAZINES

Very little work has been done on the simple derivatives of these ring systems, and most of this concerns the reduced 1,4-compounds.

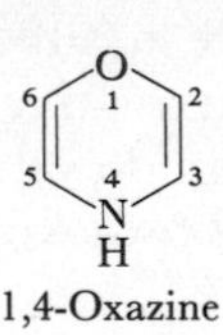

1,4-Oxazine 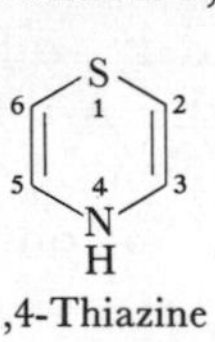   1,4-Thiazine

The most important simple oxazine is morpholine (**2**), or tetrahydro-1,4-oxazine, which is prepared from diethanolamine (**1**). Morpholine is

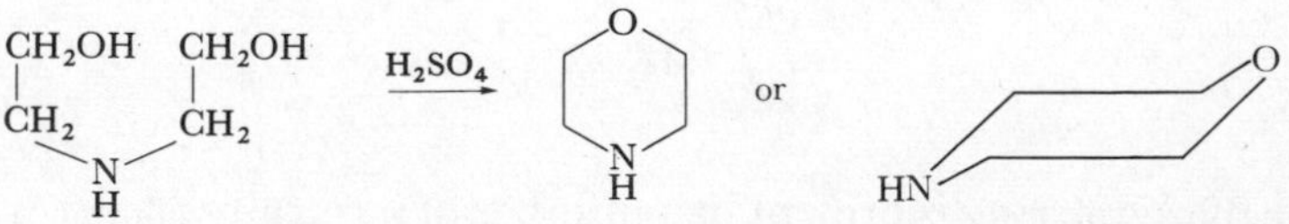

1   2   Chair form

a colourless liquid, b.p. 128°, which is miscible with water. It is an extremely powerful solvent and has many uses because of this property. It is a moderately strong base (pK_a 8·7), and from calculations of the dipole moments for various conformations and the observed value (1·48 D) it has been concluded that the molecule adopts the chair form with the heteroatoms at the extremities. Morpholine is not attacked at 160° by either concentrated hydrochloric acid or 10% aqueous sodium hydroxide and has the chemistry of a typical aliphatic secondary amine. Thiamorpholine (4), obtainable from mustard gas (3) and ammonia, is similar.

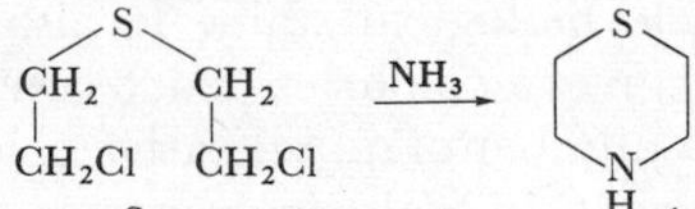

While the monobenzo-oxazines and -thiazines are of little interest, derivatives of phenoxazine (5) and phenothiazine (8) have attracted

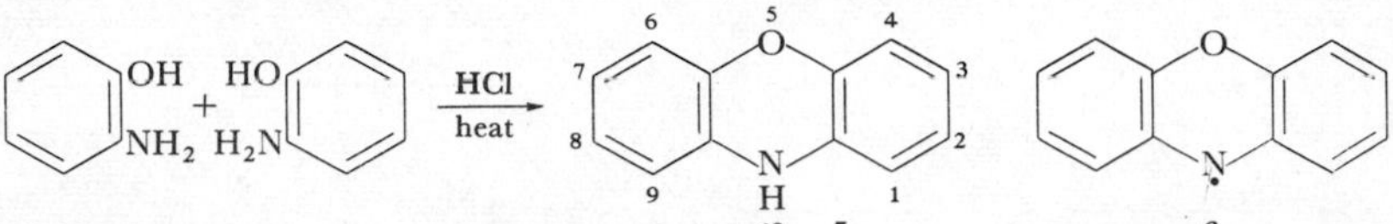

attention. Phenoxazine is a colourless solid, m.p. 156°, which is readily oxidized to a blue-green free radical (6). Many highly coloured materials, such as Meldola's blue (7), are phenoxazonium salts and have been used as dyestuffs. The positive charge is not localized on the oxygen atom, as might be inferred from structure 7, this structure is

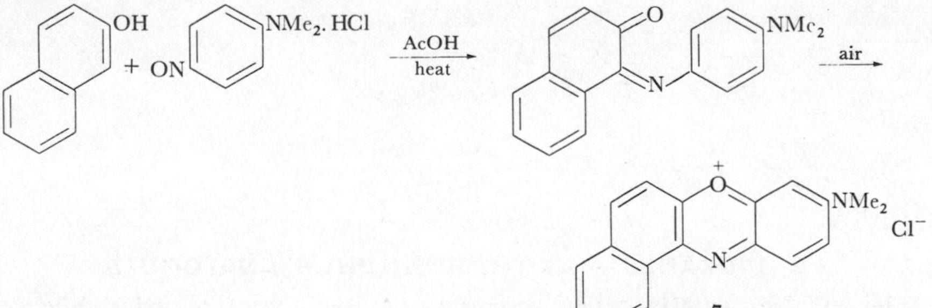

but one of many which can be written; the compound is best considered as a resonance hybrid. The phenoxazine ring also occurs in the complex peptide containing antibiotic actinomycin[26] and in the omnochromes, which are insect pigments formed from tryptophan (p. 169).

Phenothiazine (**8**), m.p. 185°, b.p. 371°, is very valuable in the control of mosquitoes, as it kills their larvae. It is used as a fruit spray and as an anthelmintic in farm animals. Methylene blue (**9**), which

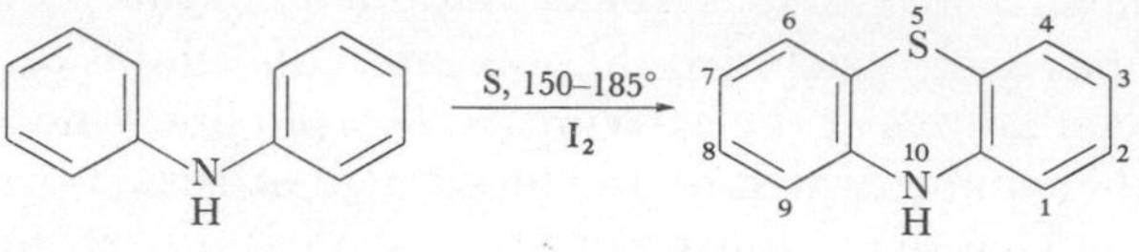

can be made as indicated and structurally resembles Meldola's blue (**7**), is a most valuable biological stain. It also has mild antiseptic properties. Reduction gives a colourless leuco compound (**10**), and this provides the basis of a number of quantitative colorimetric methods of estimating reducing agents in biological systems.

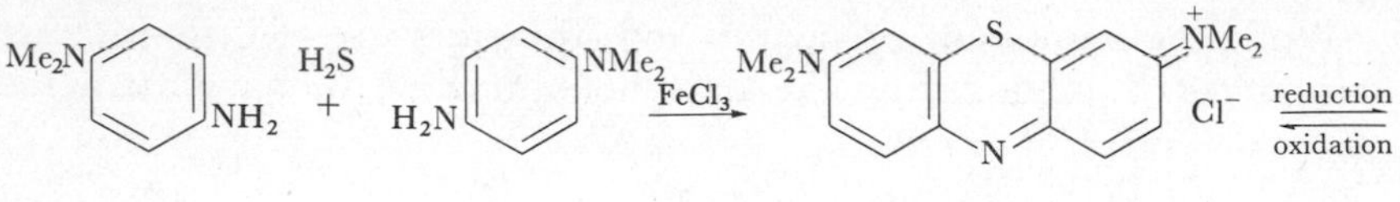

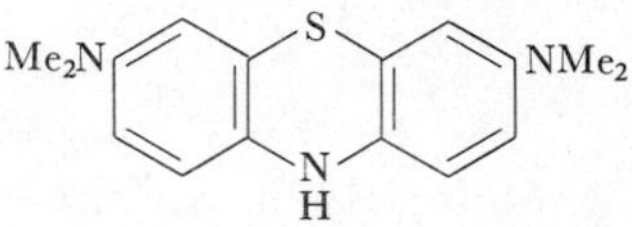

Chlorpromazine, or 'Largactil' (**11**), is a most useful tranquillizing agent and has a large number of other physiological effects.[27]

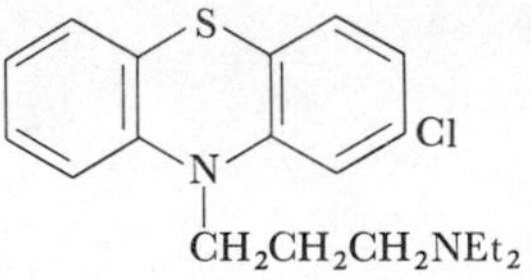

5. DIOXANES AND THEIR SULPHUR ANALOGUES

1,4-Dioxane, usually called dioxane (**1**), is a toxic colourless hygroscopic compound of m.p. 12° and b.p. 102°. Electron-diffraction studies have shown that, in the vapour, the ring adopts the chair conformation. Dioxane is miscible with water and most organic liquids, and it is a most powerful and widely used industrial solvent. It will dissolve many dyes, fats, resins, celluloid, and cellulose derivatives, and can even be used as a substitute for water in the iodoform test when the substrate is insufficiently water-soluble. Dioxane is prepared industrially from oxi-

$$\begin{array}{c} CH_2OH \\ | \\ CH_2OH \end{array} \xrightarrow[\text{(poor method, gives an impure product)}]{4\% \ H_2SO_4} \quad \text{(1)} \quad \xleftarrow{\text{NaOH aq.}} \quad \begin{array}{cc} CH_2 & CH_2 \\ | & | \\ CH_2Cl & CH_2OH \end{array} \xleftarrow{ClCH_2CH_2OH} $$

rane (ethylene oxide, p. 17) and as usually available contains impurities such as water, acetaldehyde, glycol, and 2-methyldioxolane. It is best purified by boiling with dilute hydrochloric acid, followed by treatment with sodium hydroxide and then with sodium. It has many of the properties of an aliphatic ether. The dioxane ring is opened with cold hydrogen bromide, giving 2,2'-dibromoethyl ether. Dioxane dibromide, m.p. 65°, formed with bromine, is a useful brominating agent (p.101), and is much more stable than ether dibromide, m.p. −40°. Dioxane also forms a complex with sulphur trioxide, which is a mild sulphonating agent. Chlorine reacts readily with dioxane to give a mixture of substitution products which can be separated. 2-Chlorodioxane (2) has a reactive chlorine atom in the same sense as 2-chlorotetrahydrofurans (p.103) and has similar uses. 2,3-Dichlorodioxane (3) and 2,3,5,6-tetrachlorodioxane are converted into dioxene (4)

and dioxadiene (5) respectively by a mixture of magnesium chloride and magnesium. Both 4 and 5 behave as unsaturated ethers.

1,3-Dioxane (6), which can be prepared from formaldehyde and propane-1,3-diol in the presence of an acid catalyst, is very similar to 1,3-dioxolane (p. 327). 1,3-Dioxanes can be prepared in water solution, and in general are highly resistant to acid hydrolysis.[28] 1,2-Dioxane

$$\begin{array}{c} CH_2OH \\ | \\ CH_2 \\ | \\ CH_2OH \end{array} + OCH_2 \xrightarrow{H^+, \, -H_2O} \quad \text{(6)} \qquad \text{(7)}$$

(7) is a cyclic dialkyl peroxide.[29]

1,4-Oxathiane (8) and 1,4-dithiane (9) are known. They differ from their oxygen analogues only in the special reactions of the sulphur atom, for instance in their oxidation to sulphones. X-ray studies[30] on crystalline 1,4-dithiane have shown that the ring adopts the chair form.

The 1,4-disulphoxide is *trans*.[31] 1,4-Dithiadiene (**10**), b.p. 80° at 20 mm, has been made as indicated.[32] Its structure is especially interesting, as the molecule is not planar. X-ray studies[33] have shown that the carbon–sulphur–carbon angle is 101°, that the individual halves of the boat-shaped molecule are planar, and that the angle between these planes is 137°. The carbon–carbon and carbon–sulphur distances are

1·29 Å and 1·78 Å respectively and suggest that the compound will have aliphatic properties.

The tetracyano derivative of **10** has been obtained from disodium dimercaptomaleonitrile and thionyl chloride. It decomposes at ca. 200° and does not appear to have aromatic character.[34]

GENERAL BIBLIOGRAPHY

PYRIDAZINES
  Jacobs, in *Heterocyclic Compounds*, ed. Elderfield, Vol. 6, Wiley, New York, 1956.

CINNOLINES, PHTHALAZINES, QUINAZOLINES, and QUINOXALINES
  Simpson, *Condensed Pyridazine Rings*, Interscience, New York, 1953.
  Jacobs, Elderfield, Williamson, and Wythe, in *Heterocyclic Compounds*, Vol. 6, ed. Elderfield, Wiley, New York, 1956.
    Cheeseman, 'Quinoxalines', *Advan. Heterocyclic Chem.*, **2**, 204 (1963).

PYRIMIDINE
  Brown, *The Pyrimidines*, Interscience, New York, 1962.
  Kenner and Todd, in *Heterocyclic Compounds*, Vol. 6, ed. Elderfield, Wiley, New York, 1956.
  Bendich, in *Nucleic Acids*, Vol. I, Academic Press, New York, 1955.
  Lythgoe, *Quart. Rev.*, **3**, 181 (1949).

PYRAZINES
  Pratt, in *Heterocyclic Compounds*, Vol. 6, ed. Elderfield, Wiley, New York, 1956.

PHENAZINES
  Swan and Felton, *Phenazines*, Interscience, New York, 1957.

OXAZINES
  Cromwell, in *Heterocyclic Compounds*, Vol. 6, ed. Elderfield, Wiley, New York, 1956.
  Eckstein and Urbanski, *Advan. Heterocyclic Chem.*, **2**, 311 (1963).

Thiazines
Elderfield and Harris, in *Heterocyclic Compounds*, Vol. 6, ed. Elderfield, Wiley, New York, 1956.

Dioxanes and their Sulphur Analogues
Kremer and Rochen, and Elderfield, in *Heterocyclic Compounds*, Vol. 6, ed. Elderfield, Wiley, New York, 1956.

REFERENCES

1. Tjebbes, *Acta Chem. Scand.*, **16**, 916 (1962).
2. Katritzky and Waring, *J. Chem. Soc.*, 1523 (1964).
3. Kealey, *J. Am. Chem. Soc.*, **84**, 966 (1962).
4. Clews and Cochran, *Acta Cryst.*, **2**, 46 (1949).
5. Dewar, *Electronic Theory of Organic Chemistry*, p. 36, Oxford University Press, London, 1949.
6. Tjebbes, *Acta Chem. Scand.*, **16**, 916 (1962).
7. Miller, Lykos, and Schmeising, *J. Am. Chem. Soc.*, **84**, 4623 (1962).
8. Hunt, McOmie, and Sayer, *J. Chem. Soc.*, 525 (1959).
9. Whittaker, *J. Chem. Soc.*, 1646 (1953).
10. Curphey, *J. Am. Chem. Soc.*, **87**, 2064 (1965).
11. Chesterfield, McOmie, and Tute, *J. Chem. Soc.*, 4590 (1960).
12. Lythgoe and Rayner, *J. Chem. Soc.*, 2323 (1951).
13. Parry, *Acta Cryst.*, **7**, 313 (1954).
14. Katritzky and Waring, *J. Chem. Soc.*, 3046 (1963).
15. Wierzchowski and Shugar, *Photochem. Photobiol.*, **2**, 377 (1963); Wierzchowski, Shugar, and Katritzky, *J. Am. Chem. Soc.*, **85**, 827 (1963).
16. Bolton, *Acta Cryst.*, **16**, 166 (1963).
17. Fox and Sugar, *Bull. Soc. Chim. Belg.*, **61**, 44 (1952).
18. Schwarzenbach and Irving, *Complexometric Titrations*, Interscience, New York, 1957.
19. Brown and Evans, *J. Chem. Soc.*, 527 (1962).
20. Brown, *J. Appl. Chem.*, **2**, 202 (1952).
21. Whitehead, *J. Am. Chem. Soc.*, **75**, 671 (1953).
22. Todd, in *Perspectives in Organic Chemistry*, ed. Todd, Interscience, New York, 1956; *The Nucleic Acids*, Vols. I and II, ed. Chargaff and Davidson, Academic Press, New York, 1955.
23. Koppel, Springer, Robins, and Cheng, *J. Org. Chem.*, **27**, 3614 (1962).
24. Cromer, Ihde, and Ritter, *J. Am. Chem. Soc.*, **73**, 5587 (1951).
25. Bedford, Beezer, and Mortimer, *J. Chem. Soc.*, 2039 (1963).
26. Johnson, *Symposium on Antibiotics and Mould Metabolites*, *Chem. Soc. Special Pub. No.* 5, p. 82 (1956).
27. Hopkin, *Pharm. J.*, **174**, 317 (1955).
28. Galiano, Rankin, and Mantell, *J. Org. Chem.*, **29**, 3424 (1964).
29. Criegee and Müller, *Ber.*, **89**, 238 (1956).
30. Marsh, *Acta Cryst.*, **8**, 91 (1955).
31. Shearer, *J. Chem. Soc.*, 1394 (1959).
32. Parham, Wynberg, and Ramp, *J. Am. Chem. Soc.*, **75**, 2065 (1953).
33. Howell, Curtis, and Lipscomb, *Acta Cryst.*, **7**, 498 (1954).
34. Simmons, Vest, Blomstrom, Roland, and Cairns, *J. Am. Chem. Soc.*, **84**, 4746, 4756, 4772 (1962).

CHAPTER IX

SOME COMPOUNDS WITH MORE THAN TWO HETEROATOMS

A very large number of compounds possessing more than two hetero-atoms in one, or more rings, is known. Most of these contain nitrogen atoms. In this chapter four of the more important systems, listed below, will be considered briefly.

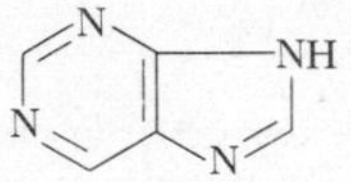

| Purine | Pteridine | 1,3,5-Triazine | Sydnone |

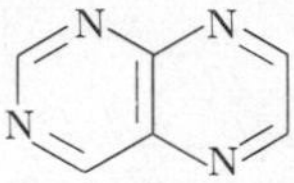

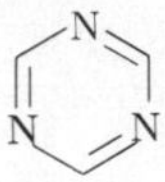

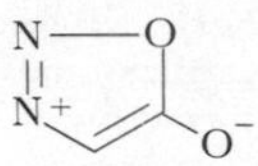

1. PURINES

A. Introduction

The purine ring system is one of the most important present in living systems, but as in the case of pyrimidine (p. 344), the parent compound has not been found in nature. The least substituted naturally occurring derivative of purine known is the 9-ribofuranoside, which is present in the fungus *Agaricus nebularis*.[1] The purine ring is present in many natural products, including several nucleotides (hydrolysis products of nucleic acids p. 344), in a number of coenzymes, in the antibiotic puromycin, in uric acid, in caffeine and related compounds (the stimulants of tea, coffee, and cocoa), and in several compounds which are valuable in the treatment of certain types of cancer.

B. The structure and chemical reactions of purine and its simple derivatives

Purine itself is a colourless compound, m.p. 212°, which is very soluble in water, but sparingly soluble in organic solvents. Its structure has not been examined by physical methods, although the dimensions of 6-aminopurine (adenine) hydrochloride have been calculated[2] from x-ray-diffraction photographs. The interatomic distances show that the purine ring is aromatic. Purine can formally be derived from a fusion of pyrimidine and imidazole rings. By analogy

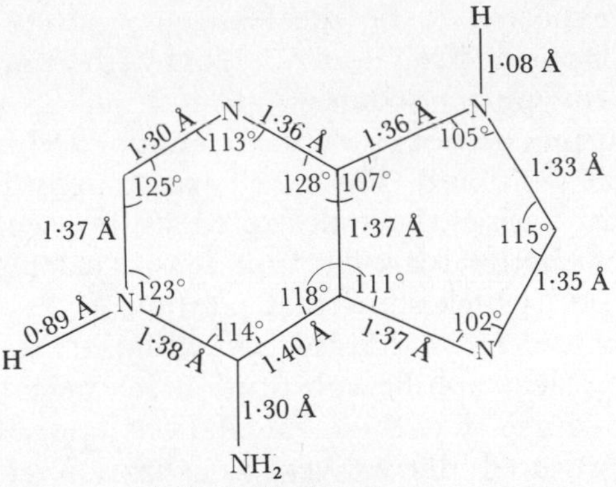

Adenine hydrochloride

positions 2 and 6 (and substituents at these positions) of purine should be similar chemically to positions 2 and 4 of pyrimidine, and position 8 to position 2 of imidazole, and in general this is the case. Purine

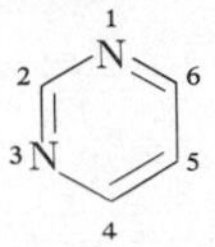

Pyrimidine 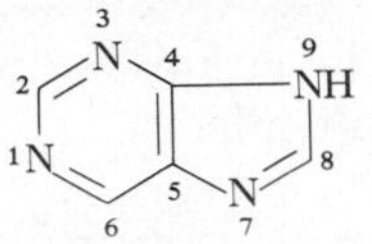   Purine 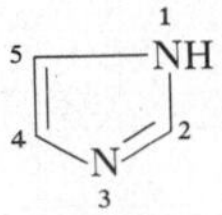   Imidazole

(pK_a 2·4) is a stronger base than pyrimidine (pK_a 1·3). It is also a much weaker base but a much stronger acid (acidic pK_a 8·9) than imidazole (p. 302); these properties are consistent with the 'pyrimidine' ring withdrawing electrons from the 'imidazole' ring of purine.

The results of molecular-orbital calculations[3] of the π-electron densities and localization energies round the isolated purine ring are of particular interest (Table 1). Position 8 has the lowest electron density

TABLE 1. Calculations on the purine molecule

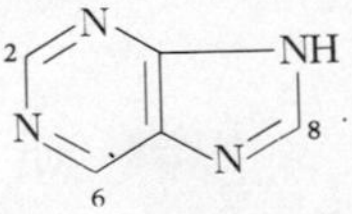

Position	Localization energy in β units for		π-Electron density in the isolated molecule
	Electrophilic attack	Nucleophilic attack	
2	2·567	2·323	0·902
6	2·482	2·176	0·907
8	2·393	2·176	0·895

N*

and would be expected to be the least susceptible to electrophilic attack. Although purine itself does not react with aromatic diazonium salts, 2,6-dihydroxypurine couples at position 8, while 2,8- and 6,8-dihydroxypurines do not react; some amino- and hydroxy-purines also brominate at position 8. This is the exact opposite of what would be expected on the basis of the π-electron densities recorded in Table 1, but it is consistent both with π-electron density calculations of a more sophisticated type,[4] which show that positions 6, 2, and 8 are in increasing order of π-electron density, and with the calculated localization energies for electrophilic substitution in the table. It must be remembered of course that these calculations apply to purine itself, and not to substituted derivatives. Localization energies measure approximately the activation energy for this type of substitution and this depends on both the polarizability of the molecule being attacked and on the properties of the molecule in the transition state. Although in a number of aromatic molecules the induced polarizability runs parallel to the permanent one, this is not always so. π-Electron densities alone can therefore be a misleading guide to the position of attack of a reagent on a molecule.

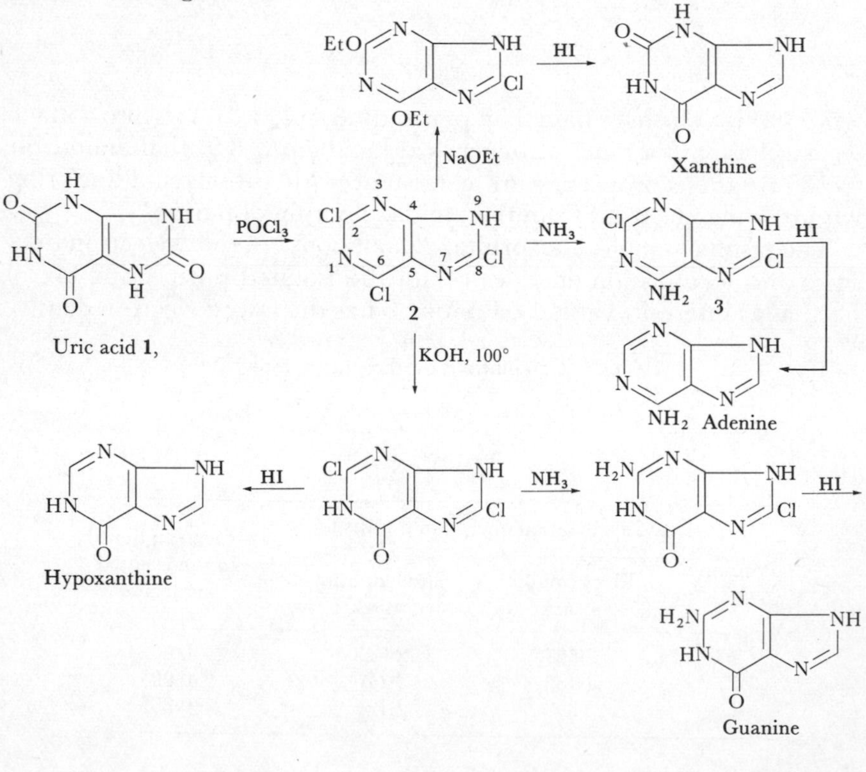
HI
Xanthine
NaOEt
Uric acid 1,
POCl3
2
NH3
3
HI
Adenine
KOH, 100°
HI
Hypoxanthine
NH3
HI
Guanine

The halogen atoms of 2,6,8-trichloropurine (**2**), obtainable from uric acid (**1**), are replaced successively in the order 6, 2, 8 by nucleophilic reagents. This successive replacement proved a most useful synthetic procedure in the earlier stages of purine chemistry, but most of the compounds obtained from 2,6,8-trichloropurine and shown in the flowsheet are more readily available from Traube's synthesis (p. 358). In contrast the 8-chlorine atom of 2,8-dichloropurine,[5] and the 2-chlorine atom of 2,8-dichloro-6-hydroxypurine,[6] are the more easily replaced in these molecules by nucleophilic reagents. Adenine is perhaps the most important purine base in living systems, and some of its derivatives are considered on pp. 359–363.

Uric acid (**1**) is excreted in human urine (ca. 600 mg per day), and is the major nitrogen-containing excretion product of birds and reptiles. It was isolated in 1776, and its general structure deduced from de-

gradation in 1875; the key degradations were with nitric acid to alloxan (**4**) and urea, and with alkaline permanganate to allantoin (**5**). The first synthesis of uric acid, in confirmation of its structure, was in 1888, but the best preparation is that of Traube (p. 358). Heating uric acid with formamide gives xanthine (**6**), while on heating with water to 190° a remarkable reaction occurs, giving some 2,4,7-trihydroxypteridine (**7**). The murexide test for uric acid is described on p. 340.

Caffeine (1,3,7-trimethylxanthine), obtained commercially from the methylation of xanthine with methyl chloride or sulphate and alkali, is the major stimulant in tea and coffee. In the formula given for xanthine (**6**) a hydrogen atom has been placed on position 9. It could equally well have been placed at position 7, as the compound is tautomeric.

1,3-Dimethylxanthine, theophylline, also occurs in tea, and 3,7-dimethylxanthine, or theobromine, is the major alkaloid of the cocoa bean.

C. Synthetic methods

(1) Purine can be obtained in a remarkable manner by heating formamide and ammonia to 200°; the yield is only 1%, but the reactants are very cheap.

(2) The most important method of purine synthesis is that of Traube, who showed that 4,5-diaminopyrimidines could be cyclized to purines. Purine itself can be obtained from 4,5-diaminopyrimidine and formic acid. 4-Aminopyrimidines, such as 8, are readily available, and on nitrosation, or diazo coupling (p. 336), followed by reduction of the

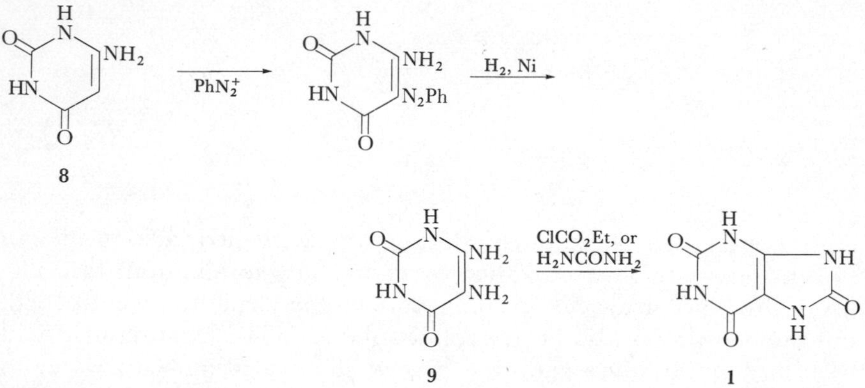

product, give the 4,5-diamino compounds (e.g. 9). In the case shown heating with urea, or better with ethyl chloroformate, gives uric acid (1). Cyclization of 9 with formic acid, or with the more vigorous mixture of acetic anhydride and ethyl orthoformate,[7] gives xanthine (6). 4,5-Diaminopyrimidines are most easily cyclized to purines unsubstituted at position 8 with sodium dithioformate. In the synthesis of adenine (11) outlined the 5-thioformamidopyrimidine (10) is first formed and easily loses hydrogen sulphide. This type of synthesis is particularly valuable, for if a 4,5,6-triaminopyrimidine is involved and either the 4- or 6-amino group is alkylated cyclization always occurs on to the alkylated nitrogen atom. A 9-substituted purine is therefore formed, and many naturally occurring purines are of this type. Other syntheses of purines from pyrimidines are available.[8]

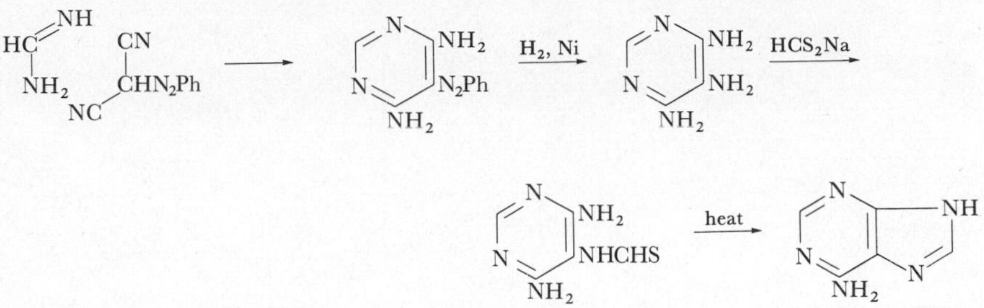

D. Purines of special interest

Several purine bases are very widely distributed in living organisms and often occur as complex derivatives of greatest biological interest. Of these bases adenine (**11**) is the most common, and the chemistry of its derivatives will be considered as an example. Adenosine derivatives are involved in oxidation–reduction (p. 231), phosphorylation (p. 361), methylation (p. 363), sulphonation (p. 363), and acylation (p. 362) systems *in vivo*.

1. *Adenosine and its phosphates*

The hydrolysis of ribo- and deoxyribo-nucleic acids under various conditions yields a number of pyrimidine (p. 344) and purine nucleosides; the terms nucleoside and nucleotide are defined on p. 344. The common purines involved are adenine (**11**) and guanine (**12**), and

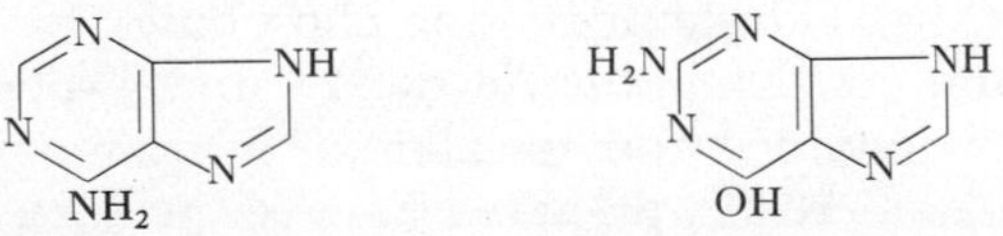

from the hydrolysis of ribonucleic acid, the nucleoside adenosine (**15**) can be obtained. The further hydrolysis of adenosine gives adenine and D-ribose, and the ribose was shown to be attached to position 9, and not to position 7, of the ring by a series of ultraviolet absorption spectrum comparisons. Periodate oxidation of adenosine gives the dialdehyde (**16**) and no formic acid, showing that the sugar ring is furanose. The first synthesis of adenosine (**15**) is outlined[9] below and starts with **3**. The ribose is connected to the purine moiety with a β-link; this has been confirmed by x-ray studies. An earlier chemical proof depended on the supposition that α-bromotetraacetylglucose, of known configuration, would undergo a Walden inversion in reaction with the silver salt

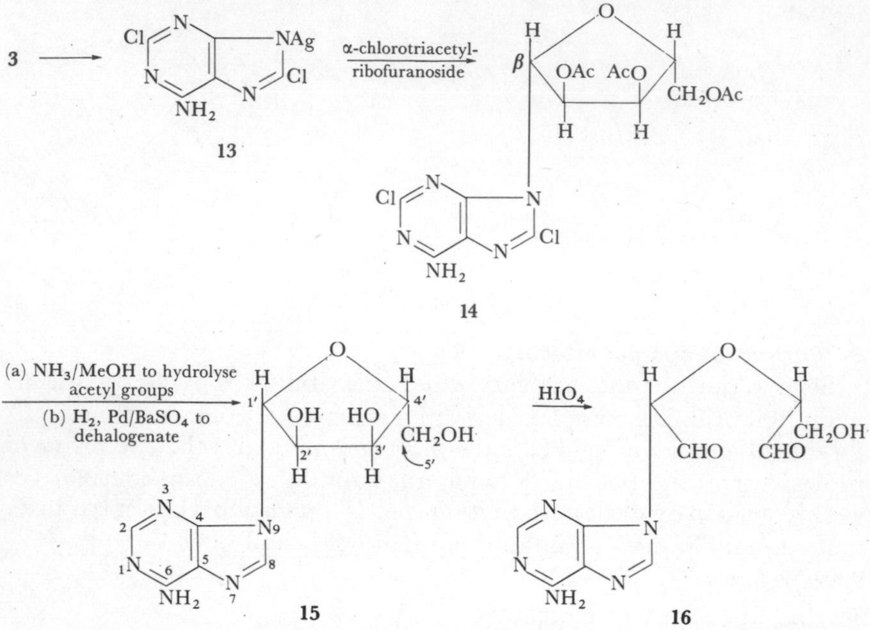

(13). Adenine-9-β-glucoside, prepared from the product of this reaction through dehalogenation, gives 16, as does adenosine, on periodic acid oxidation, thereby confirming the β-linkage in adenosine.

Several adenylic acids, or adenosine phosphates, have been isolated from natural sources. A mixture of the 2'- and 3'-phosphates, 'yeast adenylic acid', is obtained from the alkaline degradation of ribonucleic acid, which is commercially prepared from yeast. These phosphates are readily interconvertible through a cyclic intermediate and are stable to periodic acid. Adenosine-5'-phosphate, obtainable from muscle ('muscle adenylic acid') or enzymically from other adenosine phosphates, is attacked by periodic acid and readily forms a boric acid complex in confirmation of the presence of two *cis* hydroxyl groups.

The best synthesis of adenosine-5'-phosphate, of the several described, starts with adenosine (15). This, after conversion into the 2',3'-isopropylidene derivative (17) with acetone under acidic conditions, is phosphorylated with dibenzylphosphorochloridate (readily prepared from phosphorus oxychloride and two moles of benzyl alcohol). The product (18) is hydrogenated, when the benzyl groups are split off as toluene, and then mild acid hydrolysis yields acetone and adenosine-5'-phosphate (19). The synthesis of adenosine-5'-phosphate *in vivo* has been subject to a great deal of investigation[10] and is quite complex.

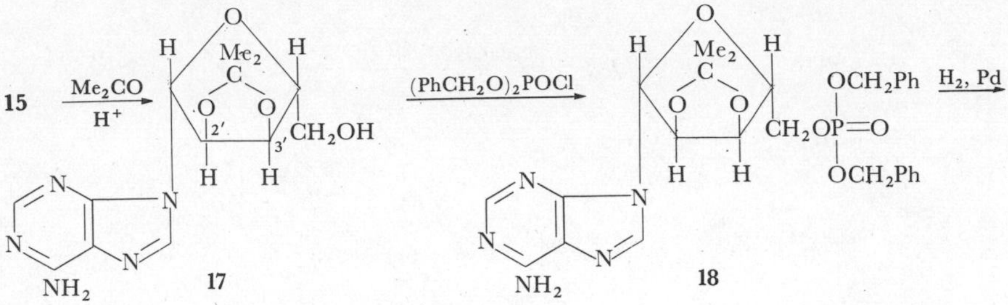

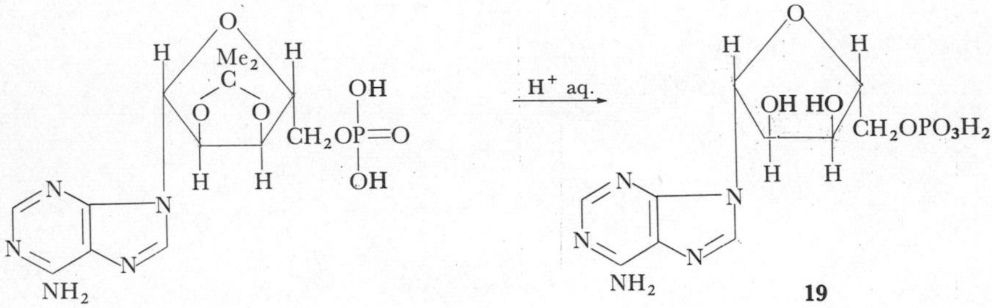

Adenosine-5′-diphosphate, ADP (**22**), and adenosine-5′-triphosphate ATP (**24**) are involved in the reversible phosphorylation of many compounds *in vivo*, and many other polyphosphates derived from guanine, uracil, cytosine, or thymine nucleosides occur in smaller quantities and play specific roles in metabolic processes. ATP is usually isolated from muscle and its structure was deduced originally from degradative studies. Acid hydrolysis yields adenine and ribose-5-phosphate, while alkaline hydrolysis gives adenosine-5′-phosphate and pyrophosphoric acids. ATP both increases the conductivity of boric acid and consumes 1 mole of periodic acid. These results prove that only the 5-hydroxyl group of the ribose moiety bears the phosphate groups and suggest a linear triphosphate. This last point is in agreement with titration studies, which show three primary and one secondary dissociation, and the structures of both ADP and ATP have been confirmed by several syntheses.

20 is obtained by careful acid hydrolysis of **18** (above), when both the isopropylidene and one benzyl group are removed. The silver salt of **20** with dibenzylphosphorochloridate gives **21**, which on catalytic debenzylation yields ADP (**22**). Heating **21** with 4-methylmorpholine (a tertiary base with powerful solvent properties) splits off one benzyl group, giving **23**, which, through the usual procedure with its silver salt followed by hydrogenation, gives ATP (**24**). It is interesting that

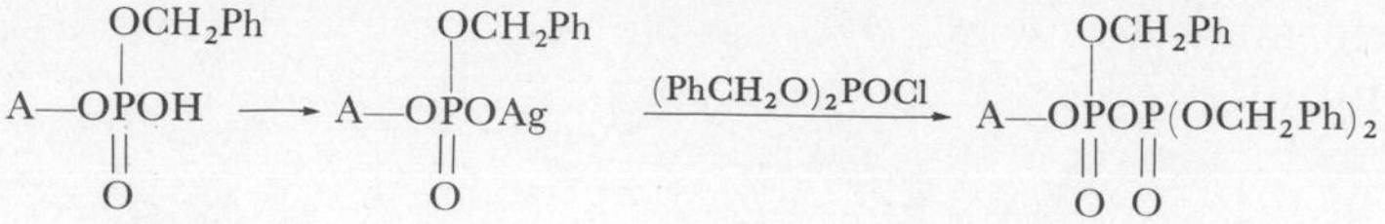

$$\begin{array}{ccccc}
\overset{OCH_2Ph}{\underset{O}{A-OPOH}} & \longrightarrow & \overset{OCH_2Ph}{\underset{O}{A-OPOAg}} & \xrightarrow{(PhCH_2O)_2POCl} & \overset{OCH_2Ph}{\underset{O\ \ O}{A-OPOP(OCH_2Ph)_2}} \\
\mathbf{20} & & & & \mathbf{21}
\end{array}$$

$$\mathbf{21} \xrightarrow{H_2,\ Pd} \overset{OH}{\underset{O\ \ O}{A-OP\ O\ P-(OH)_2}}$$

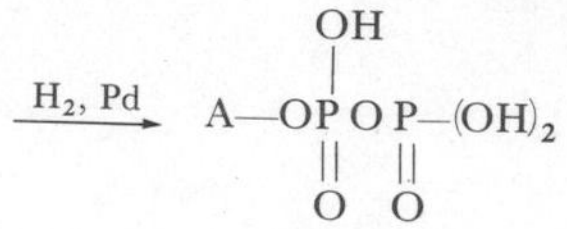

$$\mathbf{22,\ ADP}$$

$$\mathbf{21} \longrightarrow \overset{OCH_2Ph}{\underset{O\ \ O}{A-OPOP}}\overset{OCH_2Ph}{\underset{OH}{}} \xrightarrow{(PhCH_2O)_2POCl} \overset{PhCH_2O\ \ OCH_2Ph}{\underset{O\ \ \ O\ \ \ O}{A-OP\ O\ POP(OCH_2Ph)_2}}$$

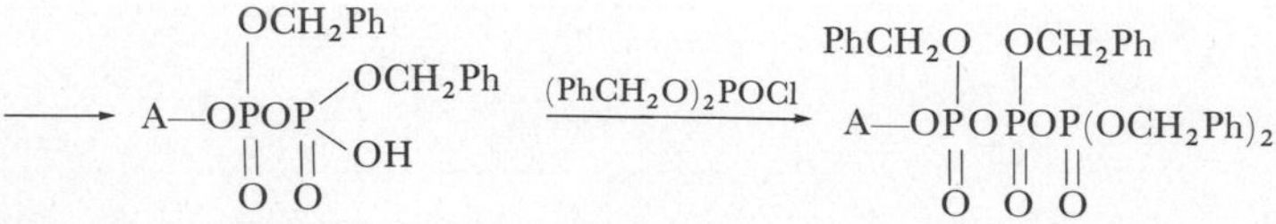

$$\mathbf{23}$$

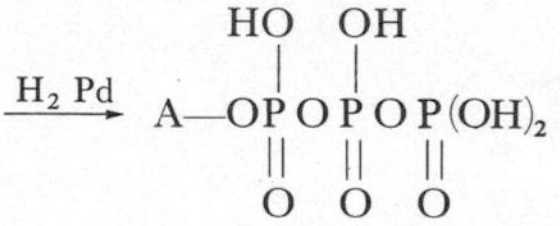

$$\xrightarrow{H_2\ Pd} \overset{HO\ \ OH}{\underset{O\ \ \ O\ \ \ O}{A-OP\ O\ P\ O\ P(OH)_2}} \qquad A = \text{Adenosine-5'-}$$

$$\mathbf{24,\ ATP}$$

a much better yield of ATP can be obtained from disilver adenosine-5'-phosphate and excess dibenzylphosphorochloridate followed by hydrogenolysis. A rearrangement occurs, probably through a cyclic intermediate after or during the debenzylation.

2. Coenzyme A

Coenzyme A (**25**) is a derivative of adenosine responsible for the transfer of acetyl and other acyl groups in living systems. An S-acyl coenzyme A is first formed, and this acylates another molecule with

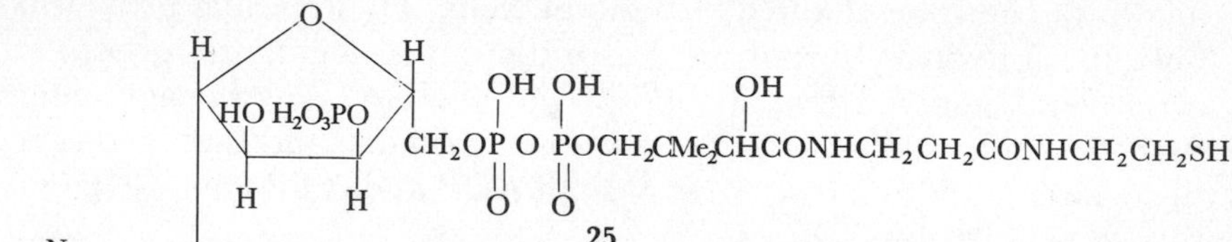

$$\text{CH}_2\text{OP O POCH}_2\text{CMe}_2\overset{OH}{\text{CHCONHCH}_2}\text{CH}_2\text{CONHCH}_2\text{CH}_2\text{SH}$$

25

↓ acid hydrolysis

Adenosine-5'-phosphate + H₂O₃POCH₂CMe₂CHCONHCH₂CH₂CO₂H + H₃PO₄

19   Pantothenic acid 4'-phosphate

+

H₂NCH₂CH₂SH

the reformation of coenzyme A. The structure of the coenzyme has been firmly established by degradation,[11] the major outlines of which are shown, and recently synthesis has been achieved.[12]

3. S-Adenosyl-L-methionine

S-Adenosyl-L-methionine, earlier called thetin (27), has been synthesized.[13] It is formed from adenosine-5′-triphosphate and methionine (26) *in vivo* and is concerned in the biological transfer of methyl groups.

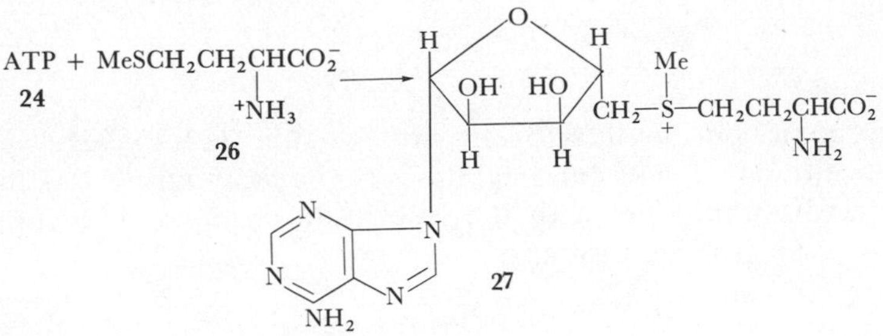

$$\text{ATP} + \underset{\underset{26}{^+\text{NH}_3}}{\text{MeSCH}_2\text{CH}_2\text{CHCO}_2^-}$$

24

4. Phosphoadenosinephosphosulphate

The nucleotide coenzyme which is involved in the conversion of phenols into their O-sulphates *in vivo* has been identified[14] as 3′-phosphoadenosine-5′-phosphosulphate (28). It has been synthesized[15] from adenosine-3′,5′-diphosphate and 1-proto-1-pyridiniumsulphonate (p. 194) in the presence of sodium bicarbonate.

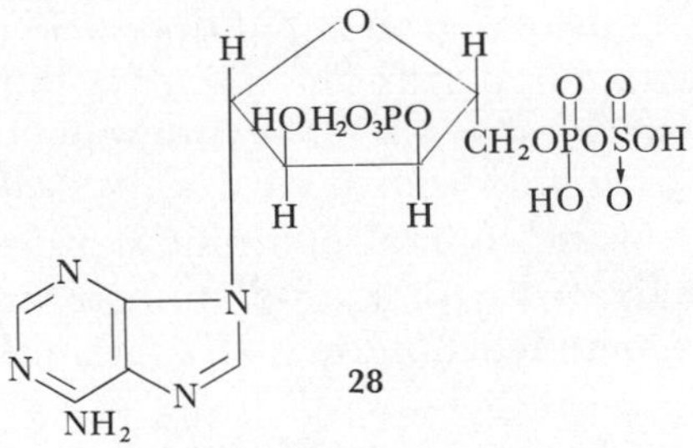

5. Oxidation–reduction coenzymes of adenine

Nicotinamide–adenine dinucleotide (NAD) and flavine–adenine dinucleotide are discussed on pp. 231 and 367, respectively.

6. Puromycin

This is a wide-spectrum fungal antibiotic derived from adenine, and has structure 29. It is a ribose derivative.

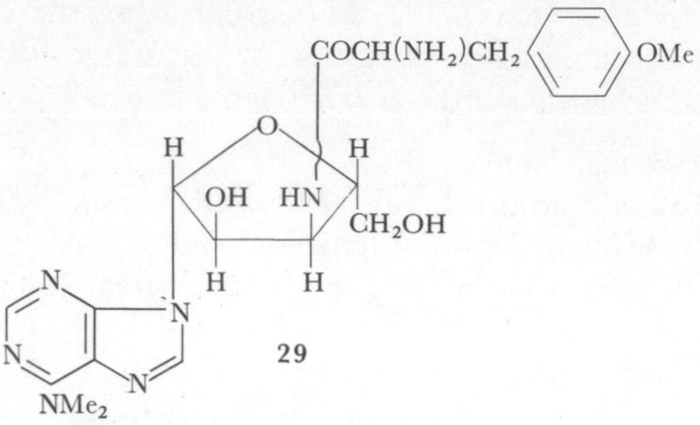

29

7. Chemotherapeutic purines

Very many purines have been synthesized in recent years as potential antitumour agents, and of these 6-mercaptopurine has limited value. It may interfere with the utilization of folinic acid (opposite page) by the growing tumour.

2 PTERIDINES

Xanthopterin (2-amino-4,6-dihydroxypteridine) and leucopterin (2-amino-4,6,7-trihydroxypteridine), derivatives of pteridine (**1**), were obtained from the wings of butterflies and other insects, in very small quantities in 1891, but their constitution was not established until 1940. This was because only very small quantities of the materials were available, and the early analytical data were erroneous owing to combustion difficulties. Pteridines are usually colourless or yellow, and account for the yellow colour of bees and wasps. Other pteridines, including 'folic acid', which is the name of a group of antipernicious anaemia factors, folinic acid, and vitamin B_2, are of immense importance in living systems. Certain pteridines are useful against some types of leukaemia.

Pteridine (**1**) is obtainable from glyoxal and 4,5-diaminopyrimidine. This is an example of the general pteridine synthesis, where a dicarbonyl compound is treated with a 4,5-diaminopyrimidine, and which has been used to prepare leucopterin and xanthopterin. Pteridine is a

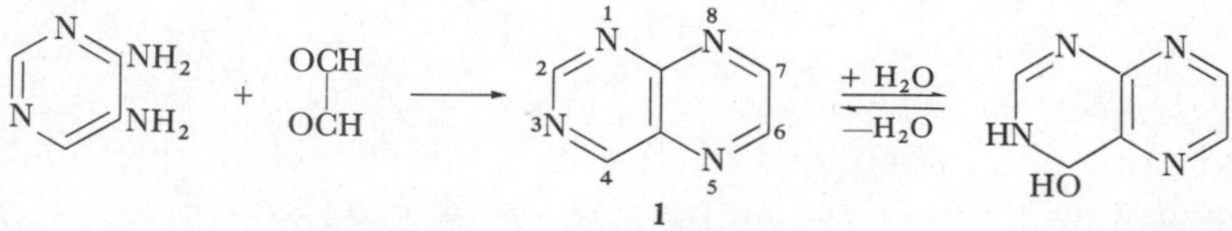

yellow solid, m.p. 139°, soluble in water and organic solvents. It adds water across the 4,5-positions reversibly. This is an example of a general type of behaviour of many heterocyclic compounds.[16] It can be considered as pyrimidinopyrazine, and its properties are consistent with this. For example, hydrogenation under alkaline conditions, which reduces pyrazine but not pyrimidine, reduces the 'pyrazine' ring of pteridine. The molecular dimensions of pteridine have been determined by x-ray methods and are in agreement with its aromatic characteristics. The 3,4-nitrogen–carbon bond is particularly short.

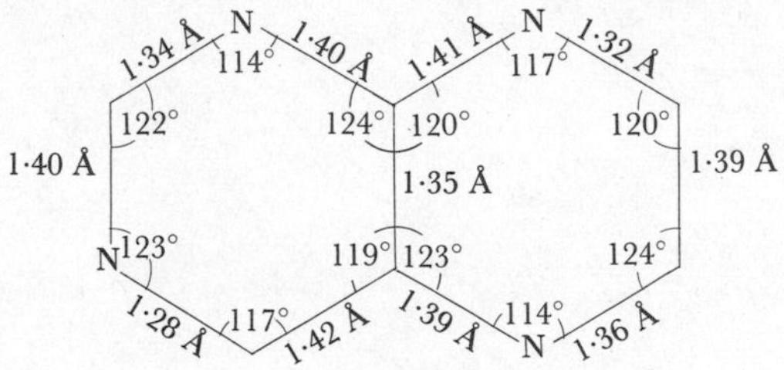

Molecular dimensions of pteridine

One of the antianaemia factors present in the mixture originally called 'folic acid', obtained from liver and yeast, is pteroylglutamic acid (3). Both it and pteroic acid (2) can be synthesized as outlined.

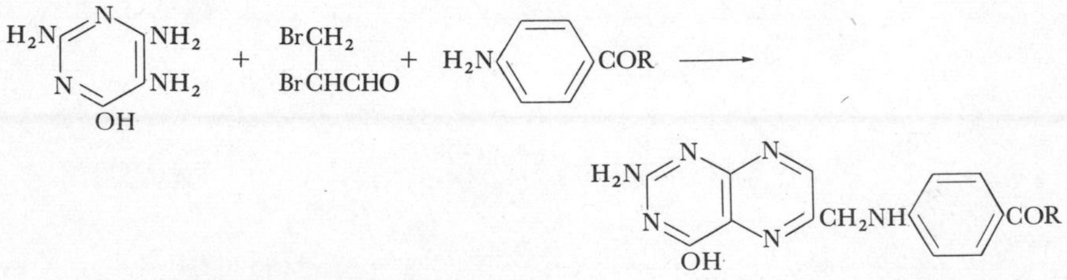

2, R = OH, Pteroic acid
3, R = NHCHCH$_2$CH$_2$CO$_2$H, Pteroylglutamic acid
    |
    CO$_2$H

Oxidation takes place *in situ*, the yields are poor, and many variants of the synthesis have been examined. The 5-formyl derivative of tetrahydropteroylglutamic acid (4) is known as folinic acid and this, and the related 10-formyl derivative, are involved in methylation in purine synthesis. It is essential for mammalian cell division. This function is

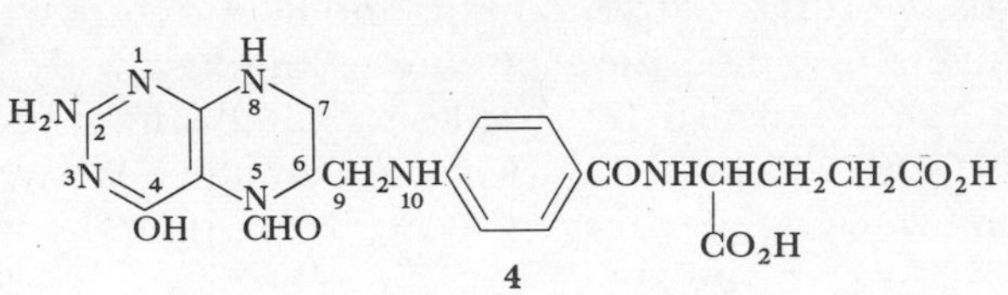

4

inhibited by 'aminopterin', the 4-amino analogue of pteroylglutamic acid, and by 'amethopterin' (4-amino-10-methylpteroylglutamic acid). These two compounds are of value in treating acute leukaemia, as are several other related pteridines.

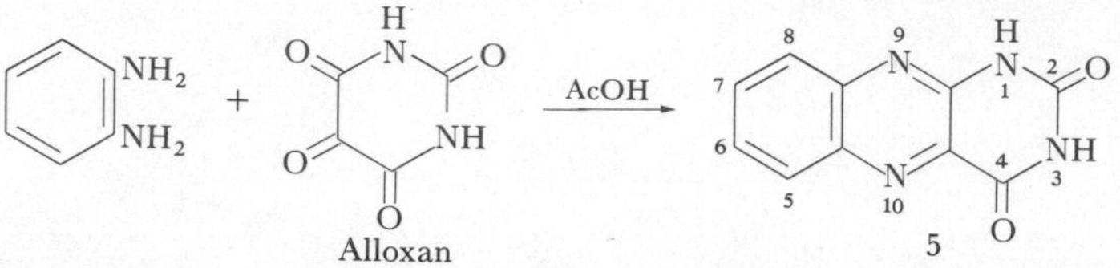

Alloxan

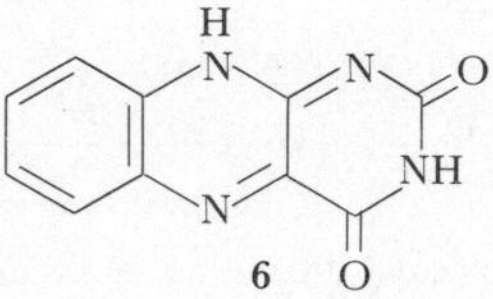

2,4-Dihydroxybenzopteridine is usually called alloxazine (5), and vitamin B_2 or riboflavin (8) is a derivative. Riboflavin is a yellow compound which gives highly fluorescent solutions and occurs in plant

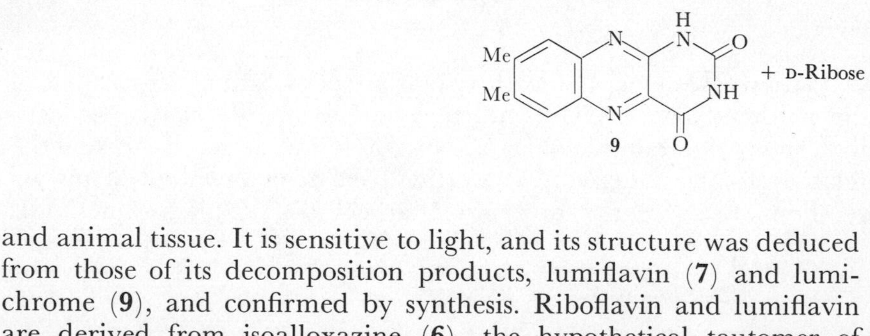

and animal tissue. It is sensitive to light, and its structure was deduced from those of its decomposition products, lumiflavin (7) and lumi-chrome (9), and confirmed by synthesis. Riboflavin and lumiflavin are derived from isoalloxazine (6), the hypothetical tautomer of alloxazine in which the hydrogen atom at position 1 is moved to position 9.

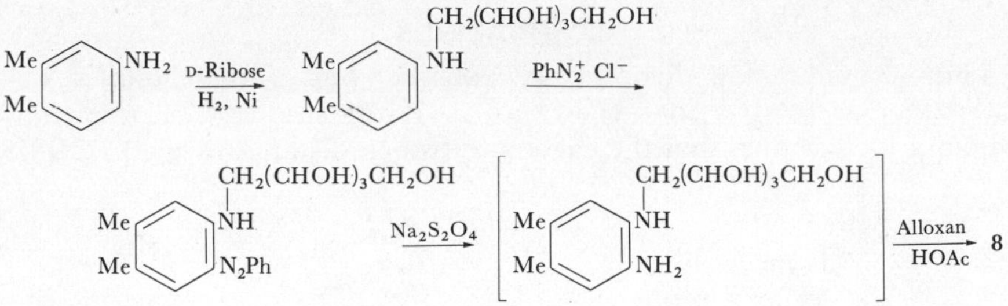

The coenzyme, flavin–adenine dinucleotide (**10**), is important in biological oxidation systems, and reduction, which affects only the isoalloxazine ring, procceds in two one-electron steps as outlined. It in-

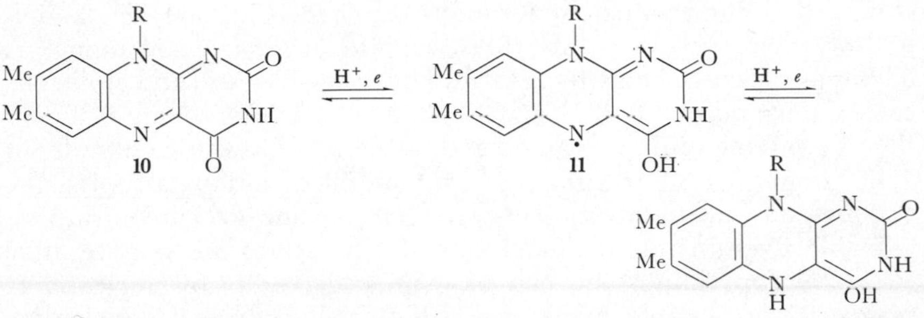

volves the formation of a free radical (**11**). Riboflavin can act as a photosensitizing agent, and the light-excited molecule can act as an electron donor.[17] The structure of the dinucleotide (**10**) is based on several degradations, including its hydrolysis to adenosine-5′-phosphate (p. 360) and riboflavin-5′-phosphate, and has been confirmed by synthesis[18].

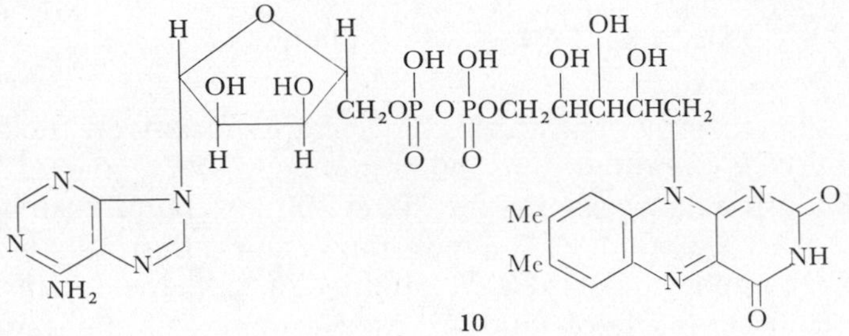

10

3. TRIAZINES

Three triazines are theoretically possible, but of these only 1,3,5-triazine, or *sym*-triazine (**1**) is known. X-ray studies[19] on this compound have shown that the carbon–nitrogen distances are all 1·319 Å

1,2,3-Triazine   1,2,4-Triazine   1,1,3,5-Triazine   2

and that the ring is planar but not a regular hexagon. The angles at whose apexes lie nitrogen and carbon atoms are 113·2° and 126·8° respectively. 1,3,5-Triazine is best prepared[20] by the thermal or base-catalysed decomposition of formamidine hydrochloride (**2**), and is hydrolysed almost instantly by dilute acids to formic acid and ammonia. This type of ring opening by acids and bases is very easy, and unlike the case of pyrimidine (p. 337), nucleophilic attack with sodamide opens the ring, giving sodium cyanide and ammonia. Cyanuric chloride, or 2,4,6-trichloro-1,3,5-triazine (**4**), is obtained industrially by the vapour-phase polymerization of cyanogen chloride on charcoal and is a valuable dyestuff intermediate. Its chlorine atoms are very reactive (cf. 2-chloropyridine) and can be displaced readily by nucleophilic reagents. For example, hydrolysis with glacial acetic acid, which gives better results than water, which has also been used, yields 2,4,6-trihydroxy-1,3,5-triazine, or cyanuric acid (**3**). This can also be obtained by the trimerization of cyanic acid or, among other products, by heating urea. Cyanuric acid gives cyanuric chloride with phosphorus pentachloride.

3   4   5

The halogen atoms of cyanuric chloride are successively replaced by ammonia (cf. 2-chloropyridine and ammonia, p. 212), giving 2,4,6-triamino-1,3,5-triazine, or melamine (**5**), at 100°. Melamine can be made in many other ways, one of the most important industrially being the thermal decomposition of urea. Melamine–formaldehyde resins are excellent electrical insulators and are used to make 'plastic' tableware.

The valuable high explosive 'RDX', or 'Cyclonite', is 1,3,5-trinitrohexahydro-1,3,5-triazine (**6**) and is obtained by nitrating hexamethylenetetramine, and various herbicides contain the triazine ring.[21]

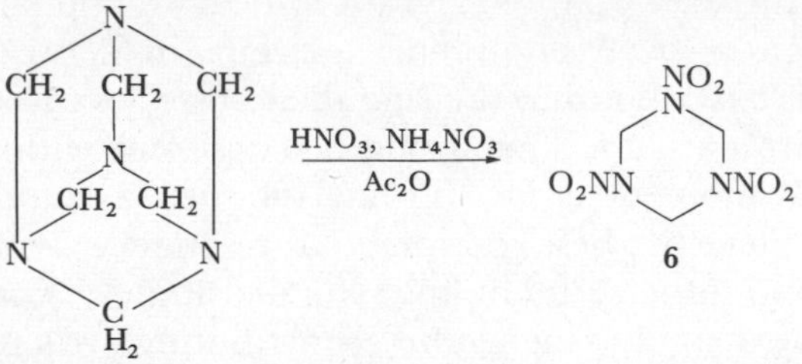

N
CH2 CH2 CH2
N
CH2 CH2
N N
C
H2
HNO3, NH4NO3
Ac2O
NO2
N
O2NN NNO2

6

The drug 'Paludrine', also called 'Proguanil' (**7**), is widely used as an antimalarial agent (see also p. 282). It has, however, been shown that 'Paludrine' itself has no action on the malaria parasite, but that it is converted into the active agent, a triazine (**8**), by the host.

H2N—C N C—NH2
NH N
HC
Cl Me Me
H2N N NH2
N N
Cl Me Me

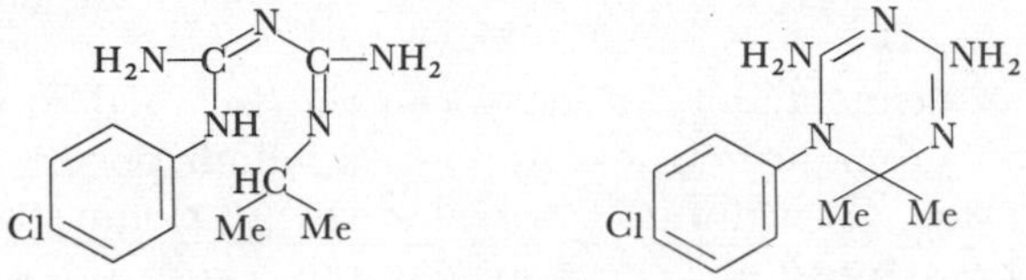

7 **8**

4. SYDNONES

N-Nitrosophenylglycine (**1**) on treatment with acetic anhydride yields 3-phenylsydnone (**3**) in a general reaction; it appears that the mixed anhydride (**2**) is an intermediate. This sydnone (**3**) is colourless, has m.p. 135°, and is easily soluble in benzene but sparingly in water. It is hydrolysed to *N*-nitrosophenylglycine by alkali, but phenylhydrazine, formic acid, and carbon dioxide are obtained with dilute acid. Bro-

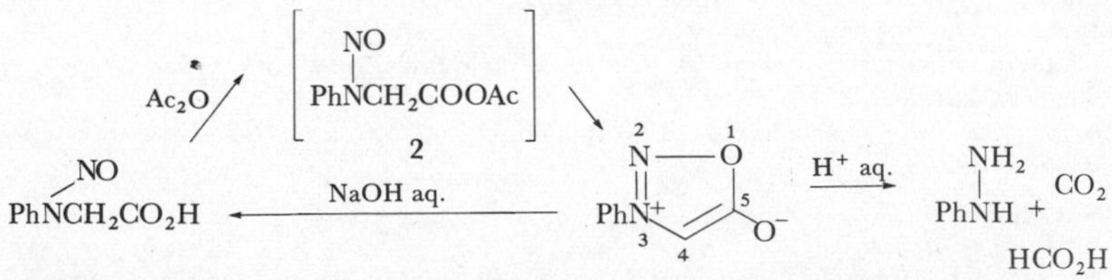

NO
PhNCH2COOAc
2
Ac2O
NO
PhNCH2CO2H
NaOH aq.
2 1
N—O
PhN+ 5
3 4
O−
H+ aq.
NH2
PhNH +
CO2
HCO2H

1 **3**

mination and nitration of 3-phenylsydnone take place in the sydnone ring, presumably at position 4. The structure, and particularly the best mode of representation of the sydnone ring, has aroused controversy.

3-Alkylsydnones have a well-defined aromatic type of absorption spectrum, and the ring has a large dipole moment (ca. 7 D) towards the exocyclic oxygen atom. Molecular-orbital calculations have shown that the ring and the exocyclic oxygen atom bear fractional positive and negative charges respectively. If one electron is in fact transferred from the ring to this oxygen atom, the ring then possesses the six π electrons required for aromaticity. This would be consistent with its chemistry, but the dipole moment is far too low for such a complete transfer. Sydnones are therefore best considered as resonance hybrids, to which structure **4** and others, including **4a**, **4b** and **4c** contribute, and represented by **4**, or by such other contributing structure as is con-

venient. The term 'mesoionic' has been put forward to describe the sydnones and other aromatic compounds which possess a degree of charge separation. It is difficult to exclude zwitterionic structures such as **5** from the definition, except in a purely arbitrary way, and because of this the new term does not appear to be essential. A new anti-malarial agent (**6**) is a sydnone derivative.[22]

6

GENERAL BIBLIOGRAPHY

PURINES

Chargaff and Davidson, *The Nucleic Acids*, Academic Press, New York, 1955.
Lythgoe, *Quart. Rev.*, **3**, 181 (1949).
Chemistry and Biology of the Purines, ed. Wolstenholme and O'Connor, *Ciba Foundation Symposium*, Churchill, London, 1957.

PTERIDINES

Albert, *Quart. Rev.*, **6**, 197 (1952).
Chemistry and Biology of the Pteridines, ed. Wolstenholme and Cameron, *Ciba Foundation Symposium*, Churchill, London, 1954.
Pfleiderer, *Angew. Chem.*, **75**, 993 (1963).

TRIAZINES

Erickson, Wiley, and Wystrach, *The 1,2,3- and 1,2,4-Triazines, Tetrazines, and Pentazines*, Interscience, New York, 1956.

Smolin and Rapoport, *s-Triazines and Derivatives*, Interscience, New York, 1959.
Grundmann, *Angew. Chem.*, **75**, 393 (1963).

SYDNONES
  Baker and Ollis, *Quart. Rev.*, **11**, 15 (1957).
  Stewart, *Chem. Rev.*, **64**, 129 (1964).

REFERENCES

1. Löfgren and Lüning, *Acta Chem. Scand.*, **7**, 225 (1953); Brown and Weliky, *J. Biol. Chem.*, **204**, 1019 (1953).
2. Cochran, *Acta Cryst.*, **4**, 81 (1951).
3. Pullman, *J. Chem. Soc.*, 1959, 1621.
4. Lykos and Miller, *Tetrahedron Letters*, 1743 (1963) and references there cited.
5. Lewis, Beaman, and Robins, *Can. J. Chem.*, **41**, 1807 (1963).
6. Lloyd, *Chem. Ind. (London)*, 953 (1963).
7. Montgomery, *J. Am. Chem. Soc.*, **78**, 1928 (1956).
8. Lister, *Rev. Pure Appl. Chem. (Australia)*, **11**, 178 (1961); Taylor and Garcia, *J. Am. Chem. Soc.*, **86**, 4720 (1964).
9. Davoll, Lythgoe, and Todd, *J. Chem. Soc.*, 967 (1948).
10. Baddiley and Buchanan, *Ann. Rept. Chem. Soc.*, **54**, 329 (1957).
11. Baddiley, *Advan. in Enzymol.* **16**, 1 (1956).
12. Khorana and Moffatt, *J. Am. Chem. Soc.*, **83**, 663 (1961).
13. Baddiley and Jamieson, *Chem. Ind. (London)*, 375 (1954).
14. Robbins and Lipman, *J. Am. Chem. Soc.*, **78**, 2652 (1956).
15. Baddiley, Buchanan, Letters, and Sanderson, *J. Chem. Soc.*, 1731 (1959).
16. Albert and Armagero, *Advan. Heterocyclic Chem.*, **4**, 1 (1965).
17. Oster, Bellin, and Holmström, *Experienta*, **18**, 249 (1962).
18. Christie, Kenner, and Todd, *Nature*, **170**, 924 (1952).
19. Wheatley, *Acta Cryst.*, **8**, 224 (1955).
20. Kreutzberger, *Fortschr. chem. Forsch.*, **4**, 273 (1962).
21. Gysin, *Chem. Ind. (London)*, 1393 (1962).
22. Nyberg and Cheng, *J. Med. Chem.*, **8**, 531 (1965).

CHAPTER X

HETEROCYCLIC COMPOUNDS WITH A
SEVEN-MEMBERED RING

Interest in seven-membered ring heterocycles, with three double bonds in the ring, has sprung up in the last few years in connexion with studies of aromaticity, of certain rearrangements, and of the valuable therapeutic properties of some compounds of this group. Compounds in which the ring is saturated, or partially saturated, have properties which are predictable from a knowledge of those of similar aliphatic compounds.

Six π electrons are provided by the six carbon atoms of the three formal double bonds, so that if no more electrons of this type are available from the heteroatom, as in borepine (1), the system might be expected to possess aromatic character. This type of structure would be similar to that of the relatively stable tropylium cation (2). Azepine

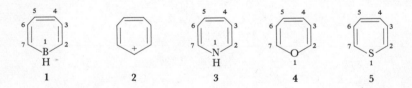

(3), oxepine (4), and thiepin (5), on the other hand do not fit Hückel's $4n + 2$ rule, and so would be expected to have high reactivity and little aromatic character, a situation which appears to pertain. Valency tautomerism has been demonstrated in both azepines and oxepines.

1. BOREPINE

Although borepanes (1, R = Cl, Et or OMe) have been synthesized, the first attempts to prepare borepines have given non-cyclic products.[1] However dibenzo[bf]borepine (2) has been obtained as an unstable easily oxidized pyridine derivative. It has been little investigated.[2]

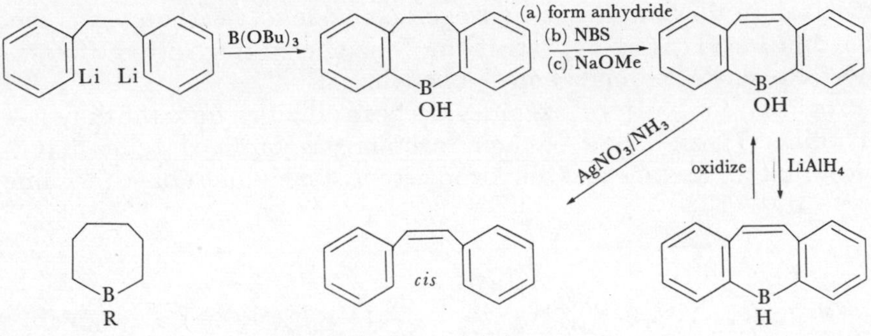

NBS = N-bromosuccinimide

2. AZEPINE

Azepine itself can be written in various tautomeric formulations, and so far it appears that the 3H-tautomers are the most stable.

Benzene with ethyl azidoformate and light gives a 70% yield of ethyl azepine-1-carboxylate (2), the structure of which has been established by hydrogenation to a hexahydro derivative of certain constitution (3).[3] Although the valency tautomer (1) of the azepine may be an intermediate in the synthesis, there is yet no evidence (contrast oxepine)

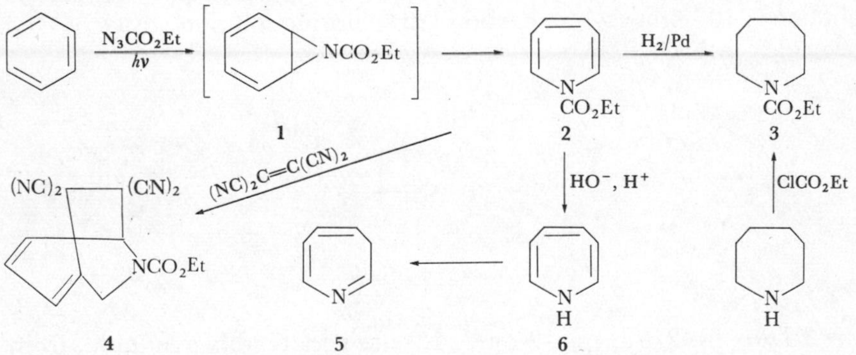

that it is present in the azepine (2) which is isolated. Careful alkaline hydrolysis of 2, followed by acidification, is thought to give 1H-azepine (6) which isomerized rapidly in solution to 3H-azepine (5), but neither compound has actually been isolated. Reduction of the ester (2) with lithium aluminium hydride gave the very unstable 1-methylazepine, while with tetracyanoethylene the ester (2) formed the Diels–Alder adduct (4).[3] 1-Cyanoazepine, obtained in good yield from the thermolysis of cyanogen azide (N_3CN) in benzene, is hydrolysed by alkali in the presence of hydrogen peroxide to 1-carbamylazepine, but dilute acid caused rupture of the 7-membered ring with the formation of phenylcyanamide and N-phenylurea.[4]

An interesting series of azepines has been obtained from the dihydropyridine (7), and some of their reactions are outlined below.[5] It is clear that the azepine and dihydropyridine systems must have the same

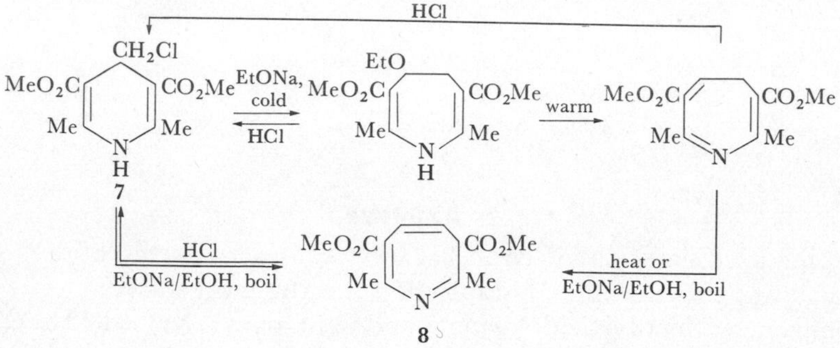

order of stability, and that of the azepines the $3H$-tautomer (8) is the most stable. The 1-methyl derivative (9) of the dihydropyridine (7) is also of special interest as with potassium t-butoxide, at different concentrations, either the azepine (11) or its valency tautomer (10) can be obtained; 10 isomerizes in carbon tetrachloride solution (trace of HCl present?) to 11.[6]

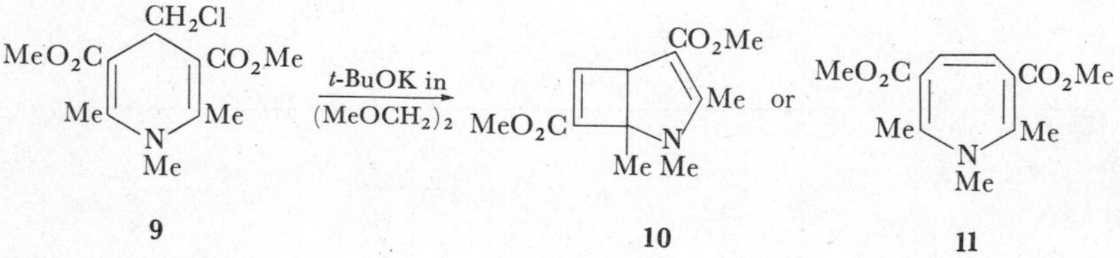

1,3-Dihydro-$2H$-azepin-2-ones (13) are very readily available[7] from the sodium salts of 2,6-dialkylphenols (e.g. 12) with chloramine, or methylchloramine, at $-70°$. Hydrogenation over platinum gives the expected cyclic amide (16). The NHCO group of the azepinone (13) is amidic in character as the compound forms sodium salts which alkylate on the nitrogen atom, is hydrolysed by acid eventually leading to the lactone (17), is reduced by lithium aluminium hydride to the corresponding amine (15), and with triethyloxonium borofluoride gives the corresponding imido ether, the 2-ethoxyazepine (14).[8] The double-bond system of the azepinone (13) possesses considerable

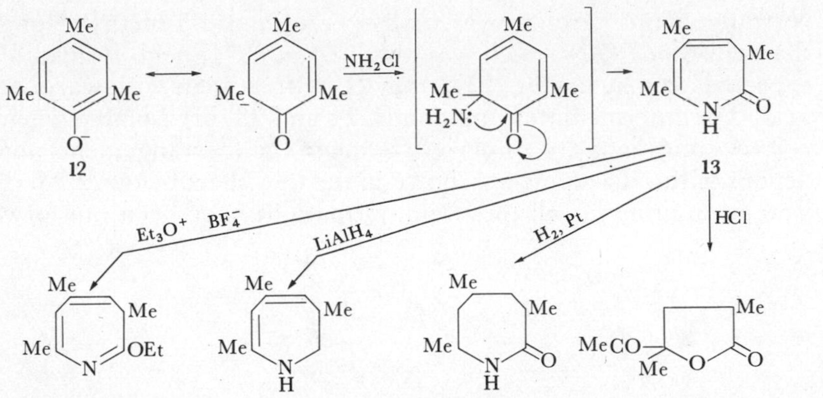

12 13 14 15 16 17

butadiene-like character and adds to dimethyl acetylenedicarboxylate yielding **18**. However, it does not react with the less vigorous *N*-phenylmaleimide which combines with the amine **15** in the normal way. Light also causes isomerization of **13** to **19**.[8] One azepinedione (**20**) has marked activity against Crocker sarcoma.[9]

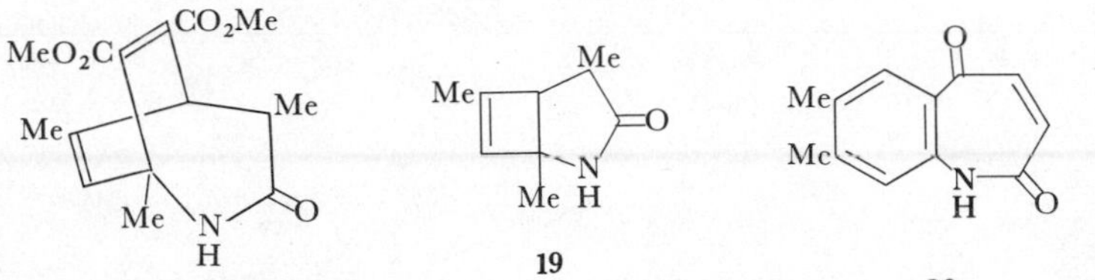

18 19 20

A very great deal of work has been done in the last few years on various diazepines, some of which undergo fascinating rearrangements. Others possess valuable pharmacological properties. Examples of the

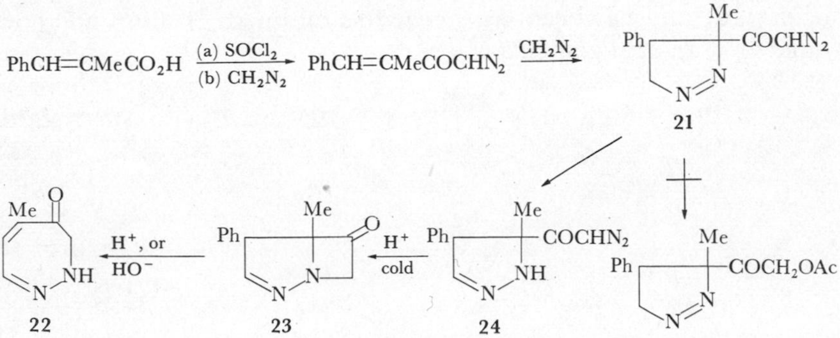

21 22 23 24 25

rearrangements are provided by 6,7-dihydro-5-methyl-4-phenyl-diazepin-6-one (**22**) which was obtained in 80% yield, instead of the expected acetoxy ketone (**25**), from **21** by treatment with warm acetic acid. The intermediate compounds, **24** and **23**, are isolable when the correct conditions are employed. Some of the rearrangements and reactions of this diazepine are shown in the flow sheet below.[10] Mechanisms accounting for all these transformations have been put forward.

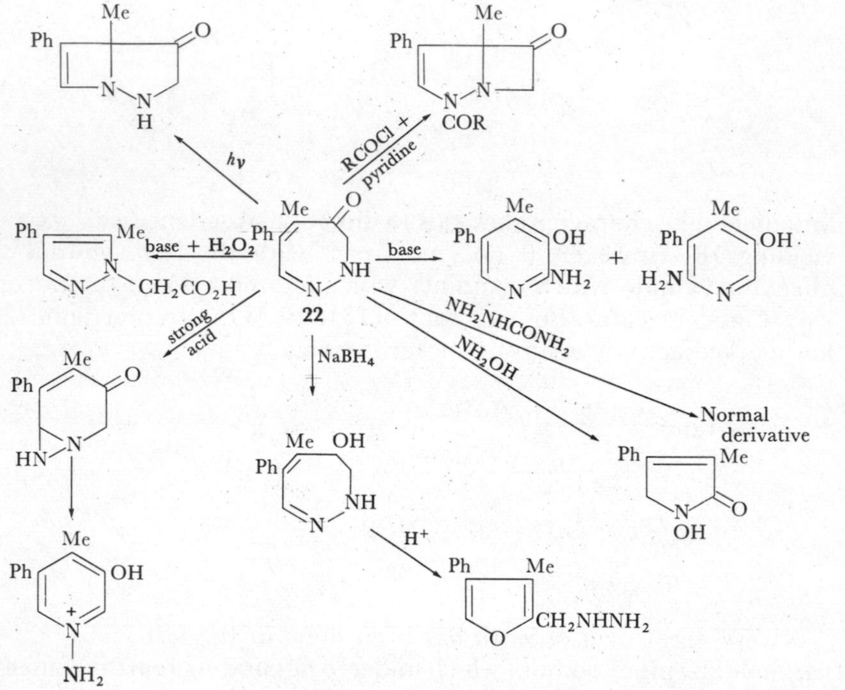

The valuable tranquilizing agent, 'Librium', is the 1,4-diazepine 4-oxide (**26**) and has been synthesized as outlined. It also undergoes a number of rearrangements.[11]

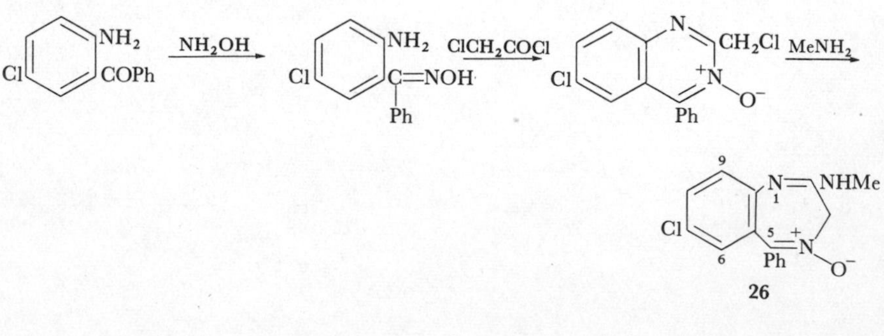

3. OXEPINE

The synthesis of oxepine was first achieved in 1964 by a method which has also been used for the preparation of some derivatives. Oxepine is an orange liquid, b.p. 38° at 30 mm. The nuclear magnetic resonance spectrum of the liquid is temperature dependent, and is interpreted to show the presence of comparable amounts of the oxirane (1) and the oxepine (2).[12] Hydrogenation of oxepine gives the known cyclic

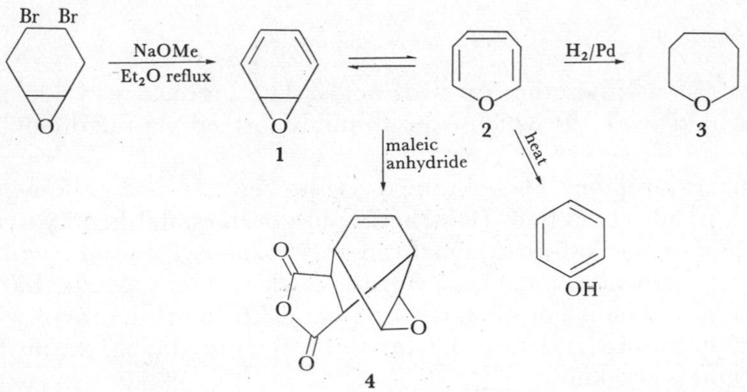

ether (3), the 7-membered ring structure thereby being established, while heating to 70° isomerizes oxepine to phenol. Oxepine undergoes the Diels–Alder reaction with maleic anhydride yielding (4).[12] The nuclear magnetic resonance spectrum of 3-chloro-6-oxooxepine (5) gives no indication of the presence of any enol, and the compound is very sensitive to both acids and bases.[13] There is therefore no doubt that there is little, if any, aromatic character present in simple oxepines.

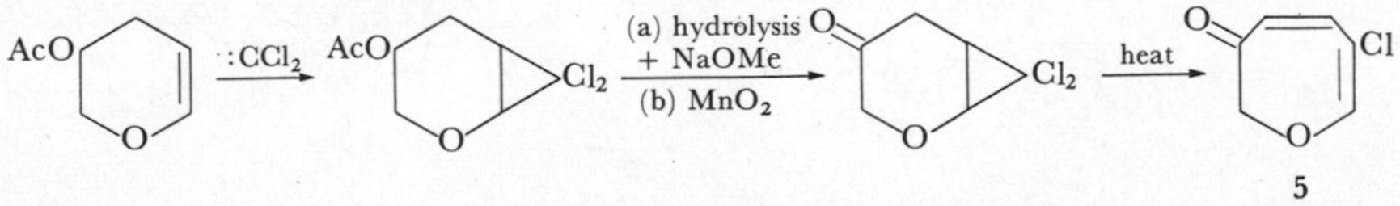

2,3-Dihydrooxepine (6) can be obtained from 4H-pyran[14] by ring expansion, but attempts to carry out similar experiments with pyrylium salts in the hope of obtaining oxepine itself failed. This dihydrooxepine undergoes a photocyclization to 10.[15] 4,5-Dihydrooxepine (7)[16]

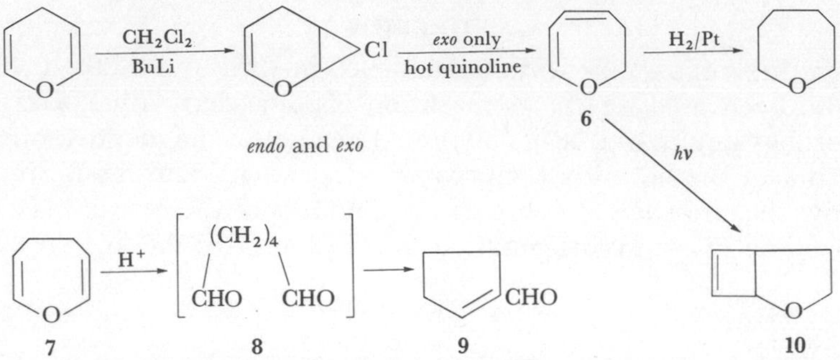

behaves as a vinyl ether towards acids. The product is cyclopent-1-
enecarbaldehyde (**9**) which is presumably formed via the dialdehyde
(**8**)

Benzo[*b*]oxepine (**11**), obtained as shown,[17, 18] is a yellow-green
oil of b.p. 50° at 0·5 mm. Its structure has been established by hydrogenation to the known homochroman,[17] and is consistent with its
nuclear magnetic resonance spectrum[17] which also suggests that the
heterocyclic ring is not planar. Compound **12**, the structure of which
seems established, is clearly an oxepine of an unusual type; the nitrogen
analogue is also known.[18a]

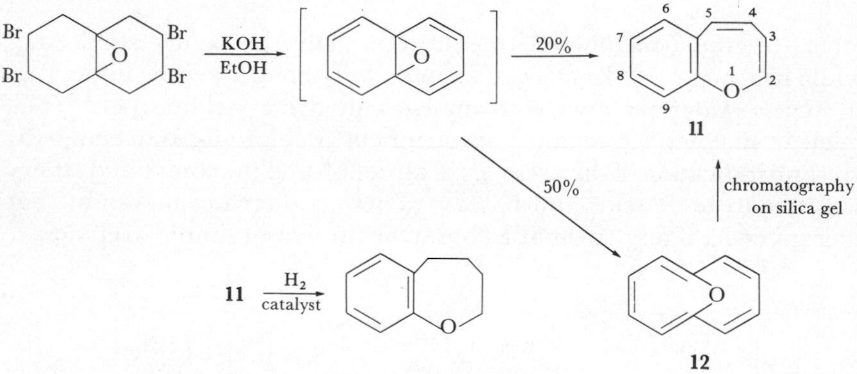

Benzo[*d*]oxepine (**13**) has been obtained[19] from the bis-Wittig
reagent derived from **14**, and is much less stable to acid than the diester
obtained from **15** with diazomethane.[20] This behaviour is parallel to
that of furan and its 2,5-dimethoxycarbonyl derivative. The structure
of the diester of **15** is consistent with its nuclear magnetic resonance
spectrum.[21]

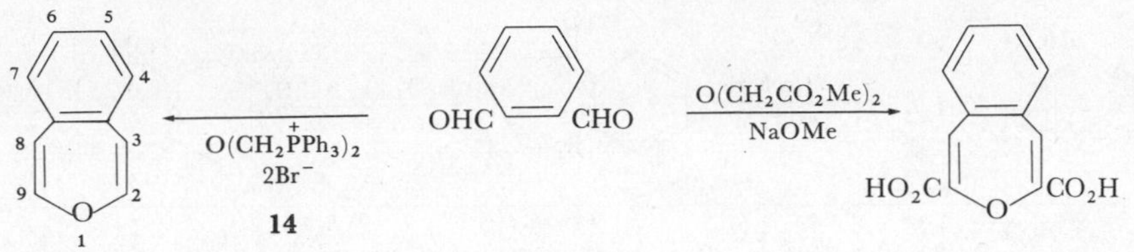

13 ← $\dfrac{O(CH_2\overset{+}{P}Ph_3)_2}{2Br^-}$ **14** | OHC CHO | $\dfrac{O(CH_2CO_2Me)_2}{NaOMe}$ | **15**

4. THIEPIN

Few compounds definitely possessing the thiepin ring are known. The benzo[*d*]thiepin (**1**) is easily obtained[22] and readily loses sulphur to form naphthalene-2,3-dicarboxylic acid (**2**); this desulphurization may be compared with a similar one in the isothianaphthene series (p. 185). The acid with a limited amount of diazomethane gives the corresponding diester, but excess diazomethane adds on to two of the double bonds in the molecule. The nuclear magnetic resonance of the diester gives no evidence for the presence of a valency tautomer, and is consistent with the structure proposed.[21]

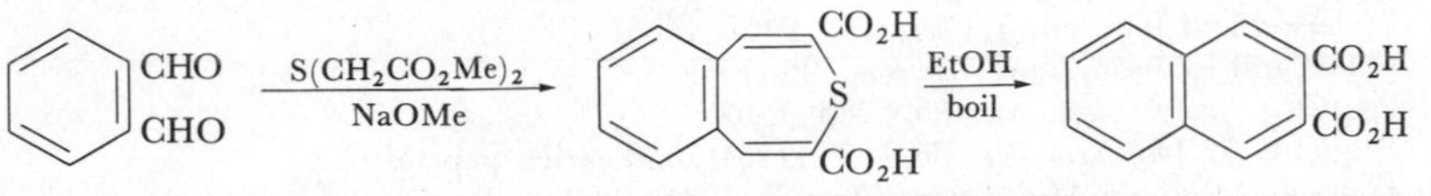

Benzo[*d*]thiepin 3,3-dioxide (**4**) has been obtained by a long route from **3**, involving cyclization of the acid chloride, oxidation to the 3,3-dioxide, and several more stages.[23] It is easily reduced by Raney nickel and hydrogen to the 1,2,4,5-tetrahydro derivative and on pyrolysis gives a good yield of naphthalene.

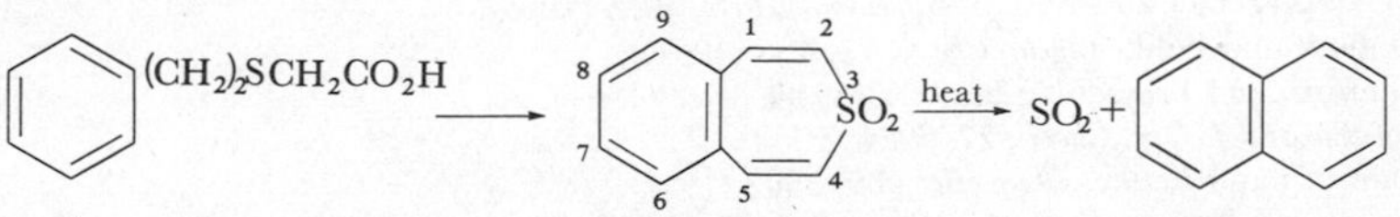

Benzo[*b*]thiepin 1,1-dioxide (**5**) has been obtained by the route outlined.[24] It is nitrated at position 8, and bromine adds to the heterocyclic ring only under the influence of light. Nucleophilic addition, which occurs easily thianaphthene 1,1-dioxide (p. 183), does not take

5

place. These observations suggest that the heterocyclic ring has some aromatic character. Attempts to decompose the thiepin to sulphur dioxide and napthalene have been unsuccessful.

REFERENCES

1. Brieger, *Diss. Abstr.*, **22**, 1824 (1961).
2. van Tamelen, Brieger, and Untch, *Tetrahedron Letters,* **8**, 14 (1960).
3. Hafner, *Angew. Chem., Intern. Ed.*, **3**, 165 (1964).
4. Marsh and Simmons, *J. Am. Chem. Soc.*, **87**, 3529 (1965).
5. Anderson and Johnson, *J. Chem. Soc.*, 2411 (1965).
6. Childs and Johnson, *Chem. Commun.*, 95 (1965).
7. Paquette, *J. Am. Chem. Soc.*, **85**, 3288 (1963).
8. Paquette, *J. Am. Chem. Soc.*, **86**, 4096 (1964), and earlier papers.
9. James and Rees, *J. Med. Pharm. Chem.*, **5**, 1234 (1962).
10. Moore and Theuer, *J. Org. Chem.*, **30**, 1887 (1965), and earlier papers. *Moore, Trans. N.Y. Acal. Sci.,* **27**, 591 (1965).
11. Metlesics, Tavares and Sternbach, *J. Org. Chem.*, **30**, 1311 (1965), and earlier papers.
12. Vogel, Böll, and Günther, *Tetrahedron Letters*, 609 (1965).
13. Masamune and Castelluci, *Chem. Ind.* (*London*), 184 (1965).
14. Schweizer and Parham, *J. Am. Chem. Soc.*, **82**, 4085 (1960).
15. Paquette, Barrett, Spitz, and Pitcher, *J. Am. Chem. Soc.*, **87**, 3417 (1965).
16. Braun, *J. Org. Chem.*, **28**, 1383 (1963).
17. Sondheimer and Shani, *J. Am. Chem. Soc.*, **86**, 3168 (1964).
18. Vogel, Biskup, Pretzer, and Böll, *Angew. Chem.*, **76**, 785 (1964).
18a. Vogel, Pretzer and Böll, *Tetrahedron Letters,* 3613 (1965).
19. Dimoth and Pohl, *Angew. Chem.*, **73**, 436 (1961).
20. Dimroth and Freyschlag, *Chem. Ber.*, **90**, 1623 (1957).
21. Jorgenson, *J. Org. Chem.*, **27**, 3224 (1962).
22. Dimroth and Lenke, *Chem. Ber.*, **89**, 2602 (1957).
23. Truce and Lotspeich, *J. Am. Chem. Soc.*, **78**, 848 (1956).
24. Traynelis and Lowe, *J. Org. Chem.*, **29**, 366 (1964), and earlier papers.

COMPOUND INDEX

This index is subdivided into compound and subject indexes. Compounds are listed under the parent heterocyclic system, where possible. The page numbers in heavy type are those which refer to major discussions of the subject or compound, and those numbered in italics refer to synthesis.

HEAVY TYPE—MAJOR DISCUSSIONS. ITALICS—PREPARATIONS

Azepine (*contd.*)
 1-carboxylic acid, ethyl ester, *373*
 1-cyano-, *373*
 2-ethoxy-, *374*
 hexahydro-, *373*
 hexahydro-1-carboxylic acid, ethyl ester
   373
 1-methyl-, *373*
  tetracyanoethylene adduct *373*
 1,2,7-trimethyl-3,6-dicarboxylic acid,
   dimethyl ester *374*
1H-Azepine,
 2,3-dihydro-3,5,7-trimethyl-, *375*
 2,3-dihydro-3,5,7-trimethyl-2-one,
   dimethyl acetylenedicarboxylate adduct,
   375
 4,5-dihydro-4-ethoxy-2,7-dimethyl-3,6-
   dicarboxylic acid, dimethyl ester, *374*
 hexahydro-3,5,7-trimethyl-2-one, *375*
2H-Azepine,
 1,3-dihydro-3,5,7-trimethyl-2-one, *375*
3H-Azepine,
 2,7-dimethyl-3,6-dicarboxylic acid,
   dimethyl ester, *374*
 2-ethoxy-3,5,7-trimethyl-, *375*
4H-Azepine,
 2,7-dimethyl-3,6-dicarboxylic acid,
   dimethyl ester *374*
Azete, 40
Azetidin-,2,4-dione,
 1,3,3-triphenyl-, *44*
Azetidine, **39–41**, *42*
 1-benzenesulphonyl-3-bromo-, 39
 1-*n*-butyl-, *42*
 2-carboxylic acid, *42*
 1-dithiocarbamic acid, azetidine salt, 40, 41
 1-hydroxymethyl-, 40, 41
 1-nitroso-, 40, 41
 1-phenyl-, *42*
 1-(4'-toluenesulphonyl)-, *42*
Azetidinium,
 1,1-diethyl-, salts, 41
Azetidin-2-one, **42**, **43**, *45*
 1-benzyl-3,3-dimethyl-4-phenyl-, *45*
 4,4-bisethoxycarbonyl-1-phenyl-, *45*
 3,3-dimethyl-1,4,4-triphenyl-, 44, *45*
 1,4-diphenyl-, *44*, *45*
 1-phenyl-, *45*
 3-phenacetamido-1-phenyl-, *44*
 1-phenyl-4,4-dicarboxylic acid, diethyl
   ester, *45*
 3-amino-1,4-diphenyl-, 44
 3,3-dimethyl-1,4-diphenyl-, *45*
Azetine, 40
Azetin-2-one,
 1,4-diphenyl-, *44*

Aziridine, 5, **6–10**, **12**, *15*, **16**, 18, 20, 29, 42
 1-acetyl-, 16
 1-(2-aminoethyl)-, *15*
 1-benzenesulphonyl-2-bromomethyl-, 39
 1-benzoyl-, 10
 2-benzoyl-1-cyclohexyl-3-phenyl-, 14
 2-benzyl-3-phenyl-, *16*
 1-bromo-, *8*
 1-*n*-butyl-, 14
 1-chloro-, *8*
 1-(2-cyanoethyl)-, *8*
 1-cyclohexyl-, 11
 2,2-dimethyl-, 13
 2,3-dimethyl-, 14
 3,3-dimethyl-2-isopropoxy-2-phenyl-, *6*
 2,3-dimethyl-1-nitroso-, *14*
 2-2',4'-dinitrophenyl-3-methyl-, *5*, *6*
 2,3-diphenyl-, 13
 1-ethyl-2,3-dimethyl-, 12
 2-ethyl-2-phenyl-, *16*
 1-lithium, *8*
 2-methyl-, 14, 32
 1-nitroso-, *8*
 1-phenyl-, 11
 2-phenyl-, 13, 14
 1-p-toluenesulphonyl-, 13
  trimethylboron complex, 40
 1,2,3-triphenyl-, 15
Aziridin-2-one,
 1-t-butyl-3-phenyl-, **12**
 1-t-butyl-3,3-dimethyl-, **12**
Aziridinium salts, **8–10**
 1,1-dimethyl-, perchlorate, *8*
Azirine, 4
 dihydro-, see aziridine
 3-(2,4-dinitrophenyl)-2-methyl-, *5*
 3,3-dimethyl-2-phenyl-, *6*
 2-2',4'-dinitrophenyl-3-methyl-, *5*, *6*
Azulene, *194*

Bacimethrin, 345
Barbituric acid, **339**, *341*, 345
 5-aryl-, 339
 5,5-dialkyl-, *339*
Benzaldehyde, .
 2-formamido-, *154*
Benzene,
 1,3,5-triphenyl-, *237*
 1,2-oxide, *377*
Benzidine, 168
Benzilic acid, 54
Benzimidazole, 91, *304*, *305*, 308, **309**
 5,6-dimethyl-, 92
  1-α-D-ribofuranoside,-3-phosphate, 91
 2-iodo-, *309*

HEAVY TYPE—MAJOR DISCUSSIONS. ITALICS—PREPARATIONS

SUBJECT INDEX, SEE PAGES 403–408

SUBJECT INDEX, SEE PAGES 403–408

Pyrimidine (*contd.*)
4-amino-2,5-dimethyl-,   324
4-amino-2,6-dimethyl-,   339
4-amino-2-ethylthio-,   *338*
4-amino-2-hydroxy-, see also cytosine,   *338*
4-amino-2-hydroxy-5-carboxylic acid ethyl ester,   *344*
2-amino-4-methyl-,   *337*
4-amino-6-methyl-,   *337*
4-amino-2-methyl-5-carboxylic acid, ethyl ester,   *343*
4-amino-2-methyl-5-methylsulphonic acid, 324
5-bromo-,   *336*
4-chloro-2-ethylthio-,   *338*
5-cyano-4-hydroxy-2-methyl-,   *343*
2,4-diamino-,   *338*
4,5-diamino-,   358, 364
4,5-diamino-2,6-dihydroxy-,   *358*
4,6-diamino-5-phenylazo-,   *359*
4,6-diamino-5-thioformamido-,   *359*
4,6-dicarboxylic acid,   335
2,4-dichloro-,   335, *338*
1,6-dihydro-6-phenyl-,   *337*
2,4-dihydroxy-, see also uracil,   337
2,4-dihydroxy-6-methyl-,   *343*
4,6-dimethyl-,   *336*
4,6-dimethyl-2-styryl-,   *338*
2-ethylthio-4-hydroxy-,   *338*
hexahydro-,   *341*
hexahydro-2,4-dioxo-6-methyl-,   *343*
5-hydroxy-,   *336, 337*
4-hydroxy-2-mercapto-,   *338*
4-hydroxy-2-mercapto-5-methoxy-,   *337*
4-hydroxy-5-methoxy-,   *337*
2-mercapto-4,6-dimethyl-,   *336*
4-mercapto-5-methoxy-,   *337*
5-methoxy-,   *337*
4-methyl-,   337
2-(4-nitrophenyl)-,   *337*
4-(4-nitrophenyl)-,   *337*
1-oxide,   *336*
4-phenyl-,   *3337*
1,4,5,6-tetrahydro-,   *341*
4,5,6-triamino-,   *358*
2,4,6-trihydroxy-, see also barbituric acid, 339
2,4,6-trimethyl-,   337, 338
2,4,6-tristyryl-,   *338*
Pyrimidinium,
1,3-diethyl-, bisborofluoride,   *336*
1-methyl-, methosulphate,   *336*
Pyromucic acid, see furan-2-carboxylic acid, 93
α-Pyrone, see 2-pyrone
γ-Pyrone, see 4-pyrone,

2-Pyrone,   236, *238*
maleic anhydride adduct,
4-Pyrone,   236, *239*
2,6-dicarboxylic acid,   *239*
2,6-dimethyl-,   *239*
2,6-dimethyl-,   **240**, 292
2,6-dimethyl-, 3-carboxylic acid,   *239*
2,6-dimethyl-, dimer,   *240*
2,6-diphenyl-,   230
Pyrrocoline, see also indolizine,   175
Pyrrole,   *62, 64,* **62–77,** *82, 85, 86,* 87, 95, 97, 101, 120, 121, 122, 125, 136, **141–145,** 151–156, 159, 160, 166, 190, 212, 302
2-acetonitrile,   *73*
2-acetoxy-4-carboxylic acid, ethyl ester,   *79*
1-acetyl-,   `70`
2-acetyl-,   *72*
5-acetyl-2,4-dimethyl-3-carboxylic acid, ethyl ester,   74
2-acetyl-1-methyl-,   *77*
1-acetyl-1-methyl-4-nitro-,   *77*
4-acetyl-1-methyl-2-nitro-,   *77*
1-allyl-,   70
2-allyl-,   *70*
1-benzoyl-,   71
1-benzyl-,   69, 78
1-benzyl-2-fumaric acid,   *69, 78*
1-benzyl-2-maleic acid,   *69, 78*
2,5-bishydroxymethyl-,   `70`
2,5-bistriphenylmethyl-2,5-dihydro-,   *68*
2-bromo-5-bromomethyl-3-methyl-4-carboxylic acid ethyl ester,   *77*
4-bromo-2-carbaldehyde,   *81*
4-bromo-2-carboxylic acid, methyl ester, *83*
2-bromo-3,5-dimethyl-4-carboxylic acid, ethyl ester,   *77*
5-bromo-3-methyl-2,4-dicarboxylic acid, diethyl ester,   *74, 83*
2-(2-butyl)-,   71
3-(2-butyl)-,   71
2-carbaldehyde,   *71, 72, 73,* 80, **81,** 82
3-carbaldehyde,   **81**
1-carboxylic acid,   84
ethyl ester,   69
2-carboxylic acid,   *73,* 144
methyl ester,   83
3-carboxylic acid,   *84*
ethyl ester,   *83*
5-chloro-2-carboxylic acid, methyl ester, *83*
1-β-cyanoethyl-,   `70`
2,5-diamino-,   *79*
2-diazo-3,5-diphenyl-,   *79*
1,2-dicarboxylic acid, diethyl ester,   *87*
2,3-dicarboxylic acid, diethyl ester,   *83*

SUBJECT INDEX, SEE PAGES 403–408

SUBJECT INDEX

HEAVY TYPE—MAJOR DISCUSSIONS. ITALICS—PREPARATIONS

HEAVY TYPE—MAJOR DISCUSSIONS. ITALICS—PREPARATIONS

COMPOUND INDEX, SEE PAGES 381–402

COMPOUND INDEX, SEE PAGES 381–402

Date Due